The A to Z of Opera

The A to Z of Opera

Introduction

It might seem that opera, as it developed in Western Europe in the late 16th century, was all a terrible mistake. The interests of the time, scientific and cultural, had brought close attention to the world of ancient Greece and Rome, but if opera was ever intended as a revival of classical Greek tragedy, then it was singularly wide of the mark. Opera, in fact, reflected elements of classical Greek and Roman thought and practice, but had an equal debt to its own immediate predecessors and to the society in which it developed.

In the 16th century there was nothing particularly new about drama and nothing new in the combination of music and drama. Such a combination had had a place, after all, in medieval Christian liturgy, with plays and music re-enacting events associated with Easter and with Christmas. From this a larger repertoire had grown, with plays based on events recorded in the Bible or derived from Christian tradition. Music was associated with dramatic action in secular performances of one sort or another. Court entertainments of various kinds took place in which elements of drama and music were combined. An extravagant example is recorded in accounts of the Feast of the Pheasant in Burgundy in 1454. A court banquet was given as an attempt was made to arouse interest in a Crusade, after the Turkish capture of Constantinople. On this occasion singers in the guise of musical blackbirds emerged from a giant pie for the edification of the guests. Such diversions, whether primarily political or artistic, took place throughout Europe. The essential difference in the new art of opera lay in its developed dramatic structure. This, in turn, was associated with a much more dramatic style of music, drawing on the classical art of rhetoric, the art of public speaking, which, nominally at least, formed part of the new education.

The period now known as the Baroque developed in the last decades of the 16th century. It is distinguished, above all, by the development of what has become known as dramatic monody. Here a simple form of melody closely follows the rhythms and intonations of speech, accompanied by simple if occasionally startling chords. The new technique of composition made opera possible. Plays with songs and dances were one thing, but works providing a dramatic combination of words and music throughout were something different.

There were three principal elements from the ancient world that influenced the new form, Greek and Roman tragedy, ancient rhetoric and the work of the philosophers Plato and Aristotle. Interest in classical Greek tragedy brought with it the understanding that music and dance had been essential elements of performance. With the music now lost, a new music was created. At the same time the rules and conventions of classical Greek and Roman rhetoric came to be reflected in drama. The new art of opera could also seek theoretical support from the works of Plato and Aristotle. From Plato came the idea that certain kinds of music were rightly associated with certain states of mind or soul. In the philosophical dialogue *The Republic* Plato's hero Socrates suggests that some kinds of music should be banned, because of the effect they have on character. Others are to be encouraged as fostering bravery or prudence. This was at the basis of what became the Doctrine of the Affections, the association of certain pieces of music with certain states of mind, so that a sad song, for example, might both express the feeling of the singer and arouse a similar feeling in those who heard it. From Aristotle came the now fundamental connection of music with poetry and rhetoric, together with the suggested moral purpose of drama. Through the proper exercise of the emotions of pity and fear, exercised on suitable subjects, an audience would undergo a moral cleansing, a catharsis. Opera, then, had a moral purpose. It was soon, of course, to have a political one.

From the very beginning opera brought together all the arts. It involved painting, poetry, drama, dance and music, making it the most complex of art forms. It was, as Samuel Johnson later pointed out, exotic and irrational, and, as many have found, remarkably expensive. It remained, nevertheless, of continuing social and political importance. In the first respect it edified and entertained, and in the second it served as an expression of the power and splendour of the monarch in an age of kings.

ITALY

Early Opera

There was always argument about who composed the first opera. Some of his contemporaries regarded the Roman composer Cavalieri's *La rappresentatione di Anima e di Corpo* (1600) (The Representation of Soul and Body) as the first true example. Written for the Oratorian movement of St Philip Neri and with a dramatic content recalling that of medieval morality plays, in its combination of drama with the new music, it had some claim to priority. Allegorical figures dispute in a work that seeks to show the superiority of the spiritual. The composer himself claimed to have been the first to unite music and drama in this way, although rivals claimed to have done the same things some years before.

While Cavalieri's work entertained and edified the entire College of Cardinals in Rome, other early operas were designed as court entertainments of a more secular kind. Works of this kind were staged, notably, for the Médici rulers in Florence and, most memorably of all, at Mantua. It was there that Monteverdi had his *Orfeo* staged in 1607, followed the next year by *Arianna*, now lost. The subject of *Orfeo* (Orpheus) had already been treated in Florence by the composers Peri and by Caccini. The story had an obvious relevance. The legendary musician Orpheus, grieving at the loss of his beloved Eurydice, attempts to save her from the Underworld by the power of his music and is almost successful, thwarted only at the last minute by his own doubts. Orpheus not only demonstrates the importance of music. He is also represented as a shepherd among shepherds, making it possible for the poet and composer to draw on an existing literary and musical tradition. Pastoral poems and romances were set in a conventional Arcadia, where the only troubles that arose came from the thwarted love of amorous shepherds, whose heart-ache often proved fatal. The Italian madrigal, the part-songs of the 16th century, often set pastoral verses, drawing on another tradition of the ancient world. Here the life of the shepherd was idealised in an urban or court view of the country, a convention that could present the ageing Queen Elizabeth of England as Oriana, Queen of the Shepherds, shortly before her death. Monteverdi and his librettist were drawing on existing literary and musical conventions.

Opera as court entertainment continued, often under enlightened patronage. It was in Venice, in 1637, that the first public opera-house was opened. Venice was a commercial republic, ruled by an oligarchy, but without a royal court. The commercial aspect of opera could here be exploited, so that by the end of the century there were seven Venetian opera-houses, dominated, after the death of Monteverdi in 1643, by the composer Cavalli, followed by Legrenzi. Venetian opera, not uninfluenced at first by the opera of Rome, spread throughout Italy and to other parts of Europe. As a more popular form than early courtly opera, it offered a mixture of the serious and the comic. Monteverdi's *Orfeo* had no comic relief, but his two later surviving operas, written for Venice in the early 1640s, include elements of comedy. They also followed a convention now established, that of the happy ending. There was still, as before, a strong element of spectacle, with elaborate stage machinery that allowed transformation scenes and grandiose effects, with a complementary extravagance of costume and décor. Leading composers of the later years of the 17th century and early years of the 18th also include Alessandro Scarlatti in Naples and Rome, father of the keyboard composer Domenico Scarlatti.

Early opera had involved madrigals, dramatic monody and set songs, or a mixture of these. As the 17th century went on, there developed a gradual distinction between recitative and aria. The first of these, lightly accompanied often simply by chords, follows the rhythm and stresses of speech without the formal structure of a melody. Recitative, in fact, is dialogue set to music. The aria is a song, often in a form that frames a middle section in identical outer sections, the second of which might be ornamented by the singer. While the plot may be carried forward by the recitative, the aria tends to embody one state of mind. Both had an important part to play in what followed, although audiences tended to pay more attention to arias and much less to recitative, which seemed tedious.

Opera Seria

The later years of the 17th century brought the beginnings of operatic reform. This came about partly as a result of French criticism, based on the Aristotelian principles that dominated French classical tragedy. There the so-called dramatic unities of time, place and plot were to be observed. These demanded a closer connection between time in the drama and time on stage, some limit on the changes of place possible, since in Greek tragedy no change of scene was allowed, and a final unity of plot, without primitive diversion into unconnected sub-plots. Under the leadership of the librettist Apostolo Zeno in Venice, the art was purged of its comic elements. The new form, later known as *opera seria*, followed clear principles of classical propriety and led to a certain stylization. There were clear categories of major and minor rôles, usually for six or seven solo singers, and of the number and type of arias to be allocated to each. Subjects tended now to be historical, rather than mythological. *Opera seria* held a central position in repertoire for three-quarters of the 18th century. It brought the rise to prominence of the *castrato*, now cast in the principal male rôles, and allowed a similar importance and scale of fees to the *prima donna*, the first lady. Each would expect a similar number of arias of varied mood, sad, angry, brave or meditative, irrespective of the demands of the plot, while the secondary singers would have their own demands to make.

After Zeno the principal librettist was Metastasio, regarded as the most outstanding dramatist and poet of his time. The new libretti, the operatic texts, were set again and again by major composers of the day, including Vivaldi. The music, in fact, became relatively expendable. It was often a case of first the words, then the music. In London Handel had *opera seria* libretti adapted for the varied requirements of London audiences. He was followed in London, later in the century, by another German composer, Johann Christian Bach, the youngest son of old Johann Sebastian, but the art remained essentially an Italian one.

Opera Buffa

In the 18th century there was a parallel development of what was later known as *opera buffa* (comic opera). This had its roots in the ancient Roman comedy of Plautus and Terence and this in turn had been derived from ancient Greek New Comedy. Features of these were stock characters, comic and cunning servants, angry and parsimonious fathers, passionate lovers, amorous daughters and bragging soldiers. With them came a preoccupation with what was recognisable as ordinary life, however simplified. Another source of Italian comedy was found in the associated improvised theatre of the *commedia dell'arte*, with its similar array of stock characters. *Opera buffa* corresponded to contemporary spoken drama and opera texts owed a great deal to the work of the playwright Goldoni. Oddly enough, the earlier historical process was now reversed. In the 17th century tragedy had acquired comic elements. Now serious characters began to find a place in comic opera, which became less comic and more realistic. These more dramatically credible plots found a place in Italian operas such as those written in Vienna by Mozart and his librettist Lorenzo da Ponte and their contemporaries.

Reform Opera

Serious Italian opera, again at first in Vienna, underwent a marked reform with the work of Gluck and the librettist Calzabigi. Between them they succeeded, largely under French influence, in introducing simplifications. The formal requirements of the old *opera seria* were reduced, allowing a greater degree of realism. Gluck, in fact, claimed that he made music the servant of poetry, never introducing novelties or distractions from the dramatic situation. He explained his principles clearly in his introduction to the opera *Alceste*, published in 1768. These had already been put into practice in 1762 with his version of the story of Orpheus, *Orfeo ed Euridice* (Orpheus and Eurydice).

From Rossini to Verdi

The 19th century in Italy brought some of the best known operas of all. These are found first of all in Rossini, a master of comedy, as in *Il barbiere di Siviglia* (The Barber of Seville), in which the barber Figaro abets his master Count Almaviva in his wooing of Rosina and the gulling of her guardian, old Doctor Bartolo. Rossini also tackled more serious subjects, as in his heroic melodrama *Tancredi*, with its ingredients of love, jealousy, misunderstanding and final resolution either, as in the first version, in a conventional happy ending, or, as in the revised version, in the hero's death. *Tancredi* provides a demanding title-rôle characteristic of the so-called *bel canto* style that Rossini so much admired. This involved a fine voice and the flexibility and evenness of tone to cope with elaborately florid vocal writing.

In Italian opera Rossini was followed by Bellini and Donizetti. The former had a mastery of extended lyrical melodies, shown in the intense romanticism of operas like *Norma*, with its story of love and heroic self-sacrifice by the Druid priestess of the title. Donizetti showed an equally marked dramatic sense, exemplified in *Lucia di Lammermoor*, based on the novel by Sir Walter Scott and including what became a popular operatic element, a mad scene for the heroine. His sense of comedy is evident in *L'elisir d'amore* (The Elixir of Love), with its quack doctor and forlorn lover, and in *Don Pasquale*, the fooling of the elderly bachelor of the title by a pair of young lovers, anxious to be united. Stock characters of Italian comedy occur in both.

The 1840s brought to prominence one of the greatest of all operatic composers. Verdi held a leading position in Italian opera for some half a century and continues to dominate operatic repertoire. From *Nabucco* (Nebuchadnezzar) in 1842 to *Falstaff* in 1893 he served, as he claimed, in the galley, to produce masterpiece after masterpiece. In these he created a very personal amalgamation of current trends of increased dramatic power and cogency, influenced at times by France and at times by Germany, but always essentially Italian in his own idiom. His career coincided with the rise of Italian nationalism and often his operas suggested a contemporary relevance. This is found, for example, in the chorus of Hebrew slaves in *Nabucco* and in the chorus of the oppressed people of Scotland in his Shakespearean *Macbeth*. It was Shakespeare, whose work had a new appeal in a period of relative freedom from earlier classical convention, who inspired Verdi's last two operas, the tragedy *Otello* and the fine comedy of *Falstaff*, based on *The Merry Wives of Windsor*.

Verismo and Puccini

The later years of the century brought *verismo* (realism), a reflection of current literary trends, in Mascagni's *Cavalleria rusticana* (Rustic Chivalry), a down-to-earth story of love and jealousy in a village, peasant setting, and Leoncavallo's *Pagliacci* (Players). This last brought to the opera a police-court murder case, in which a jealous actor had killed his faithless wife on the stage. *Pagliacci* provides a famous example of the dramatic treatment of drama itself, a contrast between the actor himself and the part he is forced to play.

Realism of this kind had its effect on Puccini, whose operas form a major part of modern repertoire, from *Manon Lescaut* and *Tosca* to *Turandot*. While he might seek the exotic in the Japanese setting of *Madama Butterfly* or the China of *Turandot*, in *Tosca*, in spite of its historical setting, he presented a story of political intrigue, murder and deception of contemporary relevance. Puccini too was able, like Verdi, to provide a successful synthesis of current musical and dramatic trends.

20th Century

Opera has, of course, continued in Italy, both in its more traditional form and in modern experiment. The story has not ended. The later 20th century offers obvious difficulties of succinct summary, with the general musical eclecticism that has characterized music and the other arts.

FRANCE

France has had its own dramatic and operatic tradition. While Italian opera has had some influence, affected itself by its contact with the principles of French classical drama, French opera has remained true to its own cultural and linguistic traditions.

Comédie-ballet and Tragédie-lyrique

Paradoxically French opera owes its origin to a composer of Italian origin. Jean-Baptiste Lully was brought to France as a boy and as time went on established himself in a leading position in the musical life of his adopted country. In collaboration with Molière he contributed to the art of the *comédie-ballet* and with the poet Quinault he created the French five-act *tragédie lyrique*, itself indebted both to earlier French forms of ballet and drama and to Italy. Lully came to hold a dominant position, with a royal monopoly that gave him control over music in the theatre. While it is now usual to perform Molière's comedies without their music or their ballet, the plays were originally conceived with a closely related element of dance and music. *Le bourgeois gentilhomme*, for example, which has had other more recent musical offshoots, finds a natural place for music as Monsieur Jourdain, the *nouveau riche* of the title, tries to acquire the arts of a gentleman. Apart from the comic musical episodes of his singing lesson and the scene in which he is supposedly ennobled by a Turkish Mufti, there is also a final comic ballet for a mixture of French, Spanish, Italian and other dancers and singers. The form was stifled when Lully claimed ownership not only of the music but of the texts and succeeded in exercising intolerable control over Molière's collaboration with another composer.

The *tragédie-lyrique* created by Lully and the poet Quinault was not necessarily tragic, but was, at least, serious in its treatment of subjects usually drawn from mythology. The tradition was continued by composers such as Campra and Charpentier and resumed with signal success by Rameau from the 1730s onwards. These operas, however, have never found a place in international repertoire. They belonged essentially to the French court of the *ancien régime* and often had political relevance in prologues that praised the King and plots that reflected recent royal successes.

Opéra Comique

As in Italy, comic opera itself developed from more popular sources in the 18th century, notably from the Paris Fair Theatres. Here existing tunes were often used for new words, as they were to be in *The Beggar's Opera* in England. Travelling companies of players and the actors of the Italian theatre played an important part in the development of a form that mixed speech and music and closely involved a popular audience. As the century went on, what had often been a coarse form of entertainment developed into something much more acceptable to the educated. Writers like Favart and the social philosopher Rousseau turned to simple country life for their plots, although the picture they offer is highly idealised.

The 1750s brought the famous quarrel between those who favoured the Italian opera and those who held to older French traditions. This revived a traditional opposition between the French and the Italian that had occurred a hundred years before, when the Italian-born Cardinal Mazarin was blamed by politicians for the high cost of Italian opera that he had had staged in Paris and forced into exile. Now, in 1752, an Italian company presented a series of Italian shorter, lighter-hearted intermezzos in Paris with reasonable success. The literary war that arose, known as the *Querelle des Bouffons*, was initiated by the German diplomat and critic, Baron Friedrich Melchior von Grimm, at one time a friend of the Mozarts. He had harsh comments to make on French opera and was later joined in his strictures by Rousseau. Their attacks led to a series of pamphlets, espousing one side or the other. While the Italian troupe engaged at the Opéra duly left Paris in 1754, Italian influence remained, to lead to a new form of French comic opera of greater musical and dramatic interest.

Reform and Revolution

In the 1770s Gluck's reformed opera was introduced to Paris, treating very differently the kind of subjects that had been the substance of the *tragédie lyrique*. French versions of his earlier Italian operas, already staged in Vienna, were now mounted in Paris. Gluck was able, in fact, to show a new compromise. The subjects of his operas might be drawn from classical mythology and legend, like the subjects chosen by Lully, but these were treated in a modern way. The operas were less stylized and very much more dramatic in their effect. At the same time the form of so-called *opéra comique* could also turn its attention to more serious subjects, as comic opera had in Italy, catering largely for a new middle-class audience. The period before the Revolution also brought the building of provincial opera-houses, where such works would provide the general repertoire.

The Revolution brought obvious changes. French serious opera, in the form of the *tragédie lyrique* was essentially associated with the monarchy, and had, in any case, been affected by the Paris operas of Gluck, with their new element of dramatic realism. The 1790s, however, demanded work of revolutionary relevance. This trend lasted only a short time. The new century brought a re-organization of opera throughout the country under Napoleon, who instituted reforms in the opera in Paris itself, exercising a limiting control over all theatres. Under the restored Bourbon monarchy opera flourished. The period saw the success in Paris of Rossini and his operas written for the French stage. At the same time there was a continuation of the *opéra comique* by composers like Auber, Halévy, Berlioz and Bizet. Subjects varied from the light-hearted to the tragically serious, with productions at the Opéra-Comique, the company established in 1714, distinguished from those at the Opéra by their less formal requirements. French *opéra comique*, in the 19th century at least, does not have to be comic; the descriptive term indicates a much wider category of work.

Grand Opera

From the later 1820s Paris saw the creation of operas of greater pretensions in the *grand opéra* staged by the Opéra, the leading official company, itself. These operas, which reach a height of grandeur and spectacle in the work of Meyerbeer, were held in the highest esteem. The first *grand opéra*, in 1828, was Auber's *La muette de Portici* (The Dumb Girl of Portici), followed in 1829 by Rossini's last opera *Guillaume Tell* (William Tell). From Meyerbeer came *Le prophète*, *Les Huguenots* and *L'africaine*. These involved elaborate and complex spectacle. The scenery offered a degree of realism and often of grandeur. Crowd scenes allowed the chorus to act, rather than stand in formal poses, while music added to general effect. Examples of *grand opéra* retain in themselves their own place in operatic history but also deserve attention for the effect they had on other opera on a similarly grand and spectacular scale, works by Verdi and by Wagner. Socially the Opéra was important. Its magnificence reflected the growing wealth and prosperity of the country and of its upper classes.

The Opéra-Comique

French opera continued in the 19th century with the official company known as the Opéra-Comique, derived from the tradition of the same name and allowing more freedom in choice of subject and treatment. The company had been established early in the preceding century, derived from the performances of the Paris Fairs. It had amalgamated with the Paris Italian Theatre and then with other establishments offering similar repertoire. In particular, the Opéra-Comique, in the various theatres in which it performed, allowed some spoken dialogue. Outstanding examples of works staged by the Opéra-Comique include Gounod's *Faust* and Bizet's *Carmen*. Neither of these, of course, are comedies. In Gounod's opera Faust sells his soul to the Devil, a bargain from which he is finally rescued by the intervention of the spirit of the girl he has seduced. *Carmen* is a story of low life in Spain, a tale of criminals, jealousy and murder that has much in common with Italian *verismo*. The tradition continued with some of the operas of Massenet, a composer of importance in the last part of the 19th century. His *Manon*, where the heroine is convicted of immorality and transported, to die in the American desert, was staged by the Opéra-Comique, as was his treatment of the story of Cinderella, *Cendrillon*.

Opéra Bouffe

It would be impossible to leave Paris without mention, at least, of the genre of French *opéra bouffe* in the second half of the 19th century. This owes its name to Jacques Offenbach and is very much lighter in style than the comedies of *opéra comique*, which, by comparison, grew in seriousness of purpose. Best known of Offenbach's works in this form is *Orphée aux enfers* (Orpheus in the Underworld). This mocks the serious legend tackled earlier by Monteverdi and by Gluck, among many others. Now Orpheus is glad to be rid of Eurydice, while she is quite happy to enjoy herself in the Underworld, where the Blessed Spirits have greeted her with a spirited can-can. *Opéra bouffe* is light-hearted operetta, designed to satirise and to entertain. As such it seems typical of the French Second Empire, the period of Napoleon III, brought to a disastrous end in the defeat at Sedan in 1870.

20th Century

The new century brought various changes. The traditional form of *opéra comique* had come to involve itself in more serious subjects, and composers understandably preferred other descriptive titles for works that lacked any trace of comedy. The early years brought Debussy's remarkable *Pelléas et Mélisande*, based on the play by Maurice Maeterlinck, set in an impressionistic pre-Raphaelite world. Other French operas reflected the interests and trends of the day. Ravel collaborated, after the First World War, with the writer Colette in his delightful *L'enfant et les sortilèges* (The Child and the Enchantments), in which a naughty child is tormented by his victims. Darius Milhaud collaborated with Paul Claudel in *Christophe Colomb* and Francis Poulenc with the surrealist poet Guillaume Apollinaire in *Les mamelles de Tirésias* (The Breasts of Tiresias). Later in life he was to tackle the weightier subject of religious martyrdom in *Dialogues des carmélites* (Dialogues of the Carmelites), while Olivier Messiaen turned to the life of St Francis for a subject.

GERMANY & AUSTRIA

The many courts of Germany and of the Habsburg Empire and its capital Vienna were open to influence from both Italy and France. It was, indeed, one of the achievements of great German composers of the late Baroque period to bring about their own synthesis of Italian, French and German. This is heard in one form in the music of Johann Sebastian Bach and in another in the music of Handel.

While Hamburg, even in Handel's brief time there, found a place for German-language opera, it was in general Italian opera that predominated. In Vienna the Emperor Joseph II attempted, principally in the 1780s, to establish a German opera, the National-Singspiel. It was to this that Mozart contributed his successful *Die Entführung aus dem Serail* (The Abduction from the Seraglio), but the Emperor's early attempts were unsuccessful.

Singspiel

The traditional German *Singspiel* had had a longer history, parallel to the popular comedy of Italy and France. As in those countries, the division between the purely popular and the more formal and literary comedy diminished. This led to a form of German-language comic opera, with some spoken dialogue, on a variety of subjects. In some, like Mozart's *Die Zauberflöte* (The Magic Flute), elements of earlier popular comedy continue. The comic bird-catcher Papageno is one of a long line of such characters, an ordinary man set in the most extraordinary surroundings. Comedy lies, as always, in the inappropriate situation and the down-to-earth reaction to it.

Singspiel continued also in a serious vein, reflecting the parallel developments in Italy and France, as well as in German theatre, with its middle-class drama, if one may so translate the word *bürgerlich* (bourgeois), without giving it a pejorative meaning. Beethoven's only opera, *Fidelio*, first staged in Vienna in 1805, deals in generally serious terms with a loyal wife's attempt to rescue her imprisoned husband. Carl Maria von Weber's work *Der Freischütz* (The Marksman), still in language and elements of spoken dialogue a *Singspiel*, includes all the elements of German romanticism and leads the way forward to full-blown German romantic opera.

German Romantic Opera

Vienna brought together Italian opera and German *Singspiel*. Gluck and his librettist Calzabigi had brought about a reform, influenced, in some respects, by French theatre and in some works by the *opéra comique*. Here, as in the major cities in Germany, two forms of opera co-existed, the Italian and the German. The 19th century, however, with all its political and cultural changes, gave a new impetus to German opera, not only to Beethoven and to Weber, but to composers like Marschner, Spohr and Lortzing.

Richard Wagner

Towering over his contemporaries in ambition and achievement, Richard Wagner introduced, from the 1840s onwards, new musical and dramatic conceptions of the art of opera or music-drama. At first he added to the existing romantic tradition in *Der fliegende Holländer* (The Flying Dutchman), *Tannhäuser* and *Lohengrin*. The first of these tells of the ghostly Dutch sea-captain, fated to sail with his phantom crew until redeemed by a woman's disinterested love. *Tannhäuser* turns to the medieval poet of that name and his temptation by the worldly pleasures offered by the Mount of Venus, while *Lohengrin* offers a story derived from the legends of the Knights of the Grail. It was, however, with his tetralogy *Der Ring des Nibelungen* (The Ring of the Nibelung), *Parsifal, Tristan und Isolde* and *Die Meistersinger von Nürnberg* (The Mastersingers of Nuremberg) that he created a new and comprehensive art-form. While the last of these praises true German art in a plot based on the activities of the Mastersingers of the 16th century, *The Ring* is a massive conception dealing with the superhuman. The four works, to be performed on successive nights in the theatre Wagner built in Bayreuth, are closely interwoven, related by recurrent themes and fragments of themes associated with ideas and characters in the drama. The plot of this massive operatic cycle is derived from Teutonic legend, stories of the old gods and the final destruction of their Valhalla.

Operetta

Operetta seems typical of Vienna in the later 19th century, exemplified by the work of Johann Strauss, in works such as *Die Fledermaus* (The Bat), with its light-hearted intrigue and attempted marital deception. The tradition of operetta found other champions in composers like Franz von Suppé, and then, leading into the new century, in Franz Lehár and his contemporaries, with parallel success in Berlin. By the 1920s, however, the formula had worn thin, gradually to be replaced by musical comedy.

After Wagner

While Wagner may overshadow his immediate successors, his influence was enormous, reflected in the operas of Humperdinck and even, however reluctantly, of the latter's pupil, Wagner's son Siegfried Wagner. The latter's operas continue to explore a German world, but rather one of Grimm's *Fairy Tales* than of gods and heroes. In 1893 Humperdinck won his first success with his opera *Hänsel und Gretel* (Hansel and Gretel), following this with other fairy-tale operas. Siegfried Wagner turns to weightier German legends in a series of operas that are only now finding an audience.

Richard Strauss

The true successor of Wagner is Richard Strauss, particularly in the remarkable series of operas in which he collaborated with the writer Hugo von Hofmannsthal, after the earlier success of *Salome*, based on Oscar Wilde's play of that name. Wilde's work had been banned in England, and *Salome* as an opera suggested new realms of sensuality to be explored, both dramatically and musically. *Elektra* in 1909 was followed by the moving nostalgia of *Der Rosenkavalier* (The Knight of the Rose), a work of comedy and poignancy, an autumnal reflection of a mood of the time, set in the age of Mozart. Strauss continued after von Hofmannsthal's death in collaboration with Stefan Zweig and others. His last opera, *Capriccio*, was first staged in Munich in 1942. His debt to Wagner may be seen as musical rather than dramatic, reflected in orchestration and harmony.

The Weimar Republic and National Socialism

The intervention of National Socialism had, in opera as elsewhere, an immensely damaging effect on the general creativity of German opera. The 1920s had brought a period of experiment, often outrageous enough in its defiance of tradition. Composers like Franz Schreker had explored the exotic world opened by Strauss's *Salome*. He was dismissed from his position in Berlin and died in 1934. Other younger composers like Schoenberg, Zemlinsky, Weill, Goldschmidt and Hindemith were driven into exile and often, therefore, into other forms of musical activity. America, where some took refuge, lacked the traditions of the German opera-house. Kurt Weill, who had collaborated with Bertolt Brecht in Berlin in *Die Dreigroschenoper* (The Threepenny Opera), a modernised and political version of *The Beggar's Opera*, turned to the American musical. Schoenberg left his great opera *Moses und Aron* unfinished.

Zemlinsky did the same, never completing his last opera. Goldschmidt in England found almost as little opportunity as Hindemith in America, both having suffered from official censorship before their forced or chosen emigration. Schoenberg's pupil Berg, however, had added his own very distinctive contribution to German opera in *Wozzeck*, a study of madness and murder. At the time of his death in Vienna in 1935 he left his second opera, *Lulu*, unfinished.

Contemporary German Opera

Germany and Austria continue to offer a fertile ground for new opera. This is encouraged by the existence of a large number of efficient provincial .opera-houses and a measure of enlightened public support. There have been notable new operas from composers such as Hans Werner Henze and remarkable experiment from Karlheinz Stockhausen, among others, expanding the possibilities of music-theatre.

BRITAIN

England, like other European countries apart from Germany, France and Italy, lacked an established national tradition of opera until the 20th century. Henry Purcell, in the later 17th century, wrote a wealth of incidental music and contributed to a genre recent scholars have called *semi-opera*, an amalgamation of spoken drama and a strong and often supernatural musical element. It was Italian opera, however, that entertained the fashionable world in the 18th century, in spite of the damaging effect of the anti-opera of John Gay, *The Beggar's Opera*. This began a new form, the English *ballad opera*, with its use of popular melodies. The musical borrowings, at least, must recall the practice of the Paris Fair Theatres.

19th Century

While there were English, Scottish and Irish composers of opera, there is relatively little trace of their work in continuing repertoire. Two Irish composers, however, Balfe and Wallace, are remembered, respectively, for *The Bohemian Girl* and *Maritana* staged in London in the 1840s. Another composer of paternal Irish origin, Arthur Sullivan, survives triumphantly in his operettas, collaborations with W.S.Gilbert.

National Opera

The 20th century brought an element of national opera through Vaughan Williams, Holst and others. Their work in this form was largely for local audiences. A more markedly international school of English opera started with Britten's opera *Peter Grimes* in 1945. The subject was local but its implications, as a study of an outsider in a closed community, were much wider. This was followed by a remarkable series of works, chamber operas and operas for the larger stage, culminating in *Death in Venice*, based on the novella by Thomas Mann.

Another element in English opera of the later 20th century has been provided by Michael Tippett and by a younger generation of composers in music-theatre and in work for the opera-house.

BOHEMIA, SLOVAKIA & MORAVIA

In those parts of the Habsburg Empire that were later subsumed in Czechoslovakia there arose, with the general nationalism of the mid-19th century, national opera. This is represented in Prague by Smetana and Dvořák. Smetana's *The Bartered Bride*, in its Czech village setting, is a comedy that continues in international repertoire. Dvořák's Czech operas have travelled less satisfactorily, with language an obvious barrier. It was primarily in the second and third decades of the 20th century that the Moravian composer Janáček came to wider notice with operas that depend, in their vocal lines, on the intonations and rhythms of speech. National traditions of Czech, Slovak and Moravian opera continue.

RUSSIA

Italian opera was brought to Russia in the 18th century and Italian composers were also involved in the setting of Russian libretti. This may be seen as part of the westernising policies of Peter the Great, much as Kemal Atatürk in Turkey in the 20th century saw the introduction of opera as a concomitant part of his programme of modernisation.

Russian Nationalism

A true Russian tradition of art-music was established in the 19th century. This was started by Glinka with the supposedly historical opera *A Life for the Tsar*, followed by *Ruslan and Lyudmila*, based on Pushkin and exploring more exotic, oriental elements, as Russian composers were to continue to do. Three, at least, of the five nationalist composers who made up what became known as the Mighty Handful, made notable contributions to Russian opera. Mussorgsky achieved this, in particular, in his historical *Boris Godunov* and Borodin in his exotic *Prince Igor*. Rimsky-Korsakov may be better known abroad for his orchestral works, but he also wrote a series of important operas, ending with the exoticism of *The Golden Cockerel*, which, after trouble with the censors, was only staged after his death. Tchaikovsky, not one of the five, but thoroughly Russian in his music, is known in international repertoire for two operas based on Pushkin, *Eugene Onegin* and *The Queen of Spades*.

Shostakovich, Prokofiev and Stravinsky

Russian opera continued in the 20th century, particularly in the work of Shostakovich, whose *A Lady Macbeth of the Mtsensk District* won official condemnation. Its subject might have seemed quite acceptable to a Communist régime that believed in the social and political purpose of the arts. The opera is based on a story by Nikolay Leskov in which a young wife murders her father-in-law, and, with the help of her lover, her husband, crimes for which she and her lover are punished. This certainly follows political teaching in showing the degeneracy of the capitalists at the heart of the drama. For Stalin, however, the score was chaos instead of music.

Prokofiev left Russia in 1917 and spent a number of years abroad, before finally returning home in 1936, in time for the official attack on Shostakovich. For Chicago he had written the opera *The Love for Three Oranges*, but the next opera, *The Fiery Angel*, was not performed until after the composer's death in 1953. His most ambitious opera in Russia was the monumental *War and Peace*, based on Tolstoy. This was completed in 1948 but not staged until 1960.

Stravinsky, in exile from Russia, contributed to the genre in very Russian style in his earlier period, but his later opera *The Rake's Progress*, however characteristic in musical language, belongs rather to English and American repertoire in subject and language. With a plot based on Hogarth's series of engravings, the work is neo-classical in form and texture, combining the Rake's progress to disaster with the legend of Faust.

AMERICA & OTHER COUNTRIES

It may seem cavalier to include the rest of the operatic world in a geographical rag-bag. South America at first inherited operatic traditions from its colonial past, from Spain and Portugal. The United States also relied on European tradition, but in the 20th century, in particular, went on to develop its own musical idiom. In opera this is reflected in the work of Aaron Copland, Samuel Barber and others. Most characteristic, although with no direct successors, is Gershwin's black opera *Porgy and Bess*, while the expatriate Italian composer Menotti has added his own very personal contribution in operas like *The Medium* and *The Consul*. Although many composers, forced into exile from Germany and German-dominated countries in Europe, found a place in the United States, there was little scope for opera. Some were able to work in Hollywood, while others, like Kurt Weill, made a dramatic contribution to the American musical in music that often had its basis in earlier operatic experience.

In Europe Spain and Portugal shared in the earlier developments of Italian opera and provided inspiration for other countries in choice of setting. The popular Spanish *zarzuela*, with its song, dance and spoken dialogue, has a long history, but flourished particularly in the second half of the 19th century. Composers who wrote operas drawing on national sources of inspiration include Enrique Granados, Manuel de Falla and Roberto Gerhard.

Countries of Eastern Europe have again built on national musical and cultural traditions. In Hungary Kodály offered what has been described as a *Singspiel* in the very Hungarian *Háry János*, dealing with the comic exaggerations of a boastful old soldier. His contemporary Bartók left only one opera, *Duke Bluebeard's Castle*, a work that makes greater demands on an audience. In Poland Szymanowski made his own distinctive contribution to operatic repertoire with *King Roger*, a medieval drama based on the *Bacchae* of Euripides. echoing the conflict that the philosopher Nietzsche had seen again between Apollo and Dionysus, the serenely rational and the passionately irrational. While the talents of these composers may not have been primarily operatic, all three contributed to the genre in characteristic ways.

Conclusion

The three great streams that have come together in European opera have flowed from Italy, in the first place, then from France and from Germany. The same might be said of the great body of Western art-music. It was that mixture of Italian melody, French dance and German intellect and technique that created Western music as it is now known and the genre of opera that came from it. To this amalgam have been added the colours and cultural flavouring provided by other countries, with the later development of their own individual operatic traditions. Opera itself is essentially a synthesis of the arts. Its music remains a synthesis of different national cultures, absorbed and then diffused once more. Since its early development it has had its enemies, cynics who can find nothing but the ridiculous in stage performances where characters, often in extreme circumstances, sing rather than speak or scream. Yet it is arguably the highest of all arts, the sum and summit of them all, the art, as an early composer remarked, of Princes.

Note

The Naxos A to Z of Opera cannot claim to be a complete survey of operatic history. There is no mention here of the musical and dramatic arts outside the European tradition, and even within the latter there must be many omissions and many arbitrary choices. While there are notable exceptions, most composers, major and minor, have written operas, so that any reader seeking fuller information would need to consult the four substantial volumes of *The Grove Dictionary of Opera*, the most comprehensive publication on the subject, complete multi-volume dictionaries of music such as *The New Grove Dictionary of Music and Musicians* or *Musik in Geschichte und Gegenwart*, or other shorter compilations that can still afford to offer wider coverage.

The present little book contains four main sections. The first and longest of these, after the Introduction, is an alphabetic listing of operas by title, with brief information on plot and place in the scheme of things. The second section is an alphabetic list of composers who have made notable contributions to the genre, and the third is a short glossary of technical terms that may be found in the preceding text. The final section is an alphabetical index of composers and the operas mentioned. As befits a Naxos publication, the first section also includes listings of Naxos, Marco Polo and Marco Polo/Da Capo recordings of complete operas or operatic excerpts, where these are available.

Abu Hassan

- Carl Maria von Weber. *Singspiel* in one act. 1811.
- Libretto by Franz Carl Hiemer after Antoine Galland's *Le dormeur éveillé* (The Sleeper Woken), itself based on an episode in *The Arabian Nights*.
- First performance at the Residenztheater, Munich, on 4th June 1811.

Characters

Abu Hassan, cup-bearer to the Caliph	tenor
Fatime, his wife	soprano
Omar, a money-lender	bass
Caliph	speaking part
Zobeide, the Caliph's wife	speaking part

Abu Hassan is cup-bearer to the Caliph. He and his wife Fatime are being pressed for debt by Omar, a moneylender, who has designs also on Fatime. The couple plan to extract money from the Caliph. Abu Hassan seeks money for the funeral expenses of Fatime, whom he declares to be dead, while Fatime seeks funeral money from the Caliph's wife, Zobeide, for her husband. They succeed in their plan, but then both have to pretend to be dead. The Caliph promises a reward for an answer to the mystery, and Abu Hassan, hearing this, awakes from the dead. Omar, who has been shut in a cupboard by Fatime, is punished by the Caliph for his activities, and the cupboard, with Omar inside, is taken off to prison.

Weber's *Abu Hassan* was first performed in Munich in 1811. There were revivals in Gotha in 1813 and in Dresden in 1823, for both of which Weber added further songs. The work owes something to the Turkish opera, *Die Entführung aus dem Serail*, (The Abduction from the Seraglio), by Mozart, married to Weber's cousin, and there is a place in the score for what was then known as 'Turkish music', chiefly percussion. The overture is sometimes heard in concert performance and makes a lively introduction to a good piece of theatre.

Acis and Galatea

- George Frideric Handel. Masque or Serenata in one act (later two). 1718.
- Libretto by John Gay and others (perhaps Alexander Pope and John Hughes) after Ovid's *Metamorphoses*.
- First performance at Cannons, Edgware, 1718.

Characters

Acis, a shepherd	tenor
Galatea, a nymph	soprano
Damon, a shepherd	tenor
Polyphemus, a one-eyed giant	bass
Coridon, a shepherd	tenor

The nymph Galatea loves the shepherd Acis, who returns her affection. Both are counselled in their love by the shepherd Damon. The monster Polyphemus is jealous and threatens Acis, while Coridon, another shepherd, advises him against violence. Polyphemus, however, crushes Acis with a massive stone, whereupon Galatea, half-divine, uses her powers to turn him into a fountain.

Acis and Galatea was written in its first English form for performance at Cannons, the house of James Brydges, later Duke of Chandos. It follows the English pastoral genre and was described by Handel as a little opera, although it was not always fully staged, even in Handel's life-time. The work was variously revised for later performances, very fully staged, or barely staged at all, and Handel added music from his early Italian cantata on the same subject, as well as material from other cantatas. It was arranged by Mozart in 1788. Familiar songs from *Acis and Galatea* include music for Polyphemus, *I rage, I melt, I burn!* and *Ruddier than the cherry*.

Recommended Recording: Acis and Galatea ***Naxos 8.553188***

Admeto (Admetus)

- George Frideric Handel. Opera in three acts. 1727.
- Libretto adapted, probably by Haym and Rolli, from the work of Ortensio Mauro based on an earlier Italian version by the Venetian librettist Aurelio Aureli.
- First performance at the King's Theatre, London, on 31st January 1727.

CHARACTERS

Admeto (Admetus), King of Thessaly	male alto
Alceste (Alcestis), his wife	soprano
Ercole (Hercules)	bass
Orindo, a courtier	contralto
Trasimede (Thrasymedes), brother of Admeto	male alto
Antigona, a Trojan princess	soprano
Meraspe, her governor	bass
Oracle of Apollo	bass

The opera treats the legendary story of King Admetus, the subject of the play by Euripides. Admetus is dying and the oracle of Apollo tells Alcestis, his wife, that he can only be saved if someone will take his place. Matters are complicated by the arrival of the Trojan princess, Antigona. She had been betrothed to Admetus, who had never seen her, and believes his illness a punishment for not carrying out his promise to marry her. Alcestis kills herself to save her husband and Admetus asks Hercules to bring her back from the Underworld. Thrasymedes, meanwhile, has long loved Antigona, and had tricked his brother by giving him a less attractive picture of the girl he was supposed to marry, keeping Antigona's picture for himself. She disguises herself and, with her governor Meraspe, takes work in the palace gardens, disguised as a peasant, while Alcestis, returned from the dead, is now disguised as a warrior. Matters reach a considerable degree of complication before all can end in the necessary relative happiness, with Antigona possibly to be united with Thrasymedes, or so he now hopes, and Alcestis now certainly restored to her husband Admetus.

As with many of Handel's operas, *Admeto* underwent various changes to suit different theatrical circumstances. The original production at the King's Theatre employed the rival singers Faustina Bordoni and Francesca Cuzzoni in the respective rôles of Alceste and Antigona, with the famous castrato Senesino as Admeto and the castrato Antonio Baldi as his brother. Audiences were loudly divided in their support for the two rival sopranos, at the expense of the drama.

ADRIANA LECOUVREUR

- Francesco Cilea. Opera in four acts. 1902.
- Libretto by Arturo Colautti after the play *Adrienne Lecouvreur* by Eugène Scribe and Ernest Legouvé.
- First performance at the Teatro Lirico, Milan, on 6th November 1902.

Characters

Adriana Lecouvreur, of the Comédie-Française	soprano
Maurizio, Count of Saxony	tenor
Prince de Bouillon	bass
Princesse de Bouillon	mezzo-soprano
Abbé de Chazeuil	tenor
Michonnet, stage-director at the Comédie-Française	baritone

Other Members of the Company of the Comédie-Française

Quinault	bass
Poisson	tenor
Mlle Jouvenot	soprano
Mlle Dangeville	mezzo-soprano

The year is 1730, the place Paris, the scene the foyer of the Comédie-Française, where Michonnet is busily engaged. He loves Adriana, but does not declare himself, since she tells him she has a lover, an unkown admirer. The Prince de Bouillon, a patron of the theatre, has found a letter to Maurizio that they think is from the Prince's mistress, the actress Duclos, making an assignation that night at her house. The Prince resolves to arrange a party at the house, hoping to surprise the guilty pair. The letter was in fact written by the Princesse de Bouillon, who opens the second act, set at the villa of La Duclos. Here she is joined by Maurizio, her former lover, who is aware of what is happening. The Prince and his friend the Abbé arrive, and the Princess hides, leaving Maurizio to deal with a situation that is complicated by the arrival of Adriana, whose true lover he is, although she did not realise his identity. The opera continues with a story that centres on the rivalry of Adriana and the Princesse de Bouillon, but ends in tragedy when a bunch of violets that Adriana had once given to Maurizio and that he had been compelled, diplomatically, to give to the Princess, is returned to Adriana. The flowers have been poisoned by the Princess, and as, in the last act, Maurizio declares his true love for Adriana, she dies.

Francesco Cilea's opera is an example of Italian realism, *verismo*, although set in the elegance of earlier 18th century Paris. It mixes elements of comic intrigue and tragedy, the last predominating in the moving ending. The original production had Caruso in the part of Maurizio and Angelica Pandolfini as Adriana. Adriana's *Io son l'umile ancella* (I am the humble handmaid) at her entrance and her later *Poveri fiori* (Poor flowers), when she thinks Maurizio has returned the flowers to her, may be heard in concert repertoire, as may the tenor *La dolcissima effigie sorridente* (The sweetest smiling representation), sung by Maurizio in the first act.

Africaine, L' (The African Maid)

- Giacomo Meyerbeer. Grand opera in five acts. 1863.
- Libretto by Eugène Scribe.
- First performance at the Paris Opéra on 28th April 1865.

Characters

Sélika, a slave	soprano
Inès, daughter of Don Diégo	soprano
Vasco da Gama, a Portuguese naval officer	tenor
Nélusko, a slave	baritone
Don Pédro, president of the Royal Council	bass
Don Diégo, an admiral & council member	bass
Don Alvar, a member of the council	tenor
Anna, confidante of Inès	mezzo-soprano
Grand Inquisitor of Lisbon	bass
High Priest of Brahma	baritone
Anna, attendant of Inès	mezzo-soprano

The opera is set in Lisbon and on an island in the Indian Ocean: the period is the 16th century. Vasco da Gama is betrothed to Inès, and as the story opens has been away for two years. Inès recalls their parting. Her father, Don Diégo, insists that she marry Don Pédro, since now Vasco is surely dead. He returns, however, bringing with him two slaves, Sélika and Nélusko, and seeking support for further exploration, refused by the Grand Inquisitor, who finds nothing of Africa in the Bible. Vasco is imprisoned. Sélika, a queen in her own country, tries to comfort him, as he dreams of Inès, and prevents Nélusko killing him. Vasco sees in Sélika a possible companion in his enterprise, while Inès has purchased Vasco's freedom by marrying Don Pédro. Inès and Don Pédro now set sail, piloted by the treacherous Nélusko, to be joined by Vasco, who seeks to protect Inès. The vessel is wrecked in a storm and the Portuguese are taken prisoner. Sélika is now queen once more, while the male prisoners are put to death, except for Vasco, saved by Sélika, who claims him as her husband and bids him escape. He refuses, but is later seen by her with Inès, who has not died, as others have, from the poisonous scent of the manchineel tree. Sélika now believes she will lose Vasco, and kills herself, joined in death by Nélusko.

L'Africaine is a characteristic example of French grand opera, in all its magnificence of spectacle. Meyerbeer had the libretto as early as 1838, but the work was not completed until 1863 and was first performed in 1865, four years after the death of the librettist Scribe and a year after the death of the composer. The staging calls for elaborate effects, particularly in the scene on board ship, where interior cabins can be seen, and in the ship-wreck of the third act, as well as in the ceremonies at the temple of Brahma in the fourth, where the people pay homage to their queen, Sélika, the African Maid of the title. In prison Sélika tries to calm the troubled Vasco, as he sleeps, with her *Air du sommeil* (Sleep aria), *Sur mes genoux, fils du soleil* (On my knees, son of the sun). This and the tenor *Pays merveilleux* (Wonderful country), sung by Vasco in the fourth act, with Nélusko's earlier ballad *Adamastor, roi des vagues profondes* (Adamastor, king of the deep waves) may be heard in concert repertoire.

Agrippina

- George Frideric Handel. *Dramma per musica* in three acts. 1709.
- Libretto by Vincenzo Grimani.
- First performance at the Teatro S Giovanni Grisostomo, 26th December 1709.

Characters

Claudio (Claudius), Roman Emperor	bass
Agrippina, the Emperor's wife	soprano
Nerone (Nero), her son	male soprano
Pallante (Pallas), follower & lover of Agrippina	bass
Narciso (Narcissus), follower & lover of Agrippina	male alto
Lesbo (Lesbus), servant of Claudio	bass
Ottone (Otho), appointed heir to Claudio	male alto
Poppea (Poppaea), a courtesan	soprano
Giunone (Juno)	contralto

In the absence of the Emperor Claudius, presumed dead in Britain, his wife Agrippina seeks to make her son by an earlier marriage, Nero, Emperor, helped by her freedmen Pallas and Narcissus. Claudius, however, has been saved from death by Otho, now proclaimed as his heir on his return to Rome. Matters are complicated by the fact that Claudius, Otho and Nero are all in love with Poppaea, who tries to expose the machinations of the last, and of Agrippina, by arranging that all three should visit her house, each unknown to the other. Claudius seeks to put matters right by keeping Otho as his heir and allowing Nero to have Poppaea, but when this proves unacceptable, he defers to Agrippina, leaving the Empire to Nero and giving Poppaea to Otho. Juno finally blesses their marriage.

Handel's *Agrippina* was successfully staged in 1709 in Venice, where he was welcomed with cries of *Viva il caro Sassone* (Long live the beloved Saxon). In his score Handel used again music from earlier works as well as from an opera on a similar subject by Reinhard Keiser, under whom he had worked in Hamburg, before moving to Italy.

Ägyptische Helena, Die (The Egyptian Helen)

- Richard Strauss. Opera in two acts. 1927.
- Libretto by Hugo von Hofmannsthal.
- First performance at the Dresden Staatsoper on 6th June 1928 (revised version for Salzburg, 1933).

Characters

Helena (Helen of Troy), wife of Menelaus	soprano
Menelas (Menelaus)	tenor
Hermione, their daughter	soprano
Aithra, a sorceress, daughter of an Egyptian king	soprano
Altair, a nomad chieftain	baritone
Da-ud, his son	tenor
The Omniscient Sea-shell	contralto
Two Servants of Aithra	soprano & mezzo-soprano
Three Elves	two sopranos & contralto

Menelaus has taken part in the sacking of Troy and has killed the Trojan prince Paris, seducer of his wife Helen. On his way home he determines to sacrifice Helen, to expiate the bloodshed she has caused. The opera opens in Egypt, where the sorceress Aithra laments the absence of her lover, the sea-god Poseidon. An oracular Sea-shell tells her of the murderous intentions of Menelaus, and she conjures a storm that brings the couple to her palace. By her magic she deludes Menelaus into thinking the Helen abducted to Troy, whom he now is made to imagine that he has killed, is not the real Helen, but a wraith. In the second act Menelaus is jealous of the young Da-ud, son of the nomad chief Altair, and kills him, while they are out hunting. It is the magic of Aithra that eventually reconciles Menelaus and Helen. He had been deluded by a potion of forgetfulness, but now he is given a potion of remembering, and accepts Helen as she is.

Hugo von Hoffmannsthal's libretto makes use of an ancient legend, stemming from the 6th century poet Stesichorus, repeated by Euripides in his play *Helen*, referred to by Herodotus and Plato, and treated in a poem by the modern Greek poet Seferis. In this version of the story of Troy, the true Helen had never been seduced by Paris but had been kept safe in Egypt, while Troy entertained a ghost. Strauss made changes in the second act in 1932 for production at the Salzburg Festspielhaus in the following year. The oracular sea-shell and the appearance of Bedouin may be attributed to Strauss and Hoffmannsthal. Excerpts that might be heard in the concert-hall include Helen's second act *Zweite Brautnacht* (Second wedding-night).

AIDA

- Giuseppe Verdi. Opera in four acts. 1871.
- Libretto by Antonio Ghislanzoni, after an outline by Auguste Mariette (Mariette Bey), with development of the material by Verdi and by Camille Du Locle.
- First performance at the Cairo Opera House on 24th December 1871.

CHARACTERS

Aida, daughter of the King of Ethiopia, now a slave	soprano
Radames, captain of the Egyptian guard	tenor
Amneris, daughter of the King of Egypt	mezzo-soprano
Amonasro, King of Ethiopia, father of Aida	baritone
Ramfis, Egyptian High Priest	bass
King of Egypt	bass
Messenger	tenor

In the Egypt of the Pharoahs there is war with Ethiopia. The Ethiopian King's daughter, Aida, has been captured and is now a slave in the service of the Pharoah's daughter, Amneris. Radames loves Aida but is loved by Amneris. He is appointed general of the Egyptian army and in the second scene of the second act returns in triumph, to be rewarded by the unwelcome hand of Amneris in marriage. Aida's father, Amonasro, has been taken prisoner, his life spared at the intercession of Radames. In the third act he induces his daughter to help him discover the plans of the Egyptian army, which she does in a meeting with Radames, their conversation overheard by Amonasro. Aida and Amonasro take flight but the apparent treachery of Radames is now revealed and he is condemned to death, to the dismay of Amneris. In the final scene he is immured in a stone tomb, where he is joined by Aida. As they die, Amneris, above the tomb, prays for peace for her beloved Radames.

Verdi wrote his Egyptian opera *Aida* in response to a commission from the Khedive of Egypt for the opening of the new Cairo Opera House, after rejecting requests for an anthem to celebrate the opening of the Suez Canal a year earlier. The first performance was conducted by the famous double-bass player Bottesini. Spectacle, of which some stage directors have made much, is provided particularly in the return of the victorious Radames in triumph. The story was the invention of the French egyptologist Auguste Mariette, elaborated in French prose by Camille Du Locle, before the final Italian text was drafted. *Aida* remains a popular part of Italian opera repertoire. Familiar concert excerpts from *Aida* inevitably include the tenor *Celeste Aida* (Heavenly Aida) and Aida's *Ritorna vincitor* (Return victorious). The grand march has celebrated many an unoperatic festivity and has allowed spectacular extravagance in more ostentatious productions of the opera. *O patria mia* (O my homeland) for Aida in the third act adds a particular poignancy, while the final death scene of Radames and Aida is also sometimes to be heard in dramatic isolation.

Recommended Recordings:

Aida (2 CDs)	***Naxos 8.660033-34***
Highlights	***Naxos 8.554706***

AKHNATEN

- Philip Glass. Opera in three acts. 1984.
- Libretto by Philip Glass, Shalom Goldman, Robert Israel and Richard Riddell.
- First performance at the Stuttgart Staatsoper on 24th March 1984.

CHARACTERS

Akhnaten, King Amenhotep IV of Egypt	countertenor
Nefertiti, Akhnaten's wife	contralto
Queen Tye, Akhnaten's mother	soprano
Horemhab, general and future king	baritone
Aye, Nefertiti's father, adviser to Akhnaten	bass
High Priest of Amon	tenor
Akhnaten's six daughters	female voices
Funeral party of eight men	male voices
Tourist guide	speaking part

Funeral rites of King Amenhotep III are celebrated, before the new King is crowned. The latter rejects the old god, Amon. In the temple of Amon the old gods are overthrown by Akhnaten, his mother and their followers. The Queen Mother, Queen Tye, takes a leading part in promoting the new religion and teaches her son a new poem to the sole god, Aten. Akhnaten teaches the poem to his wife. A new city is built, Akhetaten, and Akhnaten sings his hymn to the sun. The third act, twelve years later, introduces the family of Akhnaten and Nefertiti, their six daughters. The King will not listen to pleas for help from his ministers and generals and is deserted by all but two of his daughters. Akhnaten is overthrown and the god Amon is restored. In modern times the voice of a tourist guide is heard showing visitors the remains of Akhetaten. In an Epilogue the spirits of Akhnaten, Queen Tye and Nefertiti haunt the ruins of the city.

Akhnaten is the third of Philip Glass's operas and makes use of American minimalist techniques in its hypnotic repetitions of musical cells. The text is in various languages, English, Egyptian and Hebrew, with Akhnaten's hymn to the sun, Aten, in the language of the audience. The hypnotic effect of the score and the choice of subject has proved particularly effective in the theatre.

ALBERT HERRING

- Benjamin Britten. Comic opera in three acts. 1947.
- Libretto by Eric Crozier, after Guy de Maupassant's *Le rosier de Madame Husson*. (Madame Husson's Rose-Bush)
- First performance at Glyndebourne on 20th June 1947.

CHARACTERS

Lady Billows, an elderly autocrat	soprano
Florence Pike, her housekeeper	contralto
Miss Wordsworth, head teacher	soprano
Mr Gedge, the vicar	baritone
Mr Upfold, the mayor	tenor
Superintendent Budd	bass
Sid, a butcher's boy	baritone
Albert Herring, from the greengrocer's	tenor
Nancy, from the bakery	mezzo-soprano
Mrs Herring, Albert's mother	mezzo-soprano
Emmie	soprano

Cis	village children	soprano
Harry		treble

Lady Billows, the dominant figure in the small Suffolk town of Loxford and self-appointed guardian of public morals, is resolved to find a candidate virtuous enough to occupy the position of May Queen, with the help of the vigilant Florence Pike, who keeps a list of miscreants and misdemeanours, and a committee of local worthies. It is eventually decided that no girl is virtuous enough but that Albert Herring, a backward boy, only son of Mrs Herring, who keeps the greengrocer's, should be made May King. Sid, the butcher's boy, suggests that Albert should break free from his mother's control, and when he and Nancy, from the baker's, resolve to meet at night, Albert is bound to wonder at what he is missing. The crowning of the new May King is duly carried out, with appropriate presents and comments from the leaders of the community. Sid, however, has laced Albert's lemonade with rum. After the ceremony Albert, now uninhibited, makes a break for freedom. The next morning his mother is distraught at his absence and is joined by others, lamenting what might well be his early death. Albert re-appears, however, free at last, thanks to Sid and Nancy, but presumably no longer fulfilling the exacting moral standards of Lady Billows.

Benjamin Britten's *Albert Herring* followed *The Rape of Lucretia* and was the first work to be written for the newly established English Opera Group, which was responsible for the first performances at Glyndebourne and then at the newly founded Aldeburgh Festival. The score of this second chamber opera is witty and apt in its allusions and parodies, with its use of traditional children's songs and with more serious elements that raise it to a level of wider significance, notably the threnody on the supposed death of Albert, togther with the idea, central to much of Britten's operatic work, of the destruction of innocence, however lightly it may be treated here..

ALCESTE

- Jean-Baptiste Lully. *Tragédie en musique* in a prologue and five acts. 1673.
- Libretto by Philippe Quinault, after Euripides' *Alcestis*.
- First performance at the Paris Opéra on 19th January 1674.

PRINCIPAL CHARACTERS

Alceste (Alcestis), Princess of Iolcos	soprano
Admète (Admetus), King of Thessaly	haute-contre
Alcide (Alcides=Hercules)	baritone
Licomède (Lycomedes), King of Scyros	bass

Charon	baritone
Pluton (Pluto)	bass
Proserpine (Proserpina)	soprano
Confidants and confidantes of the principal mortals	
Gods	

Alceste treats the subject of Alcestis, wife of Admetus, King of Thessaly, who is allowed to replace her husband, when he is about to die, but is brought back from the Underworld by Hercules. Lully's elaborate version, based on the legend, his second tragedy, has Hercules as a disappointed lover of Alcestis, eventually, after her rescue, allowing her to stay with her husband. In the first act Alcestis is abducted by another lover, Lycomedes, King of Scyros, helped by his sister, the sea-nymph Thetis, Aeolus, god of the winds and other supernatural forces. In a battle to rescue Alcestis, Hercules is victorious against Lycomedes, but Admetus is mortally wounded. Apollo now offers Admetus his life, if someone will take his place in death. Alcestis is willing to take her husband's place and is duly rescued by Hercules. The final act celebrates her triumphant return and the noble gallantry of Hercules in giving up any claim to her. The tragedy is introduced by a prologue in which nymphs long for the victorious return of Louis XIV from battle.

Alceste, offered in celebration of the victory of Louis XIV against Franche-Comté, provided a magnificent spectacle and the expected element of dance generally found in French opera. A comic sub-plot involving the secondary characters, confidants and confidantes of the leading figures in the work, gave audiences a series of tunes that won immediate popularity, however misplaced and inappropriate some critics found such comic elements in a tragedy. The work was revived on a number of later occasions.

Alceste (Italian version)

- Christoph Willibald von Gluck. *Tragedia* in three acts. 1767.
- Libretto by Ranieri de' Calzabigi, after Euripides.
- First performance at the Vienna Burgtheater on 26th December 1767.

Characters

Alceste (Alcestis), Queen of Pherae in Thessaly	soprano
Admeto (Admetus), her husband	tenor
Eumelo & Aspasia, their children	sopranos
Evandro, confidant of Admeto	tenor

Ismene, confidante of Alceste	soprano
Herald	bass
High Priest of Apollo	baritone
Apollo	baritone
Oracle	baritone
God of the Underworld	bass

Admetus is about to die, to the distress of the people of Thessaly and of his wife Alcestis and their two children. Ceremonial prayer to Apollo elicits the answer that Admetus will die that day, unless someone will take his place. Alcestis offers herself, in the forest at night, in a place sacred to the gods of the Underworld. Admetus, ignorant, as are others, of what Alcestis has done, recovers, rejoined now by his wife, who eventually reveals the sacrifice she has made. As she dies, Admetus tries to kill himself, but is prevented, reminded of his royal duty. Alcestis appears above, with the god Apollo, who allows her to return to her husband.

Gluck's *Alceste*, in contrast to the elaborate version of the story by Lully and Quinault, offers a much simpler and more human version of the legend. It is the second of Gluck's three reform operas, in which he collaborated with Ranieri de' Calzabigi. Choreography was by Noverre, allowing a greater degree of realism, relative simplicity of language, the elimination of conventional exit arias and of other elements perpetuated in the formal libretti of Metastasio. Gluck's 1769 Preface to his opera sets out his principles, and those of Calzabigi, very clearly, their aim for classical simplicity, in accordance with views current about the classical world, with which *Alceste* was intended to be more akin.

Recommended Recording:
Alceste (3 CDs) — ***Naxos 8.660066-68***

Alceste (French version)

- Christoph Willibald von Gluck. *Tragédie opéra* in three acts. 1776.
- Libretto by Marie François Louis Gand Leblanc Roullet, after Calzabigi.
- First performance at the Paris Académie Royale de Musique on 23rd April 1776.

Changes in the French version presented the two children of Alcestis and Admetus in silent rôles, cut out the parts of Ismene and the High Priest of Apollo and introduced Hercules (bass).

The French version of *Alceste* differs principally in the third act, although there are significant changes in the earlier scenes. In the French version Hercules appears, visiting Admetus, and finding him in mourning offers his services. Alcestis enters the Underworld, with Admetus attempting to

follow her in death. Hercules intervenes and defeats in battle the infernal gods. In a final scene Apollo appears to set matters right. There is an extended final divertissement, with part of the music written by Gossec. It is this later version that, on the whole, has been retained in current repertoire, rather than the Italian version.

Gluck's overture to the opera may be heard in concert repertoire, with the dramatic air of Alceste *Divinités du Styx* (Gods of the Styx).

Alceste

Other operatic treatments of the story of Alcestis were made by a number of composers, including Pietro Andrea Ziani, Pietro Alessandro Guglielmi, and Anton Schweitzer. Modern versions of the legend include a music drama by Rutland Boughton, using Gilbert Murray's translation of Euripides (London, 1922) and the opera by Egon Wellesz, with a libretto by Hugo von Hoffmannsthal (Mannheim, 1924).

Alcina

- George Frideric Handel. Opera in three acts. 1735.
- Anonymous libretto, based on Ariosto's *Orlando Furioso*, adapted from the libretto of Riccardo Broschi's *L'isola di Alcina*.
- First performance at Covent Garden Theatre, London, on 16th April 1735.

Characters

Alcina, a sorceress	soprano
Morgana, her sister	soprano
Ruggiero, a knight	male alto
Bradamante, his betrothed	contralto
Oronte, commander of Alcina's army	tenor
Melisso, Bradamante's guardian	bass
Oberto, a young nobleman	treble

The crusader Ruggiero is captivated by Alcina and held by her on her magic island. Bradamante, disguised as a man, and Melisso come in search of him. Morgana is attracted to the disguised Bradamante, to the jealousy of her lover Oronte. Ruggiero, with no memory of the past, seeks to persuade Alcina to bewitch Bradamante. Ruggiero recovers his senses, through the agency of

Melisso and a magic ring that shows the island to be barren. Ruggiero and Bradamante try to make their escape and succeed in destroying the magic power of Alcina and Morgana. The opera includes an additional rôle for Oberto, a boy seeking his father, who has been bewitched by Alcina but is eventually rescued from his predicament.

An *opera seria*, *Alcina* nevertheless has elements of spectacle and dance. It won success at its first staging in London and was revived on a number of occasions, with appropriate revisions by the composer. It remains among the most popular of Handel's operas. Concert excerpts may include Morgana's *Tornami a vagheggiar* (Return to dreaming) and Ruggiero's *Verdi prati* (Green meadows).

ALEKO

- Sergey Vasil'yevich Rachmaninov. Opera in one act. 1892.
- Libretto by Vladimir Ivanovich Nemirovich-Danchenko, after Pushkin's *Tsïganï*
- First performance at the Moscow Bolshoy Theatre on 27th April (old style) 1893.

A graduation piece for Rachmaninov, *Aleko* deals with the liaison between the young Aleko, tired of his life, with a gypsy girl, her rejection of him in favour of another and his murder of the couple. Rachmaninov's early career in Russia brought work with the Mamontov opera, although in later life his name came to be associated above all with the piano.

ALESSANDRO

- George Frideric Handel. Opera in three acts. 1726.
- Libretto by Paolo Antonio Rolli, based on Ortensio Mauro's *La superbia d'Alessandro*.
- First performance at the King's Theatre, London, on 5th May 1726.

CHARACTERS

Alessandro Magno (Alexander the Great)	male alto
Tassile (Taxiles), King of India	male alto
Clito (Cleitus), a Macedonian captain	bass
Cleone (Cleon), a Macedonian captain	contralto
Leonato (Leonatus), a Macedonian captain	tenor
Rossane (Roxana)	soprano
Lisaura	soprano

Alexander captures the Indian city of Oxidraca. There he is loved by a captive princess, Roxana, and by Lisaura. The client King Taxiles, who loves Lisaura, entertains Alexander and his captains. Cleon loves Roxana and tries to interest Alexander in Lisaura. Cleitus refuses to accept the deification of Alexander, who strikes him. In the second act Alexander declares his love to both women, each overhearing the other. He distributes the conquered territory, but Cleitus refuses his share, objecting once more to Alexander's proclamation of himself as son of Jupiter. Cleitus is imprisoned and Alexander leads his soldiers in battle against a popular uprising. In the third act Leonatus releases Cleitus and imprisons Cleon, planning to overthrow Alexander, who is warned by Cleon, now released by others. Alexander forgives everyone, declares his love for Roxana and allows Taxiles to marry Lisaura, as a reward for his loyalty during the conspiracy.

Handel's ninth full opera for the Royal Academy of Music provided rôles for the two rival sopranos, Faustina Bordoni and Francesca Cuzzoni, whose jealous enmity is reflected in the work.

Alessandro Severo

- A libretto by Apostolo Zeno on the subject of the Roman Emperor
- Alexander Severus was set in whole or in part by a number of composers, including Antonio Lotti (Venice, 1717) and Handel (London, King's Theatre, 1738).

Alexander

Other operas on the subject of Alexander the Great include settings of the libretto by Metastasio, *Alessandro nell'Indie* (Alexander in India) by Leonardo Vinci (Rome, 1730), Handel (*Poro*, London, 1731), Johann Adolf Hasse (*Cleofide*, Dresden, 1731), Nicola Porpora (*Poro*, Turin, 1731), Francesco Corselli (Madrid, 1738), Baldassare Galuppi (Mantua, 1738), Giuseppe Ferdinando Brivio (Milan, 1742), Christoph Willibald von Gluck (*Poro*, Turin, 1744), Nicolò Jommelli (Ferrara, 1744), David Perez (Genoa, 1744; Lisbon, 1755), Georg Christoph Wagenseil (Vienna, 1748), Niccolò Piccinni (Rome, 1758), Johann Christian Bach (Naples, 1762), Tommaso Traetta (Regio Emilia, 1762), Antonio Sacchini (Venice, 1763), Luigi Gatti (Mantua, 1768), Ferdinando Bertoni (Genoa, 1769), Ignaz Holzbauer (Milan, 1769), Johann Antonin Kozeluch (Prague, 1769), Domenico Corri (London, 1774), Domenico Cimarosa (Rome, 1781), Luigi Cherubini (Mantua, 1784).

Alfonso und Estrella

- Franz Schubert. Romantic opera in three acts. 1821.
- Libretto by Franz von Schober.
- First performed at the Weimar Hoftheater on 24th June 1854.

Characters

Mauregato, a usurper, now King of León	baritone
Estrella, his daughter	soprano
Adolfo, royal army commander	bass
Froila, the exiled King of León	baritone
Alfonso, his son	tenor
Young girl	soprano
Young boy	tenor

The opera deals with the love of Alfonso, exiled with his father and living in an idyllic valley, and Estrella, who is the object of Adolfo's attentions. Mauregato demands that Estrella's husband must bear the Chain of Eurich, which Alfredo gives her, when they meet in the valley. Adolfo, meanwhile, repulsed by Mauregato, leads an army against him and is victorious, taking Estrella prisoner. She is rescued by Alfredo, who overpowers Adolfo. Unlike Prospero, in Shakespeare's *Tempest*, to which there are other narrative resemblances, Froila gives up any claim to the throne now restored to him by a repentant Mauregato, and gives it to his son, as both fathers bless the marriage of their children.

There are Singspiel elements in Schubert's romantic opera, although there is no spoken dialogue in it. The work was written by Schubert and his friend von Schober during a short holiday in the country in the summer of 1821. It was not accepted by the Vienna Court Opera and had its first performance only in 1854 at Weimar, under the direction of Franz Liszt.

Almira

- George Frideric Handel. *Singspiel* in three acts. 1704.
- Libretto by Friedrich Christian Feustking, after Giulio Pancieri's *L'Almira*.
- First performance at the Hamburg Theater am Gänsemarkton, 8th January, 1705.

The young Almira is crowned Queen of Castile. She must marry the son of her guardian, Consalvo, but has no interest in allying herself to the ambitious Osman. She is loved, however, by Fernando, who turns out, by a happy accident, also to be a son of Consalvo, so that, after a variety of intrigues, all ends happily.

Almira was Handel's first attempt at opera, written in Hamburg to replace a work that, seemingly, Reinhard Keiser, the lessee and director of the Hamburg Goosemarket Opera, had been forced to abandon, while he took refuge from his creditors.

ALZIRA

- Giuseppe Verdi. *Tragedia lirica* in a prologue and two acts. 1845.
- Libretto by Salvadore Cammarano, after Voltaire's *Alzire ou Les Américains*.
- First performance at the Teatro S Carlo, Naples, on 12th August 1845.

CHARACTERS

Alvaro, father of Gusmano, Governor of Peru	bass
Gusmano, son of Alvaro and his successor as Governor	baritone
Ovando, a Spanish duke	tenor
Zamoro, a Peruvian tribal leader	tenor
Ataliba, a Peruvian tribal leader	bass
Alzira, his daughter	soprano
Zuma, her maid	mezzo-soprano
Otumbo, an American warrior	tenor

Set in 16th-century Peru, the opera *Alzira* opens with a prologue in which Alvaro, a prisoner of the Peruvians, is released at the command of their returning leader Zamoro, himself cruelly treated before as a prisoner of Guzman. The latter succeeds his father as Governor of Peru and proclaims peace with his former prisoner Ataliba, whose daughter Alzira he claims in marriage. She, however, remains in love with Zamoro, in spite of her father's pleas. The lovers are found together and Guzman orders Zamoro's execution, but at the approach of the opposing army, releases him, in return for his father's earlier release. In the second act the Incas are defeated by the Spaniards and Zamoro, again a prisoner, is again condemned to death, to be released if Alzira will marry Guzman, a bargain to which she agrees. Otumbo claims to have engineered Zamoro's release, but when the latter re-appears among his men he is furious to learn of Alzira's coming marriage. At the wedding in the Governor's palace, Zamoro, disguised as a Spanish soldier, bursts in and stabs Guzman to death. Dying, the latter is magnanimous, forgiving Zamoro and blessing his union with Alzira.

Important as the first collaboration between Verdi and the librettist Cammarano, *Alzira* was not in other respects particularly successful and has not held its place in operatic repertoire. Later collaborations with Cammarano were *La bataglia di Legnano* (The Battle of Legnano) in 1849, *Luisa Miller* for Naples later the same year and, in 1853, *Il trovatore* (The Troubadour).

Amadigi di Gaula

- George Frideric Handel. Opera in three acts. 1715.
- Libretto, perhaps by Haym, was adapted from Antoine Houdar de Lamotte's *Amadis de Gréce*, set by Destouches in 1699.
- First performance at the King's Theatre, London, on 25th May 1715.

Principal Characters

Amadigi (Amadis)	male soprano
Dardano (Dardanus), Prince of Thrace	(male) alto
Oriana, a princess	soprano
Melissa, a sorceress	mezzo-soprano
Orgando, uncle of Oriana	male soprano

Amadis of Gaul is in love with Oriana, who is also loved by Dardanus, all being in the power of the sorceress Melissa, who loves Amadis. Matters are resolved by the suicide of Melissa and the appearance of Uncle Orgando, who descends from the clouds to unite Amadis and Oriana in happiness.

Amadigi di Gaula enjoyed moderate success and was revived, with the usual alterations, in the following years. It was written at a time when Handel, relatively newly established in London, enjoyed the particular patronage of the Earl of Burlington. In 1713 or 1714 he had moved into Burlington House in Piccadilly, where it is possible that the work was written.

Amadis

- Jean-Baptiste Lully. *Tragédie en musique* in a prologue and five acts. 1684.
- Libretto by Philippe Quinault, based on Nicolas Herberay des Essart's adaptation of Garcí Rodríguez de Montalvo's *Amadis de Gaula*.
- First performance at the Paris Opéra on 18th January 1684.

Characters

Alquif, sorcerer	baritone
Urgande, sorceress, his wife	soprano
Amadis, son of Perion, King of Gaul	haute-contre
Oriane, daughter of Lisuart, King of Britain	soprano
Florestan, natural son of Perion	baritone
Corisande, confidante of Oriane	soprano
Arcabonne, sorceress	soprano
Arcalaus, sorcerer, her brother	baritone
Ghost of Ardan Canile, his brother	baritone

Lully's opera centres on the medieval hero Amadis of Gaul, whose adventures are recounted in the early 16th-century narrative of Garcí Rodríguez de Montalvo, for much of which that writer claims earlier literary authority. *Amadis* deals with the knight of that name, much admired by Don Quixote, and his relationship with his beloved Oriana, betrothed to another and doubting her lover's sincerity. An encounter with demons leaves the hero unscathed, but he is seduced by the softer magic charms of nymphs, one in the form of Oriana. The sorceress Arcabonne seeks revenge for the death of her brother, killed by Amadis, with whom, unwittingly, she has fallen in love. The vicissitudes of both hero and heroine are ended by the intervention of the good sorceress Urganda, and all ends happily.

The subject for Lully's *tragédie en musique* was chosen by Louis XIV, whose glory is praised in the prologue to the opera. The work contains the expected elements of spectacle, particularly in the scenes of enchantment, and of dance. The second act *Bois épais* (Dense forest) of Amadis provided a vehicle for Caruso, while Arcabonne's *Amour que veux-tu de moi?* (Love, what do you want of me?) once enjoyed even greater popularity.

Amadis de Gaule

- Johann Christian Bach. *Tragédie lyrique* in three acts. 1779.
- Libretto by Philippe Quinault in a version revised by Alphonse-Denis-Marie de Vismes du Valgay.
- First performance at the Paris Opéra on 14th December 1779.

Johann Christian Bach's version of Quinault's *Amadis de Gaule* omits, in its original version, the intrigues of minor characters and is the only French opera by this composer. It won very little success, in spite of the necessary inclusion of elements of spectacle and dance.

Amadis de Grèce

- André Cardinal Destouches. *Tragédie en musique* in a prologue and five acts. 1699.
- Libretto by Antoine Houdar de Lamotte.
- First performance at the Paris Opéra on 26th March 1699.

The same libretto was adapted for Handel's Italian opera *Amadigi* in 1715. Destouches belongs to the generation between Lully and Rameau. He received encouragement from King Louis XIV and brought about certain developments in French lyric theatre, notably in the form of the *ballet-héroique*.

Amahl and the Night Visitors

- Gian Carlo Menotti. Television opera in one act. 1951.
- Libretto by Gian Carlo Menotti.
- First performance with NBC, New York, on 24th December 1951.

Characters

Amahl, a lame shepherd-boy	treble
Amahl's mother	soprano
Kaspar, one of the three kings	tenor
Melchior, one of the three kings	baritone
Balthazar, one of the three kings	bass
Page to the kings	baritone

Amahl and his mother live in poverty. The boy is imaginative and when he tells his mother he has seen a bright star, she thinks this another one of his lies, still more so when he reports the approach of three kings, who seek shelter for the night. As they sleep, Amahl's mother tries to steal from her guests, seeking money to alleviate their poverty. The page wakes up and seizes her, while Amahl tries to defend her with his crutch. When the kings take leave, Amahl offers them his crutch as a present for the Holy Child that is the object of their journey. At this the boy is miraculously cured and joins the kings on their journey to Bethlehem.

Menotti's television opera presents events through the eyes of a child, in clear, attractive tonal musical language. The work has proved widely popular with television and theatre audiences.

AMAYA

- Jesús Guridi. Drama lirico in three acts and an epilogue. 1920.
- Basque libretto by José de Arrué after Francisco Navarro Villoslada's novel *Amaya o los vascos en el siglo VIII* (Amaya of the Basques in the Eighth Century).
- First performance at the Coliseo Albia, Bilbao, on 23rd May 1920.

Set in the Basque Country in the eighth century, the opera deals with the fate of Amaya, heir to the pagan Patriarch Aitor and betrothed as a child to Asier, adopted son of the pagan priestess Amagoya, destined by this marriage to be king. The Christian Teodosio has been chosen to champion the country against Moorish invaders. In Asier's long absence he marries Amaya, but Asier, on his return, by trickery induces him to doubt her constancy, leading him, in error, to murder his own parents. Condemned to expiate his crime as a hermit, he is eventually released from his penance, able to forgive Asier, as the latter dies, and to be reunited with Amaya, now a Christian, through the agency of St Michael.

Guridi's opera has had limited international success, at least with its original Basque libretto. The work draws on Basque folk-elements, both musically and, clearly, in its story.

Recommended Recording: Amaya ***Marco Polo 8.225084-85***

AMELIA AL BALLO (AMELIA GOES TO THE BALL)

- Gian Carlo Menotti. *Opera buffa* in one act. 1937.
- Libretto by Gian Carlo Menotti.
- First performance at the Philadelphia Academy of Music on 1st April 1937.

CHARACTERS

Amelia	soprano
Amelia's husband	baritone
Amelia's lover	tenor
Chief of police	bass

Amelia is preparing to go to the ball, when her husband bursts in, angry at having found letters to her from her lover. He goes out and her lover enters, through the window. When her husband returns, tempers rise, and matters reach a climax when Amelia breaks a vase over her husband's head. He is taken to hospital, her lover to prison, and Amelia to the ball, by the Chief of Police.

Menotti's *opera buffa*, in traditional number form, was first performed in an English translation in Philadelphia.

AMICO FRITZ, L' (FRIEND FRITZ)

- Pietro Mascagni. *Commedia lirica* in three acts. 1891.
- Libretto by P. Suardon, after the story *L'ami Fritz* of Erckmann-Chatrian.
- First performance at the Teatro Costanzi, Rome, on 31st October 1891.

CHARACTERS

Fritz Kobus, a land-owner	tenor
David, rabbi and match-maker	baritone
Suzel, daughter of steward to Fritz Kobus	soprano
Beppe, a gypsy	mezzo-soprano
Hanezò, a friend of Fritz Kobus	bass
Federico, a friend of Fritz Kobus	tenor
Caterina, housekeeper to Fritz Kobus	soprano

Fritz Kobus is a confirmed bachelor, but his friend David, the rabbi, tells him that within a year he will be married. Fritz is ready to stake his vineyard on the matter, since he is content as he is. Suzel, the daughter of his steward, eventually becomes his bride, when Fritz seeks to save her from a supposed marriage that she does not want.

L'amico Fritz was staged the year after the great success of Mascagni's *Cavalleria rusticana*. It provides music of great charm for Suzel, not least in the cherry-picking duet between the two principal characters in the second act, *Suzel, buon dí* (Suzel, good day), Suzel's *Son pochi fiori* (A few flowers), the instrumental *Intermezzo* that starts the third act and Fritz's *O Amore, o bella luce* (O Love, o fair light).

Recommended Recording: Intermezzo ***Naxos 8.550240***

ANDREA CHÉNIER

- Umberto Giordano. *Dramma istorico* in four acts. 1895.
- Libretto by Luigi Illica.
- First performance at Teatro alla Scala, Milan, on 28th March 1896.

Characters

Andrea Chénier, a poet	tenor
Carlo Gérard, a servant turned revolutionary	baritone
Maddalena de Coigny	soprano
La Contessa de Coigny, her mother	mezzo-soprano
Bersi, her mulatto maid	mezzo-soprano
Madelon, an old woman	mezzo-soprano
Roucher, a friend of Chénier	bass
Pietro Fléville, a novelist	baritone
Fouquier Tinville, public prosecutor	baritone
Mathieu, a waiter turned revolutionary	baritone
Dumas, president of the tribunal	baritone
Schmidt, gaoler at St Lazare prison	baritone
Incredibile (Incroyable), an informer	tenor
The Abbé, a poet	tenor
Major-domo	baritone

The first act is set in pre-revolutionary France, where Charles Gérard, a servant to the de Coigny family, reveals his contempt for his employers and his love for their daughter. The poet André Chénier is present at a party at the Château Coigny and is induced to recite, at the request of Madeleine de Coigny, but in doing so criticizes the injustices of inequality he sees around him. The second act takes place after the revolution has started. Chénier sits in a café, with the servant Bersi at another table, both observed with suspicion by the informer Incroyable. Rouchet enters with a passport for Chénier, urging him to escape, but he is both confident and, at the same time, intrigued by letters he has received from a woman, whom he now seeks. She is revealed as Madeleine, also the object of the now revolutionary Gérard's search. Gérard and Chénier meet and fight. The former falling wounded warns Chénier of his danger but denies knowledge of his assailant when questioned by the police, summoned by Incroyable. Chénier is to be arraigned, and Gérard is persuaded to sign the indictment. Madeleine promises her love to Gérard, if he will intercede for Chénier with the tribunal. He does so, but in vain, and Chénier is condemned to death, joined on the scaffold by Madeleine, who has changed places with a woman prisoner.

Andrea Chénier offers a fictional account of the French poet, who took part in the French revolution and was later executed. It is an example of Italian *verismo*, operatic realism, and contains musical allusions to the old régime in the first act and to music associated with the revolution in later acts. Particularly well known are Chénier's two arias, the so-called *Improvviso di Chénier*, his revolutionary song in the first act, and his *Come un bel dí di Maggio* (As a fine day in May), a poem written in prison.

Recommended Recordings:

Come un bel dì di Maggio	*Naxos 8.550497*
La mamma morta	*Naxos 8.551171*

ANDROMACHE

The dramas of Euripides and of Racine, as well as studies of the tragic wife of the Trojan hero Hector by Seneca and Corneille, gave rise to a number of 18th-century operas, notably settings of libretti by Apostolo Zeno and by Antonio Salvi. They deal generally with the fate of Andromache after the fall of Troy and that of her son Astyanax. Saint-Saëns, among others, wrote incidental music for Racine's *Andromaque*, the work that was the source of Salvi's libretto.

ANDROMEDA

The legendary heroine Andromeda, daughter of Cassiopeia, chained to a rock in order to be sacrificed to a sea-monster, was rescued by Perseus. This exploit and the following events were treated in opera, and were popular with painters, as exemplified by Titian and later by Ingres. Principal operatic versions of the legend are those by Lully and Quinault in the opera *Persée* and, from a historical rather than a musical point of view, by Manelli for the opening of the first public opera house in Venice in 1637, the beginning of commercial opera.

ANIARA

- Karl-Birger Blomdahl. Revue about man in time and space. 1958.
- Libretto by Erik Lindegren, after a poem by Harry Martinson.
- First performance at the Royal Opera, Stockholm, on 31st May 1959.

Controlled by the computer Mima, the space-ship Aniara leaves the poisoned Earth, heading for Mars. The vessel is thrown off course, forcing a journey to Lyra which will last for the rest of the lives of crew and passengers. Mima destroys the Earth and cannot contiune, while the commander deals as he can with the increased despair of those aboard and their moral deterioration. The twentieth anniversary of the voyage is celebrated and death is near, as the journey comes to its end.

A score of much variety makes full use of a range of musical idioms, including jazz, serial writing and an electronic tape. The narrartive is entrusted principally to Mimaroben, a bass-baritone, who operates the electronic tape, Mima, and to the chorus. This very successful work treats, according to Blomdahl, the relationship between the individual and the group in regard to time.

ANNA BOLENA (ANNE BOLEYN)

- Gaetano Donizetti. *Tragedia lirica* in two acts. 1830.
- Libretto by Felice Romani, after works by Ippolito Pindemonte and by Alessandro Pepoli.
- First performance at the Teatro Carcano, Milan, on 26th December 1830.

CHARACTERS

Enrico VIII (Henry VIII), King of England	bass
Anna Bolena (Anne Boleyn), his second wife	soprano
Giovanna Seymour (Jane Seymour), her lady-in-waiting	soprano
Lord Rochefort, brother of Anna Bolena	bass
Lord Riccardo Percy (Lord Richard Percy)	tenor
Smeton (Smeaton), the Queen's page	contralto
Hervey, a court official	tenor

Anne Boleyn is uneasy at the King's coolness towards her, while Jane Seymour is equally disturbed by his warmth towards her. Lord Percy returns to court, anxious about his former mistress, Anne Boleyn. Percy's return is part of the King's plot to entrap his wife, which he does when Percy is threatening to kill himself for love, observed by Smeaton, who also loves her. In spite of the efforts of Jane Seymour and others, Anne is duly imprisoned, to be executed, together with Percy and Rochefort.

Anna Bolena was the first of Donizetti's operas to win international acclaim and establish his reputation in Paris and London. It provides a fine vehicle for the soprano Anna Bolena, not least in her mad scene in prison, from which she is brought to her senses by the sound of cannons celebrating, prematurely, it would seem, the marriage of King Henry and Jane Seymour.

Best known of all excerpts must be the finale, *Piangete voi?* (Do you weep?).

ANTIGONE

Antigone, daughter of Oedipus, was put to death by Creon, father of her lover Haemon and successor to her own father as King of Thebes, for disobedience to the state, when she followed religious duty in making symbolic burial of her brother Polynices, killed by his own brother in rebellion against Thebes.

The play by Sophocles ends with the death of Antigone, while Euripides allowed her survival in hiding, to bear a child to Haemon, a daughter called after her grandmother, also her great-grandmother, Jocasta. The subject of Antigone and of her daughter was used by a number of 18th-century composers. In the 20th century Honegger, Carl Orff, John Joubert and others have based operas on a subject of contemporary relevance, the conflict between duty to conscience and duty to the state.

ANTONY AND CLEOPATRA

- Samuel Barber. Opera in three acts. 1966.
- Libretto by Franco Zeffirelli, based on Shakespeare's *Antony and Cleopatra.*
- First performance at the New York Metropolitan Opera on 16th September 1966.

Samuel Barber's *Antony and Cleopatra*, revised in 1975 for a more successful production by Gian Carlo Menotti, uses a condensed version of Shakespeare's play in a work of some lyrical intensity.

APOLLO ET HYACINTHUS

- Wolfgang Amadeus Mozart. Intermezzo in three acts. 1767.
- Libretto by Rufus Widl.
- First performance at the Salzburg Benedictine University on 13th May 1767.

CHARACTERS

Oebalus, King of Lacedonia	tenor
Hyacinthus, his son	treble
Melia, his daughter	treble
Zephyrus	alto
Apollo	alto

Hyacinthus, son of Oebalus, is killed by Zephyrus in an attempt to cast blame on Apollo, his rival for the hand of Melia, daughter of Oebalus. As he dies, Hyacinthus reveals the truth. Zephyrus is banished, Apollo and Melia marry and the god turns Hyacinthus into the flower that bears his name.

The eleven-year-old Mozart wrote this first dramatic piece, with a Latin text by a member of the Salzburg University staff, for performance by a young student cast, including treble and alto boys' voices for four of the leading parts, to which, even at this stage, he made little concession.

Recommended Recording: Overture — ***Naxos 8.550185***

ARABELLA

- Richard Strauss. *Lyrische Komödie* in three acts. 1929-32.
- Libretto by Hugo von Hofmannsthal.
- First performance at the Dresden Staatsoper on 1st July 1933.

CHARACTERS

Arabella	soprano
Zdenka, her younger sister	soprano
Count Waldner, her father, a retired cavalry officer	bass
Adelaide, her mother	mezzo-soprano
Mandryka, a Croatian land-owner	baritone
Matteo, a young officer	tenor
Count Elemer, a suitor of Arabella	tenor
Count Dominik, a suitor of Arabella	baritone
Count Lamoral, a suitor of Arabella	bass
The Fiakermilli, belle of the coachmen's ball	soprano
Fortune-teller	soprano

The fortunes of the Waldner family now depend on the marriage of Arabella to a rich husband. Her younger sister Zdenka is disguised as a boy, but loves one of Arabella's suitors, the young officer Matteo. Arabella has no interest in him, nor in her three other noble suitors. She is attracted, however, by the young Mandryka, nephew of her father's old comrade, a rich if eccentric land-owner to whom Count Waldner had offered his daughter. At a ball she is now in love with Mandryka, who seeks her hand in marriage. Matteo is disconsolate, but Zdenka re-assures him, giving him what she claims is a key to Arabella's room, overheard by Mandryka, who now dances with the Fiakermilli, the pretty belle of the ball. Matteo duly visits the girl he thinks to be Arabella, in fact Zdenka, and the latter eventually reveals the truth, when Matteo and Mandryka are on the verge of fighting a duel. All ends happily.

Arabella is the last collaboration between Strauss and von Hofmannsthal, who died before any revision of the second and third acts was possible. Set in Vienna in 1860, it centres in part on the characteristic coachmen's ball of the second act, the whole opera a counterpart to *Der Rosenkavalier*, the obverse to the grandeur of that opera in its relatively impoverished setting. The opera evokes a world still redolent, however, of the past, the fading glories of Habsburg Vienna.

ARBORE DI DIANA, L' (THE TREE OF DIANA)

- Vicente Martin y Soler. *Dramma giocoso* in two acts. 1787.
- Libretto by Lorenzo Da Ponte.
- First performance at the Vienna Burgtheater on 1st October 1787.

The chaste goddess Diana is induced to fall in love in an opera designed for the marriage of Maria Theresa, niece of the Emperor Joseph II.

ARDEN MUST DIE (ARDEN MUSS STERBEN)

- Alexander Goehr. Opera in two acts. 1967.
- Libretto by Erich Fried, based on Holinshed and on the Elizabethan play *Arden of Feversham*.
- First performance at the Hamburg Staatsoper on 5th March 1967.

Alexander Goehr's opera had and retains a distinct contemporary relevance, in its study of the abdication of moral involvement by the good neighbours of Arden, whose murder has been arranged by his wife and her lover. At its first performance in Hamburg the opera seemed to make its point very clearly, arousing a consequent reaction in its audience.

ARIADNE

Ariadne, daughter of King Minos of Crete, helped the Athenian hero Theseus to escape from the bull-monster, the Minotaur, and from the surrounding labyrinth. Eloping with him, she was abandoned by her lover on the island of Naxos, where she later joined the followers of Bacchus (Dionysus). Her sad fate on the apparently deserted island, the subject of one of Ovid's *Heroides*, letters from women to their absent husbands or lovers, inspired a variety of music, from one of the earliest operas to a cantata by Haydn, and the opera by Richard Strauss. Her fate was depicted by many artists, including Titian, Poussin, Tintoretto and Raphael, while for André Gide she epitomized the eternal, clinging feminine.

Other operatic treatments of the subject, apart from those mentioned below, include:

ARIADNE AUF NAXOS (ARIADNE ON NAXOS)

- Jiři Antonín (Georg) Benda. *Duodrama* in one act. 1775.
- Text by Johann Christian Brandes, following a cantata by Heinrich Wilhelm von Gerstenberg.
- First performance at Schloss Friedenstein, Gotha, on 27th January 1775.

CHARACTERS

Ariadne	speaking part
Theseus	speaking part

In speech accompanied and interrupted by the orchestra, Ariadne awakes on the shore of Naxos, to find herself deserted by the faithless Theseus.

Georg Benda was an important figure in the development of the melodrama, the use of speech with orchestral accompaniment that found a place in, for example, Beethoven's *Fidelio* or in Weber's *Der Freischütz* and in many later dramatic works. The form appealed to Mozart, who planned but never wrote a melodrama on the subject of *Semiramide*. There have been and continue to be strong elements of melodrama in 20th-century cinema.

Recommended Recording: Ariadne auf Naxos **Naxos 8.553345**

ARIADNE AUF NAXOS (ARIADNE ON NAXOS)

- Richard Strauss. Opera in one act. 1912.
  Revised as an opera in a prologue and one act in 1916.
- Libretto by Hugo von Hofmannsthal.
- First performance of the first version after Molière's *Le bourgeois gentilhomme* (*Der Bürger als Edelmann*) at the Stuttgart Hoftheater on 25th October 1912.
- First performance of the second version at the Vienna Hofoper on 4th October 1916.

Characters Prologue

Major-domo	speaking part
Music-master	baritone
Composer	mezzo-soprano
Dancing-master	tenor
Wig-maker	bass
Footman	bass
Officer	tenor
Prima donna (later Ariadne)	soprano
Tenor (later Bacchus)	tenor

Commedia dell'arte Players of the Intermezzo

Zerbinetta	soprano
Harlequin	baritone
Scaramuccio	tenor
Truffaldino	bass
Brighella	tenor

Characters in the Opera

Ariadne (see above)	soprano
Bacchus (see above)	tenor
Naiad	high soprano
Dryad	contralto
Echo	soprano

The Prologue written for the second version of *Ariadne auf Naxos* is set in the house of a rich man, where preparations are being made for an evening entertainment. This is to allow the performance of a serious opera, a comic *commedia dell'arte* piece and fireworks. To save time, the patron has ordered the tragedy and comedy to be performed simultaneously. This distresses the composer, but his teacher, the music-master, advises compromise.

The opera starts, as it should, with Ariadne lamenting her fate, to the boredom of listening nymphs. The comedians, however, now intervene to console her, ignored by Ariadne, even when Zerbinetta interrupts. The comedians seek Zerbinetta's favour. The approach of the god Bacchus (Dionysus) arouses Ariadne and the two sing ecstatically, against a starry heaven. Zerbinetta has her own comment to make on all this in the first version, followed then by the bourgeois gentleman, Monsieur Jourdain himself. In the second version, now usually followed, Bacchus and Ariadne have the last word.

Molière's comedy concerns the gulling of the unfortunate Monsieur Jourdain, who has little idea how to employ his newly acquired wealth. *Ariadne auf Naxos* was originally intended to follow a performance of the German translation of the comedy, for which Lully had provided the original music in 1670. The work by Strauss and von Hofmannsthal provides a contrast between the comic and the tragic, the latter originally treated ironically, but more high-flown in the second version that now prevails, lacking, as it does, the deflation of Zerbinetta's final comments and the re-appearance of a bewildered Monsieur Jourdain.

Ariane (Ariadne)

- Bohuslav Martinů. Opera in one act. 1958.
- Libretto by Martinů after Georges Neveux's play *Le voyage de Thésée* (The Voyage of Theseus).
- First performance at Gelsenkirchen on 2nd March 1961.

Ariane ou Le mariage de Bacchus (Ariadne or The Marriage of Bacchus)

- Robert Cambert & Louis Grabu. *Opéra* in a prologue and five acts. 1674.
- Libretto by Pierre Perrin.
- First performance at the Theatre Royal, Drury Lane, London, on 30th March 1674.

Arianna (Ariadne)

- Claudio Monteverdi. *Tragedia* in one act, 1608.
- Libretto by Ottavio Rinuccini.
- First performance at the Palace of the Duke of Mantua on 28th May 1608.

Monteverdi's opera on the subject of Ariadne is lost, although the libretto survives, with contemporary accounts of the spectacular and moving performance. Of the original music only the famous *Lament* survives, an immensely influential work, published by Monteverdi also as a madrigal and, towards the end of his life, with a sacred text. The *Lament of Arianna* was much imitated. A new work based on the libretto, and making use of the *Lament*, has been written by

Alexander Goehr and was first performed at the London Royal Opera House, Covent Garden, in 1996.

ARIANNA IN CRETA (ARIADNE IN CRETE)

- George Frideric Handel. Opera in three acts. 1734.
- Libretto adapted from earlier operas with text by Pietro Pariati.
- First performance at the King's Theatre, London, on 26th January 1734.

ARIANNA IN NASSO (ARIADNE ON NAXOS)

- Nicola Porpora. *Dramma per musica* in three acts. 1733.
- Libretto by Paolo Antonio Rolli.
- First performance at Lincoln's Inn Fields, London, on 29th December 1733.

ARIODANT

- Etienne-Nicolas Méhul. *Drame mêlé de musique* in three acts. 1799.
- Libretto by François Hoffman, after Ariosto's *Orlando Furioso*.
- First performance by the Paris Opéra-Comique on 11th October 1799.

ARIODANTE

- George Frideric Handel. Opera in three acts. 1734.
- Libretto adapted from a work by Antonio Salvi, after an episode in Ariosto's *Orlando Furioso*.
- First performance at Covent Garden Theatre, London, on 8th January 1734.

CHARACTERS

Ariodante, a prince	male mezzo-soprano
King of Scotland	bass
Ginevra, his daughter	soprano
Lurcanio, Ariodante's brother	tenor

Polinesso, Duke of Albany	male alto
Dalinda, a lady of the court	soprano
Odoardo, a courtier	tenor

The opera is set in Edinburgh, where Ginevra, object of Polinesso's unwelcome attentions, is willingly to be betrothed to Ariodante. Polinesso, meeting Ariodante, claims to be loved by Ginevra; in proof he lets the latter see him enter Ginevra's room, admitted by Dalinda, who loves him. Lurcanio, Ariodante's brother, who has overheard the encounter, urges revenge, but Ariodante instead attempts to kill himself. Lurcanio explains what he knows to the King, who disowns Ginevra. Ariodante, who has survived, is told by Dalinda what has really happened. In a tournament, Polinesso is killed by Lurcanio and Ariodante appears, saving Ginevra from the death to which she has been condemned and, with Dalinda, putting matters right.

Ariodante opened Handel's first season at Covent Garden and won some success in the war against the rival Opera of the Nobility, supported by the Prince of Wales. Handel had the tacit and financial support of the King and Queen and, more vocally, of the Princess Royal, whom the Prince of Wales was particularly anxious to spite.

Arlecchino (Harlequin)

- Ferruccio Busoni. *Theatralisches Capriccio* in one act. 1916.
- Libretto by Ferruccio Busoni.
- First performance at the Zürich Stadttheater on 11th May 1917.

Characters

Arlecchino	speaking part
Columbine, his wife	mezzo-soprano
Ser Matteo del Sarto, a tailor	baritone
Abbate Cospicuo	baritone
Dottor Bombasto	bass
Leandro	tenor
Annunziata	silent rôle

The first part, Arlecchino as Rogue, has Harlequin flirting with Annunziata, wife of the elderly tailor Matteo. Harlequin tells him that the barbarians are upon them and locks him up out of harm's way. Arlecchino as Warrior has Matteo enlisted for military service and the third section,

Arlecchino as Husband, brings a confrontation between Harlequin and his Columbine, followed by her flirtation with Leandro. Harlequin interrupts and in a duel wounds Leandro. The final section, Arlecchino as Victor, has Leandro taken to hospital by the passing Priest and Doctor, while Harlequin makes off with Annunziata.

Busoni's original intention was to provide comic interludes, in the old German Casperl tradition, for his *Doktor Faustus*, in this following 16th-century puppet-theatre practice. The score is allusive, with references to earlier operas and contemporary music.

Arlesiana, L' (The Girl from Arles)

- Francesco Cilea. Opera in four acts. 1897.
- Libretto by Leopoldo Marenco, after Alphonse Daudet's *L'arlésienne* (The Girl from Arles).
- First performance at the Milan Teatro Lirico on 17th November 1897.

In an opera that gave Enrico Caruso his first great success, Cilea sets the story of love and despair by Daudet, in which Federico eventually takes his own life, when it seems that the girl from Arles is another's. The original play by Daudet was staged with incidental music by Georges Bizet in Paris in 1872.

Most familiar of all is the tenor *E la solita storia* (It is the accustomed story).

Arme Heinrich, Der (Poor Heinrich)

- Hans Pfitzner. *Musikdrama* in three acts. 1893.
- Libretto by James Grun and Hans Pfitzner, after the poem by the 12th century poet Hartmann von Aue.
- First performance at the Mainz Stadttheater on 2nd April 1895.

Characters

Heinrich, a German knight	tenor
Dietrich, one of his vassals	baritone
Hilde, his wife	soprano
Agnes, their young daughter	soprano
Physician, a monk of Salerno	bass

Heinrich is sick and, as Dietrich reports after visiting the Physician, can only be cured by the blood of a young virgin. Agnes pleads with her parents to allow her to be the one to heal their lord. In the monastery at Salerno she is about to be sacrificed, when Heinrich miraculously regains his strength, breaks into the sacrificial chamber and prevents her death. All welcome the miracle.

Hans Pfitzner's opera is akin, in subject and treatment, to other works of the period, not least, in its medieval setting and imagery, to the work of Siegfried Wagner. Hartmann von Aue's poem has Heinrich, an admirable character, suffer from leprosy. The cure is similarly effected, leading to his marriage to the girl who has been willing to save him. The original poem is also the basis of a play by Gerhart Hauptmann, written in 1902.

Armida

The Saracen sorceress of Torquato Tasso's poem *Gerusalemme liberata*, Armida, was the subject of some hundred operas or ballets. Through her wiles she lures crusaders into her power, pursuing a vendetta, in particular, against Rinaldo, whom she takes to her magic island. When he is brought again to his senses, he leaves her, but when she is finally defeated by the crusaders, he saves her from death, gives her back her kingdom and there is a final reconciliation. The story is treated with various degrees of freedom by librettists, with operas on the subject by Traetta, Salieri, Sacchini, Naumann, Jommelli and many others. The same story appears in opera under the name of the Christian hero, *Rinaldo*, the title of Handel's first opera for London.

Armida

- Joseph Haydn. *Dramma eroico* in three acts. 1784.
- Libretto by Nunziato Porta, after an episode in Torquato Tasso's *Gerusalemme liberata*.
- First performance at Esterháza on 16th February 1784.

In Haydn's opera, performed on many occasions at Esterháza during the years immediately following its composition, Rinaldo offers to help Armida defend Damascus against the crusaders. Resolving to follow duty rather than love, Rinaldo deserts her but is almost won over to her again, through her magic and the power of the magic myrtle in the enchanted wood. Rinaldo strikes the tree and is saved, still suffering pangs of love, but following the dictates of duty.

Armida

- Gioachino Rossini. *Dramma* in three acts. 1817.
- Libretto by Giovanni Schmidt, after an episode in Torquato Tasso's *Gerusalemme liberata*.
- First performance at the Teatro S Carlo, Naples, on 11th November 1817.

Armida, in an attempt to deceive the crusaders, seeks help against the supposed usurper of the throne of Damascus. Rinaldo, elected leader, kills his rival in single combat and takes refuge with Armida in her enchanted palace. Two of Rinaldo's comrades arrive and show him his reflection in the polished surface of a shield, an event related in Tasso's poem. Coming to his senses, he leaves Armida, who is now torn between love and desire for revenge.

The casting of Rossini's *Armida* has presented problems, since it calls for seven tenors, although two pairs of rôles at least have traditionally been shared between two singers. The soprano aria *D'amore al dolce impero* (The sweet empire of love) has proved effective in concert, too.

Armida

- Antonín Dvořák. Opera in four acts. 1903.
- Libretto by Jaroslav Vrchlichký, after an episode in Torquato Tasso's *Gerusalemme liberata*.
- First performance at the Prague National Theatre on 25th March 1904.

In a Czech version of Tasso's narrative, Armida is sent to distract Rinald and his comrades from an attack on Damascus. In love they try to elope from the camp of the crusaders, and are spirited away eventually by the sorcerer Ismen. It is he who provides the magic shield so that his comrades who have come in search of him may bring Rinald to his senses, allowing him to rejoin battle with the enemy and to kill Ismen. In combat Rinald also kills Armida, who, like Clorinda in the Tasso story of Tancredi and Clorinda, dies penitent and seeking conversion.

The subject of Dvořák's *Armida* appealed, no doubt, through its treatment of conflict between Christian and non-Christian and between love and duty. The opera enjoyed no great success and the composer was by now too ill to sit through the whole of the first performance on 25th March 1904. He died on 1st May.

Recommended Recording: Overture — ***Marco Polo 8.223272***

ARMIDE

- Jean-Baptiste Lully. *Tragédie en musique* in a prologue and five acts. 1686.
- Libretto by Philippe Quinault, after an episode in Torquato Tasso's *Gerusalemme liberata*.
- First performance at the Paris Opéra on 15th February 1686.

In the prologue the allegorical figures of Glory and Wisdom proclaim their power over their hero, the unnamed Louis XIV, who has called upon them to see the conflict of love and duty resolved by Renaud (Rinaldo). Armide has taken prisoner most of the crusaders, but loves Renaud, who has not fallen into her power and now succeeds in setting his comrades free. He is lured away by Armide, who would kill him as he sleeps, but is, instead, prevented by the power of love. Renaud's comrades attempt to find him, making their way through the snares that delay them in the desert. In the end they find the hero, in Armide's magic palace, and when the spell is broken, he leaves, allowing Armide her final rage and despair, before herself departing in her flying chariot.

Lully and Quinault's last tragedy allows the usual place for spectacle and for ballet, with a series of divertissements and the intervention of monsters and demons, as well as the transformation scene, as Armide's palace is finally destroyed. The work represents Lully and Quinault at the very height of their powers.

ARMIDE

- Christoph Willibald von Gluck. *Drame béroique* in five acts. 1777.
- Libretto by Philippe Quinault, after an episode in Torquato Tasso's *Gerusalemme liberata*.
- First performance at the Paris Opéra on 23rd September 1777.

CHARACTERS

Armide, a sorceress, Princess of Damascus	soprano
Phénice, her confidante	soprano
Sidonie, her confidante	soprano
Renaud, a crusader	tenor
Hidraot, King of Damascus, a magician	baritone
La Haine (Hatred)	contralto
Danish Knight	tenor

Ubalde, a knight	baritone
Demon in the form of Lucinde, beloved of the Danish Knight	soprano
Demon in the form of Mélisse, beloved of Ubalde	soprano
Artémidore, prisoner of Armide	tenor
Aronte, guard of Armide's prisoners	bass
Naiad	soprano
Shepherd	soprano
A Pleasure	soprano

In his *Armide* Gluck set Quinault's libretto of 1686 and the action of the opera therefore follows that of the earlier work, without the prologue. In Lully's version Renaud and the Danish Knight were haute-contres and La Haine a tenor. Gluck considered the opera as perhaps his best.

ARMINIO

- George Frideric Handel. Opera in three acts. 1736.
- Libretto adapted from an earlier libretto by Antonio Salvi.
- First performance at Covent Garden Theatre, London, on 12th January 1737.

Handel's *Arminio* deals with the German hero Hermann or Arminius, who defeated the Roman legions under their general Varro, events recounted in the *Annales* of Tacitus. The opera won no very great success, but enjoyed the support and attendance of the Prince and Princess of Wales.

AROLDO

- Giuseppe Verdi. Opera in four acts. 1857.
- Libretto by Francesco Maria Piave, after his earlier *Stiffelio*.
- First performance at the Teatro Nuovo, Rimini, on 16th August 1857.

CHARACTERS

Aroldo, a Saxon knight	tenor
Mina, his wife	soprano
Egberto, her father	baritone
Godvino, a knight	tenor
Briano, a holy man	bass

Enrico, Mina's cousin	tenor
Elena, Mina's cousin	mezzo-soprano

Set in Kent and in Scotland, the opera opens with Aroldo's return from the crusades and Mina's fears, since she has been inconstant. At a celebration a letter, apparently from Enrico, is handed to Mina, concealed in a book, and the incident is seen by Briano, who warns Aroldo of what he thinks is happening. Aroldo seeks to open the book, as he tells the story of a knight who acted dishonourably by sending a love-letter to the lady of the house concealed in a book. Egberto believes Godvino, who had handed the book to Mina, to be her seducer and kills him as Aroldo confronts Mina. On the banks of Loch Lomond Aroldo and Briano, dressed as hermits, give shelter to travellers who have sailed over the loch through a storm. These are Egberto and Mina, exiled after the death of Godvino. Mina seeks and finally receives Aroldo's forgiveness.

Aroldo transforms the Protestant pastor Stiffelio into a 13th-century crusader, Aroldo, winning with the new opera relative success at the time.

Artaserse

The libretto *Artaserse* by Metastasio was set by some fifty composers in the 18th century, including Vinci, Hasse, Arne, Galuppi, Jommelli, Graun, Paisiello, Piccinni, Sacchini, Cimarosa, Anfossi, Isouard, Gluck and Johann Christian Bach. It deals with the machinations that followed the murder of the Persian Emperor Xerxes. Thomas Arne's version, *Artaxerxes*, staged in London in 1762, was the composer's only full opera in English and continued in repertoire into the 19th century.

Ascanio in Alba

- Wolfgang Amadeus Mozart. *Festa teatrale* in two acts. 1771.
- Libretto by Giuseppe Parini.
- First performance at the Regio Ducal Teatro, Milan, on 17th October 1771.

Characters

Ascanio	male soprano
Venere (Venus)	soprano
Silvia	soprano

Fauno (Faun)	male soprano
Aceste, a priest	tenor

Ascanius, the son of Aeneas, grandson of Venus, is to marry Silvia, who is allowed, in a pastoral setting, to see her future husband's image. In spite of her uncertainties, all ends well.

Mozart wrote *Ascanio in Alba* for the wedding celebrations of the Habsburg Archduke Ferdinand to Maria Ricciarda Berenice d'Este in Milan. The piece contains complimentary references to the couple and their ancestry.

Recommended Recording: Ascanio in Alba (2 CDs) ***Naxos 8.660040-41***

Assedio di Calais, L' (The Siege of Calais)

- Gaetano Donizetti. *Melodramma lirico* in three acts. 1836.
- Libretto by Salvadore Cammarano, after Luigi Marchionni's *L'assedio di Calais*, based on Pierre du Belloy's *Le siège de Calais*.
- First performance at the Teatro S Carlo, Naples, on 19th November 1836.

Donizetti's opera deals with the siege of Calais by the English King Edward III and the offered sacrifice by the seven burghers of the town, reprieved by the intercession of the Queen.

At the Boar's Head

- Gustav Holst. Interlude in one act. 1924.
- Libretto drawn from Shakespeare's *King Henry IV, Part I and Part II* and from the *Sonnets*.
- First performance at the Opera House, Manchester, on 3rd April 1925.

Gustav Holst drew on traditional songs for his musical interlude based on the episode at The Boar's Head tavern in which Falstaff boasts of his courage as a highway robber in front of Prince Hal and Poins, who had trapped Falstaff into a notable display of cowardice. Falstaff woos Doll Tearsheet, watched by the Prince and his companion.

Atalanta

- George Frideric Handel. Opera in three acts. 1736.
- Libretto adapted anonymously from Belisario Valeriano's *La caccia in Etolia* (The Hunt in Aetolia)
- First performance at Covent Garden Theatre, London, on 12th May 1736.

Meleager, King of Aetolia, loves Atalanta, Princess of Arcadia, whose principal interest is the hunt, an activity pursued in a pastoral setting under the name of Amaryllis. Meleager, disguised as the shepherd Thyrsis, follows her, and is eventually successful in his pursuit.

The opera was part of the celebration offered for the marriage of the Prince of Wales to Augusta, Princess of Saxe-Gotha. The Prince supported the opposing opera company, the so-called Opera of the Nobility, and Handel was now turning his attention increasingly to English oratorio. Meleager, a breeches rôle at the first performance of the opera, is given the well known *Care selve* (Dear woods), heard often enough in recital.

Attila

- Giuseppe Verdi. *Dramma lirico* in a prologue and three acts. 1846.
- Libretto by Temistocle Solera and Francesco Maria Piave, after the play *Attila, König der Hunnen* (Attila, King of the Huns) by Zacharias Werner.
- First performance at the Teatro La Fenice, Venice, on 17th March 1846.

Characters

Attila, King of the Huns	bass
Ezio, a Roman general	baritone
Odabella, daughter of the ruler of Aquileia	soprano
Foresto, a knight of Aquileia	tenor
Uldino, Breton slave of Attila	tenor
Leone, an old Roman	bass

Attila urges his warriors to sing a hymn of victory. Odabella, with her female fighters, praises the courage of Italian women. The Roman general Ezio offers Attila the Roman Empire, if he will leave Italy free, but Attila rejects the proposal. Elsewhere Foresto musters the soldiers in Aquileia that have survived Attila's attack and wonders sadly about the fate of his beloved Odabella, now a captive. Odabella, meanwhile, plans to kill Attila, and is now joined by Foresto, who no longer doubts her fidelity. Foresto and Ezio join together against Attila, who announces his intention of marrying Odabella, but as the Romans and Italians attack the Huns, she stabs Attila to death.

In the circumstances of the time, Verdi's *Attila* has clear contemporary political relevance, with the words of Ezio, *Avrai tu l'universo, resta Italia a me* (You shall have the universe, Italy remains mine), striking a particular resonance, as nationalists sought Italian freedom and unity.

Atys

- Jean-Baptiste Lully. *Tragédie en musique* in a prologue and five acts. 1676.
- Libretto by Philippe Quinault, after Ovid's *Fasti*.
- First performance at the French court, St Germain-en-Laye, on 10th January 1676.

Characters

Le Temps (Time)	baritone
Flore (Flora), a goddess	soprano
Melpomène (Melpomene), the Muse of tragedy	soprano
Iris, a goddess	soprano
A Zephyr	haute-contre
Hercule (Hercules) Antée (Antaeus) Ethéocle (Eteocles) Polinice (Polynices) Castor Pollux	dancers
Atys (Attis), Sangaride's kinsman, favourite of Célénus	haute-contre
Idas, his friend, brother of Doris	bass
Sangaride, nymph, daughter of the River Sangarius	soprano
Doris, a nymph, her friend, sister of Idas	soprano
Cybèle (Cybele), a goddess	soprano
Mélisse, her confidante and priestess	soprano
Célénus (Celaenus), King of Phrygia, son of Neptune	baritone
Le Sommeil (Sleep)	haute-contre
Morphée (Morpheus), son of Le Sommeil	haute-contre
Phobétor, son of Le Sommeil	bass

Phantase, son of Le Sommeil	tenor
Sangar, god of the River Sangarius	bass
Alecton (Alecto), a Fury	silent rôle

The opera opens with a prologue set in the palace of Time, where there is praise of the King from Flora, unseasonable in mid-winter, other gods and goddesses, with heroes, represented by dancers. In the tragedy itself Attis, disclaiming his love, is actually in love with Sangaride, who loves him, rather than her betrothed, Celaenus, as she admits to him. The goddess Cybele, in whose honour the Phrygians are gathered, appears. In her temple Celaenus seeks reassurance from Attis, whom, it now seems, Cybele loves and has chosen as Sacrificer. She reveals her love to Attis in a dream, induced by Sleep and his sons, and waking he warns Sangaride to keep their love secret. Mistaking his motives, she pledges her faith to Celaenus, with her father, the River God's approval. Attis, now Sacrificer to Cybele, forbids the match and he and Sangaride are spirited away by zephyrs. In the last act Cybele summons up the Fury Alecto, who turns Attis mad. In frenzy he kills Sangaride and, coming to his senses, stabs himself to death, to be transformed by Cybele into a pine-tree.

Atys, apparently a favourite work of Louis XIV, is the fourth of the tragedies by Lully and Quinault. It involves a large element of spectacle in the dance divertissements and in general lacks the sub-plots that are part of many other operas of the period on the model of the Venetian theatre. In 1780 the same libretto was adapted by Jean François Marmontel for an opera by Niccolò Piccinni.

Aucassin et Nicolette (Aucassin and Nicolette)

- André-Ernest-Modeste Grétry. *Comédie mise en musique* in four acts. 1779.
- Libretto by Michel-Jean Sedaine, after the fable *Les amours du bon vieux temps* (Loves of the Good Old Days) by Jean-Baptiste de la Curne de Sainte-Palaye.
- First performance at Versailles on 30th December 1779.

Aucassin et Nicolette deals with the seemingly ill-fated love of the lovers of the title, eventually resolved when parental approval is secured with the revelation of Nicolette's true parentage. The opera is set in the Middle Ages and Grétry from time to time makes use of musical elements that suggest the period.

- Kurt Weill. Opera in three acts. 1929.
- Libretto by Bertolt Brecht.
- First performance at the Leipzig Neues Theater on 9th March 1930.

CHARACTERS

Leokadja Begbick	contralto
Fatty, the book-keeper	tenor
Trinity Moses	baritone
Jenny	soprano
Jim Mahoney	tenor
Jake Schmidt	tenor
Alaska Wolf Joe	bass
Pennybank Bill	baritone
Toby Higgins	tenor

On the run from the police, Leokadja Begbick, Trinity Moses and Fatty decide to set up a city of their own, with prize-fights every three days. The place attracts malcontents from far and wide, including the Cuban mulatta Jenny and her friends and the lumberjacks Jim, Jake, Bill and Joe. Jim falls in love with Jenny, for whom he pays $30, but Mahagonny is threatened by a hurricane and by the police in pursuit of Mrs Begbick. The hurricane passes and now nothing is barred in Mahagonny, with gluttony, love turning to lust and prize-fights to the death. Jim, with Jenny and Bill, tries to sail away, but cannot pay Mrs Begbick what he owes. He is captured and tried. Toby Higgins, arraigned before Mrs Begbick for murder, bribes his way out of it, but Jim has no money to do this, and Bill will not lend him anything. He is condemned to death for not paying for his whisky and is sent to the electric chair, while others act out the idea of God coming to Mahagonny. The opera ends with protest banners, seeking general licence, the world of capitalism and the words *Können uns und euch und niemand helfen* (Can't help us and you and anyone).

The opera came from an earlier collaboration with Brecht, resulting in the *Songspiel: Kleine Mahagonny*. In essence an attack on capitalism, it gave rise to protests from National Socialist Party supporters in 1930 and the following years, to be banned in Germany, with other works of Weill and Brecht, from 1933. Weill's music uses a variety of idioms, including rag-time, jazz and formal counterpoint, capturing a particular popular idiom notably in the *Alabama Song*. The controversial text drew particular opposition on both moral and political grounds.

Aureliano in Palmira

- Gioachino Rossini. *Dramma serio* in two acts. 1813.
- Libretto by Felice Romani, after Gaetano Sertor's libretto *Zenobia di Palmira*, set by Anfossi in 1789.
- First performance at the Teatro alla Scala, Milan, on 26th December 1813.

The Roman Emperor Aurelianus has seized Antioch and taken prisoner, then released, the ambitious Queen Zenobia and her lover, the Persian prince Arsace. Nobly suppressing his own feelings, the Emperor allows the lovers to be united and to live in the pastoral simplicity that the young prince prefers. It is this element that gives rise to the most characteristic music.

Axur, re d'Ormus (Axur, King of Ormus)

- Antonio Salieri. *Dramma tragicomico* in five acts. 1787.
- Libretto by Lorenzo Da Ponte, after the play *Tarare* of Beaumarchais.
- First performance at the Vienna Burgtheater on 8th January 1788.

In origin intended as an Italian version of the successful Paris opera *Tarare* by Salieri, *Axur, re d'Ormus* reworked the Beaumarchais original. The opera, which ends in tragedy but includes comic elements, was very successful in Vienna and elsewhere in German-speaking countries, winning particular favour with the Emperor Joseph II.

BALLO IN MASCHERA, UN (A MASKED BALL)

- Giuseppe Verdi. *Melodramma* in three acts. 1858.
- Libretto by Antonio Somma. after Eugène Scribe's *Gustave III, ou Le bal masqué*.
- First performance at the Teatro Apollo, Rome, on 17th February 1859.

CHARACTERS

Riccardo, Count of Warwick (Gustavus III of Sweden)	tenor
Amelia, wife of Renato	soprano
Renato, secretary to the Governor (Anckarström)	baritone
Samuele (Count Ribbing)	bass
Tommaso (Count Horn)	bass
Silvano, a sailor (Cristian)	baritone
Oscar, a page	soprano
Ulrica, a fortune-teller (Arvidson)	contralto

Originally set in late 18th-century Sweden, the plot dealt with a conspiracy against Gustavus III and his assassination. Verdi and his librettist were compelled by censorship in Naples, for which the work was originally intended, to change the scene from Sweden to Boston and the King to the English Governor. In the Boston version first performed, Riccardo is in love with Amelia, wife of his friend and secretary, Renato, who has discovered a plot against the Governor. Riccardo consults the fortune-teller Ulrica and overhears Amelia seek from the old woman a remedy for her love for Riccardo. The woman tells Riccardo he will be killed by a friend. At midnight by the gallows, Amelia seeks the magic herb that will cure her, meeting there Riccardo, who has overheard her plan. Renato approaches, warning Riccardo of a plot to kill him, and is told to escort the veiled woman back, without seeking her identity. The conspirators seize them both and reveal Amelia's identity, leading to the tragedy of the third act, where, at a masked ball, Renato kills Riccardo, who had resolved to part with Amelia and now, as he dies, assures her husband of her fidelity.

Un ballo in maschera is often performed in its Swedish setting, rather than the improbable Boston. Others have transposed the work elsewhere, notably to Naples. In its dramatic music it combines elements of French and Italian style, the light and dark of Oscar and Ulrica and the more deeply characterized Renato and Amelia. The overture offers elements of the first scene, a chorus, a fugato and the first aria of Riccardo. Recital repertoire includes the tenor *La rivedrà nell'estasi* (I shall see her again in delight) and the baritone *Alla vita che t'arride* (To the life that gives us joy), the tenor's Neapolitan *Di'tu se fedele il flutto m'aspetta* (Tell me if the sea faithful awaits me), as Riccardo confronts the sorceress, and his moving *Ma se m'è forza perderti per sempre* (But if I am forced to lose you for ever) in an opera where the tenor has a predominant rôle. Amelia has the demanding scene at the gallows, with her recitative and aria *Ma dall'arido stelo divulsa* (But parted from its dry stem), as she picks the magic herb, followed by her love duet with Riccardo, and her moving scene in which she asks Renato for pity *Morrò, ma prima in grazia deh! mi consenti* (I die, but first of your kindness grant me), pleading to be allowed to see her son.

Recommended Recordings:
Overture — ***Naxos 8.553018***
Ma se m'è forza / Di'tu se fedele — ***Naxos 8.550497***

Banadietrich

- Siegfried Wagner. Opera in three acts. 1909.
- Libretto by the composer.
- First performed at the Hoftheater, Karlsruhe, on 23rd January 1910.

Derived from the 9th century *Hildebrandlied*, *Banadietrich* deals with the hero Dietrich and his beloved Schwanweiss (Swan-White), whom he is induced to betray in return for victory, offering to the Devil the thing most dear to him. Wittich, pardoned for his apparent treachery, offers his protection to Schwanweiss, while the evil Raunerath succeeds in his plan to divert Dietrich into diabolical courses, causing his excommunication and his life as a cursed outlaw, condemned to the wild hunt. Through Schwanweiss he is eventually saved and is able to join her, with other water-nymphs, Raunerath and the Devil now put to flight.

Banadietrich is characteristic of Siegfried Wagner's preoccupation with German legend, with a Mephistophelean figure, a tempter, who finds a place elsewhere in his work, as in that of his near contemporary Pfitzner and others.

Recommended Recording: Banadietrich (2 CDs) — ***Marco Polo 8.223895-96***

Barbe-bleue (Bluebeard)

- Jacques Offenbach. *Opéra bouffe* in three acts. 1866.
- Libretto by Henri Meilhac and Ludovic Halévy.
- First performance at the Paris Théâtre des Variétés on 5th February 1866.

Bluebeard has met his match in the impossible Boulotte, his sixth wife, of whom he attempts to rid himself with the help of his alchemist Popolani. Romance is provided by the match arranged by King Bobèche between his daughter, once living as a shepherdess, and Prince Safir, once disguised as a shepherd, and in fact her lover. All ends happily for the lovers, while Bluebeard suffers the indignity of the re-appearance of his earlier wives, who had been drugged by Popolani, and with them five courtiers who were to have been executed for alleged dalliance with the Queen. All are paired off, leaving Bluebeard to put up with Boulotte.

Barbiere di Siviglia, Il (The Barber of Seville)

- Gioachino Rossini. *Commedia* in two acts. 1815.
- Libretto by Cesare Sterbini, after *Le barbier de Séville* by Beaumarchais.
- First performance at the Teatro Argentina, Rome, on 20th February 1816.

Characters

Count Almaviva	tenor
Bartolo, a doctor in Seville	basso buffo
Rosina, ward of Dr Bartolo	mezzo-soprano
Figaro, a barber	baritone
Don Basilio, a singing teacher	bass
Fiorello, servant to the Count	bass
Ambrogio, servant to Dr Bartolo	bass
Berta, Dr Bartolo's housekeeper	mezzo-soprano
Officer	baritone
Notary	silent rôle

Originally entitled *Almaviva, ossia L'inutile precauzione* (Almaviva, or The Useless Precaution), to avoid the obvious comparison with the popular treatment of the same plot by Paisiello, Rossini's opera deals with the plan by Count Almaviva to woo Rosina and win her hand in marriage. With the help of the barber and general factotum Figaro, he carries out his plan to outwit her guardian, Dr

Bartolo, who has his eye on his ward's fortune. Almaviva woos Rosina under the guise of a student, Lindoro, exchanging notes with her, and gains entry to Dr Bartolo's house disguised as a drunken officer, billeted on him, he alleges. The doctor claims exemption and summons the guard, who allow the Count to go, when the officer in charge learns his identity, still concealed from Rosina and her guardian. The Count next finds his way into the house as a substitute for the officious music-master Don Basilio, giving Rosina a singing lesson, until Don Basilio appears and has to be bribed to keep silent. After other turns of fortune, Dr Bartolo is thwarted in his intention to marry Rosina, who is reconciled to the real identity of her lover.

Il barbiere di Siviglia remains the most popular of Rossini's comic operas, providing a witty and lively score to accompany a series of incidents worthy of any farce. The first performance was unsuccessful as a result of objections made by supporters of Paisiello's opera on the same subject. The usual overture was that originally written for the opera *Aureliano in Palmira*, and the work includes some of the best known of all operatic elements in Figaro's *Largo al factotum* and in Rosina's *Una voce poco fa* (I heard a voice a little while ago), as well as the fulminations of Dr Bartolo and Don Basilio's *La calunnia* (Slander), praise of a useful way to dispose of the Count. Other well known elements in the score include the Count's first act serenade *Ecco ridente in cielo* (Lo, smiling in the heaven), while the music-lesson scene may include a coloratura aria, if Rosina is sung by a soprano, such as Alabyev's *Nightingale*, an opportunity for vocal display.

Recommended Recordings:

The Barber of Seville (3 CDs)	***Naxos 8.660027-29***
Highlights	***Naxos 8.553436***

Barbier von Bagdad, Der (The Barber of Baghdad)

- Peter Cornelius. *Komische Oper* in two acts. 1858.
- Libretto by Peter Cornelius, after *The Arabian Nights*.
- First performance at the Weimar Hoftheater on 15th December 1858.

Characters

The Caliph	baritone
Baba Mustapha, a Cadi	tenor
Margiana, his daughter	soprano
Bostana, his servant	mezzo-soprano
Nureddin	tenor

Abul Hassan Ali Ebn Bekar, a barber	bass
Three Muezzins	bass & two tenors

Nureddin is in love with Margiana. The barber Abul Hassan is summoned to prepare him for his meeting with her, but his talkative nature and attempts to help Nureddin induce the latter to pretend to his servants that Abul Hassan is ill, leaving him in their care. The Cadi has intended to marry his daughter to an old friend, but he is called to prayer and the lovers are left alone, their meeting interrupted by the re-appearance of Abul Hassan, trying to help, and the return of the Cadi. Nureddin hides in a trunk that had contained the presents sent by Margiana's other suitor and Abul Hassan, thinking Nureddin dead, tries to remove the trunk, to the anger of the Cadi, who thinks Abul Hassan is a thief. Matters are settled by the arrival of the Caliph.

Cornelius wrote his opera with the encouragement of Liszt, then employed at the Weimar court. The work underwent various changes at the hands of others but in its restored original form retains a place in German operatic repertoire. The part of the barber offers a fine comic rôle.

Barbiere di Siviglia, Il (The Barber of Seville)

- Giovanni Paisiello. *Dramma giocoso* in four acts. 1782.
- Libretto by Giuseppe Petrosellini, after *Le barbier de Séville* of Beaumarchais.
- First performance at the Hermitage, St Petersburg, on 26th September 1782.

Paisiello dedicated his opera to Catherine II of Russia. It was mounted in Vienna in 1783 and won great popularity there and elsewhere. Rossini, in his opera of 1816 on the same subject and possibly indebted to the same libretto, did his best to avoid comparison with his predecessor. In this he was initially unsuccessful.

Bärenhäuter, Der (The Man in the Bear's Skin)

- Siegfried Wagner. Opera in three acts. 1898.
- Libretto by Siegfried Wagner, based on the Grimms' *Fairy Tales*.
- First performance at the Königliches Hof- und Nationaltheater, Munich, on 22nd January 1899.

Characters

Hans Kraft	tenor
Devil	bass
Stranger (St Peter)	baritone
Melchior Fröhlich, the mayor	bass
Nikolaus Spitz, a landlord	tenor
Lene, the mayor's daughter	soprano
Gunda, the mayor's second daughter	soprano
Luise, the mayor's third daughter	soprano
Kaspar Wild, corporal	baritone

Hans Kraft, a returning soldier, accepts employment from the Devil, guarding the souls in Hell. Gambling with a stranger, St Peter in disguise, he loses the souls to heaven and is punished by the Devil by being forced to wander the earth dressed in the skin of a bear, unwashed and despised. He helps the mayor discharge his debt to the rapacious inn-keeper Spitz and is promised the hand of one of his daughters in marriage. Only Luise will agree to marry him, but they are finally united after Hans Kraft has played a heroic rôle in the battle at Plassenburg.

A pupil of Humperdinck, Siegfried Wagner continued a very German tradition of magic opera, here basing his work on traditional fairy-tales, set in the Middle Ages. In the very German nature of his work he follows his father, but in other respects he creates a very different form of opera.

Recommended Recording: Der Bärenhäuter (2 CDs) ***Marco Polo 8.223713-14***

Bartered Bride, The

- Bedřich Smetana. Comic opera in three acts. 1866.
- Libretto by Karel Sabina.
- First performance at the Prague Provisional Theatre on 30th May 1866.

Characters

Krušina, a peasant	baritone
Ludmila, his wife	soprano
Mařenka, their daughter	soprano
Mícha, a landlord	bass
Háta, his wife	mezzo-soprano

Vašek, their son	tenor
Jeník, Micha's son by his first wife	tenor
Kečal, a marriage-broker	bass
Ringmaster of a visiting circus	tenor
Esmeralda, a dancer in the circus	soprano
Indian	bass

A marriage is arranged between Mařenka and the son of Micha, Vašek, a match strongly supported by the marriage-broker Kečal, who stands to gain by it. Mařenka is in love with Jeník, whose parentage is unknown to her. Jeník is bought off by Kečal, on the understanding that Mařenka will marry the eldest son of Micha. Vašek, who stutters and is a simple-minded boy, has at first no desire to marry Mařenka, but is captivated by the circus dancer Esmeralda, in whose act he agrees to appear as a bear. Mařenka is angry when she learns of the supposed bargain that Jeník has made with Kečal, the more so when he insists that she sign the contract to marry Micha's eldest son. All comes right when he reveals his identity, leaving Kečal to storm out in anger at the trick played on him.

Smetana's opera is essentially Czech in its story, its language and its music and represents an important element in the development of Czech musical nationalism. The overture enjoys great popularity as a concert opener, while the *Polka*, *Furiant* and *Dance of the Comedians* have a firm place in concert repertoire.

Recommended Recording:
Overture, Polka, Furiant, Dance of the Comedians ***Naxos 8.550376***

Bassarids, The

- Hans Werner Henze. *Opera seria* in one act (four movements) with an intermezzo. 1966.
- Libretto by W.H.Auden and Chester Kallman, after *The Bacchae* of Euripides.
- First performance at the Salzburg Grosses Festspielhaus on 6th August 1966.

Characters

Dionysus, A Voice, A Stranger	tenor
Pentheus, King of Thebes	baritone
Cadmus, his grandfather, founder of Thebes	bass
Tiresias, a blind prophet	tenor
Captain of the Royal Guard	baritone

Agave, daughter of Cadmus, mother of Pentheus	mezzo-soprano
Autonoe, her sister	soprano
Beroe, an old slave, former nurse to Semele	mezzo-soprano
Young woman, slave to Agave	silent rôle
Child, her daughter	silent rôle

Pentheus, succeeding his grandfather as King of Thebes, plans to establish a form of monotheism. Dionysus, reputed son of Zeus and Semele, daughter of Cadmus, arrives and wins followers, the Bassarids, joined by Agave, Tiresias and others. Pentheus tries to suppress the cult, taking prisoner the disguised Dionysus. The latter shows Pentheus, in an intermezzo, the erotic fantasies that lie hidden in his own mind and induces him to follow and watch the Bassarids and Maenads, followers of Dionysus. In the fourth movement Agave returns bearing the head of her son Pentheus, whom she has killed, thinking him a lion. She comes to her senses, but Dionysus now banishes the royal house of Thebes and destroys their palace, raising his mother Semele from the dead to become a goddess on Mount Olympus.

Henze uses symphonic form in the four movements of the opera. This was his second collaboration with Auden and Kallman and is again a work of clear contemporary significance, reflecting psychological problems in human nature if sensual aspects of the mind are repressed.

Bastien et Bastienne (Bastien and Bastienne)

- Wolfgang Amadeus Mozart. *Singspiel* in one act. 1768.
- Libretto by Friedrich Wilhelm Weiskern and Johann Müller, with revision by Johann Andreas Schachtner, after *Les amours de Bastien et Bastienne* (The Loves of Bastien and Bastienne) by Marie-Justine-Benoîte Favart and Harny de Guerville.
- First performance at the house of F.A.Mesmer in Vienna in September and October 1768.

Characters

Bastien	tenor
Bastienne	soprano
Colas, a magician	bass

Bastienne, taking the advice of the magician Colas, wins back the heart of Bastien, whose amorous intentions have wandered.

Mozart's *Singspiel*, written when he was twelve, makes use of a text familiar in Vienna for some years, based on a parody of Rousseau's *Le devin du village* (The Village Soothsayer). Like that work, it reflects, dramatically and musically, pastoral innocence, suited well enough to the little theatre in Mesmer's Vienna garden, where the work was first performed.

Recommended Recording: Overture **Naxos 8.550185**

Battaglia di Legnano, La (The Battle of Legnano)

- Giuseppe Verdi. *Tragedia lirica* in four acts. 1848
- Libretto by Salvadore Cammarano, after *La bataille de Toulouse* by Joseph Méry.
- First performance at the Teatro Argentina, Rome, on 27th January 1849.

Characters

Federico Barbarossa	bass
First Consul of Milan	bass
Second Consul of Milan	bass
Mayor of Como	bass
Rolando, a Milanese leader	baritone
Lida, his wife	soprano
Arrigo, a soldier from Verona	tenor
Marcovaldo, a German prisoner	baritone
Imelda, maid to Lida	mezzo-soprano
Squire to Arrigo	tenor
Herald	tenor

Arrigo and Rolando, with their fellow-soldiers, the Lombard League, swear to defend their country against Barbarossa. Lida, with whom the German prisoner Marcovaldo is in love, to her annoyance, was formerly betrothed to Arrigo, before her marriage to Rolando, when she thought her lover dead. Arrigo and Rolando, in Como, try to muster support against Barbarossa, who himself shows them the power of his army. In Milan Arrigo joins a band of patriots, swearing to fight to the death to rid Lombardy of foreign domination. Rolando is their leader. Lida writes a letter to Arrigo, intercepted by Marcovaldo, who gives it to Rolando. He now swears revenge on Arrigo and his wife Lida, finding them, innocently enough, together. Putting personal feelings aside, he leaves for battle, shutting Arrigo in his room, to dishonour him. Arrigo leaps down from the balcony, but in battle, in which the Lombards are victorious, is mortally wounded, brought back to die in Milan Cathedral. He is reconciled to Rolando and Lida as he dies.

Verdi's opera celebrates the national aspirations of the Italy of his own time against Austrian domination. It was, at the time, topical, and has since then suffered from this. The overture is occasionally heard in the concert-hall, while the oath scene by the patriots has its own place in operatic literature.

Recommended Recordings:

Overture	***Naxos 8.553089***
Preghiera / Oath Scene	***Naxos 8.550241***

BEATRICE DI TENDA

- Vincenzo Bellini. *Tragedia lirica* in two acts. 1833.
- Libretto by Felice Romani, after the play of the same name by Carl Tedaldi-Fores.
- First performance at the Teatro La Fenice, Venice, on 16th March 1833.

CHARACTERS

Filippo Maria Visconti, Duke of Milan	baritone
Beatrice di Tenda, his wife	soprano
Agnese del Maino, loved by Filippo	mezzo-soprano
Orombello, Lord of Ventimiglia	tenor
Abichino, his friend, former minister to Facino, Duke of Milan	tenor
Rizzardo del Maino, brother of Agnese	tenor

Filippo Visconti has married the widow of Facino, Duke of Milan, Beatrice di Tenda, becoming Duke himself. He loves Agnese del Maino. Orombello vows to support her, and is surprised together with Beatrice by Visconti. Under torture Orombello implicates Beatrice, who herself must be tortured, to elicit a confession of infidelity. Visconti hesitates briefly, but resolves to put his wife to death. Agnese confesses her part in a plot to discredit Beatrice, who forgives her and Visconti as she goes to her death.

The work is Bellini's penultimate opera, coming after *Norma* and to be followed in 1835 by *I Puritani*. The overture makes use also of Beatrice's prayer before the statue of her first husband, *Deh! se mi amasti un giorno* (Ah! If once you loved me), before she is joined by Orombello and surprised together with him by her second husband, Visconti.

Béatrice et Bénédict (Beatrice and Benedick)

- Hector Berlioz. *Opéra* in two acts. 1862.
- Libretto by Berlioz, after Shakespeare's *Much Ado about Nothing*.
- First performance at the Theater der Stadt, Baden-Baden, on 9th August 1862.

Characters

Don Pedro, a general	bass
Léonato, governor of Messina	speaking part
Héro, his daughter	soprano
Béatrice, his niece	mezzo-soprano
Ursula, her companion	contralto
Claudio, an officer	baritone
Bénédict, an officer	tenor
Somarone, a conductor	bass

Benedick, a confirmed bachelor, exchanges jibes with Beatrice, refusing to follow the example of Claudio, who is to marry Hero. Attempts are made, by subterfuge, to persuade Beatrice and Benedick that each is in love with the other, and, with apparent reluctance, they agree to marry, as Claudio and Hero are married.

The opera by Berlioz sets one element in Shakespeare's play, introducing a further comic element in the maestro di cappella Somarone, but omitting the intrigue of Don John, with Hero's supposed dishonour and death, before all ends well. The overture makes use of melodies from the opera and is sometimes heard in concert performance.

Beggar's Opera, The

- Johann Christoph Pepusch (arranger). Ballad opera in three acts. 1728.
- Libretto by John Gay.
- First performance at Lincoln's Inn Fields on 29th January 1728.

Characters

Macheath, a famous highwayman	tenor or baritone
Peachum, a fence	bass

Mrs Peachum, his wife	soprano
Polly Peachum, his daughter	soprano
Lockit, a corrupt prison-keeper	baritone or bass
Lucy Lockit, his daughter	soprano
Filch, a thief employed by Peachum	tenor
Diana Trapes	soprano
Beggar	speaking rôle
Player	speaking rôle

An anti-opera, with an anti-hero, like Fielding's satirical novel *Jonathan Wild, The Beggar's Opera* has the highwayman Macheath as its hero. Peachum, a thief-taker and fence, deplores his daughter's flirtation with Macheath, now revealed as a secret marriage. Peachum resolves to have Macheath betrayed to the law. Macheath is taken, as he consorts with women of the town, and is imprisoned in Lockit's gaol. He tries to persuade Lucy Lockit, promising marriage, to help him bribe his way out of prison. Escaping, he is taken again, while Lucy and Polly make no secret of their rivalry. Macheath is to be hanged, until the Beggar who is presenting the work is persuaded by the Player to provide a happy ending with a reprieve.

The Beggar's Opera, a satire on contemporary political corruption, made use of popular tunes of the time. These have been realised in various ways, most notably in the version of the work by Benjamin Britten, which makes of it an original and characteristic work of its own, first staged in 1948.

Belfagor

- Ottorino Respighi. Comic opera in a prologue, two acts and epilogue. 1923.
- Libretto by Claudio Guastalla, after a play of the same name by Ercole Luigi Morselli.
- First performance at the Teatro alla Scala, Milan, on 26th April 1923.

The Devil, Belfagor, tries to discover the truth of the allegation that sinners sin through the influence of their wives. In the guise of a rich merchant, he marries Candida, who is in love with a young sailor, Baldo, with whom she escapes, on his return from sea. Disguised as a tramp, Belfagor tries to make Baldo jealous, but Candida's virtue is established as the church bells, silent since her forced wedding, now ring out again.

Belisario

- Gaetano Donizetti. *Tragedia lirica* in three acts. 1836.
- Libretto by Salvadore Cammarano, after an adaptation of Eduard von Schenk's *Belisarius* by Luigi Marchionni.
- First performance at the Teatro La Fenice, Venice, on 4th February 1836.

Belisarius is accused by his wife of having their son killed and as a result of forgeries, which she will not repudiate, is imprisoned as a traitor to the Byzantine Empire that he has served. Blinded, he is sent into exile, but is instrumental in saving the Empire from attack by his friend and supporter Alamiro, with his own son, who had not been killed. The opera ends with the death of Belisarius and his exoneration from blame as either traitor or killer of his own son.

Eclipsed by more popular operas, *Belisario* remains a rare element in current operatic repertoire.

Bella dormente nel bosco, La (The Sleeping Beauty in the Forest)

- Ottorino Respighi. *Fiaba musicale* in three acts. 1921.
- Libretto by Gian Bistolfi, after the fairy-story by Charles Perrault.
- First performance by puppets at the Teatro dei Piccoli di Podrecca, Palazzo Odescalchi, Rome, on 9th April 1934.

First designed for puppets and then revised for children, the opera follows the original fairy-story, but includes its own wide-ranging allusions, musical and literary, as Sleeping Beauty sleeps her way into the 20th century, before being awakened.

Recommended Recording: La bella dormente nel bosco — ***Marco Polo 8.223742***

Belle Hélène, La (The Fair Helen)

- Jacques Offenbach. *Opéra bouffe* in three acts. 1864.
- Libretto by Henri Meilhac and Ludovic Halévy.
- First performance at the Paris Théâtre des Variétés on 17th December 1864.

CHARACTERS

Hélène (Helen), Queen of Sparta	soprano
Oreste (Orestes), son of Agamemnon	mezzo-soprano
Pâris (Paris), son of King Priam of Troy	tenor
Ménélas (Menelaus), King of Sparta	tenor
Agamemnon, King of Kings	baritone
Calchas, soothsayer to Jupiter	baritone
Achille (Achilles), King of Phtiotis	tenor/baritone
Ajax I, King of Salamis	tenor/baritone
Ajax II, King of the Locrians	tenor/baritone
Bacchis, maid of Hélène	soprano

Helen, wife of the dullard Menelaus, is promised to Paris, after his winning decision in the beauty contest between the three goddesses on Mount Ida. With the help of Calchas, Paris hides in Helen's bedroom and they are surprised by the unexpected return of Menelaus, who, with his fellow kings, denounces the seducer. In the third act all have gone to the seaside, Helen still protesting her innocence. A priest of Venus appears to take her away to make sacrifice to the goddess, but he is later revealed as Paris, with whom Helen happily sails to Troy.

As with light operas such as *Orphée aux enfers* (Orpheus in the Underworld), Offenbach and his librettists take a quizzical view of contemporary society in their witty treatment of the traditional story of Helen of Troy.

Recommended Recording: Overture ***Naxos 8.550473***

BENVENUTO CELLINI

- Hector Berlioz. *Opéra semi-seria* in two acts. 1837. Revised twice in 1852, the first time for Weimar under Liszt.
- Libretto by Léon de Wailly and Auguste Barbier, after the memoirs of Benvenuto Cellini.
- First performed at the Paris Opéra on 10th September 1838.

Cellini, commissioned by Pope Clement VII to make a statue of Perseus, is opposed by the papal treasurer Balducci, who prefers the sculptor Fieramosca and whose daughter Teresa plans to elope to Florence with Cellini. Fieramosca, jealous of Cellini and eager for Teresa's favours, is revealed hiding in her room and makes his escape. Thinking of his love, now his aim in life, Cellini receives money for the statue, which he promises to cast the next day, although Balducci has sent too little. He plans to elope with Teresa in the guise of a monk at the next day's carnival. Balducci is lampooned in a play arranged by Cellini, but the disguised monks bring confusion in which the bravo Pompeo, in monastic garb, is killed by Cellini, who escapes, while Fieramosca, who has overheard the plan of elopement and himself appeared in monk's habit, is arrested. Safe at home, Cellini tells Teresa of his escape, but Balducci and Fieramosca burst in, intent on Teresa's marriage to the latter. Meanwhile the statue remains unfinished, with no metal for the casting. Cellini seizes everything he can, including his own statues, and triumphantly creates the statue of Perseus.

The opera was unsuccessful at its first production in Paris and fared little better in revision in Weimar. In spite of the confusions engendered by the complexities of the plot, particularly in the second act, there is much in the score that deserves attention. The overture is a frequent part of concert repertoire. The overture *Le carnaval romain* (The Roman Carnival) is based on material from the opera.55

Recommended Recording: Overture ***Naxos 8.550999***

BERENICE

- George Frideric Handel. Opera in three acts. 1737.
- Libretto adapted from *Berenice, regina d'Egitto* (Berenice, Queen of Egypt) by Antonio Salvi.
- First performance at Covent Garden, London, on 18th May 1737.

Cleopatra Berenice, Queen of Egypt, and her sister Selene are involved in a plot of some complexity, as the Romans intervene in the affairs of the country. Matters end happily, in the opera if not in history, when Berenice marries her cousin Alexander and her sister marries the prince Demetrius.

The opera enjoyed little success and was given only four performances in the season. Handel himself had suffered on 13th April some form of paralytic stroke that immobilised four fingers of his right hand, forcing him to travel in the summer to Aix-la-Chapelle to take the waters. The minuet from the overture to the opera remains well known in various arrangements.

BESUCH DER ALTEN DAME, DER (THE VISIT OF THE OLD LADY)

- Gottfried von Einem. Opera in three acts. 1971.
- Libretto by Friedrich Dürrenmatt, after his own play of that title.
- First performance at the Vienna Staatsoper on 23rd May 1971.

Claire Zachanassian, now a very rich woman, returns to her native town, seeking revenge on her former lover Alfred Ill and for the unjust treatment she received from the courts. She offers the town a billion marks in return for the death of Ill, a proposal that in the end is accepted.

The opera is a satire on the venality of the townspeople and the corruption of attitudes to money in a plot in which the Kafkaesque Alfred Ill has no real chance of escape. It won some international popularity with music in an accessibly conservative idiom.

Betly

- Gaetano Donizetti. *Dramma giocoso* in one act. 1836. Revised in two acts in 1837.
- Libretto by Donizetti, after *Le châlet*, a libretto for Adolphe Adam by Eugène Scribe and Mélesville, based on Goethe's *Jery und Bätely*.
- First performance at the Teatro Nuovo, Naples, on 21st August 1836.

In an opera set in Switzerland, the innocent Daniele, later with the support of Max, woos the latter's sister, Betly, with final success.

Betly, ossia La capanna svizzera (Betly, or The Swiss Chalet) is an attractive work, if not among the greatest of Donizetti's achievements. The score contains elements of local colour.

Betrothal in a Monastery

- Sergey Prokofiev. Lyrico-comic opera in four acts. 1941.
- Libretto by Prokofiev and Mira Alexandrevna Mendelson, after Sheridan's *The Duenna*.
- First performance at the Prague National Opera Theatre on 5th May 1946.

Characters

Don Jerome, a grandee of Seville	tenor
Ferdinand, his son	baritone
Louisa, his daughter	soprano
The Duenna (Margaret)	contralto
Don Antonio, in love with Louisa	tenor
Clara d'Almanza, friend of Louisa	mezzo-soprano
Mendoza, a rich fish-merchant	bass
Don Carlos, his friend, an impoverished nobleman	baritone
Monks and servants	

Don Jerome plans to marry his daughter Louisa to Mendoza, for business reasons. Ferdinand, his son, is in love with Clara, while Antonio loves and serenades Louisa. Her duenna, with whom Louisa discusses her predicament, has her own designs on Mendoza. After a series of complications, the result of a variety of disguises, Antonio and Louisa, Ferdinand and Clara and Mendoza and the Duenna marry, a result with which Don Jerome must be content.

Sheridan's ballad opera was adapted by Mira Mendelson, who wrote verses for the set songs of Prokofiev's opera, while the composer himself wrote the prose passages. This was the first operatic collaboration between Prokofiev and Mira Mendelson, who lived with him after the break-up of his marriage until his death in 1953. The music is lyrical and the general treatment of the story makes something of the satire immediately acceptable to then Soviet thinking. The score includes settings of six translations of Sheridan's original songs.

Bettelstudent, Der (The Beggar Student)

- Carl Millöcker. Komische Operette in three acts. 1882.
- Libretto by F. Zell (Camillo Walzel) and Richard Genée, after *The Lady of Lyons* by Edward Bulwer-Lytton and *Les noces de Fernande* (Fernande's Marriage) by Victorien Sardou.
- First performance at the Theater an der Wien, Vienna, on 6th December 1882.

Colonel Ollendorf, Saxon governor of the prison in Krakow, plans revenge against a Polish noblewoman by presenting two impoverished Polish students to her, in the guise of Polish noblemen. True romance intervenes, and with the ennoblement of the student of the title all ends happily.

The operetta retains a place in popular repertoire. Well known songs from the work include *Ich knüpfte manche zarte Bande* (I tied many delicate ribbons), *Ich setzt' den Fall* (I put the case) and *Ich hab'kein Geld, bin vogelfrei* (I have no money, I'm free as a bird), all for tenor.

Bianca e Falliero (Bianca and Falliero)

- Gioachino Rossini. *Melodramma* in two acts. 1819.
- Libretto by Felice Romani, after *Les Vénitiens, ou Blanche et Montcassin* (The Venetians, or Blanche and Montcassin) by Antoine-Vincent Arnault.
- First performance at the Teatro alla Scala, Milan, on 26th December 1819.

Bianca loves the young Venetian general, Falliero, but her father has promised her in marriage to Capellio. She refuses to sign the wedding contract, but Falliero, who has supported her, takes refuge in the Spanish Embassy, thus breaking the law of Venice. He is to be judged by the council of three of the full alternative title of the opera, *Il consiglio di tre*, Capellio, her father and another official. It is Capellio's perception of Bianca's sincerity that leads, in the opera at least, to Falliero's release and a happy ending.

The opera is no longer in general current repertoire, although excerpts are occasionally heard, including the quartet from the climax of the work, *Cielo, il mio labbro ispira* (Heaven, inspire my lips) and perhaps the soprano *Della rosa il bel vermiglio* (The fair crimson of the rose).

Bianca e Fernando (Bianca and Fernando)

- Vincenzo Bellini. *Melodramma* in two acts. 1826.
- Libretto by Domenico Gilardoni, after *Bianca e Fernando alla tomba di Carlo IV duca di Agrigento* (Bianca and Ferdinand at the Tomb of Charles IV, Duke of Agrigento) by Carlo Roti.
- First performance at the Teatro S Carlo, Naples, on 30th May 1826.

The usurper Filippo banishes the son of Carlo, the old duke, and plans to marry his daughter. Duke Carlo is released from prison by his son and daughter, Fernando and Bianca, while Filippo has his just deserts.

The opera is not among the best known of Bellini's work, although the soprano aria *Sorgi, o padre* (Rise, father) may be heard in recital.

Billy Budd

- Benjamin Britten. Opera in four acts. 1951. Revised version in two acts. 1960.
- Libretto by E.M.Forster and Eric Crozier, after Herman Melville's story of the same title.
- First performance at Covent Garden, London, on 1st December 1951.
- First performance of the revised version at Covent Garden on 9th January 1964.

Characters

Captain Vere, commander of the Indomitable	tenor
Billy Budd, a sailor	baritone

John Claggart, master-at-arms	bass
Mr Redburn, first lieutenant	baritone
Mr Flint, sailing master	bass-baritone
Lieutenant Ratcliffe	bass
Red Whiskers, an impressed man	tenor
Donald, a sailor	baritone
Dansker, an old sailor	bass
Novice	tenor
Squeak, ship's corporal	tenor
Bosun	baritone
First and Second Mates	baritones
Maintop	tenor
Novice's friend	baritone
Arthur Jones, an impressed man	baritone
Four Midshipmen	trebles
Cabin boy	speaking part

Set on HMS Indomitable in 1797, during the French wars, the drama involves the relationship between Edward Fairfax Vere and the seaman Billy Budd, a sailor who has been taken to serve in the navy. Billy Budd, a character of radiant innocence, is in conflict with Claggart, the evil master-at-arms, who resolves to destroy him. Struck by Billy Budd, Claggart is killed and Captain Vere, who is aware of Billy Budd's innate goodness and innocence, is compelled by duty to sentence him to death.

The opera, set on a warship, has only men in the cast. It deals, as so often in Britten's operas, with the destruction of innocence, both that of the Novice, forced through fear to betray Billy Budd, and that of Billy Budd himself, while Captain Vere is presented with what might be seen as the traditional conflict between duty and love, current in earlier operatic tradition. The technical problem of writing only for male voices is triumphantly overcome, while the work provided a moving rôle for Peter Pears as Captain Vere in the original production and a chance for Britten again to evoke the sea, as he had done in *Peter Grimes* six years before.

Bluebeard's Castle

- Béla Bartók. Opera in one act. 1911.
- Libretto by Béla Balázs, after the fairy-story by Charles Perrault.
- First performance at the Budapest Opera on 24th May 1918.

CHARACTERS

Duke Bluebeard	bass
Judith, his wife	mezzo-soprano
Prologue	spoken
Bluebeard's three other wives	silent rôles

Newly married to Duke Bluebeard, Judith opens a series of doors, revealing, behind the seventh, Bluebeard's three former wives, representing the morning, noon and evening of his life: Judith represents night. Bluebeard dresses her in the crown and robes from the third door, the Treasury, and she passes with the others through the seventh door, leaving Bluebeard to solitude and the coming eternal darkness.

Bluebeard's Castle is Bartók's only opera and has been seen as representing the conflict between male and female, the rational and the emotional.

BOCCACCIO

- Franz von Suppé. *Operette* in three acts. 1879.
- Libretto by F. Zell (Camillo Walzel) and Richard Genée, after a play based on an episode in Boccaccio's *Decameron*.
- First performance at the Carltheater, Vienna, on 1st February 1879.

Boccaccio, an object of scandal to his fellow citizens in 14th century Florence, arranges for his friends to cuckold two worthy citizens, while he makes love with Fiametta, foster-daughter of one of them. She is to marry the Prince of Palermo, but agrees, instead, to marry the man she really loves, the scandalous writer Boccaccio.

Recommended Recordings:

Overture	***Marco Polo 8.223648***
March	***Marco Polo 8.223683***

BOHÈME, LA

- Giacomo Puccini. Opera in four acts. 1895.
- Libretto by Giuseppe Giacosa and Luigi Illica, after the novel *Scène de la vie de bohème* (Scene of Bohemian Life) by Henri Murger.
- First performance at the Teatro Regio, Turin, on 1st February 1896.

CAFEMOMUS

Characters

Rodolfo, a poet	tenor
Mimi, a seamstress	soprano
Marcello, a painter	baritone
Schaunard, a musician	baritone
Colline, a philosopher	bass
Musetta, a singer	soprano
Benoit, their landlord	bass
Alcindoro, state councillor	bass
Parpignol, toy vendor	tenor
Custom-house sergeant	bass

In an attic apartment in the Latin Quarter of Paris, a group of young artists are living together in poverty. Their neighbour, the little seamstress Mimi, introduces herself, seeking a light for her candle, when Rodolfo is left alone. They fall in love. At the Café Momus Rodolfo presents Mimi to his friends, while the singer Musetta abandons her elderly rich lover Alcindoro in order to join Marcello. Alcindoro is left to settle the bill for all of them. Time has passed. Mimi has lived with Rodolfo, but they quarrel, because of his apparent jealousy. He has planned to leave her, as we learn in a scene set on a cold winter morning by the city gates. Musetta, a contrast in character to the gentle Mimi, later returns to the attic apartment of the four young men, bringing with her the dying Mimi, whom they now try to comfort, but in vain, as she dies before their eyes of the consumption that has racked her.

Ruggero Leoncavallo claimed priority in his own operatic version of *La Bohème*, with a libretto of his own devising, based on the novel by Murger. His version was first performed on 6th May 1897 at the Teatro La Fenice, Venice, and won immediate, if not lasting success of the same degree as Puccini's opera. The latter version is among the best known of all works in the current repertoire, a thoroughly romantic treatment, with an element of realism in its setting. The score has provided singers with operatic recital repertoire, in particular the tenor *Che gelida manina* (Your tiny hand is frozen), Mimi's *Mi chiamano Mimi* (They call me Mimi), Rodolfo's *O soave fanciulla* (O sweet girl) and Musetta's *Waltz*.

Recommended Recordings:

La Bohème (2 CDs)	***Naxos 8.660003-04***
Highlights	***Naxos 8.553151***

Bohemian Girl, The

- Michael William Balfe. Grand opera in three acts. 1843.
- Libretto by Alfred Bunn, after the ballet pantomime *La gypsy* by Joseph Mazilier and Jules-Henri Vernoy de Saint-Georges, based on the story by Cervantes, *La gitanilla* (The Gypsy Girl).
- First performance at Drury Lane, London, on 27th November 1843.

Arline, daughter of the governor of Pressburg, is saved, as a child, by the disguised Polish nobleman Thaddeus and the gypsy leader with whom he is associated. Twelve years later Arline, who has been abducted by the gypsies, and Thaddeus are in love, but he is loved by the Queen of the gypsies, who marries the couple, but seeks the girl's downfall. Arline is accused of theft but is then recognised by her father. He at first refuses to sanction a marriage between a gypsy and his daughter, at which point Thaddeus reveals his true identity. Attempts by the gypsy Queen to kill Arline result in her own death, as the bullet she shoots hits her instead.

The opera follows the earlier tradition of the English ballad opera, and includes such well known songs as *I dreamt that I dwelt in marble halls.*

Bomarzo

- Alberto Ginastera. Opera in two acts. 1967.
- Libretto by Manuel Mujica Laínez, after his own novel of the same name.
- First performance at the Lisner Auditorium, Washington D.C., on 19th May 1967.

The 16th century Duke of Bomarzo, Pier Francesco Orsini, his own appearance and sins reflected in the grotesque stone figures in his garden, drinks a potion to bring immortality, but is poisoned. He sees episodes from his past life, his despised childhood, his ominous horoscope, his meeting with a courtesan, at his father's instigation, his failure to save his brother from death in the Tiber and his reign, in consequence, as Duke, with its jealousy and murder.

Ginastera's opera makes use of various 20th century techniques of composition, including serial variations, tone clusters and elements of chance.

Boréades, Les (The Descendants of Boreas)

- Jean-Philippe Rameau. *Tragédie en musique* in five acts. 1763.
- Libretto attributed to Louis de Cahusac.
- Intended for performance in 1764, but seemingly abandoned.

Alphise, Queen of Bactria, should marry a son of Boreas, the North Wind, but is in love with Abaris, whose parentage is unknown. She is punished by the winds for her impiety, to be rescued by her lover. He calms the angry Boreas with Cupid's magic arrow and now reveals himself as the son of Apollo and a daughter of Boreas. Alphise can now follow tradition and the dictates of her heart.

The opera contains the expected episodes of ballet and of the spectacular. The reasons for the cancellation of its intended performance in 1764 are unknown, although French fashions in opera were by then changing.

Recommended Recording: Les Boréades (Suite) — ***Naxos 8.553388***

Boris Godunov

- Modest Petrovich Mussorgsky. Opera in seven scenes. 1869.
- Revised version in four acts and a prologue. 1872, rev. 1873.
- Libretto by Mussorgsky, after Pushkin's tragedy, with historical information drawn from the work of Nikolay Mikhaylovich Karamzin.
- First performance at the Mariinsky Theatre, St Petersburg, on 8th February 1874.

Characters

Boris Godunov	bass or baritone
Fyodor, his son	mezzo-soprano
Xenia, his daughter	soprano
Her old wet-nurse	mezzo-soprano
Prince Vasily Ivanovich Shouysky	tenor
Andrey Shchelkalov, clerk to the Duma	baritone
Pimen, monk and chronicler	bass
Pretender, the false Dmitry, Grigory	tenor
Marina Mniszek, a Polish princess	mezzo-soprano
Rangoni, a Jesuit	bass
Varlaam, a vagabond	bass

Missail, a vagabond	tenor
Hostess of the inn	mezzo-soprano
Nikitich, a constable	bass
Yurodiviy, the simpleton (Holy Fool)	tenor

Boris Godunov has had the rightful heir to the empire, Dmitry, murdered and now is proclaimed Tsar. Time passes and Russia is in turmoil, in spite of the Tsar's efforts to rule well. In a monastery cell the monk Pimen, who has been writing a history of the times, tells his young novice Grigory of the events leading to the triumph of Boris. Grigory, now inspired to seek justice and identifying himself with the murdered prince, is sought by the authorities, but seeks to cast suspicion on the disreputable wandering monk Varlaam. Boris Godunov, in the Kremlin palace, suffers torments of remorse, as revolt threatens from Poland. There Dmitry declares his love for Marina Mniszek, and they are urged by the Jesuit Rangoni to march on Moscow, leading an army of Polish nobles. In the Kremlin Boris is haunted by his fears, more so when he learns of miracles worked at the grave of Dmitry, the boy whose murder had brought him the throne. As monks chant their prayers and the council of boyars gather round him, Boris dies. In a final scene the pretender Dmitry leads his army to victory, while the Simpleton laments the fate of Russia.

The two versions of *Boris Godunov* differ in many respects. In addition to this, the work was rescored by Rimsky-Korsakov for performance in 1896. The first version ends with the death of Boris, while the Polish scenes and the final success of the false Dmitry belong to the later version, although in this the two scenes of the fourth act are often reversed, to allow the opera still to close with the death of Boris. The opera provides a major rôle in that of Boris Godunov, famously taken by singers such as Chaliapin, Nicolai Ghiaurov and Boris Christoff. In whatever version it is a monumental element in Russian operatic repertoire.

BOULEVARD SOLITUDE

- Hans Werner Henze. *Lyrisches Drama* in seven scenes. 1951.
- Libretto by Grete Weil, after the work of the same name by Walter Jockisch, based on the Abbé Prévost's *Manon Lescaut*.
- First performance at the Hanover Landestheater on 17th February 1952.

Henze's opera is an updated version of the story of Manon Lescaut, the subject of operas by Puccini and Massenet. Here Manon is on her way to a finishing school, accompanied by her brother, when she meets Des Grieux, a student. They share a Paris attic room together, but have no money. Lescaut finds a rich lover for his sister, but both of them are turned out when Lescaut is found stealing from him. Des Grieux and Manon are together again, but Lescaut now brings her lover's son as a new client. All ends in disaster for the lovers, when Lescaut again attempts to steal and, apprehended, shoots the old man, leaving Manon to face imprisonment and separation from Des Grieux.

Henze's interesting re-use of such a familiar story derives its music from a twelve-note series, although the opera is not exclusively atonal and, as with the operas of Berg, makes use of earlier traditional forms.

BRANDENBURGERS IN BOHEMIA, THE

- Bedřich Smetana. Opera in three acts. 1863.
- Libretto by Karel Sabina.
- First performance at the Prague Provisional Theatre on 5th January 1866.

In a patriotic opera that, nevertheless, lacks the thoroughly Czech mood of *The Bartered Bride*, the story deals with the conflict between the Brandenburgers, the abduction of the young prince and his mother, and the Czechs. The Brandenbugers withdraw from Bohemia, while all ends happily for the mayor's daughter, Ludiše and her lover Junoš, in spite of the machinations of the wicked Jan Tausendmark, who has also had designs on her.

The opera has some historical importance as the first of Smetana's Czech stage works for the new Prague Provisional Theatre.

BRAUTWAHL, DIE (THE BRIDE'S CHOICE)

- Ferruccio Busoni. *Musikalisch-fantastisches Komödie* in three acts and an epilogue. 1911.
- Libretto by the composer after the story by E.T.A.Hoffmann.
- First performance at the Hamburg Stadtheater on 13th April 1912.

Edmund Lehsen, a young painter, is in love with Albertine, daughter of a rich merchant, but Edmund's protector, the goldsmith Leonhard, objects to the match, while others have designs on Albertine. Like Portia in Shakespeare's *The Merchant of Venice*, she makes her choice by the use of three caskets, allowing Edmund the victory against the son of old Manasse and a comic minor official.

Busoni's score contains a wide range of musical allusions, reflecting the involved nature of the original story. The work has never won any lasting success in the theatre.

Brigands, Les (The Brigands)

- Jacques Offenbach. *Opéra bouffe* in three acts. 1869.
- Libretto by Henri Meilhac and Ludovic Halévy.
- First performance at the Théâtre des Variétés, Paris, on 10th December 1869.

Fragoletto, captured by Italian brigands, falls in love with their leader's daughter and, to prove himself, becomes involved in the interception of marriage plans between the Princess of Granada and the Prince of Mantua. The brigand chief substitutes his daughter's portrait for that of the Princess and provides his own wedding delegation to Mantua. Eventually matters are sorted out, the brigands revealed and pardoned, and Fragoletto married to the chief brigand's daughter.

As the Second Empire came to an end, Offenbach won great success with his operetta containing witty satire on elements in contemporary society.

Buona figliuola, La (The Accomplish'd Maid)

- Niccolò Piccinni. *Opera buffa* in three acts. 1760.
- Libretto by Carlo Goldoni, after Samuel Richardson's *Pamela, or Virtue Rewarded.*
- First performance at the Teatro delle Dame, Rome, on 6th February 1760.

As in Samuel Richardson's novel, a servant-girl is wooed by a man of higher social class, here the Marchese della Conchiglia, but, while Pamela holds out for marriage, her virtue eventually rewarded, Goldoni's heroine, Cecchina, marries when her true, noble parentage is revealed.

La buona figliuola enjoyed enormous contemporary success and, through the good offices of the Jesuits, was even performed in Peking by the palace eunuchs for the edification of the Chinese court, although Richardson's epistolary novel itself was on the Index. The music is attractive and tuneful and the opera's popularity led to translations of the libretto into French, German and English.

BUONA FIGLIUOLA MARITATA, LA (THE ACCOMPLISH'D MAID MARRIED)

- Niccolò Piccinni. *Opera buffa* in three acts. 1761.
- Libretto by Carlo Goldoni.
- First performance at the Teatro dei Formagliari, Bologna, in May 1761.

Goldoni and Piccinni devised a sequel to *La buona figliuola*, continuing the story of Cecchina in further conflicts with her noble husband's family. The work enjoyed some success, but never rivalled that of the earlier work.

BÜRGSCHAFT, DIE (THE PLEDGE)

- Kurt Weill. Opera in three acts. 1931.
- Libretto by Caspar Neher, after Johann Christian Herder's *Der afrikanische Rechtspruch* (The African Judgement).
- First performance at the Berlin Städtische Oper on 10th March 1932.

The moral tale on which the opera is based proposes the principle that man does not change, although society may, and all is subject to the law of money and power. The leading characters are the improvident and dishonest Mattes and the grain-dealer Orth, who stands security for him. By the end of the opera, when war and inflation have taken their toll, Anna, the wife of Mattes, has died, Luise, his daughter earns her living as a dancer and Mattes himself, injured in a fight with Orth, is killed by the people of the city, whom he has exploited.

Die Bürgschaft marks Weill's definitive break with Brecht and the end of his career as a composer of opera in Europe. It represents, in almost classical musical terms, a strong political statement, of particular relevance towards the end of the German Weimar Republic.

Burning Fiery Furnace, The

- Benjamin Britten. Church parable. 1966.
- Libretto by William Plomer.
- First performance at Orford Church, Suffolk, on 9th June 1966.

The Abbot and a group of monks and acolytes enter to the sound of plainchant, before performing their play. The three Israelites, Ananias, Misael and Azarias, have, on the advice of Daniel, been appointed to high office, now renamed in Babylonian style, Shadrach, Meshach and Abednego. Their refusal to bow down before the golden image of the god of Babylon, Merodak, leads to their condemnation to die in the burning fiery furnace. When they emerge unscathed, King Nebuchadnezzar is converted to their religion, while the Astrologer is rejected.

The second of Britten's church parables, like the first, *Curlew River*, opens with plainchant, the Advent sequence *Salus aeterna* (Eternal salvation) and this provides a unifying theme, associated particularly with the three. The score includes riddles, proposed by boy singers and an acrobat, at the royal entertainment and a skilfully varied hymn to Merodak.

Cadi dupé, Le (The Duped Cadi)

- Christoph Willibald von Gluck. *Opéra comique* in one act. 1761.
- Libretto by Pierre-René Lemonnier.
- First performance at the Vienna Burgtheater on 8th November 1761.

The judge (Cadi) tries to divorce his wife Fatime in order to marry Zelmire, who herself has a lover, Nouradin. The Cadi is tricked into marrying Ali, a woman of great ugliness, veiled and substituted at the wedding for Zelmire. The Cadi realises his foolishness and all ends well.

Gluck's opera belongs to the Turkish fashion of the period and involves the use of so-called janissary music, represented by piccolo, drums and cymbals in a witty score.

Cadmus et Hermione (Cadmus and Hermione)

- Jean-Baptiste Lully. *Tragédie en musique* in a prologue and five acts. 1673.
- Libretto by Philippe Quinault, after Ovid's *Metamorphoses*.
- First performance at the Paris Jeu de Paume de Béquet on 27th April 1673.

With the usual prologue in praise of the King, with Louis XIV represented as Apollo killing the Python, the opera deals with the legendary Cadmus, King of Thebes, and his love for Hermione, daughter of Venus and Mars. There is considerable divine intervention from Pallas Athene and Cupid on the one side and Juno on the other, but all ends well in the marriage of the happy pair and the reconciliation of Juno and Jupiter.

Cadmus et Hermione establishes the new form of *tragédie en musique*, here including elements of comedy among the servants, as in contemporary opera in Venice, a mixture later avoided by Lully and by subsequent reformers in Italian opera. A contemporary transcription of the overture by Jean-Henri d'Anglebert remains a possible part of harpsichord repertoire.

Calife de Bagdad, Le (The Caliph of Baghdad)

- Adrien Boieldieu. *Opéra comique* in one act. 1800.
- Libretto by Claude de Saint-Just.
- First performance by the Paris Opéra-Comique at the Salle Favart on 16th September 1800.

The Caliph of Baghdad woos Zétulbe in disguise, wishing to be loved for himself, winning the object of his affections in spite of misunderstandings occasioned by Zétulbe's mother, who mistakes him for a well known robber.

Boieldieu won great contemporary success with his opera, for which he avoided overt orientalism, although the story itself follows a fashion given new impetus in France by the exploits of Napoleon.

Calisto

- Francesco Cavalli. *Dramma per musica* in a prologue and three acts. 1651.
- Libretto by Giovanni Faustini, after Ovid's *Metamorphoses*.
- First performance at the Teatro S Apollinare, Venice, on 28th November 1651.

Jupiter falls in love with the nymph Callisto, a votary of the chaste goddess Diana, a guise that Jupiter, on the advice of Mercury, assumes, thereby achieving his purpose. Diana, meanwhile, falls in love with the shepherd Endymion and is angry when Callisto approaches her again, demanding her embraces. Juno, jealous of her husband's affairs, calls on the Furies, who turn Callisto into a bear, a metamorphosis at once reversed by Jupiter, who now wins Callisto's heart in truth, setting her finally among the stars.

Cavalli's opera won immediate success in Venice and has continued to do so in modern revivals. The tenor aria *Cor mio, che vuoi tu?* (My heart, what do you want?) and the mezzo-soprano *Dolcissimi baci* (Sweetest kisses) may be heard in recital repertoire.

Cambiale di matrimonio, La (The Bill of Marriage)

- Gioachino Rossini. *Farsa comica* in one act. 1810.
- Libretto by Gaetano Rossi, after a play by Camillo Federici and a libretto by Giuseppe Checcherini.
- First performance at the Teatro S Moisè, Venice, on 3rd November 1810.

Tobias Mill, a rich English merchant, agrees to marry his daughter Fanny to a Canadian, Mr Slook, whom he has never seen. Fanny, however, has given her heart to the young and impoverished Edward Milfort. The comedy develops when Slook, in colonial garb, with manners to suit, arrives and is confronted by Milfort, who is anxious to prevent the match, and by Mill, who is determined to enforce the contract. All ends well, as Slovak makes Fanny over to Milfort.

A witty comedy, *La cambiale di matrimonio* was Rossini's first opera for the professional stage. The overture is heard with some frequency in the concert-hall.

CAMPANELLO DI NOTTE, IL (THE NIGHT BELL)

- Gaetano Donizetti. *Melodramma giocoso* in one act. 1836.
- Libretto by the composer, after *La sonnette de nuit* (The Night Bell) by Brunswick, Mathieu-Barthélemy Trion and Victor Lhérie.
- First performance at the Teatro Nuovo, Naples, on 1st June 1836.

Enrico, lover of Serafina, who has married the old chemist Don Annibale Pistacchio, resolves to keep the old man from the marriage-bed by a series of demands, using the chemist's night-bell, which he is obliged, by his trade, to answer.

Humour is engendered by the various disguises assumed by Enrico, as he summons the chemist to his aid, including an appearance as an opera-singer out of voice, allowing room for topical musical parody.

CAMPIELLO, IL (THE LITTLE SQUARE)

- Ermanno Wolf-Ferrari. *Commedia lirica* in three acts. 1935.
- Libretto by Mario Ghisalberti after the play by Carlo Goldoni.
- First performance at the Teatro alla Scala, Milan, on 12th February 1936.

A variety of characters meet around the small square in Venice where the opera is set, encounters that result in amorous intrigue and conflict.

In a score of particular charm, Wolf-Ferrari evokes the spirit of Venice, with a libretto in Venetian dialect.

Candide

- Leonard Bernstein. Comic operetta in two acts. 1956. One act revision in 1973.
- Libretto (1956) by Lillian Hellman, after Voltaire, with additional lyrics by various writers.
- Libretto (1973) by Hugh Callingham Wheeler, with further additional lyrics also by Stephen Sondheim.
- First performance in Boston on 29th October 1956.
- First performance of revised version at the Chelsea Theater Center, New York, on 20th December 1973.

Bernstein's work follows the disastrous adventures of the innocent Candide, under the guidance of his tutor Pangloss, who believes that everything happens for the best, a maxim that the hero is eventually persuaded by circumstances to reject.

The revised versions of *Candide*, the last of which was made in 1988, differ very considerably in musical and dramatic content. The sparkling overture is heard often enough in the concert-hall, while songs from the operetta include *It must be so*, with words by Richard Wilbur and *Candide's Lament* with words by John Latouche. *The Venice Gavotte* sets words by Dorothy Parker and Richard Wilbur.

Canterina, La (The Singer)

- Joseph Haydn. *Intermezzo in musica* in two acts. 1766.
- Libretto by Carl Friberth, after an opera by Piccinni.
- First performance in Eisenstadt (?) in 1766.

Gasparina is wooed by her landlord, the singing-teacher Don Pelagio, but prefers the rich young Don Ettore, with whom she is finally united.

Haydn finds occasion to parody serious opera in this light-hearted intermezzo, written relatively early in his career in the service of the Esterházy family.

Capriccio

- Richard Strauss. *Konversationsstück für Musik* in one act. 1942.
- Libretto by the composer and Clemens Krauss, on a subject suggested by Stefan Zweig and the libretto by Giovanni Battista Casti for Salieri's *Prima la musica e poi le parole* (First the music and then the words).
- First performance at the Munich Bayerische Staatsoper on 28th October 1942.

Characters

Countess Madeleine, a young widow	soprano
Clairon, an actress	contralto
Flamand, a musician	tenor
Olivier, a poet	baritone
The Count, brother of Countess Madeleine	baritone
La Roche, a theatre director	bass
Monsieur Taupe, a prompter	tenor
Two Italian singers	soprano & tenor
A young dancer	silent part
Major-domo	bass
Eight servants	tenors & basses
Three musicians	violin, cello & harpsichord

In a château near Paris, about the year 1775, the birthday of Countess Madeleine is being celebrated. Her interests tend towards music, but her brother, the Count, favours rather poetry and the actress Clairon. The entertainment to be given includes music by Flamand, a play by the poet Olivier and a theatrical piece by the whole company. Alone with the Countess, Olivier declares his love, while Flamand, returning with a setting of a sonnet translated from Ronsard by Olivier, now in turn declares his own love for the Countess. It is the enthusiasm of the theatre director La Roche for the grandiose and spectacular in opera that leads Olivier and Flamand to collaborate on an opera, while the Countess herself is left at the end of the work still unable to decide between the poet and the composer, words or music.

Typical of the later period of Strauss's music, *Capriccio* opens with a string sextet, a prelude that takes the place of an overture. A later interlude provides another part of the work that may be heard outside the opera-house, with the intense final aria of the Countess, as she ponders the old dilemma.

Capuleti ed i Montecchi, I (The Capulets and Montagues)

- Vincenzo Bellini. *Tragedia lirica* in two acts. 1830.
- Libretto by Felice Romani.
- First performance at the Teatro La Fenice, Venice, on 11th March 1830.

Characters

Tebaldo, betrothed to Giulietta	tenor
Capellio, leader of the Capuleti, father of Giulietta	bass
Lorenzo, doctor to the Capuleti	tenor/bass
Romeo, leader of the Montecchi	mezzo-soprano
Giulietta, daughter of Capellio	soprano

The story of Romeo and Juliet, familiar from Shakespeare, has earlier Italian sources. The Guelph Tebaldo is to marry Giulietta, but vows revenge on the Ghibelline Romeo, who has killed Capellio's son. Romeo, disguised as a messenger, conveys apologies for the killing and offers marriage with Giulietta as a means of reconciliation. In her room, Romeo urges flight, but she refuses and in the following scene preparations are under way for her wedding, interrupted by the factional disputes of the Montecchi, who burst in. The doctor Lorenzo offers Giulietta a draught that will simulate death, a seeming event mourned, as Romeo and Tebaldo are about to fight. Approaching Giulietta's tomb, which his followers force open, Romeo takes poison, dying as Giulietta revives. As he falls dead, Giulietta too dies.

Bellini's opera provides a demanding breeches part for a mezzo-soprano, to be heard notably in *Se Romeo t'uccise un figlio* (If Romeo killed your son), while Giulietta's romanza *O quante volte* (O how many times) expresses her love for Romeo and her dilemma. The work was composed in a period of six weeks and both librettist and composer make use in it of earlier material.

Recommended Recording: O quante volte **Naxos 8.550605**

Caravane du Caire, La (The Caravan of Cairo)

- André-Ernest-Modeste Grétry. *Opéra-ballet* in three acts. 1783.
- Libretto by Etienne Morel de Chédeville.
- First performance at Fontainebleau on 30th October 1783.

The enslaved Frenchman Saint-Phar loves a fellow-slave, Zélime, daughter of an Indian chief. Saint-Phar's father, Florestan, has won favour with the Pasha in Cairo, who buys Zélime, while Saint-Phar himself is released by his captor, after he has helped defend the caravan against marauding Arabs. Saint-Phar abducts Zélime, is discovered, but, at the pleading of Florestan is released.

Grétry's opera enjoyed considerable success for nearly half a century. It is light-hearted and makes some use of supposed oriental effects with the harp and triangle in a deftly written score.

CARDILLAC

- Paul Hindemith. Opera in three acts. 1926. Four act version. 1952.
- Libretto by Ferdinand Lion, after E.T.A.Hoffmann's *Das Fräulein von Scuderi* (The Girl from Scutari). Revised and rewritten by Hindemith in 1952.
- First performance at the Dresden Staatsoper on 9th November 1926.
- Revised version first performed at the Zürich Stadttheater on 20th June 1952.

In 17th century Paris the goldsmith Cardillac kills to retrieve any object he has made and sold. His daughter is divided in her heart between her father and her lover, an Officer who buys a gold chain from Cardillac, and is stabbed by him. Wounded, the Officer lays blame on the Gold Dealer, a witness of the attack, but Cardillac reveals his own guilt and is killed by the crowd. In the revised version Cardillac's daughter is replaced by the Opera Singer and her lover by Cardillac's Journeyman, who is suspected by the Police Officer as the murderer. A gold diadem is sought from Cardillac for the Opera Singer and in the third act there is a performance of Lully's *Phaëton* in which she wears it, giving it back to Cardillac after the opera. The Police Officer makes off with the diadem and Cardillac wounds him in an attempt to recover it. The Journeyman is accused, but Cardillac, as in the earlier version, reveals himself as the murderer, to be killed by the crowd.

Scored for what is virtually a chamber orchestra, *Cardillac* studies the relationship of the artist and society, the subject of the later *Mathis der Maler* (Matthias the Painter). Hindemith uses a number of traditional forms, culminating in a last act *passacaglia*. Some have deplored the revised version, which they see as weakening the drama.

Carmen

- Georges Bizet. *Opéra comique* in four acts. 1874.
- Libretto by Henri Meilhac and Ludovic Halévy, after the novel by Prosper Mérimée.
- First performance by the Paris Opéra-Comique at the Salle Favart on 3rd March 1875.

Characters

Carmen, a gypsy	mezzo-soprano
Don José, a corporal of dragoons	tenor
Escamillo, a matador	baritone
Micaëla, a peasant girl	soprano
Zuniga, a lieutenant	bass
Moralès, a sergeant	baritone
Frasquita, a gypsy	soprano
Mercédès, a gypsy	soprano
Lillas Pastia, an inn-keeper	spoken part
Andrès, a lieutenant	tenor
Le Dancaïre, a smuggler	tenor/baritone
Le Remendado, a smuggler	tenor

Set in Seville around the year 1830, the opera deals with the love and jealousy of Don José, who is lured away from his duty as a soldier and his beloved Micaëla by the gypsy factory-girl Carmen, whom he allows to escape from custody. He is later induced to join the smugglers with whom Carmen is associated, but is driven wild by jealousy. This comes to a head when Carmen makes clear her preference for the bull-fighter Escamillo. The last act, outside the bull-ring in Seville, brings Escamillo to the arena, accompanied by Carmen, there stabbed to death by Don José, who has been awaiting her arrival.

Carmen, the most famous of Bizet's operas, with its exotic Spanish setting, introduced a note of realism into opera that proved unacceptable to many who saw the first performances. Objection was taken to the wild and immoral behaviour of Carmen, the chorus of cigarette factory-girls and their smoking and the final murder of Carmen on the stage. Orchestral suites have been derived from the score, while popular excerpts must include Carmen's seductive *Habanera* and *Séguidilla*, the famous *Toreador's Song* and Don José's later reference to the flower Carmen had once thrown him, *La fleur que tu m'avais jetée* (The flower that you threw me), with Micaëla's moving aria *Je dis que rien ne m'épouvante* (I say that nothing frightens me).

Recommended Recordings:

Carmen (3 CDs)	**Naxos 8.660005-07**
Highlights	**Naxos 8.550727**

CASTOR ET POLLUX

- Jean-Philippe Rameau. *Tragédie en musique* in a prologue and five acts. 1737.
- Libretto by Pierre-Joseph Bernard.
- First performance at the Paris Opéra on 24th October 1737.

Pollux, immortal twin of the mortal Castor, takes revenge on the killer of his brother and suggests marriage to Castor's mourning widow Telaira, but she seeks the restoration of Castor to life. Jupiter agrees to bring this about, if Pollux will take his brother's place in death, whereupon Hebe, goddess of youth, summons up visions of what Pollux will lose thereby. Pollux prepares to enter Hades, followed by the princess Phoebe, who loves him. Castor, not content in the Elysian fields, does not want his brother's sacrifice, but agrees to return to Telaira for one day. Eventually both brothers are granted immortality, taking their place in the sky as the heavenly twins.

The opera won greater acclaim at its revival in 1754. The third of Rameau's operas, it represents the height of his achievement, with the expected element of display usual in French opera of the period.

CATERINA CORNARO

- Gaetano Donizetti. *Tragedia lirica* in a prologue and two acts. 1843.
- Libretto by Giacomo Sacchéro, after the libretto for Halévy's *La reine de Chypre* by Jules-Henri Vernoy de Saint-Georges.
- First performance at the Teatro S Carlo, Naples, on 18th January 1844.

The Venetian Caterina Cornaro is compelled by Mocenigo to marry Lusignano, King of Cyprus, although she loves the young Frenchman Gerardo. Lusignano saves the life of Gerardo, neither realising the identity or rôle of the other in Caterina's affections. The two men vow friendship and matters are settled when Gerardo defeats Lusignano's enemies, as the latter, dying, leaves the kingdom to his wife.

A later revision of the opera allows Gerardo to die as he defends Cyprus. Notable is Lusignano's aria *Ah! non turbarti a questi accenti* (Ah! Do not be disquieted at these accents).

CATONE IN UTICA (CATO IN UTICA)

- Johann Christian Bach. *Opera seria* in three acts. 1761.
- Libretto by Pietro Metastasio.
- First performance at the Teatro di S Carlo in Naples on 4th November 1761.

Metastasio's libretto was set by Leonardo Leo in 1729, Niccolò Piccinni in 1770 and others. It deals with the hostilities between Cato and Caesar and the former's final suicide.

CAVALLERIA RUSTICANA (RUSTIC CHIVALRY)

- Pietro Mascagni. *Melodramma* in one act. 1889.
- Libretto by Giovanni Targioni-Tozzetti and Guido Menasci, after the play and story by Giovanni Verga.
- First performance at the Teatro Costanzi, Rome, on 17th May 1890.

CHARACTERS

Santuzza, a peasant girl	soprano
Turiddu, a young soldier	tenor
Alfio, the village teamster	baritone
Lola, his wife	mezzo-soprano
Mamma Lucia, mother of Turiddu	contralto

In a Sicilian village it is Easter Sunday. Santuzza's former lover Turiddu is in love with Lola, Alfio's wife. Santuzza seeks revenge by telling Alfio of Lola's unfaithfulness and he kills Turiddu in a fight, after the latter has left Santuzza in the charge of his mother.

An example of realism (*verismo*), Mascagni's opera is a concentrated study of love and jealousy, unified in its music and offering a strong contrast between normal village life, with its church celebration of Easter, and the strong feelings of the principal characters, a contrast that has its counterpart in other operas, not least in Britten's *Peter Grimes*. Popular excerpts include the tenor *O Lola*, Santuzza's *Voi lo sapete* (You know it), the central instrumental *Intermezzo*, the drinking-song *Viva il vino* (Long live wine) and Turiddu's poignant *Mamma, quel vino è generoso* (Mother, this wine is generous). *Cavalleria rusticana* is often coupled in performance with Leoncavallo's *Pagliacci*.

Recommended Recording: Cavalleria Rusticana **Naxos 8.660022**

Cendrillon (Cinderella)

- Jules Massenet. *Conte de fées* in four acts. 1896.
- Libretto by Henri Cain, after the fairy-tale by Charles Perrault.
- First performance by the Paris Opéra-Comique at the Salle Favart on 24th May 1899.

Characters

Cendrillon (Cinderella)	soprano
Madame de la Haltière, her step-mother	mezzo-soprano
Pandolfe, her father	bass
Noémie, her step-sister	soprano
Dorothée, her step-sister	mezzo-soprano
Le Prince Charmant (Prince Charming)	soprano
La Fée (Fairy Godmother)	coloratura soprano
Le Roi (The King)	bass

The familiar story unfolds with a first act in which Madame de la Haltière prepares her two daughters for the ball, leaving Cendrillon alone, when they have gone, to be encouraged and transformed by her Fairy Godmother. At the ball the Prince rejects other possible contenders for his hand, falling in love with the unkown Cendrillon. At home again, Madame de la Haltière boasts of the success of her daughters. Cendrillon, comforted by her father, resolves to run away and in a second, magic scene dreams of her love for the Prince. The fourth act brings Cendrillon home again, the whole episode now to her a dream. News comes of the search for the owner of the missing glass slipper and Cendrillon enjoys the reality of final success.

There is an element of pastiche in Massenet's witty score of *Cendrillon*, with its magic scenes. Cendrillon's *Ah! que mes soeurs sont heureuses* (Ah! how happy my sisters are) may be heard in recital.

Recommended Recording: Cendrillon (Suite) ***Marco Polo 8.223354***

Cenerentola, La (Cinderella)

- Gioachino Rossini. *Dramma giocoso* in two acts. 1817.
- Libretto by Jacopo Ferretti, after the fairy-tale by Charles Perrault and other libretti on the same subject.

◆ First performance at the Teatro Valle, Rome, on 25th January 1817.

CHARACTERS

Cenerentola, Angelina (Cinderella)	contralto
Don Magnifico, Baron of Monte Fiascone, her step-father	baritone
Clorinda, his daughter	soprano
Tisbe, his daughter	mezzo-soprano
Don Ramiro, Prince of Salerno	tenor
Dandini, his valet	bass
Alidoro, a philosopher, his tutor	bass

In a slightly different form of the fairy-tale, Cenerentola shows kindness to Alidoro, who calls at Don Magnifico's castle in the guise of a beggar, and he advises Don Ramiro that here is a girl worthy of his hand. The ugly sisters and Don Magnifico are ready to attend the ball at the palace, while it is Alidoro who comes to the aid of Cenerentola and takes her there, after a scene in which Dandini and the Prince have changed places. Continuing the same imposture, Dandini, as the Prince, greets Don Magnifico at Don Ramiro's country-house, and appoints him court vintner, while the Prince and his valet cannot understand Alidoro's praise of Don Magnifico's daughter, seeing only the two ugly sisters. Cenerentola admits that she prefers the Prince's servant, the real Prince, who now reveals to her his true identity. She gives him a bracelet that matches her own and tells him to find her, once she has gone. Forced by a storm to seek shelter in Don Magnifico's castle, the Prince recognises Cenerentola, who seeks forgiveness for her step-father and step-sisters. The opera ends in Don Ramiro's palace, where Cenerentola is finally enthroned, as she deserves.

Rossini's deft and witty opera avoids the magic element of the original story and provides interesting contrasts in the casting of Cenerentola as a contralto. The overture is a popular concert item, while Cenerentola's *Nacqui all'affanno, al pianto* (Born to worry and complaining) adds a moving element to the last scene. Rossini is said to have written the opera in three weeks.

Recommended Recording: Rondò finale (Act II) ***Naxos 8.553543***

Cherevichki (The Slippers)

- Pyotr Il'yich Tchaikovsky. Comic-fantastic opera in four acts. 1874.
- Libretto by Yakov Polonsky and Nikolay Chayev, after Gogol's story *Christmas Eve*.
- First performance at the Moscow Bolshoy Theatre on 31st January 1887.

A revised version of *Vakula the Smith*, *Cherevichki* is Tchaikovsky's only comic opera, a story of love and trickery, in which Vakula's mother Solokha, a witch, and the Devil of the Stove have a part to play.

Chérubin (Cherubino)

- Jules Massenet. *Comédie chantée* in three acts. 1905.
- Libretto by Henri Cain and Francis de Croisset, after a play by the latter.
- First performance at the Monte Carlo Opéra on 14th February 1905.

Massenet's comedy explores the love affairs of Cherubino, the amorous page of *The Marriage of Figaro*, the second play in the Beaumarchais Figaro trilogy. The title-rôle was designed for Mary Garden, Debussy's first Mélisande.

Christmas Eve

- Nikolay Andreyevich Rimsky-Korsakov. A carol brought to life in four acts. 1895.
- Libretto by the composer, after the story by Gogol.
- First performance at the Mariinsky Theatre, St Petersburg, on 10th December 1895.

Based loosely on the story used by Tchaikovsky for *Vakula the Smith* and *Cherevichki*, the opera by Rimsky-Korsakov explores regions of even greater fantasy.

Recommended Recording: Christmas Eve (Overture and Suite) ***Naxos 8.553789***

Christophe Colomb (Christopher Columbus)

- Darius Milhaud. Opera in two parts. 1930. Revised version 1968.
- Libretto by Paul Claudel.
- First performance at the Berlin Staatsoper on 5th May 1930.

A work of some complexity, Milhaud's opera brings, in its first version, reminiscences of the dying Columbus, the explorer's career and discovery. The work demands large forces and elaborate staging.

CHRISTOPHORUS

- Franz Schreker. Opera in a prologue, two acts and an epilogue. 1927.
- Libretto by the composer.
- First performance in Freiburg on 1st October 1978.

Christophorus, oder Die Vision einer Oper (Christophorus or The Vision of an Opera) is dedicated to Arnold Schoenberg and involves a mixture of fantasy and realism, as a young composer tries to write an opera on the subject of St Christopher, a character who takes over before the composer returns to the original request, for a string quartet, a medium that he can control.

CHUTE DE LA MAISON USHER, LA (THE FALL OF THE HOUSE OF USHER)

- Claude Debussy. Opera (unfinished). 1911.
- Libretto by the composer, after the story by Edgar Allan Poe.
- First performed in a reconstructed version at Yale University on 23rd February 1977.

The work of Edgar Allan Poe exercised considerable influence over the imagination of French writers and musicians at the turn of the century. Debussy's unfinished opera treats the morbid fascination of Roderick Usher with Madeline, whom he buries alive only to see her return, as the old house falls in ruins.

CID, LE

- Jules Massenet. *Opéra* in four acts. 1885.
- Libretto by Adolphe d'Ennery, Edouard Blau and Louis Gallet, after the play by Corneille.
- First performance at the Paris Opéra on 30th November 1885.

Loved by Chimène, Rodrigue swears to avenge his father's honour, an oath that leads him to kill Chimène's father. Rodrigue leads the Spanish armies against the Moors, leaving Chimène to resolve the conflict in her heart between filial duty and love. Matters seem to have been resolved when news is brought of Rodrigue's death in battle, but finally he returns triumphant, to be forgiven by Chimène.

The ballet-music of the second act has a place in concert repertoire, while Chimène's *Pleurez, pleurez, mes yeux* (Weep, weep, my eyes), an expression of the dilemma in which she finds herself in the third act, is well known.

Recommended Recording: Le Cid (Ballet Music) **Naxos 8.550086**

Cinesi, Le (The Chinese Girls)

- Christoph Willibald von Gluck. *Azione teatrale* in one act.
- Libretto by Pietro Metastasio.
- First performance at the Vienna Schlosshof on 24th Sepember 1754.

Using a libretto set by Antonio Caldara for the imperial family in 1735, Gluck offers a new version of a work that allows fashionable chinoiserie display in costume, setting and, in the use of percussion, a supposed Chinese style of music. The piece is a contrast of manners, brought about by the return of the young man Silango from a visit to Europe with new ideas he has gathered there. His sister Lisinga, and her two friends parody the operatic tragic aria, the pastoral and the comic, and the piece ends in a ballet.

Ciro in Babilonia (Cyrus in Babylon)

- Gioachino Rossini. *Dramma con cori* in two acts. 1812.
- Libretto by Francesco Aventi, after the biblical narrative of Belshazzar's feast.
- First performance at the Teatro Communale, Ferrara, probably on 14th March 1812.

An early work, Rossini's opera treats the story of the captivity of Cyrus in Babylon, the writing on the wall that warns his captor Belshazzar of what is to come and the defeat of the latter, leading to the release of Cyrus and his family.

Clemenza di Scipione, La (The Clemency of Scipio)

- Johann Christian Bach. *Opera seria* in three acts. 1778.
- Anonymous libretto.
- First performed at the King's Theatre, Haymarket, London, on 4th April 1778.

The last of Johann Christian Bach's Italian operas, written for the London stage, deals with the mercy shown by the Roman general Scipio to Spanish prisoners, taken after the capture of Carthage.

His final clemency results in the willingness of his prisoners to swear allegiance to Rome, something that, under threat of death, they had been unwilling to do.

CLEMENZA DI TITO, LA (THE CLEMENCY OF TITUS)

- Wolfgang Amadeus Mozart. *Opera seria* in two acts. 1791.
- Libretto adapted by Caterino Mazzola from Metastasio.
- First performance at the Prague National Theatre on 6th September 1791.

CHARACTERS

Tito (Titus, Roman Emperor)	tenor
Vitellia, daughter of the former Emperor Vitellius	soprano
Sesto (Sextus), friend of Tito, in love with Vitellia	male soprano
Servilia, sister of Sesto, in love with Annio	soprano
Annio (Annius), friend of Sesto, in love with Servilia	soprano
Publio (Publius), Praetorian prefect of the Guard	bass

Vitellia, jealous of Titus, persuades Sextus, who is in love with her, to plot against his friend, the Emperor. Annius seeks from Sextus the hand of his sister, which he grants. Titus, rejecting a foreign marriage, now declares that he will marry Servilia, in order to honour Sextus. She tells Titus that she loves Annius, and he releases her from marriage with him. Vitellia still urges Sextus to assassinate Titus, but when she learns that she is to be the wife of Titus, she becomes anxious to prevent the plot, which is now afoot. Titus survives and Sextus is found guilty, still refusing to implicate Vitellia, who finally admits her guilt, to be forgiven by the magnanimous Emperor.

Mozart's opera was commissioned by Prague for the coronation of Leopold II as King of Bohemia, after no such work had been sought to mark the Emperor's coronation in Vienna. The Empress Maria Luisa notoriously described the work as *porcheria tedesca* (German piggery), claiming that the music was very bad, and that most of the audience slept through the performance, but the work certainly enjoyed later popularity. It makes use of an old libretto, in a revised version of the *opera seria* libretto of Metastasio, suggesting new ways in which the older form might now be treated. The overture is familiar in concert repertoire, while *Parto, parto* (I go, I go) of Sextus, with its basset clarinet obbligato for Anton Stadler, and Vitellia's *Non più di fiori* (No more with flowers), with the same obbligato instrument, may also be heard in recital as part of present soprano repertoire.

Recommended Recording: Overture ***Naxos 8.550185***

Cloches de Corneville, Les (The Bells of Corneville)

- Robert Planquette. *Opéra-comique* in three acts. 1877.
- Libretto by Clairville and Charles Gabet.
- First performance at the Paris Folies-Dramatiques on 19th April 1877.

The drama treats the predicament of the Marquis de Corneville, returning to claim his inheritance, and of Germaine, both of them cheated by the steward Gaspard. The work enjoyed very great popularity for many years, but has now fallen out of general favour.

Colas Breugnon

- Dmitry Borisovich Kabalevsky. Opera in a prologue and three acts. 1937.
- Revised version, 1968.
- Libretto by V.G.Bragin, after the story by Romain Rolland.
- First performance at the Maliy Theatre, Leningrad, on 22nd February 1938.

Colas Breugnon, Master of Clamecy opens with a prologue for the carpenter of the title, introducing episodes from his past, his flirtation with Selina, her jealousy of Mademoiselle de Termes, who admires the craftsmanship of Colas at the Duke's castle. He turns his attention to Jacqueline, who, in the second act, has been his wife for some years. Now he makes a statue of Selina, whom he still loves, and this is taken by the jealous steward Gifflard for the Duke's castle. Returning soldiers bring plague to the town and Colas is left alone to suffer the disease. Revived, he learns that everything has been burned by the soldiers, and now attends the death-bed of his wife, vowing to take continuing care of his grand-daughter, who has been spared. He meets Selina and their love is renewed. The Duke and Gifflard are burning the town, including the works carved by Colas. The latter has his revenge when the statue of the Duke that has been commissioned is revealed as showing him seated backwards on a donkey.

Colas Breugnon contains obvious elements of appeal to the authorities in the Soviet Union, with its satire on the ruling classes. The overture remains popular in concert repertoire.

Recommended Recording: Colas Breugnon (Orchestral Suite) ***Naxos 8.553411***

Comte d'Ory, Le (Count Ory)

- Gioachino Rossini. *Opéra* in two acts. 1828.
- Libretto by Eugène Scribe and Charles-Gaspard Delestre-Poirson, after a play by the same writers.
- First performance at the Paris Opéra on 20th August 1828.

Set in 13th century France, the opera deals with the attempts of Count Ory to woo the Countess Adèle, whose brother is away on a crusade. She and her ladies have abjured love in his absence. Ory disguises himself as a hermit, deceiving even his tutor and his page, Isolier. The latter is also in love with the Countess and gains admission to the castle, with Ory, who warns the Countess against him, while absolving her from her vow, only to have his identity revealed by his tutor. In the second act Ory and his men, disguised as nuns, seek shelter from a storm in the castle, where they alternate their behaviour between emptying the wine-cellar and an appearance of prayer. Isolier tricks Ory into an assignation that he supposes is with the Countess, but is in fact also with his page, and he and his men make their escape as the husband of the Countess is heard returning.

The wit of Rossini is evident in his opera for the French theatre, a work that shows a complete mastery of the form and of the Paris stage. The score includes a fine trio in the scene between Ory, Isolier and Adèle in which the first is outwitted by the page, *A la faveur de cette nuit obscure* (Thanks to this dark night).

Consul, The

- Gian Carlo Menotti. Musical drama in three acts. 1950.
- Libretto by the composer.
- First performance at the Schubert Theatre, Philadelphia, on 1st March 1950.

In an unnamed European city John Sorel, wounded, takes refuge at home from the secret police and urges his wife Magda to find a visa for him from a foreign consulate, where, in the following scene, she experiences delay after delay, but meets the Magician. In the second act Magda sleeps, while John's mother nurses her dying baby. A stone through the window signals news of John, who has sought safety in the mountains. The baby dies. At the consulate Magda waits, entertained with others by the Magician. She faints when she sees the secret police agent leave the Consul's office, fearing danger. At the consulate again, she is encouraged when another applicant is given a visa. She leaves, while John plans to return and is arrested. The Secretary agrees to telephone Magda with the news. As Magda, home again, commits suicide, the telephone rings. Her dying brings hallucinations and a dance of death led by the Magician.

The Consul is a powerful work, couched in Menotti's very direct musical style, generally tonal but here allowing for some harshness of idiom. The subject is as apt now as it was at the time of the original composition.

CONTES D'HOFFMANN, LES (THE TALES OF HOFFMANN)

- Jacques Offenbach. *Opéra fantastique* in five acts. 1880.
- Libretto by Jules Barbier, after the play by Barbier and Michel Carré, based on stories by E.T.A.Hoffmann.
- First performance by the Paris Opéra-Comique at the Salle Favart on 10th February 1881.

CHARACTERS

Hoffmann, a poet	tenor
The Muse	soprano
Nicklausse, Hoffmann's friend	mezzo-soprano
Lindorf, a councillor of Nuremberg	bass-baritone
Stella, a prima donna	soprano
Andrès, her servant	tenor
Luther, an innkeeper	baritone
Spalanzini, an inventor	tenor
Cochenille, his servant	tenor
Olympia, a doll	soprano
Coppélius, Spanzini's rival	baritone
Antonia, a singer	soprano
Crespel, her father, a violin-maker	baritone
Frantz, his servant	tenor
Dr Miracle, a doctor	baritone
Voice of Antonia's mother	mezzo-soprano
Giulietta, a courtesan	soprano
Schlemil, her lover	bass
Dapertutto, a magician	baritone
Pitichinaccio, Giulietta's servant	tenor
Crespel	

The Tales of Hoffmann takes a series of separate stories, linked by the presence of the poet himself, with his companion Nicklausse. In the first act, which serves as a prologue, Hoffmann's muse takes the form of his student friend Nicklausse. In Luther's tavern in Nuremberg, Hoffmann sees his rival Councillor Lindorf with his beloved Stella, enjoying apparent success. He tells the assembled students the story of Klein Zach and then agrees to tell them more. The second act deals with Hoffmann's love for the doll Olympia, the invention of Spalanzini, frustrated by Coppélius, who claims part of the profits from Spalanzini's invention, for his contribution of eyes. He is fobbed off with a worthless cheque and returns to break the doll, leaving Hoffmann to lament his folly, brought about through the magic spectacles that Coppélius had provided. Hoffmann now falls in love with the singer Antonia, daughter of the violin-maker Crespel. Here he is frustrated by Dr Miracle, who induces Antonia to sing, an activity which brings about her death from the lung complaint from which she suffers. In Venice Hoffmann is attracted by the courtesan Giulietta. The magician Dapertutto urges her to seize Hoffmann's reflection for him. In a duel Hoffmann kills his rival, Giulietta's former lover Schlemil, only to find his beloved in the arms of her servant Pitichinaccio. In a final act set in Luther's tavern again, Hoffmann rejects Stella, who leaves with Councillor Lindorf, while his muse returns, urging him to further literary effort.

Offenbach achieved something of his more serious ambition in *The Tales of Hoffmann.* In performance the bewilderingly large number of characters is reduced by allowing the same singer to take the parts of those who serve to frustrate Hoffmann, Lindorf, Coppélius, Dr Miracle and Dapertutto. The same tenor may take the character parts of the servants Cochenille, Frantz and Pitichinaccio, while in some productions the four soprano rôles, Stella, Olympia, Antonia and Giulietta may be taken by one singer. In instrumental repertoire arrangements of the famous *Barcarolle* of the fourth act have proliferated, as in its vocal form as *Belle nuit, ô nuit d'amour* (Fair night, o night of love). Other excerpts heard in operatic recitals include *Il était une fois à la cour d'Eisenach* (Once upon a time at the court of Eisenach), Hoffmann's tale of the impish Klein Zach, Olympia's *Les oiseaux dans la charmille* (The birds in the garden walk) and Antonia's *Elle a fui, la torterelle* (She has flown, the little dove).

Coq d'or, Le (see Golden Cockerel, The)

Corregidor, Der (The Magistrate)

- Hugo Wolf. Opera in four acts. 1895.
- Libretto by Rosa Meyreder, after Pedro de Alarcón's novel *El sombrero de tres picos* (The Three-Cornered Hat).
- First performance at the Mannheim Nationaltheater on 7th June 1896.

The miller Uncle Lukas and Frasquita are happily married, but the magistrate, Don Eugenio, has designs on the latter, who teases him and makes a fool of him. In revenge Don Eugenio has Lukas lured away to the mayor's house, but he has no success with Frasquita, who eludes his grasp, escaping to try to find her husband, but pestered now by Don Eugenio's servant Repela. Returning home Lukas finds the magistrate in his bed and suspecting the worst, resolves on revenge by donning Don Eugenio's clothes and seducing the magistrate's wife. Don Eugenio wakes and is forced to dress in the clothes of Lukas, now refused admission to his own house. All ends happily enough, with Lukas and Frasquita re-united and Don Eugenio subdued by his wife.

Wolf's opera is not performed very often and was initially refused by Vienna and Berlin, being staged in the former only in 1904 under the direction of Gustav Mahler, who made various changes in the work. The *Prelude* and *Intermezzo* from the opera have a place in orchestral repertoire.

Corsaro, Il (The Corsair)

- Giuseppe Verdi. Opera in three acts. 1848.
- Libretto by Francesco Maria Piave, after Byron's poem *The Corsair*.
- First performance at the Teatro Grande, Trieste, on 25th October 1848.

The corsair captain Corrado is unhappy with his life. A message received, he rallies his men and in a second scene parts from Medora, who has premonitions of disaster. In the harem of Seid, Pasha of Coron, his beloved Gulnara is anxious to escape, and Corrado and his men seek to free her and her companions by force, but are taken prisoner. Corrado is condemned to death and Gulnara pleads for him. She visits Corrado in his dungeon and offers to kill Seid, but Corrado will not allow this, avowing his love for Medora. Gulnara kills Seid and escapes with Corrado to the pirate island. There Medora is near to death, and as she dies Corrado leaps from the cliffs to his own death.

Not among the best of Verdi's operas, the score nevertheless provides the tenor Corrado with *Eccomi prigionero* (Here I am, a prisoner) and the soprano Medora with a winning *romanza* in the first act. The overture has a place in concert repertoire.

Cosa rara, Una (A Rare Thing)

- Vicente Martín y Soler. *Dramma giocoso* in two acts.
- Libretto by Lorenzo Da Ponte, after the play *La luna della Sierra* (The Moon of the Sierra) by Luis Vélez de Guevara.
- First performance at the Vienna Burgtheater on 17th November 1786.

The second libretto by Da Ponte for the Spanish composer Martín deals with marriage intrigue in a Spanish village and royal intervention. The work became enormously popular in Vienna, where it had had the active encouragement of the wife of the Spanish ambassador. Mozart quoted from it in the last act of *Don Giovanni*.

Così fan tutte (All Women do the Same)

- Wolfgang Amadeus Mozart. *Opera buffa* in two acts. 1789.
- Libretto by Lorenzo Da Ponte.
- First performance at the Vienna Burgtheater on 16th January 1790.

Characters

Fiordiligi, a lady of Ferrara, living in Naples	soprano
Dorabella, her sister	soprano
Guglielmo, an officer, Fiordiligi's lover	bass
Ferrando, an officer, Dorabella's lover	tenor
Despina, the sisters' servant	soprano
Don Alfonso, an old philosopher	bass

Set in 18th century Naples, the opera opens with Don Alfonso's wager that the two girls, Fiordiligi and Dorabella, are no more trustworthy in matters of love than any other women. In their garden the girls sing of their love, interrupted by Don Alfonso, who tells them that their lovers are to be called away to the war. The couples part, faithfulness now pledged again. Despina, bribed by Don Alfonso, urges the girls to find other lovers, but they declare their constancy. Guglielmo and Ferrando return, disguised as Albanians, but the girls remain firm. When the men pretend to take poison, necessitating the attentions of Despina disguised as a doctor and using the magnetic techniques of Mozart's friend Dr Mesmer to effect a cure, they seem to waver. In the second act they agree to Despina's suggestion of harmless flirtation, each unwittingly choosing the other's partner. The success of the two Albanians, in spite of Fiordiligi's more prolonged resistance, leads to a wedding, with Despina now disguised as the notary. The men now appear as themselves and pretend shock and horror at what is afoot, before revealing their plot. All ends happily, as Don Alfonso urges the power of reason in these circumstances.

The first run of *Così fan tutte* in Vienna was interrupted by the death of Joseph II, allowing only ten performances in the season. In the following century the alleged immorality of the plot led to a number of changes in the work, which has been firmly re-established in the 20th century as one of

the great masterpieces of operatic repertoire. The lively overture has a place in the concert-hall, while vocal excerpts must include the trio *Soave sia il vento* (Gently blow the wind) for the two girls and Don Alfonso, as the lovers pretend to sail away to the wars, Fiordiligi's dramatic *Come scoglio* (Like a rock) in which she proclaims her unshakable constancy, Ferrando's *Un'aura amorosa* (A loving breeze) and the common sense of Despina in *Una donna a quindici anni* (A lady at fifteen) and *E Amore un ladroncello* (Love is a little thief).

Recommended Recordings:

Così fan tutte (3 CDs)	***Naxos 8.660008-10***
Highlights	***Naxos 8.553172***

Cox and Box

- Arthur Sullivan. Operetta in one act. 1866.
- F.C.Burnand, after the farce of the same name by J.Maddison Morton.
- Probably first performed privately in London on 26th May 1866.

Sullivan's first operetta deals with the comic activities of a landlord who lets the same room to two lodgers, alternating, unknown to them, by day and night. It was later elaborated for public performance.

Crociato in Egitto, Il (The Crusader in Egypt)

- Giacomo Meyerbeer. *Melodramma eroico* in two acts. 1824.
- Libretto by Gaetano Rossi.
- First performance at the Teatro La Fenice, Venice, on 7th March 1824.

Palmide, daughter of Aladino, Sultan of Damietta, is promised in marriage to Elmireno, the disguised knight Armando, to whom she is already married and whose child she has borne. Armando reveals his true identity as a Knight of Rhodes and as lover of Felicia, a kinswoman of the Grand Master, Adriano, who upbraids Armando for his attachment to Palmide. There is consternation at the planned wedding of Armando and Palmide, when the former appears in European dress and the Sultan orders the imprisonment of all the Knights present. Later relenting, he sets them free, but Adriano now rejects Armando, having learned of the existence of his son. Armando and Palmide plan flight, but are forestalled by the Sultan, who again imprisons the Christians, now armed by the traitor Osmino to kill their ruler. Led by Armando they protect the Sultan, instead of killing him, and thanks to the latter's clemency and gratitude Armando and Palmide are allowed to marry and leave for Europe.

Il crociato in Egitto was Meyerbeer's last opera for the Italian theatre. The part of Armando was written for a male soprano, echoing earlier practice, but was taken by the famous prima donna Giuditta Pasta at the first Paris performances in 1825.

Csárdásfürstin, Die (The Gypsy Princess)

- Emmerich Kálmán. Operetta in three acts. 1915.
- Libretto by Leo Stein and Béla Jenbach.
- First performance at the Johann-Strauss Theater, Vienna, on 17th November 1915.

Sylva Varescu, a well known cabaret singer, is in love with Prince Edwin von und zu Lippert-Weylersheim, who has had another match arranged by his disapproving family. Matters are happily resolved when it turns out that the Prince's mother had also once been a cabaret singer.

Among the most popular of operettas, *Die Csárdásfürstin* (The Gypsy Princess) includes a charming entrance song for Sylva, as she sings of her home, her unsuccessful suitor Count Boni's farewell to her, as she plans her departure for America, *Ganz ohne Weiber* (Quite without women) and the famous duet between Countess Stasi, Edwin's proposed wife, and her reluctant cousin, *Machen wirs den Schwalben nach* (Let us copy the swallows).

Recommended Recording:
Sylvia's Entrance / Ganz ohne Weiber / Machen wirs den Schwalben nach / Tanzen möcht' ich ***Naxos 8.550942***

Cunning Little Vixen, The

- Leoš Janáček. Opera in three acts. 1923.
- Libretto by the composer, after the novel *Liška Bystrouška* by Rudolf Těsnohlídek.
- First performance at the Brno National Theatre on 6th November 1924.

In a forest glen the Badger sits smoking, Flies dance around, joined by the Blue Dragonfly, the Cricket and Grasshopper, with the Mosquito, making a waltz. The Frog is chased by the little Vixen, and the Forester wakes up, catching the latter to take home. In the Forester's yard the Vixen is advised by others to reconcile herself to captivity, but instead she kills the Cock, so admired by the subservient Hens, and escapes. In the second act the Vixen fouls and occupies the Badger's sett, after a quarrel. In the inn the Schoolmaster plays cards with the Forester. The Priest teases the former about his coming marriage, and the Schoolmaster makes fun of the Forester over the escape of the Vixen, who now observes the three men as they make their way home. At home the Vixen is wooed by the Fox and after spending time together they are married. In the third act the Vixen and Fox and their cubs avoid a trap set by the Forester and plunder the poultry basket of the chicken-seller and poacher Harašta. He fires at them and the Vixen is killed. In the final scenes the Forester and Schoolmaster are together, the latter sad at the wedding of the girl he had loved. Walking home, the Forester remembers the happy past and seems to see the little vixen and the frog that had wakened him in the first act.

The Cunning Little Vixen, with its mixture of the animal and the human, presents obvious problems of staging, which have not always been overcome. It offers a nostalgic and wise view of life in music of great humanity. A concert suite by Vaclav Talich has been drawn from the first act of the opera.

Cunning Peasant, The

- Antonín Dvořák. Comic opera in two acts. 1878.
- Libretto by Josef Otakar Veselý.
- First performance at the Prague Provisional Theatre on 27th January 1878.

The amorous Prince, with designs on the peasant-girl Bětuška is outwitted by the Princess, with the aid of the cunning peasant, Martin.

Cupid and Death

- Matthew Locke and Christopher Gibbons. Masque in five entries. 1653. Revised in 1659.
- Text by James Shirley.
- First performance in London on 26th March 1653.

The arrows of Cupid and of Death are exchanged, with predictable results, until matters are put right by Mercury.

The masque was staged to entertain the Portuguese Ambassador, then present in London for the signing of a treaty between Oliver Cromwell and the King of Portugal. While lacking the splendour of a court masque, it provides varied music from the two composers. It is possible that Locke was responsible for the surviving second version only, revising the earlier work of Christopher Gibbons.

Curlew River

- Benjamin Britten. Church parable. 1964.
- Libretto by William Plomer.
- First performance in Orford Church, Suffolk, on 12th June 1964.

Monks enter the church, chanting the plainchant evening hymn *Te lucis ante terminum* (Thee before the ending of the day). They present a play in which the Ferryman carries pilgrims across to a miraculous shrine. They are joined by the Madwoman, who believes the grave to be that of her son, abducted and murdered a year before. The voice of the boy is heard, as she prays at the tomb, and her wits are restored. The Abbot, leader of the monks, points the moral of the tale, before the monks leave, chanting their hymn.

Based on the Japanese play *Sumidagawa* that Britten had seen in Tokyo in 1956, *Curlew River* derives much of its material from the opening plainchant. Scored for a small group of musicians, it is performed without a conductor, various players or singers taking the lead, as in chamber music performance. The church setting and the necessary simplicity of action and staging make this first of Britten's church parables an intensely moving work.

D

Dafne

- Marco da Gagliano. Opera in a prologue and six scenes. 1608.
- Libretto by Ottavio Rinuccini, after Ovid's *Metamorphoses*.
- First performance at the Mantuan court in February 1608.

Ovid, in a prologue, declares the power of love. Apollo defeats Pithone (the Python) and boasts of his power to Cupid, who, with his smaller arrows, plans to take revenge. Shot by Cupid's dart, Apollo falls in love with Daphne, chaste devotee of Diana. Cupid boasts to his mother Venus of his achievement. A messenger, Thyrsis, describes Apollo's pursuit of Daphne and her metamorphosis into a laurel tree. In a final scene Apollo laments his loss.

One of the earliest operas, Gagliano's *Dafne* exalts the power of love and the power of art. It treats again the subject used earlier by Rinuccini and set in 1598 by Peri and Corsi in Florence. The work, with its chorus of nymphs and shepherds, is rather an extension of the pastoral than a re-creation of Greek drama.

Dalibor

- Bedřich Smetana. Opera in three acts. 1867.
- Libretto by Josef Wenzig.
- First performance at the Prague New Town Theatre on 16th May 1868.

Based on events in Czech history, the opera deals with the arraignment of the knight Dalibor before King Vladislav, accused of the killing of the Burgrave of Ploškovice, whose sister Milada pleads for vengeance. Dalibor had killed the Burgrave, seeking revenge for the death of his friend, the musician Zdeněk. Dalibor is condemned to prison for life, but Milada, moved by his account, now intercedes for him, and the peasant-girl Jitka proposes means for his escape. In the second act she tells her lover Vítek how Milada has disguised herself as a musician and gained admission to the castle where Dalibor is held. Dalibor's thoughts, in his dungeon, of Zdeněk are interrupted by the appearance of Milada, now in love with him. Fearing imminent rebellion, Vladislav now orders the death of Dalibor, who is expecting freedom. Milada dies in an attempt to rescue him, and Dalibor himself dies in battle against his enemies, hoping now to be re-united in death with Zdeněk and Milada.

With distinct echoes in its plot of Beethoven's *Fidelio*, Smetana's *Dalibor* celebrates heroic friendship rather than the eternal feminine. Its Czech subject, with certain Czech elements in the score, give the work national importance, with *The Bartered Bride*.

DAME BLANCHE, LA (THE WHITE LADY)

- Adrien Boieldieu. *Opéra comique*. 1825.
- Libretto by Eugène Scribe, after Walter Scott's *Guy Mannering*.
- First performance by the Paris Opéra-Comique at the Salle Feydeau on 10th December 1825.

Dickson, a tenant of Count Avenel, learns from the English officer George Brown that the wicked steward of the estate, Gaveston, plans to buy the late Count's castle and title. Dickson's wife Jenny sings the ballad of the White Lady, guardian spirit of the Avenels, who now summons Dickson to the castle. Brown offers to go in his place. In the castle Anna, orphan ward of the Avenels, disguised as the White Lady, meets Brown, whom she recognises as a wounded soldier she had once tended and who reminds her of the lost Avenel heir. At auction Gaveston is outbid by Brown, who must now find the money, revealed eventually by the White Lady herself. Brown turns out to be the Avenel heir and is united with Anna.

La Dame blanche won great popularity in 19th century France. Most frequently heard now in operatic recital repertoire is the tenor *Viens, gentille dame* (Come, gentle lady).

DAMNATION DE FAUST, LA (THE DAMNATION OF FAUST)

- Hector Berlioz. *Légende dramatique* in four parts. 1846.
- Libretto by the composer and Almire Gandonnière, after Gérard de Nerval's translation of Goethe's *Faust*.
- First performance in concert by the Paris Opéra-Comique at the Salle Favart on 6th December 1846.

Designed initially for concert performance, *La Damnation de Faust* is an expansion of the composer's 1829 *Huit scènes de Faust* (Eight Scenes from Faust). It opens on the plains of Hungary, an opportunity for the use of the patriotic *Rákóczi March*. Faust in his study draws comfort from the singing of the church congregation revealed to him, but is persuaded by

Méphistophélès to seek pleasure instead. In Auerbach's cellar Brander sings the *Song of the Rat*, with a drunken Amen fugue to cap it. Méphistophélès sings his *Song of the Flea*. Sleeping by the banks of the Elbe, Faust sees the *Dance of the Sylphs* and a vision of Marguérite. In her house, where Faust is concealed, she sings the ballad of the King of Thule, a *chanson gothique*. Méphistophélès sings a serenade, and Faust and Marguérite join in a love duet. In the following scene she laments her unhappiness, now deserted. In a final scene Faust invokes nature, there is a *Ride to the Abyss*, a vision of Hell, with the redemption of Marguérite, taken up to Heaven.

In concert the *Rákóczi March* is very familiar, followed by the *Ballet des Sylphes* (Ballet of the Sylphs), while *Une puce gentille* (A gentle flea), the song of Mephistopheles, has a special place in bass repertoire. The whole work was first staged in Monte Carlo in 1893 and has subsequently been mounted in various opera-houses throughout the world.

Recommended Recording: La Damnation de Faust (2 CDs) ***Naxos 8.554385-86***

DANTONS TOD (DANTON'S DEATH)

- Gottfried von Einem. Opera in two parts. 1946.
- Libretto by the composer and Boris Blacher, after the play by Georg Büchner.
- First performance at the Salzburg Festspielhaus on 6th August 1947.

Robespierre is reported to have brought about the execution of twenty people for no just reason. Danton is urged to oppose him openly, but does not do so, while Saint-Just tries to persuade Robespierre to eliminate his rival. He agrees and will also, once he learns of a newspaper attack on him, agree to the execution of Desmoulins, whom he had earlier sought to protect. Danton and Desmoulins are imprisoned and the former is brought before the tribunal, where he defends himself but is condemned after the intervention of Saint-Just. He is taken to execution with Desmoulins, and, the execution completed, Lucile, the wife of Desmoulins, mounts the scaffold, knowing that the guillotine is the only end.

Inspired by the unsuccessful attempt to assassinate Hitler in 1944, von Einem's opera, in a somewhat eclectic 20th century style, gives particular musical and dramatic importance to the volatile Paris mob, with its changing loyalties, a comment on contemporary popular attitudes.

Daphne

- Richard Strauss. *Bukolische Tragödie* in one act. 1938.
- Libretto by Joseph Gregor, with advice from Stefan Zweig.
- First performed at the Dresden Staatsoper on 15th October 1938.

Characters

Daphne	soprano
Peneios, a fisherman, her father	bass
Gaea, her mother	contralto
Leukippos, a shepherd	tenor
Apollo	tenor
Four Shepherds	tenor, baritone & two basses
Two Maids	sopranos

A pastoral prelude ushers in the preparations for the feast of Dionysus. Daphne is wooed, against her will, by the shepherd Leukippos, for whom she had entertained merely childish affection. Her mother Gaea tells her that one day her heart will blossom like a flower, but Daphne refuses the robes and flowers brought her for the festival and runs away. Leukippos resolves to wear the robes and thus further his intent. Peneios invokes the gods, summoning them to the banquet, at which Apollo appears, in the guise of a cowherd. He is greeted by Daphne, but his embraces confuse her. In the dance in honour of Dionysus, Leukippos is unmasked by Apollo, who, challenged, now reveals himself, shooting Leukippos dead with his arrow. Daphne's sadness persuades Apollo to pray Zeus to make Leukippos his flute-player on Olympus and to make the chaste Daphne a sacred laurel tree, whose leaves may crown his devotees.

The evocative closing scene has found its own place outside the opera-house. The opera itself, intended originally as a companion piece for the one-act *Friedenstag*, proved too long for that purpose, but remains too short for a whole evening. The suggested opposition of Dionysus and Apollo, a commonplace from Nietzsche, remains unrealised, with neither god true to form. Nevertheless the work contains much music of nostalgic beauty, not least in the pastoral prelude and the idyllic setting.

Dardanus

- Jean-Philippe Rameau. *Tragédie en musique* in a prologue and five acts. 1739. Revised in 1744 and 1760.
- Libretto by Charles-Antoine Le Clerc de La Bruère.
- First performance at the Paris Opéra on 19th November 1739.

Characters

Vénus	soprano
L'Amour (Cupid)	soprano
Dardanus, son of Jupiter and Electra	haute-contre
Teucer, king of Phrygia	bass
Iphise, his daughter	soprano
Anténor, a prince	bass
Isménor, magician and priest of Jupiter	bass
Phrygian Woman	soprano
Phrygian	bass
Three Dreams	soprano, haute-contre & bass
A Pleasure	soprano

The Pleasures, invited by Venus to her son Cupid's palace, send them all to sleep, to be aroused by the advent of Jealousy. In the first act Iphise is in love with Dardanus, enemy of her father Teucer, who proposes her marriage to Antenor. Dardanus, in love with Iphise, is warned by the magician Ismenor, whose form he now assumes, advising Antenor and learning, before he reveals his true identity, of Iphise's love for him. News comes to Iphise of the capture of Dardanus, his imprisonment provoking divine anger and the intervention of Neptune. Dreams divert Dardanus and urge him to fight the sea-monster, which he does, rescuing Antenor, who gives him his sword in gratitude. Dardanus enters Teucer's palace and is welcomed as the killer of the monster and consequent husband of Iphise.

The fifth of Rameau's operas, *Dardanus* represents a musical if not a dramatic triumph, its libretto later simplified and made marginally more credible. The concert suite from the opera may be heard in the concert-hall.

DAVID ET JONATHAS (DAVID AND JONATHAN)

- Marc-Antoine Charpentier. Sacred opera in five acts. 1688.
- Libretto by François Bretonneau.
- First performance at the Collège Louis-le-Grand in Paris on 28th February 1688.

Charpentier's sacred opera deals with the final battle between Saul and Jonathan and the Philistines and their death, and served as an interlude during the performance of a sacred drama on the subject of Saul staged at the Jesuit Collège Louis-le-Grand, following the then custom of Jesuit plays on religious subjects.

DEATH IN VENICE

- Benjamin Britten. Opera in two acts. 1972.
- Libretto by Myfanwy Piper, after the novella by Thomas Mann, *Der Tod in Venedig*.
- First performance at the Snape Maltings on 16th June 1973.

CHARACTERS

Gustav von Aschenbach	tenor
The Traveller	
The Elderly Fop	
The Old Gondolier	
The Hotel Manager	bass-baritone
The Hotel Barber	
Leader of the Players	
Voice of Dionysus	
Voice of Apollo	counter-tenor
Polish Mother	silent rôle
Tadzio, her son	dancer
Jaschiu, his friend	dancer

The writer Aschenbach, tired and unable to work, is induced to travel south. On the boat to Venice he encounters the rouged Elderly Fop and doubts the efficacy of Venice. He travels to the Lido, rowed by a truculent and obstinate old gondolier. At the hotel he notices the beautiful Polish boy Tadzio and later watches him playing on the beach. Finding the heat oppressive he plans to leave, but a mistake with his luggage persuades him to stay, particularly when he sees Tadzio again. He watches the games of Apollo, marked by the sound of the God's voice, in which Tadzio triumphs. He admits his love for the boy. In the barber's shop he hears rumours of disease in Venice and in the city itself hears more of an epidemic of cholera. The leader of a troupe of actors entertaining the hotel guests is evasive, when the question is raised. Aschenbach learns at the travel bureau that there is an epidemic and is urged to leave. He plans to warn Tadzio's mother, but cannot. In his dreams he hears Dionysus disputing with Apollo and finally triumphant. The beach is empty, and Tadzio and his friends soon abandon their games. At the barber's he is rouged and has his hair dyed, resembling now the elderly fop. Now he follows the Polish family to Venice, thinking he has encouragement from Tadzio. The guests leave the hotel and Aschenbach sees Tadzio's game with Jaschiu now turn rough. He calls out to him, Tadzio beckons, but Aschenbach falls back in his chair, dead.

Dedicated to the tenor Peter Pears, who created the rôle of Aschenbach, Britten's opera explores the Dionysian and Apollonian, the wildness of inspiration and the calm serenity of Apollo, following the dichotomy suggested by Nietzsche and implicit in Thomas Mann's novella. While the characters represented by the bass-baritone, with their related music, suggest Aschenbach's pre-ordained fate, the dancers, Tadzio and his friends, represent the Dionysian element to which the restrained, classical Aschenbach, the Apollonian, cannot speak. *Death in Venice* was Britten's last opera.

DEIDAMIA

- George Frideric Handel. Opera in three acts. 1740.
- Libretto by Paolo Antonio Rolli.
- First performance at the Lincoln Inn Fields Theatre, London, on 10th January 1741.

Achilles, fated to die in the Trojan war, has been brought up as a girl, together with Deidamia, daughter of King Lycomedes, with whom he has fallen in love. Ulysses , in disguise, comes to seek out Achilles, whose identity becomes apparent when he shows his skill in hunting. He declares his identity, when challenged, and resolves to go to the war, in spite of the protestations of Deidamia, who is equally unsuccessful when she turns her attention to Ulysses, a faithful husband to Penelope.

A relatively late work in Handel's career, *Deidamia*, in its handling of the plot and in its music, represents a lighter style than that of the earlier *opera seria*.

Demetrio e Polibio (Demetrius and Polybius)

- Gioachino Rossini. *Dramma serio* in two acts. 1808.
- Libretto by Vincenzina Vigano-Mombelli.
- First performance at the Teatro Valle, Rome, on 18th May 1812.

Rossini's first opera deals with the enmity between the kings of Syria and Parthia and the love of their daughter and son.

Demon, The

- Anton Grigor'yevich Rubinstein. Opera in a prologue, three acts, an epilogue and apotheosis. 1875.
- Libretto by Pavel Alexandrovich Viskovatov, after preliminary work by the composer and Apollon Nikolayevich Maikov, following the poem by Lermontov.
- First performance at the Mariinsky Theatre, St Petersburg, on 25th January 1875.

Characters

The Demon	baritone
The Angel	mezzo-soprano
Tamara	soprano
Prince Gudal, her father	bass
Prince Sinodal, her betrothed	tenor
Old Servant	bass
Nanny	soprano
Messenger	tenor

The Demon is disillusioned and rejects the Angels' suggestion of redemption through love. By the riverside Tamara dreams of her future marriage, but hears the voice of the Demon, whom, for a moment she sees in his brilliance and glory. Meanwhile Prince Sinodal travels towards her, held up on his journey in a mountain region. The Demon lulls him to sleep with dreams of Tamara, but the Tartars attack, Sinodal is wounded and dies. In Prince Gudal's castle news of Sinodal is awaited. A messenger announces his death and the body is brought in. The weeping Tamara is consoled by the voice of the Demon, who promises to come to her that night. She pleads with her father to allow her to enter a convent and he reluctantly yields to her entreaties. In the convent the Demon appears, but

his way is barred by the Angel. He enters Tamara's room and confesses his own suffering. Feeling pity, Tamara demands that he forswear evil. Finally she gives way, declaring her love for him. In an epilogue she is saved by the Angel and in a final apotheosis ascends to Heaven.

Rubinstein's opera is thoroughly Russian in its oriental exoticism and choice of voices. It exercised influence on Tchaikowsky's *Eugene Onegin* but in many respects is a highly original work. The *Caucasian Dance* and ballet music from the opera are sometimes heard in the concert-hall, while the Demon's romance *Nye plach' ditya* (Do not weep, my child) and *Na vozdushnom okeanye* (On the ocean of air) were favourites of Chaliapin's repertoire.

Recommended Recording: The Demon (2 CDs) — ***Marco Polo 8.223781-82***

DEUX JOURNÉES, LES (THE TWO DAYS)

- Luigi Cherubini. *Comédie lyrique* in three acts. 1800.
- Libretto by Jean-Nicola Bouilly.
- First performance at the Théâtre Feydeau, Paris, on 16th January 1800.

Tactfully transported to an earlier period of French history, the plot allows the water-carrier Mikéli to shelter two political refugees from Cardinal Mazarin, Armand and his wife Constance, who are helped by his family to escape from Paris. Armand's identity is revealed, as he defends the honour of Constance, but news comes of the repeal of the order against Armand. All ends happily.

Beethoven and Goethe both thought highly of *Les deux journées*, a work believed to have had influence on the former's *Fidelio*, as an 'escape' opera.

DEVIL AND KATE, THE

- Antonín Dvořák. Comic opera in three acts. 1899.
- Libretto by Adolf Wenig, after a Czech folk-tale.
- First performance at the Prague National Theatre on 23rd November 1899.

The spinster Kate expresses her willingness to dance with the Devil, who appears. The devil Marbuel persuades her to elope with him. In Hell Kate is disappointed, while the shepherd Jirka comes in search of her, suggesting that the devils buy her off, to avoid her nagging. Eventually Jirka dances her away. In the world above the Princess agrees to free the serfs in her kingdom and when Marbuel comes, as Lucifer has bidden him, to take the Princess to Hell, Kate jumps out on him and frightens him away, to be suitably rewarded by the Princess.

The Devil and Kate has enjoyed limited success abroad, but is thoroughly Czech in character, while, unusually, having no real love interest in its plot. Sometimes known, with English gallantry and consequent inaccuracy, as *Kate and the Devil*, the work is occasionally represented by its overture in concert repertoire.

Recommended Recording: Overture, Preludes and Infernal Dance ***Marco Polo 8.223272***

Devil to Pay, The

- Seedo (Sidow). Ballad opera. 1731.
- Play by Charles Coffey.
- First performance at Drury Lane, London, on 6th August 1731.

The Irish playwright Charles Coffey's ballad opera concerns the punishment of the bad-tempered Lady Loverule, transformed into the wife of the village cobbler, whose own sweet-tempered wife Nell is transformed into the lady of the manor. In a shortened form the opera became extremely popular and won a place in popular German repertoire as *Der Teufel ist los*, where it influenced the development of the *Singspiel*. It also provided, in the 19th century, the basis of a ballet by Adolphe Adam, *Le diable à quatre*.

Devil's Wall, The

- Bedřich Smetana. Comic-romantic opera in three acts. 1882.
- Libretto by Eliška Krásnohorská.
- First performance at the Prague New Czech theatre on 29th October 1882.

The opera deals with plans for the marriage of Vok Vítkovic, whose courtiers desire an heir for him, while the hermit Beneš prefers that he stay single, to ensure the bequest of his property to the church. Beneš is helped by the devil Rarach, who sometimes assumes his identity and brings Vok into danger by damming the river Vltava, an event recounted in local Czech legend. All comes out well enough in the end, when Hedwika shows her love by crossing the flooded area, a demonstration of her love for Vok, who marries her, while Beneš breaks the curse of the dam.

Devils of Loudun, The

- Krzysztof Penderecki. Opera in three acts. 1969. Revised in 1975.
- Libretto by the composer after the dramatized version of Aldous Huxley's novel of the same name in German by Erich Fried and subsequently in English by John Whiting.
- First performance at the Hamburg Staatsoper on 20th June 1969.

The opera deals with the downfall of Father Grandier, accused of bewitching the nuns of Loudun and implicated in opposition to the royal command to tear down the walls of the city. Grandier is innocent of witchcraft, but has human weakness when it comes to women. He is tortured and put to death in scenes of lurid intensity, matched by Penderecki's inventive atonal score.

Devin du village, Le (The Village Soothsayer)

- Jean-Jacques Rousseau. *Intermède* in one act. 1752.
- Libretto by the composer.
- First performance at Fontainebleau on 18th October 1752.

The love of Colin and Colette, disrupted by the intervention of the nobility, is mended, largely through the intervention of the Soothsayer.

Rousseau's work reflects contemporary interest in the natural man, while also offering the Paris Opéra an alternative to the *tragédie lyrique* in the Querelle des Bouffons, the quarrel between those who favoured the traditional French form and those who preferred Italian *opera buffa*. Rousseau's piece offers a French version of the latter, while endowing the continuing pastoral convention with some philosophical and even political justification.

Diable à quatre, Le (The Devil To Pay)

- Christoph Willibald von Gluck. *Opéra comique* in three acts.
- Libretto by Michel-Jean Sedaine and Pierre Baurans, after the ballad opera by Charles Coffey.
- First performance at Laxenburg on 28th May 1759.

The bad-tempered Marquise is transformed into the wife of the surly cobbler Jacques, whose own sweet-tempered wife is transformed into the Marquise through the magic of an astrologer who has been refused shelter at the château. Once the Marquise has learned her lesson, the spell is reversed.

Gluck's attractive theatre-piece won popularity in Vienna, where it was seen by Haydn in 1761, when he used the air *Je n'aimais pas le tabac beaucoup* (I didn't like tobacco much) in his symphony *Le soir* (Evening).

DIALOGUES DES CARMÉLITES (CARMELITE DIALOGUES)

- Francis Poulenc. Opera in three acts. 1956.
- Libretto by the composer, after the play by Georges Bernanos.
- First performance in Italian at the Teatro alla Scala, Milan, on 26th January 1957.

CHARACTERS

Marquis de la Force	baritone
Chevalier de la Force, his son	tenor
Blanche de la Force, his daughter	soprano
Thierry, a valet	baritone
Madame de Croissy, Prioress	contralto
Sister Constance of St Denis, a novice	soprano
Mother Marie of the Incarnation, assistant prioress	mezzo-soprano
Madame Lidoine, the new prioress	mezzo-soprano
M. Javelinot, a doctor	baritone
Mother Jeanne of the Child Jesus	contralto
Sister Mathilde	mezzo-soprano
Father Confessor	tenor
First and Second Commissary	tenor & bass
Officers, gaoler and eleven Carmelite nuns	

The brother and father of Blanche de la Force fear for her, since she is easily frightened and her carriage has been held up by a mob, as the French revolution begins. Blanche is admitted as a Carmelite novice, her demeanour a contrast with that of the cheerful peasant-girl Sister Constance, who believes they will both die on the same day. The Prioress dies, committing Blanche to the care of Mother Marie. The Requiem for the Prioress is celebrated. Blanche is frightened, when told to watch over the body, while Constance imagines that we die for others. In the chapter-house the new Prioress warns the nuns of danger to come and the Chevalier de la Force, Blanche's brother, visits her and begs her to leave with him, as the Terror draws near. The Father Confessor leads the nuns in prayer, before going into hiding himself. The revolutionaries enter the convent and expel the nuns. Under the guidance of Mother Marie the nuns vote for martyrdom, with Blanche dissenting in a secret vote, her dissent claimed and changed by the intervention of Constance. Blanche runs away, returning to her home, now looted, her father executed. Mother Marie tells her that by running away she may not have saved her soul. Blanche hears that the nuns have been arrested. In prison the Prioress urges courage on the sisters, while Mother Marie is consoled by the Father Confessor, since she is now not with her sisters. The nuns sing the *Salve regina* as they go to the scaffold, joined now by Blanche, who also goes to her death.

The play by Bernanos was based on the novel by Gertrud von Le Fort, *Die letzte am Schafott* (The Last to the Scaffold). Poulenc provided an elaborately orchestrated score for a work of high drama, powerful in its choice of subject and the treatment of it, as much as in its music.

Dido

Dido, Queen of Carthage, who killed herself when deserted by her lover, the Trojan prince Aeneas, is a tragic figure whose fate was a popular subject of opera and of other musical genres. The subject is treated in Book IV of Virgil's epic *Aeneid* and by Ovid in his *Heroides*, imaginary complaints by heroines in straits of one sort or another. Metastasio's libretto *Didone abbandonata* enjoyed great popularity, with settings by Leonardo Vinci, Giuseppe Sarti and many other composers. In France the tragedy of Dido was treated by Henry Desmarets in 1693 and by Niccolò Piccinni in 1782, as well as in the massive *Les troyens* of Berlioz.

Dido and Aeneas

- Henry Purcell. Tragic opera in three acts. 1689 or earlier.
- Libretto by Nahum Tate, after his play *Brutus of Alba* and Virgil's *Aeneid*.
- First performance at Josias Priest's school in Chelsea, London,
before December 1689, with a possible earlier performance as a court masque in 1684.

Characters

Dido, Queen of Carthage	soprano
Aeneas, a Trojan prince	baritone
Belinda, Dido's confidante	soprano
Sorceress	mezzo-soprano or baritone
Spirit, in the form of Mercury	soprano
Sailor	soprano or baritone

Dido, the widowed Queen of Carthage, entertains the Trojan Prince Aeneas, shipwrecked on his way to Italy, where he will found a new Troy. Dido and Aeneas are in love. Witches plot Dido's destruction and the Sorceress conjures a storm, to break out when the royal couple are hunting, and the impersonation of Mercury by one of her coven. The storm duly breaks and the courtiers hasten back to town, while the false Mercury tells Aeneas he must leave Dido and sail for Italy. Aeneas and his sailors prepare to leave, to the delight of the witches. Aeneas parts from Dido, who kills herself once he has gone, her death lamented by mourning cupids.

It has been plausibly suggested that Purcell's short opera *Dido and Aeneas* was originally designed as a court masque, and possible topical political allusions have been proposed, notably in the light of the future James II's Catholicism, seen to deflect him from his duty as a future king, a hypothetical intrigue that casts the Jesuits as witches. The work owes something to John Blow's *Venus and Adonis* of 1683. Most famous of all elements in the opera is Dido's lament, *When I am laid in earth*, with its descending ground bass borrowed from current Venetian practice.

Recommended Recording: Dido and Aeneas ***Naxos 8.553108***

Didone

- Francesco Cavalli. Opera in a prologue and three acts. 1641.
- Libretto by Francesco Busenello, based on Virgil's *Aeneid*.
- First performance at the Teatro S Cassiano, Venice, in 1641.

In Cavalli's opera Dido does not die, but is saved by the intervention of her lover Iarbas, King of the Getuli, whom she marries, but only after she has sung a recitative lament. The opera ends, like Monteverdi's *L'incoronazione di Poppea*, with a love duet.

Dimitrij

- Antonín Dvořák. Grand opera in four acts. 1882. Revised in 1894.
- Libretto by Marie Červinková-Riegrová.
- First performance at the Prague New Czech Theatre on 8th October 1882.

Dvořák's opera deals with the rising against Boris Godunov, led by the pretender Dimitrij, eventually revealed as an impostor and killed, after attempts to repudiate his Polish wife Marina and to marry Xenie, daughter of Boris Godunov.

The overture to *Dimitrij* may be heard occasionally in concert performance, while the opera itself is rarely heard in international repertoire.

Dinner Engagement, The

- Lennox Berkeley. Opera in two scenes. 1954.
- Libretto by Paul Dehn.
- First performance at the Jubilee Hall, Aldebugh, on 17th June 1954.

A witty libretto presents impoverished members of the English nobility cooking to entertain the visiting Grand Duchess of Monteblanco, the amorous propensities and money of whose son they are anxious to divert towards their daughter Susan. The short opera, with music that matches its libretto, ends with the engagement of Phillipe and Susan.

Dinorah

- Giacomo Meyerbeer. *Opéra comique* in three acts. 1859.
- Libretto by Michel Carré and Jules Barbier, after the former's play *Les chercheurs de trésor* (The Treasure-Seekers).
- First performance by the Paris Opéra-Comique at the Salle Favart on 4th April 1859.

Dinorah or *Le pardon de Ploërmel* (The Pardon of Ploërmel) deals with the disappearance of Hoël on the day of his wedding with Dinorah. He finds a treasure which will bring death to the first to touch it, a fate for which he enlists Corentin, but eventually all ends well, once Hoël has realised the value of love over wealth.

The best known music from Meyerbeer's opera must be the waltz that Dinorah dances with her own shadow, *Ombre légère qui suis mes pas* (Light shadow that follows in my steps), with the heroine's search for her pet goat, *Bellah! ma chèvre chérie* (Bellah! My dear goat) and Hoël's *Ah! mon remords te venge* (Ah! My remorse takes revenge).

Dioclesian

- Henry Purcell. Semi-opera in five acts. 1690.
- Text by Thomas Betterton, from the play by Fletcher and Massinger.
- First performance at the Queen's Theatre, Dorset Gardens, London, in May 1690.

The play, written in 1622, deals with the seizure of imperial power by Diocles, transformed thereupon to Dioclesian, following a prophecy that seems so improbable that he has agreed, if it comes true, to marry Drusilla, unattractive niece of the prophetess Delphia. Dioclesian's wedding with Princess Aurelia is magically disturbed by a storm and the appearance of a monster, and Delphia also sees to it that Aurelia falls in love with Dioclesian's nephew Maximinian, and, as if this were not enough, helps a Persian army to attack. Dioclesian gives way, marries Drusilla and shares his power with Maximinian.

The Prophetess, or The History of Dioclesian, in the popular English form of semi-opera, spoken drama with an additional musical and choreographic element, includes a final masque to mark the idyllic retirement of Diocles to his country retreat. The score includes the countertenor *Since from my dear Astraea's sight, Sound Fame*, with trumpet obbligato, the duet *Tell me why, Let us dance, let us sing* and the strophic *What shall I do to show how much I love her.*

Divara – Wasser und Blut (Divara – Water and Blood)

- Azio Corghi. Opera in three acts. 1993
- Libretto by the composer and José Saramago.
- First performed in the City Theatre, Münster, on 31st October 1993.

Divara – Wasser und Blut (Divara – Water and Blood) deals with the Anabaptist seizure of Münster in 1534, under their leader Jan Matthys, with his wife Divara, and the former's gradual betrayal of his earlier principles as Jan van Leiden is declared king, before his final defeat and the reversion of the city to its Catholic rulers.

Azio Corghi, in collaboration with the distinguished Portuguese writer José Saramago, was commissioned to write *Divara – Wasser und Blut* to commemorate the city of Münster's foundation. The drama of the Anabaptist capture of the city and the ensuing events is matched with dramatic music in an effective contemporary idiom.

Reommended Recording: Divara (2 CDs) ***Marco Polo 8.223706-07***

Djamileh

- Georges Bizet. *Opéra comique* in one act. 1871.
- Libretto by Louis Gallet, after *Namouna* by Alfred de Musset.
- First performance by the Paris Opéra-Comique at the Salle Favart on 22nd May 1872.

Haroun, in his Cairo palace, seeks pleasure in a monthly change of slave-girls. Djamileh, due to be discarded, loves Haroun and helped by his servant takes the place of the new girl, thus winning the love of Haroun.

Bizet's opera enjoyed only limited success in Paris. The score contains elements of exoticism and uses, at times, the device of melodrama, with words spoken to musical accompaniment.

DOCTEUR MIRACLE, LE (DOCTOR MIRACLE)

- Georges Bizet. *Opérette* in one act. 1856.
- Libretto by Léon Battu and Ludovic Halévy.
- First performance at the Bouffes-Parisiens on 9th April 1857.

Silvio, with amorous designs on the daughter of a magistrate, succeeds in gaining admittance to the house as a servant, cooks an omelette that he later claims has been poisoned, and returns as Dr Miracle in order to cure everyone, in return for the hand of Laurette, the magistrate's daughter.

Addicts of musical cookery will find an Omelette Quartet in a work designed for four singers, which includes an overture and six set pieces.

DOKTOR FAUST

- Ferruccio Busoni. Opera, with a prologue, two preludes, a scenic intermezzo and a main play of three scenes. 1924.
- Libretto by the composer, after the 16th century Faust puppet plays.
- First performance at the Sächsisches Staatstheater, Dresden, on 21st May 1925.

In a prologue the poet addresses the audience, followed by a first prelude in Faust's study, where he is given a magic book, and a second prelude in which Faust summons Mephistopheles, with whom he signs a pact. The intermezzo shows the vow of revenge by Gretchen's brother and his murder, through the intervention of Mephistopheles. The principal action shows Faust at the court of the Duke of Parma, demonstrating his magic power through visions of the biblical past and eloping with the infatuated Duchess. The second scene brings a theological dispute in a Wittenberg tavern, the burning of the body of the Duchess's child and the intimation that Faust must die that night. In the streets at night Faust gives alms to a beggar, the Duchess, and as midnight falls gives his soul to the dead child, which in turn enters his body, to continue living as Faust dies.

Busoni's work, described as a poem for music and unfinished at the time of his death in 1924, makes use of a number of other completed compositions and sketches, including his *Divertimento for flute, Op. 52, Sonatina seconda, Tanzwalzer, Op. 53* and *Sarabande and Toccata, Op. 51*.

Dom Sébastien, roi de Portugal (Dom Sebastian, King of Portugal)

- Gaetano Donizetti. *Opéra* in five acts. 1843.
- Libretto by Eugène Scribe, after Paul-Henri Foucher.
- First performance at the Paris Opéra on 13th November 1843.

Dom Sebastian plans a crusade against the Moors, while the Grand Inquisitor plots to make use of his absence to subvert his power. The King is accompanied by the poet Camoëns and by Zayda, whom he has rescued from the Inquisition and intends to return to her father. At home her father insists that she marry a Moorish chief, but she is in love with Sebastian and after his defeat by her proposed husband finds him wounded on the battlefield. She offers freely to marry the chief, Abayaldos, if he will spare the life of the wounded man, whose identity he does not suspect. In Lisbon once more, where the regent Dom Antonio has declared himself king, Sebastian reveals his identity, but is imprisoned, together with Zayda. He signs, as required, an instrument of abdication, in order to secure her release, but both of them are killed as she tries to aid his escape.

The last of Donizetti's operas, *Dom Sébastien, roi de Portugal,* has a complex and cumbersome plot. In the concert-hall the tenor *Seul sur la terre* (Alone on the earth) and baritone *O Lisbone, o ma patrie* (O Lisbon, O my country) have a secure place.

Domino noir, Le (The Black Domino)

- Daniel-François-Esprit Auber. *Opéra comique* in three acts. 1837.
- Libretto by Eugène Scribe.
- First performance by the Paris Opéra-Comique at the Salle Bourse on 2nd December 1837.

The black domino is the disguise of Angèle, of the royal convent, wooed at a ball by Horace de Massarena. She takes refuge at the house of the reprobate Count Juliano, where she poses as the housekeeper's niece and meets Massarena again. She is finally freed from her convent, when she inherits a fortune of her own and can marry him.

A work that enjoyed enormous contemporary success, *Le domino noir*, set in Spain, includes Angèle's bolero popularly known as *La gitana* and an overture that has made its way into brass band repertoire.

Don Carlos

- Giuseppe Verdi. *Opéra* in five acts. 1867. Revised in four acts in 1884.
- Libretto by Joseph Méry and Camille du Locle, after Schiller's dramatic poem *Don Carlos, Infant von Spanien* (Don Carlos, Infante of Spain).
- First performance at the Paris Opéra on 11th March 1867.

Characters

Philip II, King of Spain	bass
Don Carlos, Infante of Spain	tenor
Rodrigue (Rodrigo), Marquis of Posa	baritone
Elisabeth de Valois, later Queen of Spain	soprano
Princess Eboli, her lady-in-waiting	mezzo-soprano
Thibault (Tebaldo), her page	soprano
Grand Inquisitor	bass
A Monk	bass
Count of Lerma	tenor
Royal Herald	tenor
Heavenly Voice	soprano
Flemish Deputies & Inquisitors	basses

Don Carlos arrives in France, in secret, anxious to see his proposed bride, Elisabeth de Valois, with whom he falls in love, revealing to her his true identity. She is warned that now the King of Spain himself desires her hand for himself and not for his son. In a monastery Don Carlos recalls the stories of how his grandfather, Charles V, did not die but remains as a monk. He is induced by his friend Rodrigo to support the people of Flanders, but is moved by the sight of the King and his Queen, as they pass the tomb of Charles V. Princess Eboli, herself in love with Carlos, imagines this love returned. A scene between Elisabeth and Don Carlos is filled with emotion, as Don Carlos rushes away distraught. Rodrigo asks the King to send him to Flanders and seeks a lessening of severity in Spain's official policy. The King warns him of the power of the Inquisition. In the palace gardens, while a masked ball is in progress within, Don Carlos waits for the arrival of the Queen, and seeing a figure whom he thinks to be Elisabeth declares his love, only to find that it is Princess Eboli, at which he cannot hide his true feelings. She is resolved on revenge. As heretics are to be put to death, Don Carlos pleads for Flanders before the King and has to be disarmed by Rodrigo. The Inquisitor advises the King that Rodrigo must be punished rather than Don Carlos. Finding the portrait of his son in the Queen's jewel-case, the King accuses her of adultery, and left together with

Princess Eboli, who confesses her rôle in this and her adultery with the King, the Queen dismisses her from her service. Imprisoned, Carlos is visited by Rodrigo, who takes the blame for letters sent to Carlos from the Flemish patriots. Rodrigo is shot by an assassin who has followed him. The opera ends as the Queen and Don Carlos meet by the tomb of Charles V. The King has overheard and emerges from behind the tomb, with the Grand Inquisitor, demanding the death of his son. The voice of the old Emperor is heard and a figure comes forward, the old Emperor or a monk in disguise, to take Don Carlos into the safety of the monastery.

Verdi was induced to shorten his opera by omitting the ballet scene for the palace ball in the original third act and the first act, set in France. The score includes, for Princess Eboli, the Moorish romance, the *Veil Song*, *Au palais des fées* (At the fairies' palace), the tale of a Moorish king who by mistake wooed his own wife in the garden, a premonition of the mistake that Don Carlos is to make himself, when he mistakenly woos Princess Eboli. *Elle ne m'aime pas* (She does not love me), sung by the King, is followed by his duet with the old blind Grand Inquisitor, *Suis-je devant le Roi?* (Am I before the King?). There is much else in a powerful work, representative throughout of Verdi at the height of his powers.

Recommended Recordings:

Overture	***Naxos 8.553089***
Scene & Duet: Dio, che nell'alma	***Naxos 8.550684***
Io la vidi	***Naxos 8.550497***
Spuntato ecco il dì	***Naxos 8.550241***

Don Giovanni

- Wolfgang Amadeus Mozart. *Dramma giocoso* (*opera buffa*) in two acts. 1787.
- Libretto by Lorenzo Da Ponte.
- First performance at the Prague National Theatre on 29th October 1787.

Characters

Don Giovanni, a dissolute nobleman	baritone
Commendatore, an old nobleman	bass
Donna Anna, his daughter	soprano
Don Ottavio, her betrothed	tenor
Donna Elvira, a lady from Burgos	soprano
Leporello, Don Giovanni's servant	bass

Masetto, a peasant	bass
Zerlina, a peasant girl, his betrothed	soprano

Don Giovanni has had his way with Donna Anna, entering her bedroom, when she mistook him for her betrothed, Don Ottavio. Leporello, outside, complains of his life as a servant. Donna Anna pursues Don Giovanni and is joined by her father, who dies as they fight. Don Ottavio joins her in vowing revenge against the unknown assailant, while Don Giovanni and Leporello make their escape. Now they come across another woman, Donna Elvira, an earlier victim of Don Giovanni, who now runs off, when they recognise each other, while Leporello reads her a catalogue of his master's conquests. Master and servant now come across a group of peasants, ready to celebrate the marriage of Zerlina and Masetto. Don Giovanni manages to be left alone with Zerlina, having invited the whole company to his palace nearby, but as they go off together Donna Elvira appears, intervening to warn the girl. Donna Anna and Don Ottavio now join them, recognising Don Giovanni by his voice. In Don Giovanni's garden Masetto reproaches Zerlina, frustrating Don Giovanni's attempts to lure her away. Donna Anna, Donna Elvira and Don Ottavio appear, masked, and are invited by Leporello to join the celebration. At the ball in the palace Don Giovanni takes Zerlina into another room and when she screams pretends that Leporello is guilty. The three masked visitors now reveal themselves and accuse Don Giovanni. Outside Donna Elvira's house, Leporello is made to impersonate his master to woo her, while Don Giovanni turns his attention to her maid, a cruel deception. Masetto, seeking Don Giovanni, has his helpers sent off in various directions by Don Giovanni, in the guise of Leporello, and when Masetto is alone he sets upon him, leaving him to be consoled by Zerlina. Leporello, taking refuge in the courtyard of the house of Donna Anna, is seized, but pleads for mercy, when they realise who he is. Don Giovanni and Leporello now come together, as night draws on, in a churchyard, where the stone statue on the tomb of the Commendatore is heard to speak. At this Don Giovanni tells Leporello to invite the statue to dinner. The statue accepts and in a final scene is heard slowly approaching the room where Don Giovanni is at dinner, to the terror first of Donna Elvira, who has been urging reform on her betrayer, and then of Leporello. The statue slowly enters and holding fast Don Giovanni's hand takes him into the fiery pit that now opens before them. There follows a brief epilogue in which the moral of the tale is pointed by those who remain.

Il dissoluto punito, ossia Il Don Giovanni (The Libertine Punished, or Don Giovanni) was written for Prague and staged in Vienna the following year, with additional arias for Don Ottavio and Donna Elvira. Lorenzo Da Ponte based his libretto on the well known story, dramatized in the 17th century by the Spanish playwright Tirso da Molina and the subject of an opera by Giuseppe Gazzaniga, with a libretto by Giovanni Bertati, that had been performed in Venice in February 1787. Da Ponte also drew on Molière's treatment of the subject. The opera opens with a sinister overture, in which the approach of the stone statue can be heard. Don Ottavio's two great arias, *Dalla sua pace* (Of her peace), written for Vienna, and *Il mio tesoro* (My treasure) are essential parts of tenor repertoire. The buffo Leporello's catalogue song, *Madamina il catalogo* (Miss, the catalogue), provides bass-baritones with superb opportunity for comedy, while Don Giovanni's *Là ci darem la mano* (You'll give me your hand, my dear), the subject, among other things, of variations by Beethoven and by Chopin and of elaboration by Liszt, is one of the most famous of all operatic songs. Don Giovanni orders celebration in an energetic *Finch'han dal vino* (Let them have wine) and woos Donna Elvira's maid in an eloquent serenade, *Deh, vieni alla finestra* (Come to the window). Donna Anna herself has her moment in *Or sai chi l'onore* (You know for sure), while Zerlina's *Batti, batti, o bel Masetto* (Beat me, beat me, fair Masetto) teases the poor man into easy submission.

Recommended Recordings:

Overture	***Naxos 8.550185***
Madamina / Vedrai carino / Deh, vieni alla finestra / Là ci darem la mano	***Naxos 8.550435***
Dalla sua pace / Il mio tesoro	***Naxos 8.550383***

Don Pasquale

- Gaetano Donizetti. *Dramma buffo* in three acts.
- Libretto by the composer and Giovanni Rufini, after an earlier libretto by Angelo Anelli.
- First performance at the Paris Théâtre Italien on 3rd January 1843.

Characters

Don Pasquale, an elderly bachelor	bass
Dr Malatesta, his doctor	baritone
Ernesto, his nephew	tenor
Norina, a young widow, loved by Ernesto	soprano
Carlino, cousin of Dr Malatesta	bass

Don Pasquale has decided to marry and have a son, hoping thereby to disinherit his nephew Ernesto, whose relationship with Norina he is against. Dr Malatesta tells him that he is fit to father children, but suggests his sister Sofronia as a candidate for marriage. Ernesto finds his uncle in high spirits but is put out when he learns that the reason for this is his intended marriage. Dr Malatesta now persuades Norina to act the part of his supposed sister. Malatesta brings the veiled Norina to Don Pasquale, whose manners cause her much amusement. Malatesta now introduces his cousin Carlino, as a notary, drawing up a document to make all the old man's possessions over to Norina.

Ernesto comes in, appalled at what he sees, until matters are explained to him. Once the supposed Sofronia is safely married, as it seems, she gives full play to her temper and extravagance, eventually dropping a note that suggests she has planned an assignation in the garden that night. Don Pasquale plots with Malatesta to catch Sofronia with her lover. Ernesto sings to her in Don Pasquale's garden, joined by Norina. Don Pasquale, who, with Malatesta, has observed the scene, emerges from hiding, ready to turn Sofronia out of his house. Malatesta now persuades Don Pasquale to tell her that the next day Norina will be mistress of the house, married to Ernesto. He tells the old man that the only way to be rid of Sofronia is to have Ernesto marry Norina, and to this he agrees. The whole plot is revealed to him and he accepts that he has fully learned his lesson.

A splendid comic opera, with its own moments of tenderness, *Don Pasquale* opens with a brilliant overture that uses some of the material that is to follow. Malatesta gives a glowing description of his supposed sister in *Bella siccome un angelo* (As beautiful as an angel) and Norina's *Quel guardo il cavaliere* (So looks the knight) marks her reading a tale of romantic chivalry in the second scene. Ernesto's serenade, *Com'è gentil* (How gentle the night) and his following duet with Norina, *Tornami a dir che m'ami* (Come and say you love me) set the final garden scene.

Don Procopio

- Georges Bizet. *Opera buffa* in two acts. 1859.
- Libretto by Carlo Cambiaggio, after a libretto by Luigi Prividali.
- First performance at the Monte Carlo Opéra on 10th March 1906.

The opera treats the successful attempt by Bettina to avoid marriage to the old miser Don Procopio and to be united with her lover Odoardo. This she manages to do, like Norina in Donizetti's *Don Pasquale*, by a display of extravagance and greed.

Bizet wrote his Italian *opera buffa* during the years he spent in Rome, after winning the Prix de Rome. He later used material from it in other works.

Don Quichotte (Don Quixote)

- Jules Massenet. *Comédie-héroique* in five acts. 1910.
- Libretto by Henri Cain, after the play by Jacques Le Lorrain, *Le chevalier de la longue figure* (The Knight with the Long Face), based on the novel by Cervantes.
- First performance at the Monte Carlo Opéra on 19th February 1910.

Characters

Don Quichotte	bass
Sancho Panza	bass-baritone
La Belle Dulcinée	mezzo-soprano
Pedro, one of her admirers	soprano
Garcias, another admirer	soprano
Rodriguez, another admirer	tenor
Juan, another admirer	tenor
Chef des bandits	baritone

Dulcinea is serenaded by her four admirers. Don Quixote and Sancho Panza appear, the former singing his praise of Dulcinea, his ideal. Preventing a duel between Juan and Don Quixote, Dulcinea demands that the latter retrieve for her a necklace, stolen by a bandit from her room. Don Quixote now sets out to find the necklace, to the disgust of Sancho Panza, but deflected momentarily from his purpose as he mistakes windmills for giants and does battle with them. Surrounded by bandits in the mountains, Don Quixote moves the bandit chief to pity, when he declares his identity as a knight errant, and is given the necklace. He blesses the bandits, as he goes, for they have understood him. Returning to Dulcinea's garden, Don Quixote gives her her necklace, hoping now for marriage and an end of his travels, but he is rejected, treated kindly by her but mocked by her guests. In the mountains Don Quixote prepares to die, bestowing on Sancho an imaginary island and seeing Dulcinea in a vision in his last moments.

The score of *Don Quichotte* contains Spanish pastiche at the very start. The rôle of Don Quixote was written for Chaliapin, particularly moving in the final death scene. Massenet was near the end of his life when he wrote the work and this is reflected in his choice of subject and his treatment of the protagonist.

Donna del lago, La (The Lady of the Lake)

- Gioachino Rossini. *Melodramma* in two acts. 1819.
- Libretto by Andrea Leone Tottola, after the poem *The Lady of the Lake* by Walter Scott.
- First performance at the Teatro S Carlo, Naples, on 24th October 1819.

Ellen, daughter of the Highland chieftain Douglas, loves Malcolm Graeme but is promised by her father to Roderick Dhu. Rowing across the lake, she meets King James V, under the guise of Uberto, and offers him shelter, but he is perturbed to learn of her rebel parentage. There follows a scene with Malcolm, who agrees to join the rebels but is angry at the news of Ellen's coming marriage.

Roderick Dhu calls them all to arms. In the second act the King expresses his love for Ellen and presents her with a ring that will give her protection, should she need it. Roderick sees their meeting and the couple are surrounded, with the King, still incognito, admitting that he is a follower of the royal cause. In the palace at Stirling, where Douglas is now held as a prisoner, the King reveals his identity, ready now to spare Douglas and Malcolm and agree to the latter's marriage with Ellen.

Scott's poem provided a text for a group of Schubert songs as well as for Rossini's opera. From the latter *Mura felici* (Happy walls) for the mezzo-soprano Malcolm and Ellen's final *Tanti affetti* (Such feelings) are part of operatic recital repertoire.

Recommended Recording: Mura felici **Naxos 8.553543**

DONNE CURIOSE, LE (THE INQUISITIVE WOMEN)

- Ermanno Wolf-Ferrari. Comic opera in three acts. 1903.
- Libretto by Luigi Sugana, after the play by Carlo Goldoni.
- First performance at the Munich Residenztheater on 27th November 1903.

Gozzi's 18th century play shows inquisitive women, anxious to find out what their men are up to, entertaining various suspicions, eventually put to rest when they find the secret club is meeting for dinner in celebration of an engagement, a banquet provided by the *commedia dell'arte* characters Pantalone and Arlecchino. In an allusive score, Wolf-Ferrari provides a witty evocation of the world of Gozzi.

DONNERSTAG AUS LICHT (THURSDAY FROM LIGHT)

- Karlheinz Stockhausen. Opera in three acts, a greeting and a farewell. 1981.
- Libretto by the composer.
- First performance at the Teatro alla Scala, Milan, on 3rd April 1981.

Introduced and ended by a ritual greeting and farewell, the opera centres on Michael, represented by tenor, trumpet and dancer, Eve, soprano, basset-horn and dancer and Luzimon/Lucifer, represented by bass, trombone, dance and mime. The first act shows Michael's Youth, representing the first twenty years of the composer's life. The second act, Michael's journey round the earth, is instrumental, for solo trumpet, played inside a globe that rotates, and orchestra. In the third act Michael returns home to dispute with Lucifer, who is expelled, and to declare his own vision, as a bridge between the music of Heaven and humanity. The fanfares sound from surrounding buildings, as the audience leaves the theatre.

Stockhausen's opera is remarkable in many ways. Musically it is based on three melodic formulae and makes use of pre-recorded tapes, while dramatically it calls for stage instrumentalists and dancers, in addition to the four singers, in a musical idiom as powerful as it is original.

DORI

- Antonio Cesti. *Dramma musicale* in a prologue and three acts. 1657.
- Libretto by Giovanni Filippo Apolloni.
- First performance at the Innsbruck Hof-Saales in 1657.

Dori, Princess of Nicaea, is to marry Oronte, Prince of Persia. She, however, is captured by pirates and, disguised as a man, sold as a slave to her own sister, now due to marry Oronte, a match that she urges. A series of misunderstandings follow, complicated by Dori's assumption of a false identity, as well as that of Tolomeo, who has assumed female guise, but is in the end to marry Dori's sister, while Dori herself finally re-appears to marry Oronte.

Dori won very great contemporary success and provides music of great diversity, within the conventions of the period.

DREI PINTOS, DIE (THE THREE PINTOS)

- Carl Maria von Weber. *Komische Oper* in three acts. 1821.
- Completed by Gustav Mahler in 1888.
- Libretto by Theodor Hell (Carl Gottfried Theodor Winkler), after *Der Brautkampf* (The Bridal Contest) by Carl Seidel.
- First performance at the Leipzig Neues Stadttheater on 20th January 1888.

The intrigue centres on Clarissa and the real Don Pinto, who is to marry her. He is made drunk and replaced by Don Gaston, who is then replaced by Clarissa's lover Don Gomez. All ends well in the betrothal of Clarissa and Don Gomez.

Weber only wrote a small part of the projected opera, which was largely the work of Mahler, using other works of Weber and his own work.

Dreigroschenoper, Die (The Threepenny Opera)

- Kurt Weill. Play with music in a prologue and three acts.
- Text by Bertolt Brecht and translation by Elisabeth Hauptmann, after *The Beggar's Opera* of John Gay.
- First performance at the Berlin Theater am Schiffbauerdamm on 31st August 1928.

A play rather than an opera, the *Dreigroschenoper* follows Gay in its treatment of the anti-hero Macheath, Mac the Knife, his marriage to Polly Peachum, friendship with the chief of police Brown and his betrayal by the whore Jenny. Brown's daughter Lucy is secretly married to Mac and quarrels with Polly. Mac escapes from prison, with Lucy's help. Peachum, arrested by Brown, blackmails him into allowing his release. Mac is again arrested and now condemned to be hanged, but is saved by a royal messenger at the last minute.

The songs of the *Dreigroschenoper* have long typified Germany of the 1920s, the age of Georg Grosz. The music, in a German jazz idiom of the period, with popular dances such as the tango and the foxtrot in its rhythms, was also recast in purely instrumental form as the *Kleine Dreigroschenmusik* (Little Threepenny Music). The score includes, in the prologue *Die Moritat von Mackie Messer* (The Ballad of Mack the Knife) and Brown's *Ballade vom angenehmen Leben* (Ballad of the Easy Life) and ends with a final *Moritat und Schlußgesang* (Ballad and Final Song).

Drottningen av Golconda (The Queen of Golconda)

- Franz Berwald. Romantic opera in three acts. 1865.
- Libretto derived from the libretto *Aline, reine de Golconde* (Aline, Queen of Golconda) by J.B.C.Vial and E.G.F.de Favières, based on a libretto by Michel-Jean Sedaine, drawing on a novel by Jean Stanislas de Bouffler.
- First performance at the Stockholm Royal Opera on 3rd April 1968.

Berwald's opera, which began as a treatment of Walter Scott's novel *The Abbot*, under the title *Lochleven Castle*, eventually was adapted to the story of Aline, widowed Queen of Golconda, and the French ambassador Saint Phar, whom she had loved in earlier years and with whom she is eventually united, once the dangers of rebellion and imprisonment have been brought to an end.

Duca d'Alba, Il (The Duke of Alba)

- Gaetano Donizetti. Opera in four acts. 1839. Completed by Matteo Salvi in 1882.
- French libretto by Eugène Scribe and Charles Duveyrier.
  Italian version by Angelo Zanardini.
- First performance at the Teatro Apollo, Rome, on 22nd March 1882.

The opera, not completed by Donizetti but intended for Paris, deals with the rising against Spanish rule under the Duke of Alba in Flanders, a revolt led by the daughter of Count Egmont and her lover. A similar libretto was derived from this by Scribe for Verdi's *Les vêpres siciliennes* in 1855.

Due Foscari, I (The Two Foscari)

- Giuseppe Verdi. *Tragedia lirica* in three acts. 1844.
- Libretto by Francesco Maria Piave, after the play by Byron.
- First performance at the Teatro Argentina, Rome, on 3rd November 1844.

Characters

Francesco Foscari, Doge of Venice	baritone
Jacopo Foscari, his son	tenor
Lucrezia Contarini, wife of Jacopo Foscari	soprano
Jacopo Loredano, member of the Council of Ten	bass
Barbarigo, senator, member of the Giunta	tenor
Pisana, confidante of Lucrezia Contarini	soprano
Officer of the Council of Ten	tenor
Doge's Servant	bass

Jacopo Foscari, illegally returning to Venice from exile, awaits the decision of the Council of Ten on his fate. His wife Lucrezia pleads with the old Doge, learning, however, that the Council has decreed exile. The Doge himself is divided between public duty and family loyalty. In prison Jacopo laments his fate, railing against his enemies. His father, the Doge, comes to bid him farewell and Jacopo Loredano, an enemy of the Foscari, comes to lead Jacopo before the Council, which condemns him, in spite of his pleas and those of his wife and children. At carnival time Jacopo is taken to the barge that will carry him into exile. Another confesses to the murder of which Jacopo was accused, but, as Lucrezia tells her father-in-law, the confession is too late, since Jacopo is now dead. The old man is forced by Loredano to resign his power, to be replaced as Doge.

The dark tragedy, set in 15th century Venice, includes well enough known tenor arias in Jacopo's *Ah sì, ch'io senta ancora . . . Dal più remoto esiglio* (Ah yes, now I feel again . . From further exile) and *Odio solo, ed odio atroce* (I hate alone and fiercely hate) and a particularly moving rôle for the eighty-year old Doge.

Recommended Recording: Overture ***Naxos 8.553089***

DUENNA, THE

- Thomas Linley, father and son. Comic opera in three acts. 1775.
- Libretto by Richard Brinsley Sheridan.
- First performance at Covent Garden London, on 21st November 1775.

The comic opera *The Duenna* is remembered rather for its libretto than its music, the latter written by Sheridan's father-in-law and by his son, a friend of the young Mozart. The libretto formed the basis of Prokofiev's *Betrothal in a Monastery* and of an opera by Roberto Gerhard.

DUENNA, THE

- Roberto Gerhard. Comic opera in three acts. 1947.
- Libretto by the composer, based on Richard Brinsley Sheridan's libretto.
- First staged at the Teatro Lirico Nacional, Madrid, on 21st January 1992.

Roberto Gerhard made use of Spanish material in his only opera, first heard in a BBC broadcast of 1949. Unlike much of Gerhard's music, the score is largely tonal.

Echo et Narcisse (*Echo and Narcissus*)

- Christoph Willibald von Gluck. *Drame lyrique* in a prologue and three acts. 1779.
- Libretto by Baron Ludwig Theodor von Tschudi, after Ovid's *Metamorphoses*.
- First performance at the Paris Opéra on 24th September 1779.

Characters

Echo, a nymph	soprano
Narcisse (Narcissus), a young hunter	tenor
Amour (Cupid)	soprano
Eglé, a nymph, friend of Echo	soprano
Aglaé, a nymph, friend of Echo	soprano
Cynire, friend of Narcisse	tenor
Two Water Nymphs & Two Wood Nymphs	sopranos

· Cupid boasts of his powers in the prologue. The first act opens with the wedding of Echo and Narcissus, but she suspects him of infidelity, particularly when she sees him gazing into the water of a fountain, where Apollo has made him see reflected a beautiful goddess. Echo is near death and Apollo brings him back to his senses in time to hear her death lamented. Now Narcissus feels remorse and is about to kill himself, when Echo returns, restored to life.

Essentially a pastoral work, set in country dominated by water and wood nymphs, *Echo et Narcisse*, Gluck's last opera and one that won little success even after its revision in 1780 and revival the following season, includes fine music, in pastoral mood.

EDGAR

- Giacomo Puccini. *Dramma lirico* in three acts. 1889. Revisions up to 1905.
- Libretto by Ferdinando Fontana, after the poem *La coupe et les lèvres* (The Cup and the Lips) by Alfred de Musset.
- First performance at the Teatro alla Scala, Milan, on 21st April 1889.

Edgar loves the village-girl Fidelia, but is seduced by his desire for the Moorish Tigrana, whom he defends and with whom he escapes the village, after wounding Frank, Fidelia's brother, in a fight. Joining the army, he seeks to make good his name, but in the third act his funeral is celebrated, with Frank and a cowled monk standing before the coffin. The latter expatiates on Edgar's sins and the angry crowd opens the coffin, which contains only armour. The monk now reveals himself as Edgar and embraces Fidelia, who has remained loyal to him. She, in turn, kills Tigrana.

Edgar was Puccini's first full-length opera. The preludes to the first and third acts are sometimes heard in the concert-hall, as is Fidelia's lament at Edgar's supposed death, *Addio, mio dolce amor* (Farewell, my sweet love).

Recommended Recording: Prelude to Act III ***Naxos 8.556670***

EDUARDO E CRISTINA (EDWARD AND CHRISTINE)

- Gioachino Rossini. *Dramma* in two acts. 1819.
- Libretto by Giovanni Schmidt, with revisions by Andrea Leone Tottola and Gherardo Bevilacqua-Aldobrandini.
- First performance at the Teatro Benedetto, Venice, on 14th April 1819.

Rossini's opera is principally a pastiche, using material from other works, supplemented by a few new numbers. The overture is occasionally heard in the concert-hall.

EDUCATION MANQUÉE, UNE (A FAULTY EDUCATION)

- Emmanuel Chabrier. Operetta in one act. 1879.
- Libretto by Eugène Leterrier and Albert Vanloo.
- First private performance for the Paris Cercle de la Presse on 1st May 1879.

In a comedy of great charm, the newly married Gontran seeks advice on marital practice from his old tutor, who is not of much help, leaving the couple to find things out for themselves.

Egisto (Aegisthus)

- Francesco Cavalli. *Favola drammatica musicale* in a prologue and three acts. 1643.
- Libretto by Giovanni Faustini.
- First performance at the Teatro S Cassiano, Venice, in 1643.

The lovers Egisto and Clori and Climene and Lidio have been captured by pirates and separated, with Egisto and Climene returning to find their original lovers. Now, however, Lidio and Clori are in love. Ipparco, brother of Climene, is also pursuing Clori. The situation drives Egisto to madness, after which Clori returns to him, Ipparco giving up his claims, while Lidio returns to Climene. The action of the opera is enriched by considerable divine intervention, represented in *intermedi* that end the first and second acts.

Cavalli's opera enjoyed great contemporary success. The lament of Egisto, *Lasso, io vivo, e non ho vita* (Weary, I live, and have no life) and of Climene, *Piangete occhi dolenti* (Weep, grieving eyes) are particularly effective examples of the genre, with the scenes of Egisto's madness.

Einstein on the Beach

- Philip Glass and Robert Wilson. Opera in four acts and five 'knee plays'. 1976.
- Libretto by Christopher Knowles, Lucinda Childs and Samuel M. Johnson.
- First performance at the Avignon Festival on 25th July 1976.

A work of some length, allowing the audience freedom to come in and go out during its performance, the opera includes a series of interludes, 'knee plays', in its treatment of aspects of Einstein, humanist, scientist and musician, a man whose work changed the world. *Einstein on the Beach* calls for two soloists, soprano and tenor, a chamber choir and an ensemble of two keyboard-players, three wind-players, a soprano and a solo violinist. The music is based on minimalist principles, with small musical cells, simple figures, varied and expanded, with repeated simultaneous but different rhythmic patterns that eventually coincide to form a cycle.

Elegy for Young Lovers

- Hans Werner Henze. Opera in three acts. 1961.
- Libretto by W.H.Auden and Chester Kallman.
- First performance at the Schwetzingen Festival on 20th May 1961.

Characters

Gregor Mittenhofer, a poet	baritone
Carolina Gräfin von Kirchstetten, his secretary	contralto
Dr Wilhelm Reischmann, a physician	bass
Toni Reischmann, his son	tenor
Elisabeth Zimmer	soprano
Hilda Mack, a widow	soprano
Josef Mauer, an Alpine guide	spoken part

At the inn Der Schwarze Adler in the Austrian Alps, Hilda Mack recalls her husband going out to climb the Hammerhorn some forty years before. Dr Reischmann and Carolina comment on their thankless service to Mittenhofer, and Reischmann awaits the arrival of his son. Carolina invites Hilda Mack into the inn, as Mittenhofer, an impressive man, brings in Elisabeth, introducing her to Toni. Hilda Mack's fantastic aria seems to foretell the death of the young lovers, but delights Mittenhofer, who takes notes on it. Mittenhofer shouts his complaints at Carolina, who faints and is helped to a chair by Reischmann. Mittenhofer looks for his money, placed for him to find by Carolina, who supports him in this way, finds it and returns to his room. Carolina, however, remains upset. Josef Mauer, an Alpine guide, comes in and tells of the discovery of the body of a young man, doubtless Frau Mack's husband. It is decided that Elisabeth should tell her. Elisabeth gently breaks the news. Toni watches and remember his own mother. Frau Mack sings ecstatically, because the crystal is now broken, and Toni joins her, realising the beginning of love. In the second act Carolina and the doctor try to discourage the young lovers, who resent their interference. Carolina tells Mittenhofer, who tries to play on Elisabeth's feelings. Toni intervenes to explain the situation and Mittenhofer begs Reischmann to bless the couple: they are to stay and the next day pick for him some edelweiss, to end the poem he has written on the young lovers. When they have all gone, Mittenhofer vents his rage on them. In the third act Frau Mack prepares to leave and the young lovers set out up the mountain. Mauer announces a sudden blizzard, but Mittenhofer tells him that nobody has gone up the mountain. Toni and Elisabeth are seen through the blizzard, remembering the long married life they will never have, as they die. In a final scene Mittenhofer prepares to attend a reading in Vienna of his new poem, dedicated to the young lovers.

Henze's opera is scored for a chamber orchestra, with a wide range of percussion and individual instruments identified with characters. The composer explained the narrative as an explosion of the 19th century notion of the artist as hero, the varied action of the work accompanying the writing of a poem, and marked by the initial madness and final inspired perceptiveness of Hilda Mack.

ELEKTRA (ELECTRA)

- Richard Strauss. *Tragödie* in one act. 1908.
- Libretto by Hugo von Hofmannsthal, after the *Electra* of Sophocles.
- First performance at the Hofoper, Dresden, on 25th January 1909.

CHARACTERS

Elektra, daughter of Agamemnon	soprano
Chrysothemis, her sister	soprano
Klytemnästra (Clytemnestra), their mother	mezzo-soprano
Her Confidante & Her Trainbearer	sopranos
Young & Old Servant	tenor & bass
Orest (Orestes), son of Agamemnon	baritone
His Tutor	bass
Aegisth (Aegisthus), Klytemnästra's lover	tenor
Overseer	soprano
Five Maidservants	sopranos, mezzo-sopranos & contralto

The Greek general Agamemnon has returned from the capture of Troy to be murdered by his wife Clytemnestra and her lover Aegisthus, who now reign in his stead. Electra, barely tolerated in the palace, mourns her dead father, dreaming of revenge. Her younger sister Chrysothemis warns her that Clytemnestra plans to have her imprisoned. Clytemnestra now seeks from Electra some release from her torments, suggesting sacrifice. Electra agrees, and outlines the pursuit of her father's murderers by her brother Orestes. Clytemnestra is relieved when a messenger brings news of the death of Orestes. Electra now tries to persuade Chrysothemis to join her in vengeance, but with no success. She digs in the ground for the axe she needs, to be found by Orestes, returned. He seeks out Clytemnestra and kills her. Electra is left to welcome the returning Aegisthus, dancing round him. He goes into the palace and is struck down. Electra dances wildly in triumph, before falling down dead, leaving Chrysothemis beating at the palace doors and calling the name of her brother.

Strauss's opera is an immensely powerful work. Various motifs re-appear in the musical texture, which opens with the chanting of the name Agamemnon. Electra herself remains on stage throughout and the opera deals with a series of confrontations, with her sister, with Clytemnestra, with her brother, leading to the climax of the recognition scene, and finally with Aegisthus, before her wild dance and her death in triumph.

Elena

- Saverio Mercadante. *Dramma tragico* in three acts. 1838.
- Libretto by Salvadore Cammarano.
- First performance at the Teatro San Carlo, Naples, on 1st January 1839.

Characters

Elena da Feltre, beloved of Guido	soprano
Guido, lover of Elene	bass baritone
Ubaldo, his friend, also in love with Elena	tenor
Sigifredo, father of Elena	bass
Imberga, daughter of Boemondo	soprano
Boemondo, minister to Ezzelino	tenor
Gualtiero, friend to Elena and Sigifredo	bass

Set in the Guelph town of Feltre in Northern Italy in 1250, in the reign of the Ghibelline Ezzelino da Romano, the story concerns Elena degli Uberti, daughter of the proscribed Guelph leader Sigifredo, who is in love with Guido, the unwitting rival in love of his friend Ubaldo. Ezzelino's minister Boemondo wants Guido to marry his daughter Imberga, whom he hates. Ezzelino and Boemondo seek to capture Elena's father, Sigifredo. When Ubaldo learns that Guido intends to marry Elena, he thinks of betraying him to Boemondo and then of abducting her. Sigifredo, a fugitive, overhears Ubaldo's attempt and when he intervenes he is taken prisoner. At the palace Boemondo makes it clear to Elena that her father's safety depends on her marriage to Ubaldo, thus persuading Guido to marry Imberga. Under threat she agrees and publicly declares her preference for Ubaldo. Guido is angry, but later suspicious of her motives. Meanwhile Sigifredo has been executed and, as the sounds of the approaching wedding of Guido and Imberga are heard, Elena learns of the deception, loses her reason and dies, while Ubaldo, grief-stricken, is left to mourn alone.

In his opera *Elena da Feltre* Mercadante abandons some of the current operatic conventions, stressing, rather, the drama in varied musical forms and avoiding longer solos that might impede the progress of the plot. Ubaldo, the leading tenor, is contrasted with his rival Guido, Elena's true lover, while she is duly allowed a moving prayer and a final mad scene.

Recommended Recording: Elena da Feltre (2 CDs) — ***Marco Polo 8.225064-65***

Elisa

- Luigi Cherubini. *Opéra comique* in two acts. 1793.
- Libretto by Jacques-Antoine Reveroni de Saint-Cyr.
- First performance at the Théâtre Feydeau, Paris, on 13th December 1794.

Elisa, ou Le voyage aux glaciers du Mont St Bernard (Elisa, or The Journey to the Glaciers of Mount St Bernard) is a rescue opera, with the hero Florindo rescued from an avalanche rather than from a dungeon for political prisoners.

Elisabetta, regina d'Inghilterra (Elizabeth, Queen of England)

- Gioachino Rossini. *Dramma* in two acts. 1815.
- Libretto by Giovanni Schmidt, after a play by Carlo Federici, based on the novel *The Recess* by Sophia Lee.
- First performance at the Teatro S Carlo, Naples, on 4th October 1815.

Characters

Elisabetta (Elizabeth), Queen of England	soprano
Earl of Leicester	tenor
Matilde	soprano
Enrico (Henry), her brother	mezzo-soprano
Duke of Norfolk	tenor
Guglielmo (Fitzwilliam), Captain of the Royal Guard	tenor

Queen Elizabeth's favourite, the Earl of Leicester, has contracted a secret marriage with the Scottish Matilde, who turns out to be the daughter of Elizabeth's rival, Mary, Queen of Scots. She and her brother Henry come to the English court, disguised as Scottish hostages. Leicester confides in the Duke of Norfolk, who uses the information to discredit him. Leicester and Matilde are imprisoned, but eventually released and pardoned by the Queen, who resolves to devote herself to affairs of state rather than of the heart.

Elisabetta, regina d'Inghilterra was Rossini's first opera for the Teatro S Carlo in Naples and the first of his to have all recitatives with string accompaniment. The overture seems immediately familiar and was used again by Rossini for *Il barbiere di Siviglia.* There is much fine music, perfectly orchestrated, in the opera, with Elizabeth's first act *cavatina Quant'è grato all'alma mia* (How welcome to my soul is the common good) an item for operatic recitals, with her condemnation of Norfolk, *Fellon, la pena avrai* (Traitor, you shall be punished).

Elisir d'amore, L' (The Elixir of Love)

- Gaetano Donizetti. *Melodramma* in two acts. 1832.
- Libretto by Felice Romani, after the text by Eugène Scribe for Auber's *Le philtre* (The Love Philtre).
- First performance at the Teatro Cannobiana, Milan, on 12th May 1832.

Characters

Nemorino, a peasant	tenor
Adina, a rich land-owner	soprano
Belcore, a sergeant	baritone
Dr Dulcamara, an itinerant quack doctor	bass
Giannetta, a peasant-girl	soprano

Nemorino, a simple-minded young man, is in love with Adina, who is impressed by the sergeant Belcore, a man of overwhelming confidence in his own charms. Dulcamara arrives in the village, offering panaceas of his own fraudulent concoction. Nemorino seeks a love potion and this Dulcamara happily provides, in fact in the form of claret. Adina, meanwhile, has agreed to marry Belcore, forcing Nemorino to seek more elixir from Dulcamara, which he can only pay for by enlisting in Belcore's troop. Rumour reaches the village that Nemorino has inherited a fortune, and he now finds himself immensely popular among the girls, arousing Adina's jealousy. When Dulcamara tells her that Nemorino has enlisted in order to find a way to her heart, she relents, dismisses Belcore and agrees to marry Nemorino, after buying him out of the regiment.

One of the best of comic operas, *L'elisir d'amore* provides Nemorino with his admiring *Quanto è bella* (How lovely she is) and, best known of all, with *Una furtiva lagrima* (A furtive tear), when he sees that his enlistment has aroused Adina's pity. Dulcamara has a winning sales pitch in *Udite, o rustici* (Hear, country people) and a second act 'barcarolle' with Adina, in the wrong rhythm, *Io son ricco, e tu sei bella* (I am rich and you are beautiful). With her earlier *Chiedi all'aura lusinghiera* (Go and ask the playful wind) Adina at first rejects Nemorino.

Recommended Recordings:

L'Elisir d'amore (2 CDs)	***Naxos 8.660045-46***
(Highlights)	***Naxos 8.554704***

Emilia di Liverpool (Emilia of Liverpool)

- Gaetano Donizetti. *Dramma semiseria* in two acts. 1824. Revised in 1828.
- Anonymous libretto based on Vittorio Trento's *Emilia di Laverpaut*, after a play by Stefano Scatizzi.
- First performance at the Teatro Nuovo, Naples, on 28th July 1824.

The opera, with the alternative title of *L'eremitaggio di Liverpool* (The Hermitage of Liverpool) set in the entirely fictional Lancashire mountains abutting on Liverpool, allows Emilia, seduced and now penitently working in a hermitage, to marry her lover Federico, after the harsh intervention of her father, Claudio di Liverpool, and consequent violence, have been avoided.

Enchantress, The

- Pyotr Il'yich Tchaikovsky. Opera in four acts. 1887.
- Libretto by Ippolit Vasil'yevich Shpazhinsky.
- First performance at the Mariinsky Theatre, St Petersburg, on 1st November 1887.

The tragedy of *The Enchantress* concerns the activities of the charming widow Nastas'ya, known as Kuma, who is loved by Prince Nikita Kurlyatev and, eventually, also by his son Yury. The Princess poisons Kuma, who dies in the arms of Yury, who is then killed by his father. The Prince then goes out of his mind.

The nature of the drama makes *The Enchantress* less than convincing. The libretto was later revised to suit the dictates of the post-Revolutionary authorities in Russia.

Enfant et les sortilèges, L' (The Child and the Magic Spells)

- Maurice Ravel. *Fantaisie lyrique* in one act. 1925.
- Libretto by Colette.

- First performance at the Monte Carlo Opéra on 21st March 1925.

Characters

The Child	mezzo-soprano
Mother	contralto
La Bergère (Louis XV Chair)	soprano
Chinese Cup	mezzo-contralto
Fire/Princess/Nightingale	soprano
She-Cat	mezzo-soprano
Dragonfly	mezzo-soprano
Bat	soprano
Owl	soprano
Squirrel	mezzo-soprano
Shepherdess	soprano
Shepherd	contralto
Armchair	bass
Grandfather Clock	baritone
Wedgwood Teapot	tenor
Arithmetic/Frog	tenor
Tomcat	baritone
Tree	bass

In the first scene the child, badly behaved, breaks crockery and tortures his pets. The furniture comes to life and retaliates, followed, in the second scene, by the plants and creatures in the garden. The boy cries out for his mother, 'Maman', the creatures attack him, but he helps the wounded Squirrel. The animals are moved by this and lead the boy back to the house.

Colette's libretto provided Ravel with wide opportunities for musical parody and caricature, with its cat serenade, belligerent English teapot and dance of the frogs.

English Cat, The

- Hans Werner Henze. A story in two acts. 1983. Revised in 1990.
- Libretto by Edward Bond, after Balzac's *Peines de cœur d'une chatte anglaise* (Heartaches of an English Cat).
- First performance at the Schwetzingen Festival on 2nd June 1983.

Characters

Cats

Minette, the cat	soprano
Babette, her sister	mezzo-soprano
Tom	baritone
Lord Puff, President of the Royal Society for the Protection of Rats	tenor
Arnold, his nephew	bass
Miss Crisp, member of the RSPR	soprano
Mrs Gomfit, member of the RSPR	soprano
Lady Toodle, member of the RSPR	mezzo-soprano
Peter, Tom's friend	tenor
Mr Keen	tenor
Mr Jones, the money-lender	bass-baritone
Mr Fawn	bass-baritone
Mr Plunkett, member of the RSPR	bass-baritone

Other Animals

Louise (mouse), member of the RSPR	soprano
Counsel for the Defence (dog)	tenor
Counsel for the Prosecution (dog)	bass-baritone
Judge (dog)	bass-baritone
Lucian (fox)	tenor
Parson (sheep)	tenor

Minette is to marry Lord Puff, to the disapproval of Arnold, who will lose by the match. The RSPR shows its hypocritical charity by its adoption of the orphan mouse Louise. Tom and Peter seek amorous adventure, and Tom woos Minette, caught out by Arnold. Arnold brings his creditor Jones disguised as a doctor, to forbid Lord Puff's marriage on medical grounds, but the wedding goes ahead, with Tom in the guise of a curate accompanying the Parson, in spite of Arnold's attempts and his revelation of Minette's apparent infidelity. Minette helps her now destitute sister Babette but is still attracted to Tom, leading the RSPR to demand a divorce. In a grossly prejudiced court Tom is disguised as the Counsel for the Defence, whom he has imprisoned but who now re-appears. Tom is to be punished, but is revealed as the heir to Lord Fairport, an old friend of the Judge and therefore exonerated. Minette is to be drowned, and Tom now leaves with Babette. In a lawyer's office he is about to make his will, when he is stabbed by the fox Lucian, dying intestate, his money therefore to go to the RSPR. The ghost of Minette sings together with the dying Tom, leaving Louise to comment on the hypocrisy of society.

Henze's very varied through-composed score draws on a number of different musical sources for its satire, basing his structure on Beethoven's *Diabelli Variations*.

English Eccentrics, The

- Malcolm Williamson. Chamber opera in two acts. 1964.
- Libretto by Geoffrey Dunn, based on the book of the same name by Edith Sitwell.
- First performance at the Jubilee Hall, Aldeburgh, on 11th June 1964.

Various English eccentrics are studied in the two acts of the opera, including the bankrupt and uncomprehending Sarah Whitehead and the one-time crony of the Prince Regent, Beau Brummell.

Entführung aus dem Serail, Die (The Abduction from the Seraglio)

- Wolfgang Amadeus Mozart. *Singspiel* in three acts. 1782.
- Libretto by Christoph Friedrich Bretzner, adapted and expanded by Gottlieb Stephanie.
- First performance at the Vienna Burgtheater on 16th July 1782.

Characters

Selim, Pasha	speaking part
Konstanze, a Spanish lady	soprano
Blonde, her English maid	soprano
Belmonte, a Spanish nobleman	tenor
Pedrillo, his servant, now the Pasha's gardener	tenor
Osmin, overseer of the Pasha's house	bass
Klaas, a sailor	speaking part
Mute, servant of Osmin	silent rôle

Belmonte seeks his betrothed, Konstanze, who, with her maid Blonde, is held prisoner by the Pasha. Pedrillo, now forced to serve as the Pasha's gardener, tells him that the Pasha loves Konstanze, but will not force his attentions on her. He introduces Belmonte to the Pasha's service as an Italian architect, any access to the palace always obstructed by Osmin, who has his own designs on Blonde. She, however, knows very well how to deal with him. Belmonte, with Pedrillo's help, plans to abduct Konstanze from the seraglio, but they are caught, much to Osmin's delight. The Pasha, however, exercises clemency, the more praiseworthy in that he now knows Belmonte's father to have been his enemy and the cause of his own exile. All ends happily for Belmonte and Konstanze, Pedrillo and Blonde, who are allowed to sail away, much to Osmin's chagrin.

Mozart's *Singspiel*, his first stage work for the Vienna theatre, after he had settled in the city in 1781, makes use of fashionable Turkish elements, with the necessary percussion and piccolo appearing at the outset in the brilliant overture. In a score of overwhelming richness of invention, Osmin's folk-song *Wer ein Liebchen hat gefunden* (The one who has found a lover), obstructive in its intention, is matched by his later hopes of revenge, *Ha, wie will ich triumphieren* (Ha, how I'll triumph). Konstanze is given two immensely demanding arias, as she laments her fate, *Traurigkeit ward mir zum Lose* (Sadness will be my lot) and the testing *Marten aller Arten* (All kinds of torture). Belmonte opens the first act with a short aria, *Hier soll ich dich denn sehen* (Here should I then see you), sings of his love in *O wie ängstlich, o wie feurig* (O how troubling, how ardent) and has a charming serenade, as a signal for escape, in *Im Mohrenland gefangen war ein Mädchen hübsch und fein* (In the land of the Moors there was imprisoned a girl, pretty and lovely). Blonde too has her own moments, particularly in the scenes in which she repulses and teases Osmin, one of the great comic characters of opera.

Recommended Recordings:

Overture	***Naxos 8.550185***
Final Chorus	***Naxos 8.550507***
Durch Zärtlichkeit	***Naxos 8.550435***
Hier soll ich dich denn sehen / O wie ängstlich / Wenn der Freude Tränen fließen / Ich baue ganz / Im Mohrenland	***Naxos 8.550383***

EQUIVOCO STRAVAGANTE, L' (THE STRANGE MISUNDERSTANDING)

- Gioachino Rossini. *Dramma giocoso* in two acts. 1811.
- Libretto by Gaetano Gasbarri.
- First performance at the Teatro del Corso, Bologna, on 26th October 1811.

Rossini's first larger scale opera, *L'equivoco stravagante* is based on a plot of love intrigue in which the thick-witted Buralicchio, a *basso buffo*, is put off marriage with the lively Ernestina, largely through slander spread about her by her lover Ermanno, with whom she is finally united.

Ercole amante (Hercules in Love)

- Francesco Cavalli. Opera in a prologue and five acts. 1662.
- Libretto by Francesco Buti, after Ovid's *Metamorphoses*.
- First performance at the Salles des Machines of the Paris Tuileries on 7th February 1662.

Cavalli's spectacular work, originally designed for the wedding of Louis XIV and the Spanish princess Maria Theresa, is based on the love of Hercules and Iole, she united by divine trickery with the son of Hercules, Hyllus. The opera nears its end when Hercules receives from Iole the fatal centaur's shirt, that burns his flesh and kills him, but the intervention of Zeus allows him to ascend to the sky and to marry Hebe, the goddess of youth.

Erismena

- Francesco Cavalli. *Drama per musica* in a prologue and three acts. 1655.
- Libretto by Aurelio Aureli.
- First performance at the Teatro S Apollinare, Venice, on 30th December 1655.

In a plot of some complexity, Erismena, ignorant of the identity of her father, King of Media, disguises herself as a man and is wounded in battle, to be tended by Aldimira, an Iberian slave loved by Erismena's father but wooed by Orimeno and by Erineo, Erismena's disguised former lover, in fact Prince Idraspe of Iberia. The opera ends in a general recognition, when the true identities of the three principal characters are revealed.

Ermione (Hermione)

- Gioachino Rossini. *Azione tragica* in two acts. 1819.
- Libretto By Andrea Leone Tottola, after Racine's *Andromaque* and Euripides.
- First performance at the Teatro S Carlo, Naples, on 27th March 1819.

Andromache, widow of the Trojan Hector, is a prisoner of Pyrrhus, who is in love with her, and intends to reject his betrothed Hermione. To save her son Astyanax, Andromache is induced to marry Pyrrhus, whereupon Hermione takes her revenge by ordering Orestes to murder him, which he does, only to be disowned by her, once the deed is done, and to be pursued, at her behest, by Furies.

The opera achieved no great success and has never held any permanent place in international operatic repertoire. Its overture includes a Trojan prisoners' chorus.

Ernani

- Giuseppe Verdi. *Dramma lirico* in four parts. 1844.
- Libretto by Francesco Maria Piave, after Victor Hugo's play *Hernani*.
- First performance at the Teatro La Fenice, Venice, on 9th March 1844.

Characters

Don Carlo, King of Spain	baritone
Don Ruy Gomez de Silva, grandee of Spain	bass
Elvira, his niece and betrothed	soprano
Giovanna, her nurse	soprano
Ernani (John of Aragon), a bandit	tenor
Don Riccardo, equerry to the King	tenor
Jago, equerry to Don Ruy Gomez	bass

In their mountain encampment Ernani tells his fellow-bandits of his love for Elvira, whom he plans to abduct. She, in turn, loves Ernani, but is also loved by the King, his attempt, in disguise, to drag her away intercepted by Ernani, then joined by Don Ruy Gomez, whose anger is tempered by the revelation of the King's identity. The latter offers Ernani his help, intending to exact his own revenge in due course. At the castle of Don Ruy Gomez, Ernani appears, disguised as a pilgrim and seeking refuge from the King. Learning of Elvira's coming marriage, he reveals his identity, but is given protection by Don Ruy Gomez, who refuses to hand his guest over to the King. Elvira seeks pardon for her uncle, but is taken away by the King as a pledge of her kinsman's loyalty. Ernani suggests that they join together against the King, giving his host and rival a hunting-horn, at the sound of which he will give himself up to Don Ruy Gomez. At a meeting of conspirators, it is decided that Ernani should kill the King, who has observed the scene in the Cathedral of Aix-la-Chapelle and now emerges from behind the tomb of Charlemagne, to their dismay. The King now receives news of his election as Emperor. He pardons all and Ernani is restored to his estates as John of Aragon, now marrying Elvira. At this point Don Ruy Gomez, implacable, sounds the hunting-horn and Ernani, given the choice now of poison or a dagger, stabs himself.

Elements of the main drama, revenge and love, are suggested in the prelude. Ernani's first act *cavatina Come rugiada al cespite* (As dew on the bud) reveals his love, as does Elvira's second scene *cavatina*, *Ernani, Ernani, involami* (Ernani, Ernani, fly to me). *Infelice! e tuo credevi* (Unhappy! And I trusted you) allows an impressive moment for Don Ruy Gomez. For the King, now the Emperor Charles V, the imposing *Oh de'verd'anni miei* (Oh my years of youth) gains power from the scene in which it is set, at the tomb of Charlemagne.

Recommended Recordings:

Overture — ***Naxos 8.553089***

Chorus: Si rideste — ***Naxos 8.550241***

Eroe cinese, L' (*The Chinese Hero*)

Metastasio's libretto, set and adapted by a number of composers in the 18th century, has a particular interest in that it is based on a Yuen Dynasty play, a translation of which appeared in Jean-Baptiste du Halde's very popular history of China, oddly enough without any reference to the music that was an essential part of the work in Chinese operatic tradition. The translation stimulated further improbable excursions into *chinoiserie*, including a play by Voltaire and a political satire by Arthur Murphy, David Garrick's son-in-law, while others deplored the failure of the dramatist to observe the Aristotelian unities and the part played in the Chinese play by a purportedly magic dog.

Erwartung (*Expectation*)

- Arnold Schoenberg. Monodrama in one act. 1909.
- Libretto by Marie Pappenheim.
- First performance at the Prague Neues Deutsches Theater on 6th June 1924.

In four scenes, *Erwartung* opens with the sole singer, a soprano, searching for her lover at night. She enters fearfully a dark wood, coming then to a clearing. In the slightly longer fourth scene she comes upon a house, its shutters closed, where her lover, she thinks, may have been visiting another woman. She finds his murdered body, going through feelings of love, of angry jealousy and final desolation, before she starts again on her search.

A psychological study influenced by preoccupations of the period in Vienna, *Erwartung* is relatively short and is usually heard in the concert-hall.

Esclarmonde

- Jules Massenet. *Opéra romanesque* in four acts. 1889.
- Libretto by Alfred Blau and Louis de Gramont, after a medieval *chanson de geste.*
- First performance by the Paris Opéra-Comique at the Théâtre Lyrique on 14th May 1889.

Daughter of the Emperor of Byzantium, Esclarmonde takes over the Empire from her father, who insists she remain veiled until she comes of age, telling her that the throne will be taken by a knight victorious in a tournament. The following events include Esclarmonde's love for the knight Roland de Blois, whom she aids in his rescue of the King of France from siege. He refuses the offer of the King's daughter, but episcopal intervention leads to the discovery and unveiling of Esclarmonde, who makes her escape. Awakened from sleep by her father, she is compelled to reject Roland de Blois, who eventually returns to win a tournament in Byzantium and be united with the princess of his choice.

The score of Massenet's Wagnerian medieval opera includes instrumental episodes that make up an orchestral suite.

Recommended Recording: Esclarmonde (Orchestral Suite) ***Marco Polo 8.223354***

Esule di Roma, L', ossia il Proscritto (The Exile from Rome or The Proscribed Man)

- Gaetano Donizetti. *Melodramma eroico* in two acts. 1828.
- Libretto by Domenico Gilardoni, after *Il proscritto romano* (The Roman Proscribed) by Luigi Marchionni, based on *Androclès ou Le lion reconnaissant* (Androcles or The Grateful Lion) by Louis Charles Caigniez and Debotière.

The grateful lion of the French title saves Settimio from death in the Roman Circus, where he has been condemned to die after the false accusations of his beloved Argelia's father. Father and his future son-in-law are pardoned by the Emperor.

Etoile, L' (The Star)

- Emmanuel Chabrier. *Opéra bouffe* in three acts. 1877.
- Libretto by Eugène Leterrier and Albert Vanloo.
- First performance by the Bouffes-Parisiens on 28th November 1877.

The light opera finds King Ouf cancelling a proposed execution when he discovers that his intended victim, Lazuli, shares the same star and will die on the same day, making it necessary to cosset him.

ETOILE DU NORD, L' (THE STAR OF THE NORTH)

- Giacomo Meyerbeer. *Opéra comique* in three acts. 1854.
- Libretto by Eugène Scribe.
- First performance by the Paris Opéra-Comique at the Salle Favart on 28th November 1854.

Peter the Great, disguised as a flute-playing carpenter, falls in love with Catherine, a vivandière, who takes her brother's place as conscript, finding herself in the disguised Tsar's regiment. Drunk, he fails to recognise her and, after striking a corporal, she escapes, later to be found in madness. She is restored to sanity by a staged recreation of the scene in her own village, to be united with the Tsar.

Developed from an earlier German opera by Meyerbeer, *L'Etoile du Nord* represents a lighter aspect of the composer, but with an effective mad scene for the heroine, with flute accompaniment.

Recommended Recording: L'Etoile du Nord (3 CDs) ***Marco Polo 8.223829-31***

ETRANGER, L' (THE STRANGER)

- Vincent d'Indy. *Action musicale* in two acts. 1903.
- Libretto by the composer.
- First performance at the Théâtre de la Monnaie, Brussels, on 7th January 1903.

A mysterious stranger exercises attraction over Vita, betrothed to the customs officer André in the fishing-village where they live. The stranger, a character of transparent goodness, has an emerald which he gives to Vita, when his own love for her compels him to leave. She throws the emerald into the sea, a great storm arises, and when the stranger will rescue fishermen in danger, she joins him, both of them overwhelmed by a great wave, to die together, like Senta and her Flying Dutchman.

Wagnerian aspects of d'Indy's score include the use of leit-motifs, although instrumentation is relatively economic.

Eugene Onegin

- Pyotr Il'yich Tchaikovsky. Opera in three acts. 1878.
- Libretto by the composer and Konstantin Stepanovich Shilovsky, after Pushkin's verse novel.
- First performance at the Moscow Bolshoy Theatre on 23rd January 1881.

Characters

Madame Larina, a land-owner	mezzo-soprano
Tatyana, her daughter	soprano
Olga, her daughter	contralto
Filipyevna, Tatyana's nurse	mezzo-soprano
Eugene Onegin	baritone
Lensky, his friend, engaged to Olga	tenor
Prince Gremin	bass
A Captain	bass
Zaretsky	bass
Triquet, a Frenchman	tenor
Guillot, a valet	silent rôle

At Madame Larina's country house, Onegin and Lensky arrive, the latter to join his betrothed, Olga, leaving Onegin to talk to Tatyana, who falls in love, as her old nurse Filipyevna realises. In her bedroom she writes a letter to Onegin, which Filipyevna is to deliver. In the garden she meets him and he discourages her, urging patient restraint and telling her he has no mind to marry. At a ball in the house to celebrate Tatyana's birthday, Onegin chooses to dance with Olga, to Lensky's increasing anger, leading to his demand for satisfaction. The next morning the two men fight a duel and Lensky is killed. The third act takes place some years later at a more fashionable ball in St Petersburg. Onegin is there, having returned from self-imposed exile, and the ball is also attended by his kinsman Prince Gremin and his wife, Tatyana, her presence arousing Onegin's love. He writes her a letter, declaring his passion, but she reminds him of his former advice to her and, whatever her real feelings, now rejects him.

Tchaikovsky's opera was written at the difficult period of his marriage to an apparently infatuated and certainly unbalanced admirer and their immediate separation. It was completed abroad in Switzerland and Italy. Of particular poignancy is Tatyana's *Letter Scene* and Onegin's subsequent answer in the garden. Prince Gremin's aria in the third act gives depth to his character, as he describes the effect on him of his marriage to the young Tatyana. The dances from the two ball scenes have provided concert audiences with orchestral excerpts from the score.

Recommended Recording: Polonaise & Waltz ***Naxos 8.550137***

EURIDICE

- Jacopo Peri. Opera in five scenes. 1600.
- Libretto by Ottavio Rinuccini, after Ovid's *Metamorphoses*.
- First performance at the Palazzo Pitti, Florence, on 6th October 1600.

CHARACTERS

La Tragedia	soprano
Euridice	soprano
Orfeo (Orpheus)	tenor
Arcetro, a shepherd	tenor
Tirsi, a shepherd	alto
Aminta, a shepherd	tenor
Dafne, a messenger	soprano
Venere (Venus)	soprano
Plutone (Pluto)	bass
Proserpina	soprano
Radamanto (Rhadamanthus)	tenor
Caronte (Charon)	bass

Peri's opera, the first to survive with its music complete, was written for the celebration in Florence of the wedding of Maria de'Medici to the French King Henri IV. Additional elements to the score were provided by Giulio Caccini, whose own version of *Euridice*, published before Peri's, was performed in Florence two years later. The figure of Tragedy, with the best of Aristotelian intentions, introduces the pitiful story, which opens with Eurydice happy at her approaching wedding, with her bridegroom Orpheus equally delighted, until a messenger appears telling him of the fatal snake-bite and the death of his beloved. A shepherd describes the grief of Orpheus, who in the following scene is led by Venus to the gates of Hades. The King of the Underworld, Pluto, is persuaded by the music of Orpheus, and by Charon and Proserpine, to allow Eurydice to accompany Orpheus back to the upper world again and all ends in rejoicing.

Peri's drama, with its continuous music, includes choruses to end each scene and notable solo elements, with the lament of Orpheus, *Non piango e non sospiro* (I weep not and sigh not) and his later expression of grief *Funeste piagge, ombrosi orridi campi* (Dreadful shores, dark terrible fields). Rinuccini avoided the usual tragic ending of the story, finding a happy ending, the *lieto fine* of later opera, more appropriate to wedding celebrations.

Euridice

- Giulio Caccini. Opera in a prologue and five scenes. 1600.
- Libretto by Ottavio Rinuccini.
- First performance at the Palazzo Pitti, Florence, on 5th December 1602.

Caccini's *Euridice* was less successful than Peri's. The work is dominated largely by recitative, the inflected dramatic monody of advanced contemporary practice. Caccini's published *Le nuove musiche* remains a particularly valuable source for information on performance practice of the period.

Euryanthe

- Carl Maria von Weber. *Grosse heroisch-romantische Oper* in three acts. 1823.
- Libretto by Helmina von Chézy, after the medieval French *roman*.
- First performance at the Kärntnertortheater, Vienna, on 25th October 1823.

Characters

King Louis VI	bass
Adolar, Count of Nevers and Rethel	tenor
Lysiart, Count of Forêt and Beaujolais	bass
Euryanthe of Savoy	soprano
Eglantine of Puiset	soprano
Rudolf	tenor
Bertha	soprano

In the presence of the King, Adolar sings his praise of his bride Euryanthe. Lysiart wagers that she is unfaithful. At Adolar's castle, Eglantine, who secretly hates Euryanthe, questions her and is told how each night she prays at the tomb of Adolar's sister, who poisoned herself for love, her poisoned ring now waiting for tears of distressed innocence to cleanse it. Eglantine decides to join with Lysiart, who secretly loves Euryanthe, in a plot. She retrieves the poisoned ring from the tomb, and Lysiart proposes marriage. At court, Euryanthe rejoins Adolar, but Lysiart arrives with the ring, claiming this as proof of Euryanthe's infidelity. Adolar has lost his lands with the wager, and now they must wander together. In a mountain scene, Adolar plans to kill Euryanthe, or desert her. She is found by a royal hunting-party and convinces the King of her innocence. In the last scene the truth is revealed, Lysiart stabs Eglantine and Adolar and Euryanthe are re-united, the ghost of his dead sister now at rest.

The overture to *Euryanthe*, which is often heard in the concert-hall, uses material from the opera, including Adolar's rebuttal of Lysiart and his second act romance. The opera itself is relatively rarely staged and, vitiated by a weak libretto, never rivalled the earlier success of *Der Freischütz*.

Recommended Recording: Overture ***Naxos 8.550146***

Excursions of Mr Brouček, The

- Leoš Janáček. Opera in two parts. 1917.
- Libretto by František Gellner, Viktor Dyk, F.S.Procházka, the composer and others, after the novels by Svatopluk Čech.
- First complete performance in Prague on 23rd April 1920.

The opera falls into two parts, the first the excursion of Mr Brouček to the moon and the second the excursion of Mr Brouček to the 15th century. The work begins with a street scene between a pair of lovers, who quarrel, Málinka threatening to marry her lover Mazal's philistine landlord, Mr Brouček. The sound of revelry is heard and Brouček appears, on his way home from the tavern, given sausages to take home with him. He is taken up to the moon on a winged horse, where Etherea is attracted to him. Avoiding an aesthetic reading from her father, they fly on to the Cathedral of All Arts, where Brouček is invited to sniff flower scents and see a moon-painting, on both occasions breaching moon etiquette. He is transported back to earth, to the Prague street outside the tavern, whence he is carried home. In the second part Brouček loses his way, returning home from the tavern, and finds himself in the jewel-chamber of Václav IV. In the street he is arrested as a suspected spy of the German Sigismund, in the Hussite wars, but is released. In battle he proves his disinclination for this kind of activity, and after the Hussite victory is denounced, condemned to death in a barrel. It is in this situation that he finds himself back again in his own time, explaining matters to the tavern landlord.

Janáček's satire on middle-class philistinism is particularly pointed in the second of Brouček's excursions. Characters in the opening scene re-appear in different guises in the two excursions. The painter Mazal is Blankytný for the journey to the moon and the Hussite hero Petřik, his beloved Málinka re-appears as Etherea on the moon and as the Hussite girl Kunka, while her father, the Sacristan, is seen again as Etherea's aesthetically minded father Lunobor and as Kunka's father and Brouček's 15th century host, Domšík. The narrative is a curious one and the original production met some hostility from the performers involved.

Ezio (Aetius)

- George Frideric Handel. Opera in three acts. 1732.
- Libretto adapted from Metastasio, perhaps after Corneille's *Maximian*.
- First performance at the King's Theatre, London, on 15th January 1732.

Metastasio's libretto tells the story of the Roman general Aetius, loved by Fulvia, but betrayed by her father, who seeks to use him in a plot against the Emperor Valentinian, who has offered Aetius his sister Honoria in marriage. All ends well, with the punishment of the wicked and the triumph of the good.

The opera provides interesting material in bass arias for Varus, the Prefect of the Praetorian Guard, including *Nasce al bosco* (Born in the wood) and *Già resonar* (Now there sounds), with a trumpet obbligato. The libretto was also set by Porpora, Hasse, Sacchini, Jommelli, Gassmann, Gluck and a series of other composers up to Mercadante in 1827.

Fairy-Queen, The

- Henry Purcell. Semi-opera in five acts. 1692. revised in 1693.
- Libretto adapted from Shakespeare's *A Midsummer Night's Dream*.
- First performance at the King's Theatre, London, on 2nd May 1692.

The first act follows Shakespeare, introducing the difficulties of the mortal lovers, the plans of the greasy mechanicals to entertain Duke Theseus at his coming wedding and the quarrel of Titania, Queen of the Fairies, with Oberon. She has with her the Indian boy she has taken from Oberon and tells her fairies to entertain him. There follows an episode in which a drunken poet is teased by fairies. In the forest a masque is presented to lull Titania to sleep, interrupted by the appearance of Night, Mystery, Secresie and Sleep. Puck, Oberon's attendant spirit, puts magic drops in Titania's eyes, as she sleeps, ensuring that she will fall in love with the first creature she sees as she awakes. In love now with Bottom the Weaver, Titania provides a fairy masque for him, including a comic episode for the shepherd couple Coridon and Mopsa. Oberon wakes Titania and asks for music, bringing a symphony for the rising of the sun and representations of the four seasons. By the fifth act the mortal lovers have suitably adjusted their affairs, now found by the Duke, who sanctions marriages according to their affections. Oberon and Titania, persuading the Duke of the truth of what has been told him, provide an entertainment that brings Juno with a blessing, a plaint, a spectacular Chinese masque and the final appearance of Hymen.

As often with other semi-operas, musical elements are entrusted to the supernatural, here to the figures that appear in a series of masques commanded by Titania. The characters of Shakespeare's play are taken by actors, with the plot framed by the proposed wedding of Duke Theseus, to be joined by the two pairs of lovers, once their problems have been solved in the forest at night, through fairy intervention. The quarrels of Titania and Oberon, the latter's magic distillation administered by Puck, and the consequent amorous entanglement of the workman Bottom, crowned with the head of an ass, are abbreviated in an elaborate and expensive entertainment that brought its original promoters near to bankruptcy.

Recommended Recording: The Fairy Queen (2 CDs) — ***Naxos 8.550660-61***

Falstaff

- Giuseppe Verdi. *Commedia lirica* in three acts. 1892.
- Libretto by Arrigo Boito, after Shakespeare's *The Merry Wives of Windsor*.
- First performance at the Teatro alla Scala, Milan, on 9th February 1893.

Characters

Sir John Falstaff	baritone
Fenton	tenor
Dr Caius	tenor
Bardolfo (Bardolph), follower of Falstaff	tenor
Pistola (Pistol), follower of Falstaff	bass
Mrs Alice Ford	soprano
Ford, her husband	baritone
Nannetta, their daughter	soprano
Mistress Quickly	mezzo-soprano
Mrs Meg Page	mezzo-soprano
Host of The Garter Inn	silent rôle
Robin, Falstaff's page	silent rôle
Ford's page	silent rôle

At the Garter Inn Falstaff quarrels with Dr Caius over an earlier drunken episode. He sends his page with love-letters to Mrs Page and Mrs Ford, who, in the following scene, plan their revenge together, while Falstaff's follower Pistol tells Ford what is happening. Nannetta, daughter of the Fords, has a brief moment of love with Fenton. The plot against Falstaff is carried forward through Mistress Quickly, who makes an appointment for him with Mrs Ford. Ford himself appears at the inn, in disguise, offering a bribe, if Falstaff will pave the way for him by seducing Mrs Ford. Learning of the assignation already arranged, Ford is jealous. In the following scene, at Ford's house, the women prepare a laundry-basket for the trick they will play on Falstaff, while Mrs Ford assures Nannetta of her opposition to her father's proposed match for her with Dr Caius. The arrival of the jealous Ford leads to Falstaff's concealment in the laundry-basket, covered with dirty linen, while attention is distracted by Nannetta and Fenton, behind a screen, and mistaken by Ford and his band for Falstaff. The scene ends with Falstaff tipped into the river, but, still believing in Mrs Ford's love for him, he is lured into a supposed assignation at midnight in Windsor Forest. There he is tormented by what he supposes to be fairies. In the end, while Fenton and Nannetta are united and Dr Caius frustrated, Falstaff accepts what has happened stoically.

Verdi's last opera was given its first performance some six years after his earlier Shakespearean opera *Otello*, staged at La Scala, Milan, in February 1887. It takes the composer, now in old age, into a new world of comedy, with a text that he can treat more responsively than ever. The score contains a wealth of rich invention and the opera ends with a fugue, introduced by Falstaff's *Tutto nel mondo è burla* (Everything in the world is a joke). A moment of pathos may be heard in Falstaff's account of his handsome youth, *Quand'ero paggio del Duca di Norfolk* (When I was page to the Duke of Norfolk). Fenton's loving *Del labbro il canto estasiato vola* (From my lips ecstatic song takes flight) opens the final scene in Windsor Forest, where Falstaff, disguised and wearing antlers, hears midnight strike, the notes striking with a fascinating harmony for each stroke of the bell.

Recommended Recording: Falstaff (2 CDs) ***Naxos 8.660050-51***

FALSTAFF

- Antonio Salieri. *Dramma giocoso* in two acts. 1799.
- Libretto by Carlo Prospero Defranceschi, after Shakespeare's *The Merry Wives of Windsor*.
- First performance at the Kärntnertortheater, Vienna, on 3rd January 1799.

Salieri's comic opera *Falstaff, ossia le tre burle* (Falstaff, or The Three Jokes) omits the young lovers Fenton and Anne and concentrates on the gulling of Falstaff by the merry wives of the title, Mrs Ford and Mrs Slender. Both receive love letters from Falstaff, whose attentions are just as much financial as amorous, and react, in the end, by taking their own revenge. The absence of Fenton allows Salieri to give something of his amorous fervour to Ford, who is both jealous and loving in a powerful tenor rôle. An additional element of local comedy is introduced into the Italian libretto when Mrs Ford appears disguised as a German girl, delivering messages of assignation with both her alleged friends, the two wives.

FANCIULLA DEL WEST, LA (THE GIRL OF THE WEST)

- Giacomo Puccini. Opera in three acts. 1910.
- Libretto by Guelfo Civinini and Carl Zangarini, after the play *The Girl of the Golden West* by David Belasco.
- First performance at the Metropolitan Opera House, New York, on 10th December 1910.

Characters

Minnie	soprano
Jack Rance, sheriff	baritone
Dick Johnson (Ramerrez), a bandit	tenor
Nick, bar-tender at The Polka saloon	tenor
Ashby, agent of Wells Fargo	bass
Miners	
Sonora	baritone
Trin	tenor
Sid	baritone
Bello (Handsome)	baritone
Harry	tenor
Joe	tenor
Happy	baritone
Larkens	bass
Billy Jackrabbit, a Red Indian	bass
Wowkle, his squaw	mezzo-soprano
Jake Wallace, a travelling minstrel	baritone
José Castro, one of Ramerrez's band	bass
Courier	tenor

Minnie, at The Polka saloon, is respected and in her turn helpful to the rough clientele of the bar, miners who drink and gamble. Posters advertise a reward for the capture of the wanted bandit Ramerrez. Jack Rance, the sheriff is in love with her and is rough with Dick Johnson, who now comes into the bar, recognised and vouched for by Minnie. Ramerrez, alias Dick Johnson, has been betrayed by a former mistress, but now a bandit attack on the camp is planned. Later in the evening Johnson visits Minnie's hut, to eat there and sleep there for the night. When a group of men come to see if she is safe, they show her the picture of Ramerrez, now identified as Johnson, who has hidden at their arrival. Leaving, he is shot, but staggers in again and is hidden in the loft by Minnie, who denies his presence to Rance. Johnson's presence is revealed by drops of blood and now Minnie gambles with Rance, her love against Johnson's life, cheating to win the game. In the third act Johnson is caught and is about to be hanged when Minnie intervenes, successfully begging his life and freedom, and finally leaving together with him.

American elements serve to create the scene in California, with elaborate instrumentation. Minnie evocatively recalls her happy childhood in *Laggiù nel Soledad* (Down there in Soledad) while Johnson pleads to his captors not to tell Minnie of his coming death in *Ch'ella mi creda libero e lontano* (So that she may think me free and far away).

Recommended Recording: Ch'ella mi creda **Naxos 8.556670**

FATE (SEE OSUD)

FATINITZA

- Franz Suppé. *Operette* in three acts. 1876.
- Libretto by F. Zell and Richard Genée, after *La Circassienne* by Eugène Scribe.
- First performance at the Carltheater, Vienna, on 5th January 1876.

Fatinitza deals with the misadventures of a young Russian officer who assumes female disguise for amorous reasons, to find himself in a Turkish harem. The lively overture is a popular concert item.

Recommended Recording: Fatinitza March **Marco Polo 8.223648**

FAUSSE ESCLAVE, LA (THE FALSE SLAVE)

- Christoph Willibald von Gluck. *Opéra comique* in one act. 1757.
- Libretto based on *La fausse aventurière* (The False Adventuress) by Louis Anseaume and Pierre-Augustin Lefèvre de Marcouville.
- First performance at the Burgtheater, Vienna, on 8th January 1758.

An *opéra comique* for Vienna, *La fausse esclave* is a story of intrigue undertaken to secure a father's assent to his daughter's marriage. The score is lost, but a keyboard score is extant.

FAUST

The character of Faust, subject of Goethe's monumental drama, had a particular appeal in the 19th century, when the medieval scientist might appear in the guise of a hero, liberated from restraints, an enemy to repression, aided in his quest by the Devil himself. Derived from popular medieval rumours and superstitions, the story of Doctor Faustus was published in Germany by Johann Spiess in 1587 and from there became the subject of Christopher Marlowe's *Tragical History of Doctor Faustus*. In the late 18th century he appeared in an unfinished drama by Friedrich Müller in Mannheim, a novel by Friedrich Maximilan Klinger and in 1836 in a poem by Nikolaus Lenau. Faust provided an analogy for Thomas Mann's novel *Doktor Faustus*, an account of the rise and fall of a composer, Leverkühn, that embodies Mann's view of German society in his own time. While Lenau's *Faust* served also as a basis for Liszt, Goethe's dramatic poem provided a source for a number of composers, from Schubert, Loewe and Spohr to Liszt, Gounod, Berlioz, Schumann, Boito, Mahler, Koechlin, Jolivet, Henze and many others. The legend itself was behind Busoni's *Doktor Faustus*, while a more general influence of the Faust legend may be discerned in the various bargains musicians have been forced to drive with the Devil to ensure some improvement in technical performance or other material assistance.

Faust

- Charles Gounod. *Opéra* in five acts. 1858. Various changes and additions until 1869.
- Libretto by Jules Barbier and Michel Carré, after a play, *Faust et Marguerite* by the latter and Gérard Nerval's translation of Part I of Goethe's *Faust*.
- First performance at the Théâtre Lyrique, Paris, on 19th March 1859.

Characters

Le docteur Faust, a philosopher	tenor
Méphistophélès	bass
Marguerite	soprano
Valentin, her brother, a soldier	baritone
Wagner, his friend	baritone
Siébel, in love with Marguerite	mezzo-soprano
Marthe, Marguerite's neighbour	mezzo-soprano

The old philosopher Faust, in his study, is tired of life, but hearing the cheerful sounds of life outside, now calls on the Devil to help him. Mephistopheles appears and grants him wealth and power and, at his request, youth, in return for his soul. Faust is transformed. At a fairground, outside a tavern, there is a lively crowd of people, joined by Valentine and Siebel. Wagner sings his *Song of the Rat*, interrupted by Mephistopheles, with his praise of the golden calf and toast to Marguerite. Valentine draws his sword, which is broken through the magic of Mephistopheles. Faust escorts Marguerite, as she leaves the church, Siebel kept at bay by Mephistopheles. In Marguerite's garden Siebel picks her a bouquet of flowers, but they wither at his touch, until he dips his fingers into holy water, breaking the spell. Faust greets the house and lays a casket of jewels on the step, in place of Siebel's bouquet. Marguerite, approaching, sings her song of the King of Thule, as she muses about the handsome stranger she has met. She sees and hesitatingly opens the casket, donning the jewels, which delight her. Her neighbour Marthe encourages her, and when Faust and Mephistopheles appear, she goes out with the latter, leaving Faust and Marguerite alone, as the couples wander in the garden. Parting from her, Faust hears her confession of love and rushes to her. In the fourth act Marguerite has been deserted. In church Mephistopheles reminds her of her sin, urging her despair. In front of her house Faust and Mephistopheles provoke Valentine, who is within, and Faust kills him. He dies cursing his sister. The revised fifth act contains the Walpurgis Night scene, where Faust sees the heroines of antiquity and, finally, Marguerite, with a red mark on her neck like the cut of an axe. Brought to her in prison, where she has been condemned to death for killing her child, Faust begs her to escape with him, but she turns instead to the angels, aware of the evil in Mephistopheles. Angels now carry her up to heaven and Mephistopheles, as Faust kneels in prayer, remains frustrated.

Gounod's *Faust* remains the most famous operatic treatment of Goethe's play. Orchestral excerpts from the work include the ballet scene from the fifth act, the Nubian dances, Cleopatra variations, Trojans' dance, Mirror variations and dance of Phryne. The second act includes Valentine's *O sainte médaille* (O holy medal), as he looks at the holy medal Marguerite has given him as protection in battle. The same scene brings *Le veaux d'or* (The golden calf) of Mephistopheles, in praise of worldly things and ends with the Faust waltz *Ainsi que la brise légère* (As the gentle breeze). In the next act, after Siebel's *Faites-lui mes aveux* (Take to her my vows), comes Faust's ecstatic song to the house of his beloved Marguerite, *Salut! demeure chaste et pur* (Hail! Dwelling chaste and pure) and Marguerite's innocent ballad *Il était un roi de Thulé* (There was a King of Thule). This is in marked contrast to her delighted Jewel Song, *Ah! je ris de me voir si belle* (Ah! I laugh to see myself so fair). In her garden she plucks the petals of a flower to see if Faust loves her, and later, in a night of love, admits *Il m'aime* (He loves me). The desolate and ominous opening of the fourth act is followed by the sound of returning soldiers and the well known Soldiers' Chorus *Gloire immortelle* (Immortal glory), leading to the duel scene and the death of Valentine.

Recommended Recordings:

Faust (Ballet Music)	***Naxos 8.550081***
Salut! demeure chaste et pur	***Naxos 8.550343***
Waltz (Ainsi que la brise)	***Naxos 8.550473***

FAUST

- Louis Spohr. *Romantische Oper* in two acts. 1813. Final revision in 1851.
- Libretto by Joseph Carl Bernard.
- First performance at the Estates Theatre, Prague, on 1st September 1816.

Spohr's opera makes use of the Faust legend rather than Goethe's extended treatment of it, his hero seeking to use his power for good as much as for selfish purposes. The work ends in his punishment, as Mephistofeles drags him down to Hell. The opera occupies a place of some importance in the development of German romantic opera. The overture is intended to represent the conflict Faust feels, weaving together a number of motifs associated with ideas in the opera.

Recommended Recording: Overture ***Marco Polo 8.223122***

Favorita, La (The Favourite)

- Gaetano Donizetti. *Opéra* in four acts. 1840.
- Libretto by Alphonse Royer and Gustave Vaëz, with addition by Eugène Scribe.
- First performance at the Paris Opéra on 2nd December 1840.

Characters

Alphonse XI (Alfonso XI), King of Castile	baritone
Léonor de Guzman (Leonora di Gusmann), his mistress	mezzo-soprano
Inès (Inez), her confidante	soprano
Fernand (Fernando), a novice	tenor
Don Gaspar, the King's minister	tenor
Balthazar (Baldassare), superior of a monastery	bass

Fernando, a novice, seeks release from his vows, since he is in love with a woman whose rank and name he does not know. Leonora has him brought to her island home, fearing that he will despise her when he learns that she is the King's mistress. She warns him, as his monastic superior had done, of suffering to come. She gives him a commission in the army, as she leaves to greet the King. In battle he distinguishes himself and is honoured by the King, who remains unaware of the relationship with Leonora. A letter from Fernando to Leonora is intercepted by Don Gaspar, who shows it to the King. He questions her angrily, although the identity of the writer is still unknown to him. Baldassare now appears with a Papal condemnation of the King, bidding him dismiss his mistress and reinstate his wife, the Queen. Reluctantly the King agrees to the command of the Church and when Fernando returns victorious he offers him his own choice of reward. Fernando seeks the hand of Leonora, who now enters, in marriage and this the King generously grants. Fernando, however, is still ignorant of her past and a letter of confession that she sends him never reaches him. After his wedding he is shunned by the courtiers and at last understands that he has married the King's mistress. In distress he casts aside his sword and chain of honour and leaves with Baldassare, intending to return to the monastery. There, as he takes his vows once more, Leonora seeks him out, disguised herself as a novice and explaining how she had tried to tell him of her past. Now he is in love once more, but she dies in his arms, leaving him to pray, with the monks, for her soul.

Fernando sings the praise of his unkown beloved in *Una vergine, un'angel di Dio* (A virgin, an angel of God). The King's *A tanto amor* (For such love) is a cynical understanding of how his problems with the Church may be solved, while Leonora's *O, mio Fernando* (O, my Fernando) expresses her intention of telling her lover of her past. Fernando's moving *Spirto gentil* (Gentle spirit) marks his returning love for her and before her death she sings *Pietoso al par del nume* (Merciful like Heaven). The original French version of the opera remains in occasional French repertoire, while abroad the Italian version is generally preferred.

Fedeltà premiata, La (Fidelity Rewarded)

- Joseph Haydn. *Dramma giocoso* in three acts. 1781.
- Libretto by Giambattista Lorenzi.
- First performance at Esterháza on 25th February 1781.

Haydn's pastoral opera centres on the sacrifice to Diana demanded of a pair of faithful lovers and the triumph of the lovers, in spite of the evil intentions of the high priest of the goddess.

Fedora

- Umberto Giordano. Opera in three acts. 1898.
- Libretto by Arturo Colauti, after the play by Victorien Sardou.
- First performance at the Teatro Lirico, Milan, on 17th November 1898.

Princess Fedora Romazov is to marry Count Vladimir Andreyevich, a match which will mend his fortunes. He is shot and dies, with suspicion falling on Count Loris Ipanov, who has fled the country. In Paris Princess Fedora finds the Count and invites him to her house, intending to unmask him. He, however, shows her a letter proving the duplicitous intentions of Count Vladimir, who had been his wife's lover. To avoid interception by those that Fedora has warned of his guilt, he stays the night with her. In the third act the couple, now settled in Switzerland, learn that the revelation of Loris's responsibility for the death of Count Vladimir to the Russian authorities has led to the death of his brother in Russia, causing the death of their mother. Fedora confesses that this is her fault for telling the chief of police of his supposed guilt and of his brother's complicity. He curses her and she poisons herself, dying in his arms.

Count Loris's *Amor ti vieta* (Love forbids you), as he declares his love of Fedora in the second act, has motivic importance in the opera, and is heard again as Fedora dies.

Feen, Die (The Fairies)

- Richard Wagner. *Tragedia lirica* in three acts. 1834.
- Libretto by the composer, after Gozzi's *La donna serpente* (The Serpent Woman).
- First performance at the Königliches Hof- und Nationaltheater, Munich, on 29th June 1888.

Prefiguring Lohengrin, Ada, half fairy, half mortal, marries Arindal, King of Tramond, who is told not to ask her name. He asks, however, and her magic kingdom disappears. To rejoin him, she must try him in a series of tests in which he is unsuccessful, leaving her turned to stone for a hundred years. Like Orpheus he brings her to life from the underworld by the power of music and lives with her thereafter in fairyland.

Wagner's first opera follows the tradition of German romantic magic opera, established by Weber and Marschner, successfully enough, although this was not a path that he was to pursue. The work was first performed in Munich five years after his death.

Fennimore and Gerda

- Frederick Delius. Opera in eleven pictures. 1910.
- Libretto by the composer, after the novel *Niels Lyhne* by J.P.Jacobsen.
- First performance at the Opernhaus, Frankfurt, on 21st October 1919.

The young painter Erik Refstrup falls in love with Fennimore, daughter of Consul Claudi. Three years later, with the couple now married, Fennimore seeks the help of his friend the writer Niels Lyhne, since Erik has tired of his marriage and, drinking, is unable to work. He goes out on the town and returns drunk and abusive. In a later picture, in autumn, Fennimore is walking with Niels and they admit their love for each other. In winter news comes to her of Erik's death and when Niels arrives she rejects him, her love now turned to hate. In the final pictures Niels has returned to the farm where he had been brought up. He visits a local family and eventually marries Gerda, the eldest daughter of the family.

Most frequently heard are the interludes for the final, Gerda scenes, evocative and characteristic orchestral pieces arranged by Delius's assistant Eric Fenby. Other interludes between the pictures tell much of the inner story of the work.

Feramors

- Anton Grigor'yevich Rubinstein. Lyric opera in three acts. 1863.
- Libretto by Julius Rodenberg, after Thomas Moore's *Lalla Rookh*.
- First performance at the Hoftheater, Dresden, on 24th February, 1863.

Rubinstein's opera treats the tale of Feramors, a poor singer who is loved by a princess, who is betrothed to the Khan of Bukhara. All ends well when it turns out that Feramors is the Khan himself.

Orchestral items from the score to be heard in the concert-hall include *Dances of the Bayaderes*, a *Torchlight Dance* and a *Bridal Procession*.

Recommended Recording: Ballet Music ***Marco Polo 8.220451***

Ferne Klang, Der (The Distant Sound)

- Franz Schreker. Opera in three acts. 1909.
- Libretto by the composer.
- First performance at the Oper, Frankfurt, on 18th August 1912.

Characters

Act I

Old Graumann, a retired minor official	bass
Frau Graumann, his wife	mezzo-soprano
Grete, their daughter	soprano
Fritz, a young artist	tenor
Landlord of The Swan	bass
A Ham Actor	baritone
Dr Vigelius, a pettifogging lawyer	high bass
Old Woman	mezzo-soprano or high contralto

Act II

Greta	soprano
Mizi, a dancer	soprano
Milli, a dancer	mezzo-soprano
Mary, a dancer	soprano
Spanish Girl	contralto

The Count, 24, a man of the world	baritone
The Baron, 50, a man of the world	bass
The Chevalier, between 30 & 35, a man of the world	tenor
Fritz	tenor

Act III

Fritz	tenor
Rudolf, his friend and doctor	high bass/baritone
Grete Graumann, known as Tini	soprano
Dr Vigelius	high bass
Actor	baritone
Two Chorus Members	tenor & bass
Waitress	mezzo-soprano
Dubious Individual	tenor
Policeman	bass
Servant	speaking part

The young composer Fritz strives towards the distant sound of his ambition. Grete seeks escape from her drunken father and nagging mother with him, but he leaves her. An old woman briefly intervenes to offer help, before Graumann comes home from the inn, with his friends. It seems he has wagered his daughter's hand on a game of skittles and lost to the landlord of The Swan. Grete escapes from home and finds herself in a wood, where she falls asleep, to be found by the old woman. The second scene is set on an island in the bay of Venice in an establishment, where the girls entertain their clients. Here Greta exercises her fascination over the men, who compete for her attention. She offers herself as a prize, as the Count and Chevalier offer their songs. As she teases them, Fritz reaches the island: he has given up his search for the distant sound, but has, instead, sought out Grete. At last realises that he is in a brothel, and rushes away.

The last act opens in the garden of a bar near the theatre, where the actor and Dr Vigelius of the first act meet. Grete, now a prostitute, is brought on, fainting, having been to the theatre, where The Distant Sound has been performed, Fritz's work. As members of the audience leave the theatre, it is clear that the work was a disaster. The last scene, in Fritz's study, brings a final meeting with Grete, who comforts him as he hears again the magic sounds and falls dead.

Schreker's remarkable opera, with its collage of sounds in the second act, as different levels of music are superimposed, was an influential work in its time and it is largely through an accident of politics that it has only recently found a place again in current repertoire. Historically it came into being following Richard Strauss's *Salome*, a work that opened new possibilities of eroticism.

Fêtes de l'Amour et de Bacchus, Les (The Festivities of Cupid and Bacchus)

- Jean-Baptiste Lully. *Pastorale* in a prologue and three acts. 1672.
- Libretto by Philippe Quinault and others.
- First performance at the Jeu de Paume de Béquet, Paris, on 15th November 1672.

A pastoral pastiche, *Les fêtes de l'Amour et de Bacchus* makes use of music written for earlier collaborations with Molière. It is Lully's first opera.

Fêtes de l'Hymen et de l'Amour, Les (The Festivities of Hymen and Cupid)

- Jean-Philippe Rameau. *Opéra-ballet* in a prologue and three entrées. 1747.
- Libretto by Louis de Cahusac.
- First performance at La Grande Ecurie, Versailles, on 15th March 1747.

Les fêtes de l'Hymen et de l'Amour, ou Les dieux d'Egypte (The Festivities of Hymen and Cupid, or The Gods of Egypt) was written to celebrate the second marriage of the Dauphin. Its three entrées each celebrate a marriage, of Osiris, Canopus and Horus respectively, with spectacular effects that include the flooding of the Nile.

Fêtes de Polymnie, Les (The Festivities of Polyhymnia)

- Jean-Philippe Rameau. *Opéra-ballet* in a prologue and three entrées. 1745.
- Libretto by Louis de Cahusac.
- First performance at the Paris Opéra on 12th October 1745.

Celebrating the French victory at Fontenoy, *Les fêtes de Polymnie* (The Festivities of Polyhymnia) offers three episodes, the first the courtship of Heracles and Hebe, the second the love of Seleucus and his son Antiochus for the same woman and the third an oriental fairy romance.

Fêtes d'Hébé, Les (The Festivities of Hebe)

- Jean-Philippe Rameau. *Opéra-ballet* in a prologue and three entrées. 1739.
- Libretto by Antoine Gautier de Montdorge and others.

◆ First performance at the Paris Opéra on 21st May 1739.

Les fêtes d'Hébé, ou Les talents lyriques (The Festivities of Hebe, or The Lyric Talents) allows Hebe to arrange the celebration in Paris of poetry, music and dance, the romance of Alcaeus and Sappho, of Iphise and the legendary musician Tyrtaeus and of Aigle, nymph of Terpsichore, Muse of the dance, and Mercury.

Feuersnot (Fire-Famine)

◆ Richard Strauss. *Singgedicht* in one act. 1901.

◆ Libretto by Ernst von Wolzogen.

◆ First performance at the Dresden Hofoper on 21st November 1901.

With a libretto by the founder of the satirical Berlin Überbrettl cabaret, Strauss's *Singgedicht* (sung poem) pokes fun at the people of Munich, where his own earlier opera *Guntram* had failed, and where Wagner had made enemies. In 12th century Munich the hero Kunrad, disciple of an older magician, is tricked by a beloved but respectable girl and takes his revenge by using a spell to extinguish all fires in the city. Consummating his love in an orchestral love-scene, Kunrad relents, to general rejoicing.

Fiamma, La (The Flame)

◆ Ottorino Respighi. *Melodramma* in three acts. 1934.

◆ Libretto by Claudio Guastalla, after the play *Anne Pedersdotter* by Hans Wiers-Jenssen.

◆ First performance at the Teatro Reale dell'Opera, Rome, on 23rd January 1934.

Set in Byzantine Ravenna, Respighi's opera deals with the love of Silvana, second wife of the exarch, for her step-son, exercised through witchcraft and earning her final condemnation to death.

Fidelio

◆ Ludwig van Beethoven. Opera in two acts (originally three). 1805.

◆ Libretto by Joseph von Sonnleithner, revised in 1806 by Stephan von Breuning and in 1814 by Georg Friedrich Treitschke, after Jean-Nicolas Bouilly's *Léonore, ou L'amour conjugal* (Leonora, or Married Love).

◆ First performances at the Theater an der Wien, Vienna, on 20th November 1805, at the same theatre on 20th March 1806 and at the Kärntnertortheater on 23rd May 1814.

Characters

Leonore, disguised as Fidelio	soprano
Florestan, her husband, a political prisoner	tenor
Rocco, gaoler	bass
Marzelline, his daughter	soprano
Jaquino, Rocco's assistant	tenor
Don Pizarro, governor of the prison	bass-baritone
Don Fernando, Spanish nobleman and minister	bass

Set in a Spanish prison, near Seville, *Fidelio*, otherwise *Leonore, oder Der Triumph der ehelichen Liebe* (Leonora, or The Triumph of Married Love), centres on the loyalty and love of Leonora, who disguises herself as a boy, Fidelio, and takes service under the gaoler Rocco, discovering in the deepest dungeon her husband, Florestan. Don Pizarro, who holds Florestan prisoner for personal reasons, orders his secret murder, which Leonora is able to prevent as the arrival of the minister Don Fernando is announced, an event that will put all to rights again. Additional complications for Leonora include the unwanted affection for her of Marzelline, who is unaware of her true identity, and the consequent rivalry of Jaquino. Rocco, a good man who obeys orders, however unjust, may be seen as a representative figure, while the prisoners in his charge have their moment in the famous prisoners' chorus that allows them to emerge for a moment into the fresher air.

The four overtures to the opera, the three earlier *Leonora* overtures now generally replaced by the 1814 *Fidelio* overture, are heard often enough in the concert-hall, in particular the third of the Leonora overtures, which anticipates the climax of the opera by the use of an off-stage trumpet heralding the arrival of the *deus ex machina*, Don Fernando. The prisoners' chorus, *O welche Lust* (Oh what pleasure), in the second scene of the later two-act version of the opera, is remarkably effective, while other vocal excerpts include the quartet for Rocco and his household, *Mir ist so wunderbar* (It is so wonderful for me), Leonora's horrified recitative and aria *Abscheulicher! Wo eilst du hin?* (Detestable man! Where are you hurrying to?) and Florestan's moving *Gott! welch'Dunkel hier!* (God! How dark it is here), as he lies shackled in his underground cell.

The work is a *Singspiel*, with spoken German dialogue. Its initial failure, owed in part to the French occupation of Vienna at the time, led to an immediate revision, with the 1814 version finding greater continuing favour. While the musical influence of Mozart may be perceived, and possibly of

other treatments of the subject by the composers Gaveaux and by Paer, the plot itself owes much to French revolutionary opera, the work of Cherubini and Méhul.

Recommended Recordings:

Fidelio (2 CDs)	***Naxos 8.660070-71***
Prisoners' Chorus	***Naxos 8.550507***

Fierrabras

- Franz Schubert. *Heroisch-romantische Oper* in three acts. 1823.
- Libretto by Josef Kupelwieser, after the *Buch der Liebe* (Book of Love) by J.G.G.Büsching and F.H.von der Hagen and Friedrich de la Motte Fouqué's *Eginhard und Emma* (Eginhard and Emma).
- First performance, in a revised version, at the Grossherzogliches Hoftheater, Karlsruhe, on 9th February 1897.

Set at the court of Charlemagne, Schubert's opera deals with the love of the young Moorish prince of the title for Emma and his imprisonment through the agency of her accepted lover, Eginhard. There is a parallel romance between the Moorish princess Florinda and the Christian champion Roland. All ends in apparent happiness, with Fierrabras now a Christian knight under Charlemagne and the other pairs of lovers united after all the vicissitudes of battle and imprisonment.

Intended for performance at the Kärntnertortheater in Vienna in 1823, *Fierrabras* was never staged there. The work includes spoken German dialogue, speech over music or melodrama, following the 18th century development of the genre with Georg Benda, and good music in a shaky and prolix plot.

Fiery Angel, The

- Sergey Prokofiev. Opera in five acts. 1923. Subsequent revisions for projected performances in 1928 and 1930.
- Libretto by the composer, after the novel by Valery Bryusov.
- First full staged performance at the Teatro La Fenice, Venice, on 14th September 1955.

At an inn the knight Ruprecht hears the cries of Renata, who tells him of the angel that visited her in childhood, her distraction by carnal pleasures and her rediscovery of the angel in the guise of Count Heinrich, who abandoned her. The hostess at the inn tells Ruprecht that Renata is wicked and a witch. Failing to seduce her, he accompanies Renata in her search for Heinrich, for which she uses what magic resources she can. Ruprecht seeks the help of the philosopher and magician Agrippa von Nettelsheim, to no avail. Finding Heinrich, Renata at first renounces him, herself again rejected, and asks Ruprecht to kill him. Heinrich appears in the radiant form of the angel, and Renata now changes her mind. Ruprecht is wounded in a duel with Count Heinrich, but now Renata tells him she will enter a convent, trying to kill herself, when he declares again his love for her. They are observed by Faust and Mephistopheles, who promise to show Ruprecht the town. In the convent Renata is accused of heresy and in a final scene of pandemonium, with the nuns apparently possessed, she is condemned as a heretic.

Prokofiev wrote *The Fiery Angel* during the early period of his career outside Russia. Difficulties of staging and the impossibility of performance later in Russia, where it was eventually mounted only in 1987, led to its neglect, allowing Prokofiev to draw on the score for elements in his *Third Symphony*.

Fille du régiment, La (The Daughter of the Regiment)

- Gaetano Donizetti. *Opéra comique* in two acts. 1840.
  Revised for an Italian version in the same year.
- Libretto by Jules-Henri Vernoy de Saint-Georges and Jean-François-Alfred Bayard.
- First performance by the Paris Opéra Comique at the Salle de la Bourse on 11th February 1840.

Characters

Marie, the so-called Daughter of the Regiment	soprano
Sulpice, French grenadier sergeant	bass
Tonio, a Tyrolean peasant	tenor
La Marquise de Berkenfeld	mezzo-soprano
Hortensius, her steward	bass
Corporal	bass
La Duchesse de Crackentorp	soprano
Peasant	tenor
Notary	speaking part
Valet	speaking part

Brought up by the regiment, after being found on a battle-field as a baby, Marie tells Sergeant Sulpice of a young man who has saved her life. This is Tonio, who is found by the soldiers and now joins the regiment. The Marquise de Berkenfeld, stranded by the war, seeks a safe-conduct, and it is realised that papers found on Marie show her to be the niece of the Marquise. The discovery cannot help her budding romance with Tonio, now qualified, by earlier rules, to marry her, since he has joined the regiment. In the second act Marie, now in the castle of the Marquise, is to marry a nobleman, but still hankers after Tonio, promoted captain. Her match with him is eventually sanctioned by the Marquise, in fact her mother, after Marie has scandalized society by an account of her life with the regiment.

Excerpts from the opera heard in the concert-hall must include the overture, not least in arrangements for brass band, the vigorous regimental song *Chacun le sait* (Each one knows it), Tonio's *Ah, mes amis* (Ah, my friends) after joining the regiment and Marie's farewell to the soldiery, *Il faut partir* (I must go). The work, once neglected, is now an established part of international repertoire.

Fille de tambour-major, La (The Drum-Major's Daughter)

- Jacques Offenbach. *Opéra comique* in three acts. 1879.
- Libretto by Alfred Duru and Henri Charles Chivot.
- First performance at the Folies-Dramatiques, Paris, on 13th December 1879.

The opera, like Donizetti's *La fille du régiment* (The Daughter of the Regiment), tells of the love of Stella, who turns out to be the daughter of the drum-major and the woman now Duchess Della Volta, and the young Lieutenant Robert. To be with her lover, Stella joins the regiment as a *vivandière*, and all ends happily with the couple united.

Filosofo di campagna, Il (The Country Philosopher)

- Baldassare Galuppi. *Dramma giocoso* in three acts. 1754.
- Libretto by Carlo Goldoni.
- First performance at the Teatro S Samuele, Venice, on 26th October 1754.

A story of disguises, love and marriage, in which Eugenia rejects the suitor, the country philosopher Nardo, proposed by her father, in favour of Rinaldo. Matters are complicated by the intrigue of Eugenia's maid Lesbina, who impersonates her in an engagement to Nardo, to his final satisfaction. Eugenia's father, Don Tritemio, is finally deceived into acquiescence, when Eugenia and Rinaldo take refuge in Nardo's house, where the two couples are safely married.

Galuppi, remembered in English-speaking countries chiefly as the subject of a poem by Robert Browning, was a composer of great importance in the development of Italian *opera buffa*, of which *Il filosofo di campagna* is a fine example.

Finta giardiniera, La (The Pretended Garden-Girl)

- Wolfgang Amadeus Mozart. *Opera buffa* in three acts. 1774.
- Author of the libretto unknown, but attributed to Raniero de' Calabigi.
- First performance at the Salvatortheater, Munich, on 13th January 1775.

Characters

Ramiro, a knight, suitor of Arminda	male soprano
Don Anchise, Podestà of Lagonero	tenor
La Marchesa Violante Onesti, disguised as the garden-girl Sandrina	soprano
Roberto, her servant, disguised as the gardener Nardo	baritone
Serpetta, chambermaid to the Podestà	soprano
Arminda, niece of the Podestà, a Milanese lady	soprano
Il Contino Belfiore	tenor

In the Mayor's garden, the disguised Marchioness seeks her former lover Belfiore, who had stabbed and deserted her, Ramiro has been rejected by Arminda and the Mayor, Don Anchise, loves the supposed Sandrina. Roberto, alias Nardo, wants to marry Serpetta, who wants to marry the Podestà. Belfiore is now in love with Arminda, who intends to keep him. The second act, in the house, finds Nardo (Roberto) wooing the reluctant Serpetta, Sandrina (Violante) describing her death to Belfiore, the Mayor attempting to attract Sandrina and Ramiro trying to have Belfiore arrested for murder of Violante (Sandrina). with the Mayor refusing to allow any niece of his to marry a murderer. In the following scene she tries to exonerate him by claiming that there was no murder. Finally abandoned through Arminda's jealous agency in a wood, she hears the others, each mistaking the other's identity. Now Sandrina, under stress, imagines herself a shepherdess, Cloris, wooing her Thyrsis, Belfiore, whom the Mayor and Ramiro both challenge to a duel, a procedure to which Nardo, Serpetta and Arminda object. Sandrina now imagines herself Medusa, while Belfiore thinks himself Hercules. Still deluded in the third act, Belfiore now addresses Nardo (Roberto) as Venus, while he himself is Mercury. Sandrina, now thinking herself Herminea, declares that she loves and will marry Nardo. In the last scene all, as might be expected, comes right. Sandrina and Belfiore are restored to their senses and united, Serpetta agrees to Nardo's suit and Arminda is happy with Ramiro.

In a plot of obvious complexity, as characters assume other identities, either consciously or in madness, Mozart, in this his second comic opera, creates more rounded figures out of the stuff of two-dimensional comedy. The overture may be heard in the concert-hall, while the musical substance of the opera allows Arminda moments of high drama, with more high flown writing for the nobility and an appropriately earthier style of relative simplicity for the lower classes.

Recommended Recording: Overture ***Naxos 8.550185***

FINTA SEMPLICE, LA (THE PRETENDED SIMPLETON)

- Wolfgang Amadeus Mozart. *Opera buffa* in three acts. 1768.
- Libretto by Carlo Goldoni, adapted by Narco Coltellini.
- First performance at the Palace of the Archbishop of Salzburg probably on the Archbishop's name-day, 1st May 1769.

CHARACTERS

Fracasso, a Hungarian captain	tenor
Rosina, a Baroness, his sister	soprano
Cassandro, a misogynist	bass
Polidoro, his brother	tenor
Giacinta, their sister	mezzo-soprano
Simone, servant to Fracasso	bass
Ninetta, Giacinta's maid	soprano

Cassandro, something of a pedant, bullies his brother Polidoro and objects to his sister Giacinta marrying Fracasso, and now Rosina, Fracasso's sister, is coming to stay in the house, seeking a husband and advised by Ninetta to set her cap at the first of the two brothers that she meets. This turns out to be Polidoro, who proposes at once, to his brother's later annoyance. Cassandro now starts to make overtures to Rosina. After a variety of incidents, including the departure of Giacinta with the family fortune, leaving the brothers unable to marry, all ends well enough. Rosina, teasing until the last minute, chooses, surprisingly, to marry Cassandro, Fracasso marries Giacinta and Simone finds again Ninetta, who also had absconded with whatever she could lay her hands on.

Mozart's opera was written for performance in Vienna, but this was prevented through what his father described as jealousy. The libretto presents a series of stock characters, in the tradition to which Goldoni was accustomed and the twelve-year-old composer dealt with this in comparable fashion, producing remarkable music and taking childish delight, in particular, in a duel scene between the braggart soldier Fracasso and the cowardly bully Cassandro, any serious outcome prevented by Rosina's timely intervention.

FLAMMEN, DIE (THE FLAMES)

- Franz Schreker. Opera in one act. 1902.
- Libretto by Dora Leen.
- First concert performance in the Vienna Bösendorfersaal on 24th April 1902.

CHARACTERS

The Prince	baritone
Irmgard, his wife	soprano
Agnes, her sister	soprano
The Singer	tenor
Old Margot	mezzo-soprano

The Prince has left for the crusades, while his wife Irmgard is wooed by the Singer, in spite of the prophecy that infidelity will bring death to the Prince, if she kiss him on his return. When the Prince re-appears, victorious, Irmgard sacrifices herself, rather than bring death to her lord.

The theme of the fallen woman recurs in Schreker's later operas, in the figure of Grete in *Der ferne Klang* (The Distant Sound) and of Carlotta in *Die Gezeichneten* (The Marked Ones). *Die Flammen*, first performed with piano accompaniment and orchestrated only in recent years for staged revival, promises much, although the composer later distanced himself from his collaboration with Dora Leen.

Recommended Recording: Die Flammen ***Marco Polo 8.223422***

FLEDERMAUS, DIE (THE BAT)

- Johann Strauss. *Komische Operette* in three acts. 1874.
- Libretto by Carl Haffner and Richard Genée, after *Le réveillon* (The Midnight Supper) by Henri Meilhac and Ludovic Halévy.
- First performance at the Theater an der Wien, Vienna, on 5th April 1874.

Characters

Gabriel von Eisenstein	tenor
Rosalinde, his wife	soprano
Alfred, a singer, her lover	tenor
Dr Falke, friend of Eisenstein	baritone
Prince Orlofsky	mezzo-soprano
Frank, governor of the prison	baritone
Adele, Rosalinde's maid	soprano
Ida, her sister	soprano
Dr Blind, Eisenstein's lawyer	tenor
Yvan, Prince Orlofsky's valet	speaking part
Frosch, a gaoler	speaking part

Eisenstein is due to report to prison, having defaulted on his taxes. He is induced, however, to attend a fancy-dress party at Prince Orlofsky's, by his friend Dr Falke, who plans revenge for having been abandoned on a previous occasion to go home in his costume of a bat. Eisenstein's wife takes the opportunity of his absence for an assignation in her house with Alfred, who is mistaken by Frank, the prison governor, for her husband and taken to prison. Adele has sought various excuses for taking time off and in a borrowed dress attends Prince Orlofsky's party, where Rosalinde also appears, disguised as a Hungarian countess. In a play of disguises and partly mistaken identities Eisenstein flirts with his own wife and toasts, under the guise of the Marquis Renard, the prison governor Frank, introduced as the Chevalier Chagrin. They leave together, Eisenstein now intending to report to the prison. There the gaoler Frosch has drunken objections to the singing of Alfred. Adele and her sister, who have dramatic ambitions, seek Frank's help in furthering their stage careers, while Eisenstein, who now arrives, cannot persuade Frank at first of his identity and when he learns that the supposed Eisenstein is already in prison is suspicious of Rosalinde. Disguised as his lawyer Dr Blind, he cross-examines Rosalinde and Alfred, but she retaliates, when he reveals his identity, by producing Eisenstein's watch, which the supposed Hungarian countess had received from him at Prince Orlofsky's. Falke admits his part in the plot, Rosalinde and Alfred claim their assignation as a part of it, and all ends in apparent satisfaction.

The operetta starts with a sparkling overture, with tunes from the last act and then the Fledermaus waltz of the second act party. Adele's laughing song, *Mein Herr Marquis* (My lord marquis) in which she rejects Eisenstein's suggestion and her true identity, and her delightful display of varied acting ability, *Spiel'ich die Unschuld* (I play the innocent) to Frank are often heard. Rosalinde's Hungarian Czárdás, *Klänge der Heimat* (Sounds of my own country) is all too convincing, while the song of friendship, *Brüderlein und Schwesterlein (Little brothers and sisters)*, as the party reaches a climax, is among the most memorable of all numbers in the best of all Viennese operettas.

Recommended Recordings:

Die Fledermaus (2 CDs)	***Naxos 8.660017-18***
Highlights	***Naxos 8.553171***

FLIEGENDE HOLLÄNDER, DER (THE FLYING DUTCHMAN)

- Richard Wagner. *Romantische Oper* in three acts. 1841.
- Libretto by the composer, after Heinrich Heine's *Aus den Memoiren des Herrn von Schnabelewopski* (From the Memoirs of Herr von Schnabelevopsky).
- First performance at the Königliches Sächsisches Hoftheater, Dresden, on 2nd January 1843.

CHARACTERS

Daland, a Norwegian sea-captain	bass
Senta, his daughter	soprano
Mary, her nurse	contralto
Erik, a huntsman	tenor
Steersman on Daland's ship	tenor
The Dutchman	bass-baritone

The mysterious Dutchman is condemned to sail the seas with his ghostly crew until redeemed by the pure love of a woman. After a stormy overture Daland's ship puts in to land, and a stranger ship puts in alongside, hailed by Daland's steersman, but not answering his call or the invitations offered by the local people, who celebrate the return of their men-folk. The Dutchman himself, captain of the ghostly ship, allowed now, after seven more years, to land in his quest for release, asks Daland for hospitality, offering him rich reward and showing an interest in Senta, his daughter. In Daland's house, where the women sit spinning, Senta has long been preoccupied by the story of the Dutchman and fascinated by his portrait. Erik, a huntsman, loves her and tells her his dream, in which he saw Daland bringing home a stranger. Senta, however, is still more preoccupied with her vision of the strange seafarer, whom her father now brings home. Senta's love, it seems, will bring the Dutchman the redemption he seeks. He overhears Erik, however, reproaching Senta for her infidelity and resolves to leave her. As The Flying Dutchman sails out into the open sea, Senta, who has struggled free from Erik and those who seek to restrain her, leaps from the cliff in a pure act of love. The Dutchman's ship and crew sink at once in the waves, and he and Senta are seen united for ever.

Wagner's opera makes use of several leading motifs, a principle of which he made much greater use in his later music-dramas. Here the Dutchman himself is represented by the striking horn call heard first in the overture, with its stormy string-writing. Part of the music of Senta's second act ballad is heard, her story of the Dutchman, a motif that represents her, and there are other elements that re-appear as the story unfolds. The overture itself, in many ways a summary of the action, is an impressive concert piece. Vocal excerpts include the Dutchman's *Die Frist ist um* (The time is here) and the Steersman's song *Mit Gewitter und Sturm aus fernem Meer* (In thunder and storm from the far sea). The second act starts with the women spinning in Daland's house, singing their lilting spinning-song *Summ und Brumm* (Hum and sing), echoing the sound of their work. Senta's moving ballad follows. Choruses include the well known *Steuermann, lass die Wacht* (Steersman, leave the watch).

Recommended Recording: Der fliegende Höllander (2 CDs) ***Naxos 8.660025-26***

FLORENTINISCHE TRAGÖDIE, EINE (A FLORENTINE TRAGEDY)

- Alexander Zemlinsky. Opera in one act. 1916.
- Libretto by the composer, after the work of the same name by Oscar Wilde, translated by M.Meyerfeld.
- First performance at the Hoftheater, Stuttgart, on 30th January 1917.

The Florentine merchant Simone is suspicious of the young Prince Guido, who he suspects has cuckolded him. He offers Guido all he has in his house, after selling him a formal robe, and Guido demands Simone's wife, Bianca. Her husband sets her spinning and when he has left the room she expresses her hatred of him, wishing him dead, sentiments that he overhears, returning to speak of death and adultery. Simone again leaves Guido and Bianca together and they express their love for each other. As Guido is about to leave, Simone gives him his sword and seizing his own, fights against the thief who has stolen from him, eventually overpowering and strangling Guido. Bianca, now understanding the strength of her husband, is reconciled to him.

Teacher and perhaps once the lover of Alma Mahler, teacher also of Schoenberg, his friend and later his brother-in-law, Zemlinsky was an important figure in the musical world of Vienna, particularly in the earlier years of the 20th century. Symphonic in structure, *Eine florentinische Tragödie* (A Florentine Tragedy) starts with an orchestral overture and makes use of Wagnerian leit-motif techniques.

Floridante

- George Frideric Handel. Opera in three acts. 1721.
- Libretto by Paolo Antonio Rolli, based on *La costanza in trionfo* (Constancy Triumphant) by Francesco Silvani.
- First performance at the King's Theatre, London, on 9th December 1721.

The Persian usurper Oronte has adopted a daughter of the murdered King Nino, Elmira, whom the victorious Thracian Prince Floridante, commander under Oronte, now expects in marriage. Oronte's own daughter, Rossane, is wooed by a prisoner of Floridante, the Tyrian Prince Tomante, earlier in disguise. Floridante is expelled from the court, without apparent reason, but it then seems that Oronte intends to marry Elmira himself. Floridante returns, in disguise, planning, with Timante, that they should elope with the two girls. Their escape is foiled and Floridante is imprisoned. After further attempts by Oronte to have his way he is dethroned by Floridante and Elmira becomes Queen of Persia, with Floridante her husband and Oronte forgiven, while Rossane and Timante return together to rule in Tyre.

As with many of Handel's operas, there were revisions for subsequent performances. The thirteenth of his operas and the eighth for the King's Theatre, *Floridante* won some success, opening in London the third season of the Royal Academy of Music, founded with the support of King George I in 1718.

Forza del destino, La (The Force of Destiny)

- Giuseppe Verdi. Opera in four acts. 1861. Revised version for the Teatro alla Scala, Milan, in 1869.
- Libretto by Francesco Maria Piave, after the play *Don Alvaro, o La fuerza del sino* (Don Alvaro, or The Force of Destiny) by the Duke of Rivas, Angel de Saavedra, with an addition from Friedrich Schiller's *Wallensteins Lager* (Wallenstein's Camp). Revision and additions for 1869 by Antonio Ghislanzoni.
- First performance at the Imperial Theatre, St Petersburg, on 10th November 1862.

Characters

Marchese di Calatrava	bass
Donna Leonora di Vargas, his daughter	soprano
Don Carlo di Vargas, his son	baritone

Don Alvaro	tenor
Preziosilla, a gypsy girl	mezzo-soprano
Padre Guardiano, a Franciscan friar	bass
Fra Melitone, a Franciscan friar	baritone
Curra, maid to Donna Leonora	mezzo-soprano
Alcalde (Mayor of Hornachuelos)	bass
Trabuco, a muleteer	tenor
Surgeon	bass

Leonora has planned to elope with her lover Don Alvaro, who accidentally shoots and kills her father, the Marquis of Calatrava, who curses him as he dies. The lovers are separated in their flight, but Leonora's brother, Don Carlo, does his best to seek them out, to take revenge. At an inn, where he is disguised as a student, Don Carlo is told by the gypsy Preziosilla that she can see he is in disguise. A muleteer brings a stranger to the inn, Leonora, who sees her brother and makes off, while he sings a ballad to the company that reflects his own story. Leonora now seeks peace in a hermitage, under the protection of a nearby monastery, counselled by the Father Guardian. At the war in Italy, of which Preziosilla had told, Don Alvaro and Don Carlo are both enlisted in the Spanish contingent, both in disguise. Don Alvaro saves Don Carlo's life and they swear friendship, still without any gleam of mutual recognition. Wounded subsequently in battle, Don Alvaro entrusts a casket and letter to Don Carlo, to be destroyed after his seemingly imminent death. Suspicious, Don Carlo opens the casket and finds there a portrait of Leonora, proof that his supposed friend is in fact Don Alvaro. Meeting him on a later occasion, Don Carlo provokes a duel, but this is interrupted. Don Alvaro resolves to seek peace in a monastery, where he joins the community as Padre Raffaello. Don Carlo seeks him out and offers considerable provocation, leading, as he had hoped, to a duel in which he himself is killed. Don Alvaro seeks help from a neighbouring cell, to discover Leonora, who now approaches her brother. In a last gesture he stabs her, leaving the Father Guardian to counsel Don Alvaro, as Leonora dies.

The overture to *La forza del destino* (The Force of Destiny) makes use of themes from the opera, notably an ominous motif suggesting Fate and Leonora's second act aria, *Madre, pietosa Vergine* (Mother, merciful Virgin). A complex plot, based on what might seem a series of remarkable coincidences and singular failures of perception on the part of the leading players, brings several important and moving duets, notably the closing scene of the second act, where the Father Guardian advises Leonora on the religious life and the duets between the two younger men, Don Alvaro and Don Carlo, *Solenne in quest'ora* (In this solemn hour), as it seems Don Alvaro is near to death and the final duel *Col sangue sol cancellasi* (Settled only by blood). Don Alvaro's third act *Oh, tu che in seno agli angeli* (Oh, you who are in the bosom of the angels), when he believes Leonora dead, is well known outside its operatic context and Leonora's *Pace, pace, mio Dio* (Peace, peace, my God) movingly expresses her continuing feelings of love, as she lives her solitary life, before the final tragedy. The earlier ending of the opera allowed Don Alvaro to kill himself in final despair, after action had been interrupted by a duet of recognition. The new ending was the result of a revision in 1869.

Recommended Recordings:

Overture	***Naxos 8.553089***
Pace, pace, mio Dio	***Naxos 8.550606***
Invano, Alvaro	***Naxos 8.553030***
Rataplan, rataplan	***Naxos 8.550241***

Four Saints in Three Acts

- Virgil Thomson. Opera in a prologue and four acts. 1933.
- Libretto by Gertrude Stein.
- First performance at Wadworth Atheneum, Hartford, Connecticut, on 8th February 1934.

After a choral prologue, the opera centres on St Teresa I, St Teresa II, St Chavez and St Settlement in a surreal period and situation, reflected in approachable and apparently ingenuous music. The saints themselves seem, in their various activities, to represent the American artists' colony in Paris, where Thomson met Gertrude Stein.

Fra Diavolo

- Daniel-François-Esprit Auber. *Opéra comique* in three acts. 1830.
- Libretto by Eugène Scribe.
- First performance by the Paris Opéra Comique at the Salle Ventadour on 28th January 1830.

The carabinieri are in search of the bandit Fra Diavolo, who appears disguised as the Marquis de San Marco. Zerline, bidden by her father to marry annother, is loved by Lorenzo, commander of the forces of order, who succeeds in killing some of the bandits and restoring stolen jewellery to two English travellers, Lord Kokbourg and Lady Pamela. Fra Diavolo plans revenge and with two of his followers goes through Zerline's room to that of the English couple, intending to rob them and have Zerline killed. Lorenzo's appearance forces him to plead a secret assignation, the cause of jealousy in both Lorenzo and Lord Kokbourg. Fra Diavolo tells his men to ring the church bell when the carabinieri have gone. Learning of this plan, Lorenzo arranges to have the bell rung and Fra Diavolo is captured.

One of the few operas by Auber to remain in current repertoire, *Fra Diavolo, ou L'hôtellerie de Terracine* (Fra Diavolo, or The Inn of Terracina) has an overture that may also be heard in the concert-hall, while the tenor Fra Diavolo is provided with an impressive aria in *Je vois marcher sous ma bannière* (I see march under my banner).

Frau ohne Schatten, Die (The Woman without a Shadow)

- Richard Strauss. *Oper* in three acts. 1917.
- Libretto by Hugo von Hoffmannsthal.
- First performance at the Vienna Staatsoper on 10th October 1919.

Characters

The Emperor	tenor
The Empress, his wife	high dramatic soprano
Nurse, her guardian	dramatic mezzo-soprano
A Spirit Messenger	high baritone
Keeper of the Temple Gates	soprano/countertenor
Apparition of a Youth	high tenor
Voice of the Falcon	soprano
Voice from Above	contralto
Barak, a dyer	bass-baritone
His Wife	high dramatic soprano
Barak's Brothers:	
The One-Eyed	high bass
The One-Armed	bass
The Hunchback	tenor
Voices of Unborn Children	three sopranos & three contraltos
Voices of Three Nightwatchmen	baritones

A messenger from Keikobad, King of the Spirits and father of the childless and hence shadowless Empress, gives her nurse the message that she must return to Keikobad after three days, and the Emperor will be turned to stone. The Emperor sings of his courtship and plans to go hunting for three days, missing still his falcon, which had disappeared the day he met his wife. The Empress too comes forward, singing of her love. The falcon now tells her that she must acquire a shadow, or the Emperor will be turned to stone. She seeks her nurse's help. In the poor hut of Barak the Dyer, where his deformed brothers squabble, he reproaches his wife for their childlessness. He goes to market and the Empress and her nurse, disguised as peasants, enter the hut, the nurse seeking to buy the woman's shadow. The woman agrees, proposing not to sleep with her husband, but then hears the voices of her unborn children. In the second act the nurse tempts Barak's wife with the apparition of a young man and Barak, returning, finds her attitude to him changed. The Emperor, out hunting, finds his falcon again and feels that his wife has had earthly contact. On the third day the nurse still tries to buy Barak's wife's shadow, leaving the Empress herself filled with pity for Barak. In her own bedroom in the falcon-house she hears the voice of warning again. In Barak's hut Barak's wife at first admits to her husband her fault, but then repents of her intended bargain, as the Empress refuses the human cost of the shadow, for which Barak will kill his wife. The earth opens and receives the hut. Now, under the ground, Barak and his wife are divided by a wall, on one side of which she struggles with her conscience, while Barak's steadfast goodness remains apparent. As the Emperor is about to be judged at the court of Keikobad, the Empress is told that if she drinks the Water of Life she will have the woman's shadow, but the sound of Barak and his wife prevent her. She sees now the Emperor turned to stone, but still refuses to do harm to Barak and his wife in return for her shadow. Her final act of self-sacrifice wins her a shadow, while the voices of unborn children join Emperor, Empress, Barak and his wife in happiness.

It was suggested that, if *Der Rosenkavalier* (The Knight of the Rose) was Strauss's *Marriage of Figaro*, then *Die Frau ohne Schatten* (The Woman without a Shadow) was his *Magic Flute*. A magic opera, it is essentially a fairy-tale. With interwoven leit-motifs, the orchestral writing is rich in allusion. Possible dramatic excerpts from the opera must include the awakening of the Empress in the second act, when she already regrets her guilt in dreaming of harming Barak and his family.

Freischütz, Der (The Marksman)

- Carl Maria von Weber. *Romantische Oper* in three acts. 1820.
- Libretto by Johann Friedrich Kind, after the *Gespensterbuch* (Book of Ghosts) of Johann August Apel and Friedrich Laun.
- First performance at the Schauspielhaus, Berlin, on 18th June 1821.

Characters

Max, a forester	tenor
Kilian, a rich peasant	baritone
Cuno, hereditary head forester	bass
Caspar, a forester	bass
Agathe, Cuno's daughter	soprano

Aennchen, her cousin	mezzo-soprano
Samiel, the Black Huntsman	speaking part
Prince Otakar	baritone
Hermit	bass
Four Bridesmaids	sopranos

Kilian is winning in a shooting competition and the company of peasants mock the young forester Max, who has lost. The following day Max's performance will determine his marriage to Agathe. The forester Caspar suggests to Max that he have recourse to Samiel, the Black Huntsman, and the powers of evil, against which Cuno, Agathe's father, is quick to warn him. Max, however, in spite of everything agrees to meet Caspar at midnight in the Wolf's Glen to seek diabolical help. Caspar's plan is to find in Max a substitute for himself in Samiel's power. In a ghostly scene magic bullets are cast, six of which will surely hit their intended mark, while the seventh will go where Samiel wills. At the contest Max has used his magic bullets to good effect, but Prince Otakar proposes that he shoot a white dove that has settled on a bough with his seventh bullet. Agathe, who has entered, cries out. The hermit touches the bough and the bird flies to another tree. Max shoots and Agathe falls down fainting, while Caspar, who had hidden in the tree, is killed, visited in death by a vision of Samiel. Max confesses what has happened and is at first banished and then put on probation for a year, after which he may, if he acquits himself well, marry Agathe.

Der Freischütz (The Marksman) is the first great German romantic opera, including the varied ingredients typical of German romanticism, the forest, the huntsman, the Devil and magic. The title, literally, if clumsily, the free-shooter, gives a clearer idea of the nature of Max's actions, since it is the *Freikügel* (free-bullet) that causes his agreement with Caspar, who demonstrates its efficacy, and his dabbling in evil. The overture contains full statements of thematic material from the opera. Max's initial failure in shooting is reflected in his *Nein! länger trag'ich nicht die Qualen* (No! I'll no longer bear this torture) with the following *scena Durch die Wälder, durch die Auen* (Through the woods, through the meadows). Caspar's coarser character is apparent in his drinking-song *Hier im ird'schen Jammerthal* (Here in this earthly vale of tears), while the most ghostly and dramatic scene must be that in the Wolf's Glen, with its sinister apparitions and the solemn casting of the magic bullets. Agathe, in the second act, has a moving recitative and aria in *Wie nahte mir der Schlummer* (Now sleep comes upon me) and in the third act expresses her misgivings and faith, as she prepares for her wedding, *Ob die Wölke* (Whether the clouds). The *Huntsmen's Chorus* has found a place in varied repertoires, choral and instrumental.

Recommended Recordings:

Overture	***Naxos 8.550146***
Bridesmaids' Chorus and Huntsmen's Chorus	***Naxos 8.550507***

FRIEDENSTAG (DAY OF PEACE)

- Richard Strauss. *Oper* in one act. 1936.
- Libretto by Joseph Gregor, with private assistance from Stefan Zweig.
- First performance at the Staatsoper, Munich, on 24th July 1938.

CHARACTERS

Commandant of the town under siege	baritone
Maria, his wife	soprano
Sergeant	bass
Corporal	baritone
Private Soldier	tenor
Musketeer	bass
Bugler	bass
Officer	baritone
Front-line Officer	baritone
Piedmontese	tenor
Cast Holsteiner, commanding the besieging army	bass
Burgomaster of the town under siege	tenor
Bishop	baritone
A Woman of the People	soprano

In 1648, in a town under siege in the Thirty Years War, the Commandant refuses suggestions by the Bishop and the Burgomaster that the town should surrender, as the people starve. Eventually he agrees, if they will wait until noon, when he will give a blazing signal that all will understand. The delegation is satisfied, but it is clear that the Commandant intends to blow up the arsenal and garrison. His wife Maria urges his confidence and he tells her to make her escape. She is unwilling to abandon her husband and they embrace. The Sergeant is about to light the fuse when a cannon shot is heard and the bells of the town at once start to ring. The Commandant still refuses to surrender, but the Holsteiner, commander of the besieging force, enters and offers his hand to the Commandant, who refuses it and draws his sword. Maria comes between the two men, who now embrace, in peace once more.

Richard Strauss was prevented by the anti-semitic policies of the ruling National Socialists from further open collaboration with the Jewish writer Stefan Zweig, whose contribution would have made any performance of the opera impossible. Zweig's friend Gregor, however, proved a very much less satisfactory collaborator, as far as Strauss was concerned, in spite of his very considerable distinction as a theatre historian and his musical and operatic experience. *Friedenstag* ends with a choral finale, a hymn of thanksgiving, a procedure that Strauss avoided in his next collaboration with Gregor, *Daphne*.

From the House of the Dead

- Leoš Janáček. Opera in three acts. 1928.
- Libretto by the composer, after Dostoyevsky's novel.
- First performance at the National Theatre, Brno, on 12th April 1930.

Characters

Alexander Petrovich Goryanshikov, a political prisoner	bass
Alyeya, a young Tartar	mezzo-soprano/tenor
Filka Morosov, in prison as Luka Kuzmich	tenor
Big Prisoner	tenor
Small Prisoner	baritone
Very Old Prisoner	tenor
Commandant	baritone
Skuratov	tenor
Chekunov	baritone
Drunken Prisoner	tenor
Cook	baritone
Blacksmith	bass
Priest	baritone
Young Prisoner	tenor
Prostitute	mezzo-soprano
Prisoner/Don Juan/Priest	baritone
Kedril	tenor
Shapkin	tenor
Shishkov	baritone
Cherevin	tenor
Guard	tenor

Starting with an overture that was originally a violin concerto, the curtain rises on a prison camp in Siberia. The political prisoner Goryanshikov is brought in and taunted by the Commandant, who orders him to be flogged. The prisoners tend an eagle with a broken wing and sing sadly of the homes they have left. Skuratov tries to entertain them, and Luka tells of the murder of his commanding officer, the crime for which he is being punished. By the river Goryanshikov befriends the young Tartar Alyeya and offers to teach him to read. The prisoners put on an entertainment, Don Juan and The Tale of the Fair Miller's Wife. Afterwards, as Goryanshikov and Alyeya drink tea, the latter is attacked and injured by a jealous prisoner, while a young prisoner goes off with a prostitute. The third act, in winter again, finds Alyeya talking of the Bible and how men should love their enemies, Luka dying, Shapkin telling of his misadventures and Skuratov lamenting the absence of Luisa. Shishkov gives an account of the murder of his wife, seduced, it now transpires, by Luka, recognised after his death. In the following scene Goryanshikov is set free, to Alyeya's dismay, and the captive eagle is freed. The prisoners are marched off to work.

Janáček's last opera was left incomplete at his death in August 1928 and at its first performance ended on a note of optimism, as the eagle is set free, in place of the grim reality that the composer intended, as prison life inexorably resumes. The nature of the work makes the possibility of concert vocal excerpts rare, although the opening prelude enjoys a separate existence and there is an orchestral suite drawn from a work that, through the nature of its subject, is not particularly cheerful.

FURIOSO NELL'ISOLA DI SAN DOMINGO, IL (THE MADMAN ON THE ISLAND OF SAN DOMINGO)

- Gaetano Donizetti. *Melodramma* in two acts. 1832.
- Libretto by Jacopo Ferretti, drawing on an episode in *Don Quixote* by Cervantes.
- First performance at the Teatro Valle, Rome, on 2nd January 1833.

The episode from *Don Quixote* on which the opera is based concerns the madness and recovery of Cardenio.

GAMBLERS, THE

- Dmitry Shostakovich. Opera (unfinished). 1942.
- Libretto after the play by Nikolay Gogol.
- First staged performance in the Chamber Music Theatre, Moscow, on 24th January 1990.

Shostakovich started, in 1942, to set Gogol's play *The Gamblers*, to music, but abandoned the attempt. A version was completed by the Polish composer Krzysztof Meyer for performance in Wuppertal in 1983, following the satirical intentions of the original work of Gogol and of Shostakovich.

GAZZA LADRA, LA (THE THIEVING MAGPIE)

- Gioachino Rossini. *Melodramma* in two acts. 1817.
- Libretto by Giovanni Gherardini, after *La pie voleuse* (The Thieving Magpie) by J.M.T.Badouin d'Aubigny and Louis-Charles Caigniez.
- First performance at the Teatro alla Scala, Milan, on 31st May 1817.

CHARACTERS

Fabrizio Vongradito, a rich farmer	bass
Lucia, his wife	mezzo-soprano
Giannetto, his son, a soldier	tenor
Ninetta, a servant in their house	soprano
Fernando Villabella, her father, a soldier	baritone
Gottardo, village mayor	bass
Pippo, a young peasant, employed by Fabrizio	contralto
Isacco, a pedlar	tenor
Antonio, the gaoler	tenor
Giorgio, servant to the mayor	bass

Ernesto, friend of Fernando, a soldier	bass
Magpie	

Ninetta hopes to marry Giannetto, returning from the war. She tries to shelter her father Fernando Villabella, who has deserted from the army, and is troubled by the attentions of the mayor, Gottardo. A missing spoon and the evidence of Isacco, the pedlar, who has bought a piece of silver from Ninetta to raise money for her father, lead to her accusation and imprisonment. She is tried and found guilty, to be saved from death at the last minute by the discovery of the thief, the thieving magpie of the title.

Given a happy ending, Rossini's opera starts with a brilliant overture, a well known concert opener. Ninetta has a charming aria in which, in the first act, she expresses her love for Giannetto, *Di piacer mi balza il cor* (My heart leaps in pleasure).

Recommended Recording: Overture — ***Naxos 8.550236***

Gazzetta, La (The Newspaper)

- Gioachino Rossini. *Dramma* in two acts. 1816.
- Libretto by Giuseppe Palomba, after *Il matrimonio per concorso* (Marriage by Competition) by Carlo Goldoni.
- First performance at the Teatro dei Fiorentini, Naples, on 26th September 1816.

The opera explores the comic possibilities of two fathers and their daughters, the first advertising in a newspaper for a husband for his daughter, who is already secretly in love with the owner of the hotel where they are staying.

Geduldige Socrates, Der (Patient Socrates)

- Georg Philipp Telemann. *Komische Oper* in three acts. 1721.
- Libretto by Johann Ulrich von König, after *La patienza di Socrate con due moglie* (The Patience of Socrates with Two Wives) by Nicolò Minato.
- First performance at the Theater am Gänsemarkt, Hamburg, on 28th January 1721.

Telemann's opera for Hamburg, where he had recently been appointed director of music to the principal city churches, provides comedy based on a supposed Athenian law that insisted that men should have two wives, an unpleasant enough situation for the philosopher Socrates and a nearly fatal one for the prince, Melito.

Gemma di Vergy (Gemma of Vergy)

- Gaetano Donizetti. *Tragedia lirica* in two acts. 1834.
- Libretto by Giovanni Emanuele Bidera, after the play *Charles VII chez ses grands vassaux* (Charles VII with his Great Vassals) by Alexandre Dumas.
- First performance at the Teatro alla Scala, Milan, on 26th December 1834.

The Count of Vergy has his marriage to the barren Gemma annulled. A faithful slave murders the Count, at his second wedding, and then kills himself, leaving Gemma to mourn for her lost husband and lost love. The score includes the soprano aria *Eccomi sola alfine* (Here am I now alone).

Geneviève de Brabant (Geneviève of Brabant)

- Jacques Offenbach. *Opéra bouffe* in two acts. 1859. Revised in three acts in 1867.
- Libretto by Louis-Adolphe Jaime and Etienne Tréfeu. Revised libretto by Hector-Jonathan Crémieux.
- First performance at the Théâtre des Bouffes-Parisiens, Salle Choiseul, on 19th November 1859.

Offenbach's comic opera deals light-heartedly with the story of Geneviève, married to the Duke of Curaçao, prevented by a curse from fathering children. All ends well, with a usurper displaced and the couple happily brought together, after various vicissitudes.

Genoveva

- Robert Schumann, Opera in four acts. 1849.
- Libretto by the composer, after Ludwig Tieck's *Leben und Tod der heiligen Genoveva* (Life and Death of Saint Genoveva), with earlier drafts by Robert Reinick and Friedrich Hebbel, after the latter's play of the same name.
- First performance at the Stadttheater, Leipzig, on 25th June 1850.

In 8th century Brabant Christian knights are summoned to join Charles Martel's crusade. Siegfried, Count Palatine, leaving for the war, entrusts his young wife to the young Golo, who is in love with her. Rejected by her, he seeks revenge by secreting the old steward Drago in her bedroom and in the middle of the night bringing others to discover her imagined infidelity. Siegfried is told of this and commands Golo to put Genoveva to death. Left to the mercy of two armed men, who are to kill her, she is saved by the intervention of a deaf and dumb boy and finally reconciled with Siegfried, who has at last been told of the plot against his and his wife's honour.

The overture to Schumann's opera is occasionally heard in the concert-hall, while the rest of the work offers no great chance for characterization or vocal display.

Recommended Recording: Overture ***Naxos 8.550608***

Gewaltige Hahnrei, Der (The Mighty Cuckold)

- Berthold Goldschmidt. Opera in three acts. 1930.
- Libretto by the composer, after the play *Le Cocu magnifique* (The Magnificent Cuckold) by Fernand Crommelynck.
- First performance in Mannheim on 14th February 1932.

The poet and scrivener Bruno is jealously in love with his attractive wife Stella, nearly raped by an oxherd and then subject, at Bruno's instigation, to the attentions of her cousin Petrus, a sailor, whom he strikes and forbids the house. He now closes the shutters and makes Stella cover her face and wear drab clothes. His jealousy reaches such a pitch that only her observed infidelity will cure it, and he calls back Petrus to sleep with her. Bruno seizes a gun and bangs on the door, but when the two emerge, he will not believe that he has been cuckolded. Stella is now the local centre of male attention, but in the third act Bruno, disguised, climbs a ladder to her bedroom. Even this does not convince him, since he suspects she has recognised him, but when the oxherd offers her his protection against the hostile women of the village and her husband, she gives herself to him. As they go off together, Bruno still suspects that this is a trick: he will not be caught by it.

Goldschmidt's opera began successfully in Mannheim, but further performances planned for Berlin were prevented by political events in Germany and the work thereafter remained unperformed until a concert revival in Berlin in 1992. The composer was a pupil of Franz Schreker, an important figure in the world of opera at the time, but, while the subject may suggest contemporary preoccupations, possibly reflecting wider social and racial problems, the general style of composition calls for something rather less exotic than Schreker's, effectively written in an idiom that avoided the serial and atonal techniques of other contemporaries.

Gezeichneten, Die (The Marked Ones)

- Franz Schreker. Opera in three acts. 1915.
- Libretto by the composer.
- First performance in Frankfurt on 25th April 1918.

Characters

Antoniotto Adorno, Duke of Genoa	bass
Count Vitelozzo Tamare	baritone
Lodovico Nardi, Podestà of Genoa	bass
Carlotta Nardi, his daughter	mezzo-soprano
Alviano Salvago, a crippled young nobleman	tenor
Genoese nobles	two tenors, two baritones & two basses
Capitaneo di Giustizia (Captain of Justice)	bass
Three Senators	tenor, baritone & bass

Alviano Salvago establishes on his island of Elysium an erotic paradise, thinking thereby to overcome his own ugliness. He kills a number of girls, before attempting to give the island to the city of Genoa. The daughter of the mayor, Carlotta, an artist, is the object of his attentions and when it seems that she has been raped, as other girls had been, Alviano is accused, but leads the people to a cave where Carlotta is dying in the arms of her true lover, Vitelozzo Tamare, now stabbed to death by Alviano.

Die Gezeichneten (The Marked Ones) was written at the request of Alexander Zemlinsky, whose own ugliness had once been a subject of conversation between Mahler and his future wife Alma, Zemlinsky's pupil. Schreker's score is masterly in its sensuality, colour and often delicacy of nuance in an opera that marks the summit of his career.

Recommended Recording: Die Gezeichneten (3 CDs) ***Marco Polo 8.223328-30***

Gianni Schicchi

- Giacomo Puccini. Opera in one act. 1918.
- Libretto by Giovacchino Forzano, after an episode in Dante's *Inferno*.
- First performance at the Metropolitan Opera House, New York, on 14th December 1918.

CHARACTERS

Gianni Schicchi, aged 50	baritone
Lauretta, his daughter, aged 21	soprano
Zita (La Vecchia), aged 60, cousin of Buoso Donati	contralto
Rinuccio, aged 24, her nephew	tenor
Gherardo, aged 40, Buoso Donati's nephew	tenor
Nella, aged 34, his wife	soprano
Gherardino, aged 7, their son	alto
Betto di Signa, of uncertain age, Buoso Donati's brother-in-law	bass
Simone, aged 70, Buoso Donati's cousin	bass
Marco, aged 45, his son	baritone
La Ciesca, aged 38, Marco's wife	mezzo-soprano
Maestro Spinelloccio, doctor	bass
Ser Amantio di Nicolao, lawyer	baritone
Pinellino, cobbler	bass
Guccio, painter	bass

Buoso Donati's relations are anxious about the property he may have left them in his will, which they search for and find, revealing that, as they had feared, Buoso Donati had left everything to a monastery. Rinuccio, who hopes to marry Lauretta, daughter of Gianni Schicchi, suggests that the latter should be called, for whatever help he can give. After due consideration, he proposes taking the place of the dead man, convincing the doctor, speaking from behind the bed-curtains, and a lawyer, who draws up a new will, making smaller bequests to the family, but leaving the major properties to himself, threatening the family with legal penalties if they reveal anything, since they have all been party to the fraud. Rinuccio is now free to marry Lauretta.

Best known of all excerpts from *Gianni Schicchi* is Lauretta's plea to her father for help, *O mio babbino caro* (O dear father), too often taken completely out of its satirical context. *Gianni Schicchi* forms part of the trilogy *Il trittico* (The Triptych), with *Suor Angelica* (Sister Angelica) and *Il tabarro* (The Cloak).

Recommended Recordings:

O mio babbino caro	***Naxos 8.550605***
Firenze è come un albero fiorito	***Naxos 8.554065***

GIASONE (JASON)

- Francesco Cavalli. *Drama musicale* in a prologue and three acts. 1648.
- Libretto by Giacinto Andrea Cicognini, after the *Argonautica* of Apollonius Rhodius.
- First performance at the Teatro S Cassiano, Venice, on 5th January 1649.

CHARACTERS

Apollo	soprano
Amore (Cupid)	soprano
Giasone (Jason)	male alto
Medea, Queen of Colchis	soprano
Delfa, her nurse	male alto
Ercole (Hercules), an Argonaut	bass
Besso, Captain of Jason's Guard	bass
Rosmina, a garden-girl	soprano
Egeo, (Aegeus), King of Athens	tenor
Demo, his servant, a hunchback	tenor
Isifile (Hypsipyle), Queen of Lemnos	soprano
Oreste (Orestes), her confidant	bass
Volàno, a spirit	tenor
Alinda, her lady-in-waiting	soprano

As in a number of other operas of the period, the prologue shows gods in dispute. Here Apollo favours Medea and Cupid her rival, Hypsipyle, in their liaisons with Jason. It is evident that Jason and his crew, the Argonauts, have spent a considerable time in Colchis in their quest for the Golden Fleece, since he has already fathered twins on Medea, but is unaware of her identity. He promises to marry her. Jason's wife, and mother of twins, Hypsipyle, comes in search of him, resolving, once she knows of his infidelity, to kill her rival, while Medea uses her magic powers to help Jason. He, successful in seizing the Golden Fleece, sets sail with Medea for Corinth, followed by Aegeus, Medea's unsuccessful suitor, and his stuttering comic servant Demo. Hypsipyle eventually finds Jason and reproaches him, but he disowns her, as deluded. He later gives orders to his Captain, Besso, to have her killed, telling her, as a password, to ask if his orders have been carried out. Medea, checking on the planned death of her rival, seeks out Besso and asks the same question, with results immediately fatal, had not Aegeus appeared to save her. Jason is saved from death at the hands of Aegeus by the intervention of Hypsipyle and when Medea re-appears, now miraculously saved, a happy ending is possible, with Jason and Hypsipyle again united, and Medea now happy to accept the attentions of Aegeus.

Giasone, with its mixture of comedy and more serious elements, enjoyed the widest popularity. The mixture had become a part of the genre, as in Monteverdi's *L'incoronazion di Poppea* in 1643. Its separation of aria and recitative marks a new stage in operatic development, a change from the earlier practice of *arioso*, the use of recitative with passages of more melodic appeal, as words and drama dictated. Now narrative and action made use of recitative, while arias allowed reflection on what had happened or revelations of feelings of a character. The plot used is very different from that of the play by Euripides, the basis of other operas, which ends in spectacular murder and tragedy.

GIOCONDA, LA

- Amilcare Ponchielli. *Dramma lirico* in four acts. 1876.
- Libretto by Arrigo Boito (disguised under the anagram of Tobia Gorrio), after Victor Hugo's play *Angélo, tyran de Padoue* (Angelo, Tyrant of Padua).
- First performance at the Teatro alla Scala, Milan, on 8th April 1876.

CHARACTERS

La Gioconda, a singer	soprano
La Cieca, her blind mother	contralto
Enzo Grimaldo, a Genoese prince	tenor
Alvise Badoero, a head of the State Inquisition	bass
Laura Adorno, his wife	mezzo-soprano
Barnaba, ballad-singer and spy of the Inquisition	baritone
Zuàne, a gondolier	bass
Isèpo, a public scrivener	tenor
Pilot	bass

In 17th century Venice it is Carnival. The spy Barnaba tries to force his attentions on the singer La Gioconda, whose blind mother, through Barnaba, is now popularly suspected of witchcraft. Alvise and his wife Laura intervene, the latter convincing her husband of La Cieca's innocence, to receive a rosary from the grateful woman. Gioconda is betrothed to Enzo, disguised as a sailor, but recognised by Barnaba as a proscribed prince of Genoa and Laura's former suitor. Enzo's love for Laura is now renewed, to the dismay of Gioconda, who overhears a plot between Enzo and Barnaba, the latter having offered to arrange a meeting for Enzo with Laura. In the second act Laura is re-united with Enzo, by night on his ship, but their meeting, arranged by Barnaba, is interrupted by Gioconda. Her anger is inevitably mollified when she sees the rosary her mother had given Laura and helps her rival to escape, when Alvise, warned by Barnaba, approaches the vessel. Enzo, spurning Gioconda once more, sets the ship on fire and leaps into the sea. In his palace Alvise plots revenge, giving Laura a phial of poison, to be drunk before the end of a gondolier's song that can be heard from the lagoon. Gioconda, coming to her aid, substitutes for the poison a narcotic that will simulate death. Guests to the palace are entertained by the Dance of the Hours. Barnaba appears, dragging in La Cieca, who warns of impending death. Alvise reveals Laura's body, telling his guests what he has done, and Enzo, who has entered secretly, rushes at him. The fourth act, on the Giudecca, finds Gioconda, with the drugged Laura, but planning her own death, having gained Enzo's release by promising to yield to Barnaba. Enzo and Laura make their escape together, while Gioconda, facing Barnaba, stabs herself, dying before she can hear Barnaba's claim that he has drowned her mother.

Ponchielli undertook various revisions to his grand opera in the years immediately following its first staging. The work, continuing in international repertoire, makes heavy demands for its staging. The third act ballet, the *Dance of the Hours*, is very familiar, with Enzo's ecstatic aria *Cielo e mar* (Heaven and sea), as he waits on his ship for the appearance of Laura. Gioconda's fourth act dilemma, *Suicidio . . . in questi fieri momenti tu sol mi resti* (Suicide . . in these cruel moments you alone remain for me) provides a moment of tense drama, as does the first act recognition scene between Barnaba and Enzo, *Enzo Grimaldo, Principe di Santafior, che pensi?* (Enzo Grimaldo, Prince of Santafior, what are you thinking?).

Recommended Recordings:

Cielo e mar	***Naxos 8.550497***
Dance of the Hours	***Naxos 8.550081***
Enzo Grimaldi, Principe di Santafior	***Naxos 8.550684***

Gioielli della Madonna, I (The Jewels of the Madonna)

- Ermanno Wolf-Ferrari. Opera in three acts. 1911.
- Libretto by Carlo Zangarini and Enrico Golisciani.
- First performance as *Der Schmuck der Madonna* at the Kurfürstenoper, Berlin, on 23rd December 1911.

In Naples the leader of the Camorrists, a criminal gang, Rafaele, forces his attentions on Maliella, adopted daughter of Carmela, threatening even to rob the statue of the Madonna of jewels for her. Gennaro, son of Carmela, warns her about Rafaele, who serenades her by night. Gennaro, a blacksmith by trade, then takes his own secret keys and steals the jewels of the Madonna for Maliella. In the garden where she had heard Rafaele, she gives herself now to Gennaro. In the third act, at the meeting-place of the Camorrists, Rafaele claims that the attraction of Maliella lies in her virginity. Maliella now appears, to be rejected by Rafaele. Followed by Gennaro, she now resolves to drown herself, and Gennaro plunges a dagger into his own heart.

Wolf-Ferrari abandons, in *I gioielli della Madonna* (The Jewels of the Madonna), his usual vein of comic opera for tragic realism, not entirely successfully. The *Intermezzo* from the second act may be heard in the concert-hall, as may, more rarely, the baritone Rafaele's Serenade, *Aprila, o bella, la fenestrella* (Open, fair one, the window), in the same act.

Recommended Recording: Intermezzos — ***Naxos 8.550240***

Giorno di regno, Un (King for a Day)

- Giuseppe Verdi. *Melodramma giocoso* in two acts. 1840.
- Libretto by Felice Romani, perhaps revised by Temistocle Solera, based on the play *Le faux Stanislas* (The False Stanislas) by Alexandre Vincent Pineu-Duval.
- First performance at the Teatro alla Scala, Milan, on 5th September 1840.

The first comic opera by Verdi, and the last for many years, *Un giorno di regno* (King for a Day), with the alternative title *Il finto Stanislao* (The False Stanislas), a failure at its first performance, for whatever reasons, deals with the actions of the French officer, the Cavalier di Belfiore, who takes the place of the claimant to the throne of Poland, Stanislas Leszczynski, in order to cover the latter's secret return to his own country. The intrigue involves the frustration of the proposed marriages of the niece and the daughter of the Baron di Kelbar by the supposed King, who re-arranges matters to his own satisfaction and that of Eduardo di Sanval, the young suitor of the Baron's daughter, Giulietta, who is in love with him.

The overture to the opera may be heard occasionally in the concert-hall, as may the aria of the tenor Eduardo, *Pietoso al lungo pianto* (Pitying my long complaining).

Giovanna d'Arco (Joan of Arc)

- Giuseppe Verdi. *Dramma lirico* in a prologue and three acts. 1845.
- Libretto by Temistocle Solera, after Friedrich von Schiller's *Die Jungfrau von Orleans* (The Maid of Orleans).
- First performance at the Teatro alla Scala, Milan, on 15th February 1845.

Characters

Carlo VII (Charles VII), King of France	tenor
Giacomo, a shepherd in Dom-Rémy	baritone
Giovanna (Joan), his daughter	soprano
Delil, an officer of the King	tenor
Talbot, commander of the English army	bass

The year is 1429 and France is suffering the depredations of foreign forces. The King laments the state of his country but dreams that he is told to lay his arms before the Madonna, as he rests under an oak-tree. Giacomo is anxious that his daughter may be under the power of the devil and as she sleeps devils and angels rival each other, seeking her loyalty. Waking, she joins the King, claiming herself now ready for the battle. In the first act Giacomo offers to betray his daughter to the now defeated English, while Joan, still tempted by devils, can now join in a duet of love with the King. Their victory is celebrated in the second act, where she is denounced by Giacomo. In the third act, as the French army seems about to be defeated, Giacomo realises that he has been wrong. Joan comes to the aid of the King, who is now victorious. She, however, has been mortally wounded and dies, reconciled to her father and ready for the Heaven that awaits her.

Verdi's opera starts with a three movement overture. Essentially unhistorical in its plot, it has provided tenors, in the rôle of the King, with *Sotto una quercia* (Under an oak-tree), as he tells of his mysterious dream, and Joan herself with a memory of her pastoral childhood in *O fatidica foresta* (O prophetic forest).

Giuditta (Judith)

- Franz Lehár. *Musikalische Komödie* in five scenes. 1934.
- Libretto by Paul Knepler and Fritz Löhner.
- First performance at the Staatsoper, Vienna, on 20th January 1934.

Judith, married to Manuele, flirts with the army officer Octavio, with whom she elopes to North Africa. When Octavio's regiment moves, she works as a night-club dancer, but is sought out by Octavio again, after he has deserted from the army, but she is beyond his reach. In later years she has achieved success but he has worked as a night-club pianist and is now broken, in spite of their love.

More serious in intention than many of Lehár's stage works, *Giuditta* provided a leading rôle for Richard Tauber in Octavio. Well known songs from the musical comedy include the tenor *Freunde, das leben ist lebenswert* (Friends, life is worth living) and the later *Welch tiefes Rätsel ist die Leben* (What a deep puzzle love is) and *Du bist meine Sonne* (You are my sun), while Giuditta must be content with the loving *Meine Lippen, sie küssen so heiss* (My lips, they kiss so hotly). Fritz Kreisler arranged his violin *Serenade* from a melody taken from *Giuditta*.

Recommended Recording: Freunde, das Leben / Meine Lippen ***Naxos 8.550941***

Giulio Cesare in Egitto (Julius Caesar in Egypt)

- George Frideric Handel. Opera in three acts. 1724.
- Libretto by Nicola Francesco Haym, after an earlier libretto by Giacomo Francesco Bussani.
- First performance at the King's Theatre, London, on 20th February 1724.

Characters

Giulio Cesare (Julius Caesar)	male alto
Cleopatra, Queen of Egypt	soprano
Tolomeo (Ptolemy), her brother, King of Egypt	male alto
Achilla (Achillas), a general, his counsellor	bass
Nireno (Nirenus), confidant of Cleopatra & Ptolemy	male alto
Curio, a Roman tribune	bass
Cornelia, widow of Pompey	contralto
Sesto (Sextus), son of Pompey	soprano

Caesar, in pursuit of Pompey, lands in Egypt, where Pompey's wife, Cornelia, and her son Sextus beg for reconciliation. Ptolemy greets him with the present of Pompey's head, an unwelcome gift. Cornelia is prevented from suicide by her would-be lover Curio and Sextus threatens vengeance. Cleopatra, meanwhile, plots to use Caesar in order to displace her brother Ptolemy. Achillas offers to kill Caesar and make Ptolemy king, if he may have Cornelia as a reward. Cleopatra disguises herself as one injured by Ptolemy and seeks Caesar's interest, while Cornelia and her son are taken prisoner by Ptolemy. Caesar and Cleopatra eventually come together, her identity now revealed, while Ptolemy presses his attentions on Cornelia. Caesar escapes, to avoid a planned attempt on his life. Cleopatra is taken prisoner by Ptolemy but Caesar, returning, promises to rescue both her and Cornelia, with the help of Sextus, who, in an assault on Ptolemy's palace, kills the despot. Caesar now allows Cleopatra the crown of Egypt, as queen and tributary of the Roman Empire.

Handel's very successful opera presents the usual difficulties of works of this period for modern performance, cast as it was for three castrato singers. Later revisions transformed Nirenus into Nirena, a handmaid for Cleopatra, and cast Sextus as a tenor. The title rôle has provided a moving part for mezzo-soprano in a work that has the expected disregard for historical accuracy. The best known arias from the opera are *V'adoro, pupille* (I adore you), as Cleopatra, in the guise of a goddess, prepares to entertain Caesar, and the moving *Piangerò, la sorte mia* (I shall weep my lot), as she laments her defeat by Ptolemy. Caesar has his own moment of desolation when he returns to the shores of Egypt, after his escape from Ptolemy, with *Aure, deh, per pietà* (In mercy, ah, breezes). All this is in a richly orchestrated score.

Giustino (Justin)

- George Frideric Handel. Opera in three acts. 1736.
- Libretto anonymously based on earlier libretti by Pietro Pariati and by Nicolò Beregan.
- First performance at Covent Garden Theatre, London, on 16th February 1737.

Set in the 6th century near what was then Constantinople, *Giustino* deals with the part played by Justin in suppressing the rebellion against the Emperor Anastasius led by Vitalian, later reconciled with Justin, who turns out to be his brother. An eventful libretto allows the widowed Empress, Ariadne, now wife of Anastasius, to be rescued from a sea-monster and Leocasta, sister of Anastasius, to be saved from the clutches of a bear. Ghosts help the progress of the story when a mountain opens and the voice of the father of Justin and Vitalian is heard, revealing their relationship.

Giustino has obvious elements of spectacle, designed to appeal to an audience. The rôles of Anastasius and Justin were designed for castrato soprano and alto respectively, and the latter's *Chi mi chiama alla gloria?* (Who summons me to glory?) provides a substantial challenge.

Gloriana

- Benjamin Britten. Opera in three acts. 1953.
- Libretto by William Plomer.
- First performance at Covent Garden, London, on 8th June 1953.

The Earl of Essex, favourite of Queen Elizabeth I of England, who is disturbed by the enmity of Lord Mountjoy and Essex, is first seen in a duel with his enemy in the opening scene. Essex begs to be sent to Ireland to put down the rebellion there but the Queen demurs. She visits Norwich and is entertained with a masque, while Essex expresses his continued impatience. His sister, Lady Penelope Rich, is in love with Mountjoy, while Essex himself complains to his wife of the Queen's unwillingness to agree at once to his demands. At a ball Lady Essex is humiliated by the Queen, who, when the ladies withdraw to change, takes her elaborate dress, worn as an intended challenge to the Queen at the insistence of Essex, and wears it herself. He is now given his wish and appointed Lord Deputy in Ireland. There he fails and returns, bursting into the Queen's dressing-room, and now makes further trouble in England. An attempted rebellion fails and he is condemned to death, in spite of the pleas of his wife and sister, leaving the Queen to prepare herself for her own lonely death.

Commissioned by the Royal Opera House, Covent Garden, to celebrate the coronation of Queen Elizabeth II in 1953, *Gloriana*, the name by which her homonymous predecessor was known to her courtier-poets, was not immediately successful at its official opening performance before an audience described by one distinguished member of the cast as 'cold fish', many of whom might rather have warmed to a less demanding *Merrie England*. The *Choral Dances* of the second act are performed sometimes out of their dramatic context, a score that combines the contemporary with allusions to the music of an earlier period and includes lute-songs for Essex and dances of the Elizabethan period in the ball scene. The rôles of Essex and Queen Elizabeth were written for Peter Pears and Joan Cross, the original Peter Grimes and Ellen Orford in the opera that established English opera in post-war Britain, *Peter Grimes*.

Glückliche Hand, Die (The Fortunate Hand)

- Arnold Schoenberg. Drama with music, in once act. 1913.
- Libretto by the composer.
- First performance at the Volksoper, Vienna, on 14th October 1924.

The protagonist, a baritone, lies on the ground with a monster on his back, observed by a chorus of twelve, their faces seen from behind the back-cloth. A young woman passes, rejecting him and turning to a well dressed gentleman. Heroically he is seen in a rocky landscape where, to the anger of workmen in a cave, he makes and throws aside a crown. The woman appears again, part of her dress torn, followed by the gentleman, who throws it to the man. The woman picks it up and leaving again, kicks a rock down onto the man. This changes into the monster, leaving the man in his original sorry state.

Schoenberg's short theatre-piece creates a new kind of *Gesamtkunstwerk*, where lighting and stage effect are of symbolic importance. The man's rejection may reflect the rejection of Schoenberg's music at this time and his desertion by his wife.

- Nikolay Andreyevich Rimsky-Korsakov. Dramatized fable in a prologue, three acts and an epilogue. 1907.
- Libretto by Vladimir Nikolayevich Bel'sky, based on Pushkin's *The House of the Weathercock*.
- First performance by the Zimin Opera Company at the Solodovnikov Theatre, Moscow, on 7th October 1909.

CHARACTERS

King Dodon	bass
Prince Guidon, his son	tenor
Prince Afron, another son	baritone
General Polkan	bass
Amelfa, royal housekeeper	contralto
Astrologer	tenore-altino
Queen of Shemakha	soprano
Golden Cockerel	soprano

The Astrologer offers a cautionary tale. Tired of war, King Dodon asks his sons for advice. Guidon advises withdrawal to the capital, which General Polkan points out cannot easily be defended, while Afron recommends calling up the army only a month before any attack. The General again points out the obvious disadvantages of this plan. The Astrologer brings in a Golden Cockerel that will warn of any impending danger, demanding the necessary reward in due course. The housekeeper brings in the King's bed and a parrot that apparently praises the King. The Cockerel raises the alarm and King Dodon's sons are despatched to lead two armies, a further alarm forcing a reluctant King to don his armour. In the mountains he finds his sons dead, their armies having fought each other to the death. The Queen of Shemakha emerges from a tent, singing her *Hymn to the Sun*, set on enslaving the King by her charms, which she does. The King, at her request, orders General Polkan to be banished, in fact beheaded, and the couple are now to rule together. They return to a royal wedding procession, but the festivities are interrupted by the Astrologer, who seeks his promised reward, demanding now the Queen. King Dodon strikes him down and kills him, but the Queen now repulses him. The Cockerel pecks the King on the head and kills him, and Cockerel and Queen disappear. In an epilogue the Astrologer assures the audience that only he and the Queen were real people, the other characters merely dreams.

Rimsky-Korsakov's opera was politically inopportune and was prevented from immediate performance by the Russian censors. The satire of the piece, coming after the Russo-Japanese War and after the disturbances of 1905 in which the composer had become involved by siding with the students, seemed too accurate for comfort. Satire lies not only in the story itself but also in the music, with its allusive use of popular songs, and in what appears to be a stroke aimed at contemporary folklorists. The best known excerpt from the score must be the famous *Hymn to the Sun*, particularly in its arrangement by the violinist Fritz Kreisler. A series of orchestral excerpts provides a picture of King Dodon in his palace, on the battlefield, with the Queen and at the scene of his wedding festivities and death.

Recommended Recording: The Golden Cockerel (Suite) ***Naxos 8.550486***

GOLEM

- John Casken. Opera in two parts. 1989.
- Libretto by the composer with Pierre Audi.
- First performance at the Almeida Theatre, London, on 28th June 1989.

In a Prelude and Legend, the opera allows the Maharal to recall his earlier creation of a Golem, a saviour symbol of Jewish legend, his rejection of the noble plans of Ometh for the betterment of the world and the Golem's desire for the wife of the Maharal, his opposition to popular desire for release from oppression and his murder of the bereaved Stoikus, under provocation. The work uses ten players and a tape and involves, in the Prelude a madrigal group, formed by the principal singers.

GONDOLIERS, THE

- Arthur Sullivan. Operetta in two acts. 1889.
- Libretto by W.S.Gilbert.
- First performance at the Savoy Theatre, London, on 7th December 1889.

The heir to the throne of Barataria, stolen as a baby and entrusted, it is supposed, to a Venetian gondolier, is now sought, but cannot be identified, since the adoptive father has another son. Both boys leave their wives, to rule jointly, proclaiming equality in their kingdom. The arrival of the Duke and Duchess of Plaza-Toro adds complications, since the ruler is to marry their daughter. She, however, loves a servant, Luiz, who turns out to be the rightful heir to the throne, after his nurse had substituted her own baby for him, giving her own child to the gondolier.

Various excerpts from *The Gondoliers* have won independent popularity, but none more than the tenor *Take a pair of sparkling eyes.*

Recommended Recording: Overture ***Naxos 8.554165***

GÖTTERDÄMMERUNG (THE TWILIGHT OF THE GODS)

- Richard Wagner. Music-drama in a prologue and three acts. Fourth opera of the tetralogy *Der Ring des Nibelungen* (The Ring of the Nibelungen). 1874.
- Libretto by the composer.
- First performance at the Festspielhaus, Bayreuth, on 17th August 1876.

CHARACTERS

Siegfried, the Volsung	tenor
Gunther, the Gibichung	bass-baritone
Gutrune, his sister	soprano
Hagen, his half-brother, son of Alberich	bass
Brünnhilde, daughter of Wotan	soprano
Alberich, a Nibelung	bass-baritone
Waltraute, a Valkyrie	mezzo-soprano
Woglinde, a Rhinemaiden	soprano
Wellgunde, her sister	mezzo-soprano
Flosshilde, another sister	contralto
Three Norns, daughters of the Goddess of Fate	contralto, mezzo-soprano & soprano

On the rock of Brünnhilde the three Norns weave fate, singing of the holy ash-tree, from which a brave god made a spear, broken by a young hero and chopped into logs at the command of Wotan, to be piled around Valhalla, where they will burn the place and bring an end to the gods. As dawn breaks Siegfried emerges from the cave with Brünnhilde, having acquired from her her strength as a Valkyrie. As he prepares to leave, he gives her his ring, a symbol of his deeds, and she gives him Grane, her horse. The first act opens in the Gibichung throne-room, where Hagen urges his half-brother Gunther to marry Brünnhilde, although she is fated to be the wife of Siegfried the Volsung, who could, by trickery, be induced to marry their sister, Gutrune. Siegfried arrives and swears friendship with Hagen. Drugged by Gutrune, he offers her marriage and then agrees, using the Tarncap which will transform him, to bring Gunther the woman he wants, in exchange for Gutrune.

They swear friendship and join together ritually as blood brothers. Siegfried and Gunther leave, in search of Brünnhilde, while Hagen guards the house, awaiting their return, with the ring. Waltraute brings Brünnhilde news of Wotan's despair, in the absence of the ring, but she refuses to part with Siegfried's pledge of love. Siegfried, in the form of Gunther, leaps through the surrounding flames to claim Brünnhilde as his wife, seizing the ring from her finger. At the hall of the Gibichungs Alberich reminds Hagen of Siegfried's defeat of Wotan and of the power that the ring will give them. Siegfried returns to claim Gutrune and Hagen calls his men to attend the coming wedding. Gunther and Brünnhilde arrive and the latter, seeing the ring on Siegfried's finger, realises that there has been trickery. She curses Siegfried and tells Hagen that the hero can be wounded only from the back, a death that can be arranged at a hunting-party. The Rhinemaidens ask Siegfried for the ring and as the hunters rest, Hagen gives Siegfried a drink that revives his memory, piercing his back with his spear and mortally wounding him. Siegfried's body is brought back, to Gutrune's distress. Gunther and Hagen fight and the former is killed, but the ring cannot be taken from Siegfried's body. Brünnhilde now orders a pyre to be raised. This is lit, and she rides into it on her horse, Grane, wearing the ring, which will return, on her death, to the Rhinemaidens, who drag Hagen down to the depths of the river. Now flames are seen as Valhalla, the home of the gods, finally burns.

The last opera of *The Ring* cycle, *Götterdämmerung* is a work of sufficient substance to provide a conclusion. Wagner uses leit-motifs, themes or fragments of themes identified with particular characters, events or ideas, drawing on the material of the earlier dramas of the cycle. The closely woven texture of a work that is through-composed, with continuous music, makes the extraction of excerpts difficult. Nevertheless orchestral elements from the score that may appear in concert programmes include the music for *Dawn*, *Siegfried's Rhine Journey*, as he goes to meet Hagen, and his *Funeral March*. Vocal excerpts must include Brünnhilde's *Zu neuen Taten* (To new deeds), as she sends Siegfried on his way, and the Rhinemaiden Waltraute's Narrative, *Höre mit Sinn* (Hear and understand). More extended excerpts might include Brünnhilde's immolation and the closing part of the work.

Recommended Recordings:

Siegfried's Rhine Journey, Death & Funeral March	***Naxos 8.550211***
Immolation of the Gods	***Naxos 8.550498***

GOYESCAS

- Enrique Granados. Opera in one act. 1915.
- Libretto by Fernando Periquet.
- First performance at the Metropolitan Opera, New York, on 28th January 1916.

For his opera *Goyescas* Granados made use of his successful piano suite of the same title. Inspired by the work of the painter Francisco Goya, *Goyescas* is thoroughly Spanish in its story and musical content, treating the love-story of the bull-fighter Paquiro and his girl Pepa and of the aristocratic Rosario and her captain, Fernando.

The *Intermezzo* from *Goyescas* has enjoyed an independent concert existence, with Rosario's attractive *La maja y el ruiseñol* (The Girl and the Nightingale).

GRAF VON LUXEMBURG, DER (THE COUNT OF LUXEMBURG)

- Franz Lehár. *Operette* in three acts. 1909.
- Libretto by A.M.Willner and Robert Bodanzky.
- First performance at the Theater an der Wien, Vienna, on 12th November 1909.

The impoverished Count of the title, René, is induced to marry the singer Angèle Didier as a temporary expedient, promising not to see her but to allow speedy divorce and remarriage to a Russian nobleman, who needs the title for his proposed wife. In the event René sees Angèle, without knowing who she is, and falls in love, while the Russian Prince Basil is safely matched with a former mistress, the Countess Kokozow.

In *Mein Ahnherr war der Luxemburg* (My forebear was the Count of Luxemburg) Count René sings of the extravagance of his father. The operetta follows the very successful *Die lustige Witwe* (The Merry Widow), with a story set in Paris that also involves an arranged marriage.

Recommended Recording: Mein Ahnherr war der Luxemburg — ***Naxos 8.550942***

GRÄFIN MARIZA (COUNTESS MARITSA)

- Emmerich Kálmán. Operetta in three acts. 1924.
- Libretto by Julius Brammer and Alfred Grünwald.
- First performance at the Theater an der Wien, Vienna, on 28th February 1924.

An impoverished nobleman, Count Tassilo, takes service under Countess Maritsa, who has attempted to deter suitors by celebrating her engagement to a supposedly fictititous Baron Koloman Zsupán, a character from Johann Strauss's operetta *Der Zigeunerbaron* (The Gypsy Baron). Difficulites occur when an uncouth Zsupán actually appears to claim his future bride. A happy ending is secured when a generous aunt restores Count Tassilo's fortunes and, his identity now revealed, he can marry the Countess.

In addition to the overture, popular numbers from *Gräfin Mariza* (Countess Maritsa) include Zsupán's *Komm mit nach Varasdin* (Come with me to Varasdin), an unlikely invitation to the Countess, whose entrance song, *Heia, heia*, sets the Hungarian mood of the work. Tassilo summons the gypsy musicians at Countess Maritsa's false engagement party, *Komm Zigány* (Come, gypsy) and in *Grüss mir die süssen* (Greet for me the sweet ladies) he regrets his earlier carefree life in the city.

Recommended Recordings:

Grüss mir / Komm Zigány	***Naxos 8.550943***
Komm mit nach Varasdin	***Naxos 8.550941***

Grand Macabre, Le (The Grand Macabre)

- György Ligeti. Opera in two acts. 1977.
- Libretto by the composer and Michael Meschke, after the play *La balade du Grand Macabre* (The Ballad of the Grand Macabre) by Michel de Ghelderode.
- First performance, in a Swedish version, at the Royal Opera, Stockholm, on 12th April 1978.

Set in an imaginary Breughelland, a country derived from Breughel's paintings, the opera, introduced by a motor-horn prelude, shows a drunken common man, Piet the Pot, and the sinister Grand Macabre, Nekrotzar, who appears to announce the coming end of the world to two lovers, Amanda and Amando, in the first scene. In an embrace he kills Mescalin, who has desired a more energetic sexual partner than her astrologer husband, and accompanies him and Piet to the palace of the young Prince Go-Go, scene of conflicting politicians. Here Nekrotzar himself dies, leaving the other players in the drama seemingly alive.

Ligeti's score is allusive, using music derived from Monteverdi, Verdi and Rossini for the lovers and the Eroica skeleton Prometheus theme in the second act in the palace.

Greek Passion, The

- Bohuslav Martinů. Opera in four acts. 1959.
- Libretto by the composer, based on *Christ Recrucified* by Nikos Kazantzakis, in an English translation by Jonathan Griffin.
- First performance at the Stadttheater, Zürich, on 9th June 1961.

In a Greek village preparations are made for the Passion play to be staged the following year. Refugees arrive, but are advised to settle outside the village. The actors take on the characteristics of the parts they are to play, the shepherd Manolios as Christ, the pedlar Yannakos as St Peter and Katerina as St Mary Magdalene. The village elders plot against Manolios, who has preached charity to the refugees and he is excommunicated by the priest. In open conflict he is killed by Panais, cast as Judas.

Griselda

- Alessandro Scarlatti. *Dramma per musica* in three acts. 1720.
- Libretto after Apostolo Zeno, perhaps by Prince Francesco Maria Ruspoli.
- First performance at the Teatro Capranica, Rome, in January 1721.

Griselda is a woman whose patience is celebrated by Boccaccio in the *Decamerone* and by Chaucer in *The Canterbury Tales*, where the story is told by the Clerk of Oxenford. In a series of cruel tests, her royal husband tries her fidelity, to understand her worthiness as queen. Zeno's libretto was originally set by Antonio Maria Bononcini in 1718 and by his more distinguished brother Giovanni for London in 1722. Vivaldi turned to the same libretto, revised by Carlo Goldoni, in 1735.

Grisélidis

- Jules Massenet. *Conte lyrique* in a prologue and three acts. 1901.
- Libretto by Armand Sylvestre and Eugène Morand.
- First performance by the Paris Opéra-Comique at the Salle Favart on 20th November 1901.

Leaving for the crusades, the Marquis de Saluces accepts the wager offered by the Devil on the fidelity of his wife Grisélidis. Tempted by the Devil in various guises, Grisélidis resists, endures trials with relative patience and is finally re-united with her husband.

Massenet's fairy-tale opera provides a varied bass rôle for the Devil, who appears as a Levantine slave-trader and as an old man, as well as in his own person.

Guglielmo Ratcliff (*William Ratcliff*)

- Pietro Mascagni. *Tragedia* in four scenes. 1894.
- Libretto based on an Italian translation of Heinrich Heine's novel *William Ratcliff* by Andrea Maffei.
- First performance at the Teatro alla Scala, Milan, on 16th February 1895.

In the MacGregor castle, the laird's daughter Mary is betrothed to Douglas, the object of Ratcliff's murderous intentions, having killed two earlier suitors in duels. Mary's nurse tells of the love of her mother for Ratcliff's father, killed in jealousy by MacGregor. The tragedy ends as Ratcliff, in madness, kills Mary, her father and himself.

Guglielmo Ratcliff has enjoyed little success in the theatre, where its exotic setting in Scotland, ghosts, madness and murders now seemed out of date, sixty years after Donizetti's operatic excursion to Scotland in *Lucia di Lammermor* and particularly after the relative realism of Mascagni's own *Cavalleria rusticana* (Rustic Chivalry).

Recommended Recording: Ratcliff's Dream — ***Naxos 8.550240***

Guillaume Tell

- Gioachino Rossini. *Opéra* in four acts. 1829.
- Libretto by Etienne de Jouy and Hippolyte-Louis-Florent Bis, with Armand Marrast and Adolphe Crémieux, based on the play by Friedrich von Schiller.
- First performance at the Paris Opéra on 3rd August 1829.

Characters

Guillaume Tell (William Tell)	baritone
Hedwige, his wife	mezzo-soprano
Jemmy, his son	soprano
Arnold Melcthal, a Swiss conspirator	tenor
Walter Furst, a Swiss conspirator	bass
Mathilde, a Habsburg Princess	soprano
Melcthal, father of Arnold	bass
Gesler, governor of Schwyz and Uri	bass
Rodolphe, commander of Gesler's archers	tenor

Leuthold, a herdsman	baritone
Ruodi, a fisherman	tenor
Huntsman	baritone

Austrian domination of Switzerland has brought resistance. Arnold Melcthal, however, has served in the Austrian army and is in love with the Habsburg Princess Mathilde. Tell saves the herdsman Leuthold from the pursuing Austrians, who take old Melcthal hostage. With Walter Furst he tries to persuade Arnold to join the resistance against the Austrians and supporters gather to swear loyalty to their cause. The killing of Melcthal forces Arnold to part from Mathilde. The governor Gesler forces celebration of a hundred years of Austrian rule and Tell, recognised as the one who helped Leuthold, is arrested, with his son, before he can carry a message urging immediate revolt. Tell is forced to shoot an apple off his son's head, which he does. With William Tell now imprisoned, Arnold takes on the leadership of the revolt, and Jemmy, released into Mathilde's care, gives the signal for the rising. Tell returns, to shoot Gesler and to celebrate with the others the freedom of his country.

Rossini's last opera, written for the Paris Opéra, makes great demands on performers, notably the high tenor rôle of Arnold Melcthal, and, with its relative length, on audiences. It opens with an overture in four movements, setting the pastoral Swiss scene with five solo cellos and proceeding to a storm, a traditional herdsman's call, the *ranz des vaches*, a trumpet-call and a rapid summons to Swiss patriots that has become all too familiar in other hippodromic contexts. The first demand made on Arnold is his address to Mathilde, the demanding *Ah! Mathilde, idole de mon âme* (Ah! Mathilde, idol of my soul). She sings of her love for him in the second act, with *Sombre forêt* (Dark forest). William Tell has a tense and moving aria as he prepares to shoot the apple from his son's head, *Sois immobile!* (Do not move), while Arnold's final resolution to lead the revolt is marked by *Asile héréditaire* (Hereditary refuge), as he sees his ruined home.

Recommended Recording: Overture ***Naxos 8.550236***

GUNTRAM

- Richard Strauss. Opera in three acts. 1893. Revised 1934-1939.
- Libretto by the composer.
- First performance at the Grossherzogliches Hoftheater, Weimar, on 10th May 1894.

Freihild, the unhappy wife of the despotic Duke Robert, is dissuaded from suicide by the knightly singer and poet Guntram, who sings in praise of peace and then urges revolt against the Duke, who attacks him, only to be killed himself. Imprisoned, Guntram considers his own action, against the principles of the Christian brotherhood to which he belongs and influenced, in any case, by his love for Freihild. He finds a solution in the renunciation of the brotherhood and Freihild.

Wagnerian in inspiration and techniques, Strauss's opera won no success and later revisions did nothing to make it better. Its failure in his home city of Munich deterred him from writing opera for some years. The rôle of Freihild was taken by Strauss's future wife, Pauline de Ahna.

Hamlet

- Ambroise Thomas. *Opéra* in five acts. 1868.
- Libretto by Michel Carré and Jules Barbier, after the play by Shakespeare.
- First performance at the Paris Opéra on 9th March 1868.

Gertrude is crowned Queen of Denmark at Elsinore, while Hamlet regrets the death of his father. He loves Ophelia, daughter of the old counsellor Polonius, but now sees his father's ghost, who tells him of his murder by Claudius. In the second act Ophelia, now neglected by Hamlet, seeks permission from Gertrude to enter a convent, but this is refused. Visiting players perform the play of King Gonzago, catching the conscience of Claudius. Hamlet watches Claudius praying and learns from Polonius that he knew of the plot against the former king. In his mother's room Hamlet is about to kill her, but for the intervention of his father's ghost. A ballet opens the fourth act, *La fête du printemps* (The Festivity of Spring), followed by Ophelia's musical madness and death. In a final act Hamlet mourns her loss and, instigated again by his father's ghost, kills Claudius, to be declared king himself.

The version of *Hamlet* devised for Thomas has a relatively happy ending, a major change in the original. It has suitable operatic ingredients in a ghost that appears with some frequency and in a mad scene that is extended to allow various aspects of histrionic dementia, before Ophelia joins the Wilis, the group of spirits of unmarried girls into which Giselle was recruited. French opera demanded a ballet, although this may not seem entirely appropriate in this dramatic context. There is a rousing baritone drinking-song in *O vin, dissipe la tristesse* (Wine, banish sorrow) and Ophelia's mad scene, *A vos jeux* (To your sport) has provided a dramatic vehicle for a number of distinguished prime donne. The opera, however, above all offers an important and impressive baritone title-rôle.

Hans Heiling

- Heinrich August Marschner. *Grosse romantische Oper* in a prologue and three acts. 1832.
- Libretto by Eduard Devrient.
- First performance at the Hofoper, Berlin, on 24th May 1833.

Characters

Queen of the Earth Spirits	soprano
Hans Heiling, her son	baritone
Anna, Hans Heiling's bride	soprano
Gertrude, her mother	contralto
Konrad, a huntsman	tenor
Stephan, a blacksmith	bass

In the underground cave of the earth spirits, Hans Heiling must leave his royal mother, giving up the throne for love of the mortal Anna. In spite of all pleas, he insists on giving up everything for mortal love. In his house Heiling keeps his magic-book and the casket of bridal jewels his mother had given him. Gertrude is eager for her daughter Anna to marry Heiling, but she is in love with the young huntsman Konrad. Anna opens the magic-book and is terrified when the pages turn of their own accord: she insists that Heiling destroy it, which he does, although this is the repository of his magic power. At a village celebration Anna wants to dance, which Heiling will not allow, and Konrad sings a song of the danger of mortals marrying earth spirits. His warning is strengthened in the second act by the spirits themselves in the deserted forest, to Anna's terror. She is comforted by Konrad, who carries her back to her mother. When Heiling offers her jewels, she rejects them, drawing back in horror and accusing him of being an earth spirit. In the third act Heiling seeks revenge, agreeing now to return to the kingdom of the earth spirits. The wedding of Konrad and Anna brings a game of blind man's buff, in which Anna takes hold of Heiling, to her horror. His revenge, however, is finally abandoned, when the Queen recalls the spirits and her son, who withdraw into the cliff that still bears the name of Hans Heiling.

Marschner's opera extends further the romantic magic of Weber's *Der Freischütz* (The Marksman). The story of Hans Heiling appears in various forms, particularly in the pages of the Brothers Grimm, and Devrient submitted his libretto to Mendelssohn, who found it not suitable for his use, in part because of a certain similarity, so it seemed, to the mood, at least, of *Der Freischütz*, an opera first staged in 1821, which had influenced his *Die Hochzeit des Camacho* (Camacho's Wedding) in

1827. Marschner's opera has a strong element of magic, with exciting music for the earth spirits and the necessary ingredient of the German forest, the huntsman and young village love.

Recommended Recording: Hans Heiling (2 CDs) ***Marco Polo 8.223306-07***

HANS SACHS

- Albert Lortzing. *Oper* in three acts. 1840. Revised in 1845.
- Libretto by the composer and Philipp Reger, with Philipp Düringer, after a play by Johann Ludwig Ferdinand Deinhardstein.
- First performance at the Stadttheater, Leipzig, on 23rd June 1840.

The 16th century cobbler and mastersinger Hans Sachs is in love with Kunigunde, daughter of the pompous goldsmith Steffen, who disapproves of the match, preferring the comic and poetically incompetent Eoban, an Augsburg town-councillor, who shares certain qualities with Wagner's Beckmesser. The difficulties that Sachs has encountered are resolved when the Emperor seeks out the author of a poem, claimed by Eoban, but demonstrably by Sachs himself.

Lortzing is a composer in the German romantic tradition and his treatment of the historical Hans Sachs invites comparison with the treatment of the same character and a similar story by Wagner in his *Die Meistersinger von Nürnberg* (The Mastersingers of Nuremberg). The two works are, of course, very different in effect and technique, and, it might be added, in durability, with Wagner's opera providing an effective use of leit-motifs and a more credible figure in a Hans Sachs who makes sacrifices for the well-being of the young lovers Eva and Walther.

Recommended Recording: Overture ***Marco Polo 8.220310***

HÄNSEL UND GRETEL (HANSEL AND GRETEL)

- Engelbert Humperdinck. *Märchenspiel* in three acts. 1893.
- Libretto by Adelheid Wette, after a fairy-tale retold by the Brothers Grimm.
- First performance at the Hoftheater, Weimar, on 23rd December 1893.

CHARACTERS

Gretel	soprano
Hänsel, her brother	mezzo-soprano
Gertrud, their mother	mezzo-soprano

Peter, their father, a broom-maker	baritone
Sandman	soprano
Dew Fairy	soprano
Witch	mezzo-soprano

Humperdinck's fairy-tale opera tells the story of the brother and sister, Hansel and Gretel, children of a poor broom-maker. The children soon leave their work to play together, until their mother returns, stops their dancing and sends them out to pick strawberries. Their father comes home with food, but both parents are anxious about the children. In the wood they are lost and eat all the berries they have picked, before falling asleep under the benign spell of the Sandman. The Dew Fairy wakens them, and as the mist clears they see a gingerbread house, but their delight is short-lived. The Witch, whose house it is, takes them captive, putting Hansel in a cage to be fattened up for the table, while Gretel can be eaten at once. When the oven is hot, the children trick the Witch into looking into the oven and push her in. The Witch explodes and gingerbread children, former victims of the Witch, now come to life again. All ends happily when Peter and Gertrud are united again with their children.

Hänsel und Gretel had its origin in musical settings for the children of Humperdinck's sister, Adelheid Wette. These were later extended into something almost too elaborate for the simple and well known story. The overture enjoys a concert-hall existence, while Gretel's folk-song *Suse, liebe Suse* (Suse, dear Suse) and the following dance duet make a particularly charming episode. The Sandman has his moment in *Der kleine Sandmann bin ich* (The little Sandman am I) with its counterpart for the Dew Fairy, *Der kleine Taumann heiss ich* (I am called the little Dew Fairy). The *Dream Pantomime*, in which the children dream of the angels, after meeting the Sandman, is a possible orchestral excerpt for concert use.

Happy End

- Kurt Weill. Comedy with music in three acts. 1929.
- Play by Elisabeth Hauptmann and lyrics by Bertolt Brecht.
- First performance at the Theater am Schiffbauerdamm, Berlin, on 2nd September 1929.

The comedy, set in contemporary Chicago, concerns the conversion of a gang of criminals by a Salvation Army girl.

The score by Weill includes some of what are now his best known songs, the heroine Lilian Holliday's *Surabaya Johnny* and *Matrosen-Tango* (Sailors' Tango) and the dance-hall owner Bill Cracker's *Bilbao Song*. For many these may be familiar in the later recording made by Lotte Lenya, who married Kurt Weill and who established a firm position for Weill's work in pre-1933 Berlin and a particular style of vocal performance. She created the rôle of Jenny in *Die Dreigroschenoper* (The Threepenny Opera), but her later singing style, in the *diseuse* tradition, seems to have been very different and it is this later style that has influenced interpretation of Weill's work in Weimar Germany.

Harmonie der Welt, Die (The Harmony of the World)

- Paul Hindemith. Opera in five acts. 1957.
- Libretto by the composer.
- First performance at the Prinzregententheater, Munich, on 11th August 1957.

Centring on the astronomer Kepler, the opera deals with his quest for the harmony of the world, a vain search, as he discovers on his death-bed. There are planetary identities for the characters, the two Emperors, Rudolf II and Ferdinand II, and others, while further planetary connections may be found in Hindemith's theories of harmony in which a tonal centre may be identified with the sun and other notes with planets near or more remote.

Háry János

- Zoltán Kodály. *Singspiel* in a prologue, four adventures and an epilogue. 1926.
- Libretto by Béla Paulini and Zsolt Harsányi, after a comic epic by János Garay.
- First performance at the Royal Hungarian Opera House, Budapest, on 16th October 1926.

János, a veteran, sitting in the village inn, boasts of his achievements, his rescue of the Emperor's daughter, his promotion to general and his single-handed defeat of Napoleon, and conquest of the heart of the Empress.

Háry János provides splendid entertainment, with the hero's very tall histories rooted largely in Hungarian folk-music, the basic thematic material of the work. The popular orchestral suite drawn from the score offers a depiction of the Vienna musical clock, a wonder of the imperial capital, the defeat of Napoleon and the entrance of the Emperor, together with a *Prelude*, *Song* and *Intermezzo*.

Recommended Recording: Háry János (Suite) **Naxos 8.550142**

Help, Help, the Globolinks!

- Gian Carlo Menotti. Opera in one act. 1968.
- Libretto by the composer.
- First performance at the Staatsoper, Hamburg, on 21st December 1968.

Menotti's opera deals amusingly with visitors from another planet, their electronic taped music in contrast to that of the inhabitants of the earth, school-children and their teachers, to which they are allergic.

Help, Help, the Globolinks! was commissioned by the Hamburg Staatsoper, then under the direction of Rolf Liebermann, and won a much wider audience through a video-recording of the Hamburg performance. It provides easily intelligible entertainment, wittily conceived.

Henry VIII

- Camille Saint-Saëns. *Opéra* in four acts. 1882.
- Libretto by Léonce Détroyat and Armand Silvestre.
- First performance at the Paris Opéra on 5th March 1883.

The opera deals with the English King Henry VIII's break with the Catholic Church, when he sought divorce from his first wife, Queen Catherine of Aragon, in order to marry a lady of the court, Anne Boleyn, herself the mistress, it seems, of the Spanish ambassador, Don Gomez. Other historical inaccuracies find strong popular support for the King in his plans, a Scottish choreographic intrusion into the English court and the death of Queen Catherine, who nobly protects to the end the reputation of Anne Boleyn, who is allowed to survive at the end of the opera.

The ballet-divertissement, with its various dances, including that of the Highlanders, may be heard on occasion in the concert hall. The opera enjoyed considerable success in the life-time of the composer, but is less often staged today.

Recommended Recording: Henry VIII (Ballet Suite) ***Naxos 8.553338-39***

HÉRODIADE (HERODIAS)

- Jules Massenet. *Opéra* in four acts. 1880. Revised in 1884.
- Libretto by Paul Milliet and Henri Grémont (Georges Hartmann), after the story by Gustave Flaubert.
- First performance at the Théâtre de la Monnaie, Brussels, on 19th December 1881.

CHARACTERS

Salomé	soprano
Hérodiade (Herodias)	mezzo-soprano
Jean (John the Baptist)	tenor
Hérode (Herod)	baritone
Phanuel, a Chaldean astrologer	bass
Vitellius, Roman Proconsul	baritone
High Priest	baritone

Salome has gone to Jerusalem, where John the Baptist, whose voice had consoled her as a child, can be heard. In Herod's palace Herodias demands that John should be punished for his effrontery in calling her a Jezebel. Salome, meanwhile, has fallen in love with John, who accepts at least a platonic affection from her. In the second act Herod reclines in his private chamber, thinking of Salome and entertained by singers and dancers. A potion offered will bring an image of Salome, a fleeting vision. Outside the palace the crowd hails Herod as a liberator from Roman rule, but the appearance of the Roman Proconsul Vitellius with imperial concessions quietens for the moment any disturbance. Phanuel, who has already counselled peace and then prophesied revolt to Herod, now shows Herodias that her own daughter, Salome, is her rival in the affections of her husband. John is arrested and brought before Herod, who thinks of using him as an ally. The accusations of the priests and Salome's confession of her own love for John, make Herod lose any interest in releasing him. In the fourth act Salome visits John in his dungeon and they embrace, interrupted by the High Priest, who tells him that his hour has come. Vitellius and his men are entertained in the palace by a lavish spectacle, with dancers from many countries. Salome pleads for John, and then expresses her willingness to die with him. An executioner enters, with a blood-stained sword, and Salome makes to stab Herodias. She, however, now declares herself to be Salome's mother, and Salome stabs herself.

Oscar Wilde's French drama *Salomé*, the basis of the opera by Richard Strauss, was written in 1893 and first staged in Paris in 1896. Massenet's opera, based on one of the *Trois Contes* (Three

Stories) of Flaubert, seems to have been written originally with an Italian libretto by Angelo Zanardini, the basis of the later French version, for which Massenet made various changes. Refused by the Paris Opéra and with Ricordi no longer interested in a previously projected performance at La Scala, Milan, the work won its first staging and substantial success in Brussels. Salome, in the first act, sings of her memories of John the Baptist, *Il est doux, il est bon* (He is gentle, he is good), while Herod's drugged vision of Salome in the second act provides the baritone aria *Vision fugitive* (Fleeting vision). The necessary *grand opéra* ballet is provided, in particular, in the fourth act sequence of exotic dances.

Recommneded Recordings:

Hérodiade (Suites 1 - 3)	***Naxos 8.553124***
Hérodiade (Suites 4 - 7)	***Naxos 8.553125***

HERZ, DAS (THE HEART)

- Hans Pfitzner. *Drama für Musik* in three acts. 1931.
- Libretto by Hans Mahner-Mons and the composer.
- First performance at the Staatsoper, Berlin, on 12th November 1931.

CHARACTERS

Daniel Athanasius, a physician	baritone
Asmodi, a devil/Counsellor Asmus Modiger	tenor
Helge von Laudenheim, a court lady	soprano
Wendelin, assistant to Athanasius	soprano
Duke	bass
Duchess	contralto
Prince Tankred, their son	speaking part
Young Knight	tenor
Prosecutor	bass

Daniel Athanasius is supposed to have magic powers, dependent on a possible compact with the devil. He is persuaded by the Counsellor Asmus Modiger, in fact Asmodi, and Helge von Laudenheim to use his power, and the devil Asmodi allows him to have at his disposal for one year the heart of a living person. This he uses to bring back to life the young Prince Tancred. As a reward he is elevated to the nobility and marries Helge, but on the anniversary of the Prince's cure Asmodi demands the heart back again, Helge's heart. The Prince dies and Athanasius is accused of sorcery,

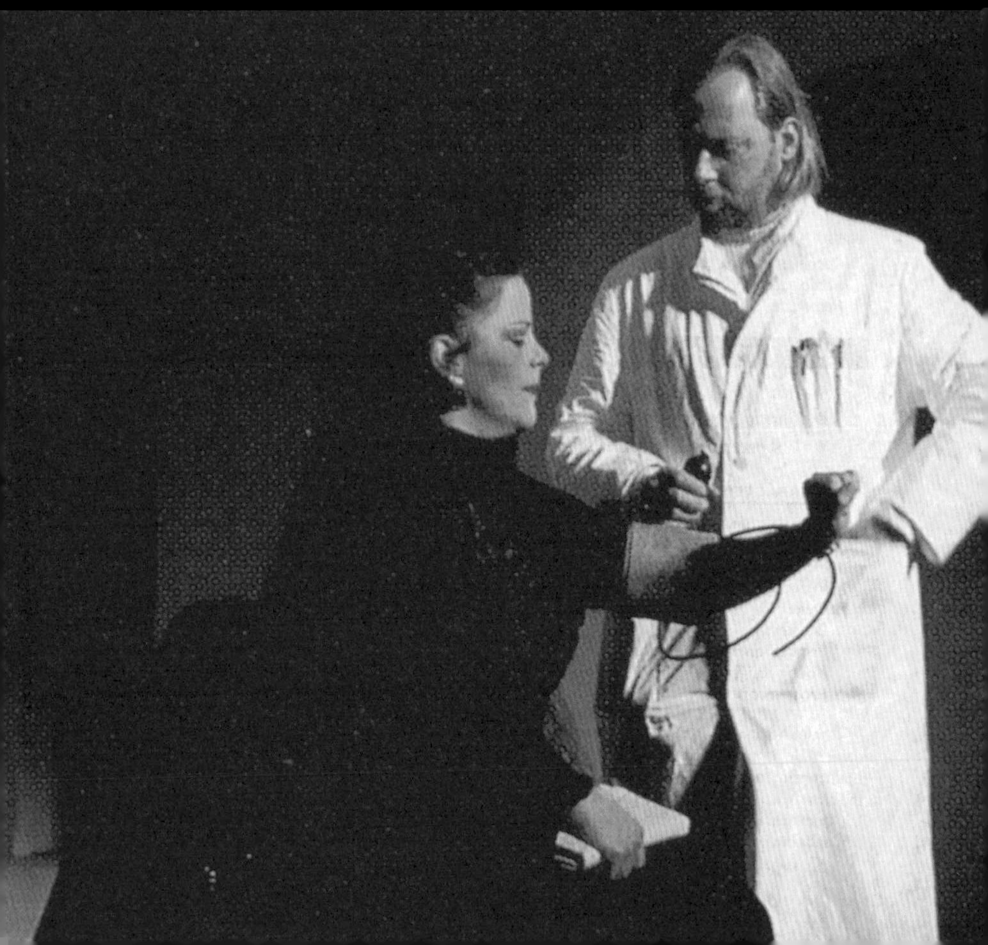

imprisoned and threatened with a painful death. Unwilling to make a second compact with Asmodi, Athanasius sees, in his dungeon, a vision of Helge, whose torments are ended when he refuses to save himself. The opera ends with the spirits of the couple moving into the distance, while the body of Athanasius lies dead before those who would have executed him.

The demonic element in Pfitzner's last opera reflects a contemporary preoccupation in the theatre and in the cinema, as does, to an extent, the novel *Doktor Faustus* of Thomas Mann. In music and in politics Pfitzner tended to conservatism, with a marked distaste for the Bolshevik in either. *Das Herz* (The Heart) has suffered undue neglect, although a recent modernised staging associated the work, not implausibly, with heart-transplant surgery. Nevertheless musical bargains with the Devil have a respectable operatic ancestry.

Recommended Recording: Das Herz (2 CDs) ***Marco Polo 8.223627-28***

HEURE ESPAGNOLE, L' (THE SPANISH HOUR)

- Maurice Ravel. *Comédie musicale* in one act. 1909.
- Libretto based on the play by Franc-Nohain (Maurice-Etienne Legrand).
- First performance by the Paris Opéra-Comique at the Salle Favart on 19th May 1911.

CHARACTERS

Torquemada, a clock-maker	tenor
Concepcion, his wife	soprano
Gonzalve, a poet	tenor
Ramiro, a muleteer	baritone
Don Inigo Gomez, a banker	bass

In 18th century Toledo, the clock-maker Torquemada is due to attend to the city clocks, his absence providing a chance of amorous freedom for his wife Concepcion. The appearance of the muleteer Ramiro with a watch to be repaired frustrates her plans, when Torquemada tells Ramiro to await his return. The latter helps by moving a large clock to her room, allowing Gonzalve to hide inside it. A second potential lover, the banker Don Inigo Gomez, comes in and is hidden in another clock, but in the end Concepcion prefers Ramiro as a lover. Returning to his shop, Torquemada finds Gonzalve and Don Inigo hidden in his clocks and sells them a clock each, accepting with apparent equanimity the return of Concepcion with her satisfied muleteer.

Ravel finds room in his score for the Spanish colour with which he was always familiar from his maternal ancestry, as well as the ticking of clocks that might be thought to reflect his Swiss paternal inheritance. The short opera, in which Ravel claimed to be aiming at a re-creation of Italian *opera buffa*, is witty and elegant, with the expected mastery of orchestration.

HIMMELSKLEID, DAS (THE GARMENT OF HEAVEN)

- Ermanno Wolf-Ferrari. *Legende* in three acts. 1925.
- Libretto by the composer, after Charles Perrault.
- First performance at the Nationaltheater, Munich, on 21st April 1927.

A Princess succeeds to the throne in a little kingdom, the wealth of which depends on a golden donkey, given to her father by a beggar, in return for his benevolence to his subjects. The beggar seeks to test the Princess, brought up to know only prosperity, telling her she must obtain the garments of heaven, of air, moon and sun. This she sets as a condition for the acceptance of a suitor, rejecting prince after prince, until war threatens. Son of the great Emperor, a Prince arrives, giving her only a flower. She demands the garments of Heaven, which he then sets out to find for her. In the air he is mocked by spirits and on the moon is banished, having rejected the advances of the Moon Fairy. The children of the sun, however, tell him that the princess will find herself what she needs. Spoilt and angry, she has destroyed the magic donkey, ruined her people and been expelled by them, to wander in the forest, dressed in a donkey-skin. She is near to death when the Prince finds her, but now she knows herself, and all ends happily.

Das Himmelskleid (The Garment of Heaven) was in part a reaction of Wolf-Ferrari to the disturbed conditions of the time and the inevitable division of loyalties he harboured, son of a German father and an Italian mother. The work is in general in the German tradition of fairy-tale opera rather than in Wolf-Ferrari's usually lighter style. It does, however, have elements of comedy in the opening scene, where rejected suitors of the Princess complain, and otherwise of lyrical romanticism.

Recommended Recording: Das Himmelskleid (3 CDs) ***Marco Polo 8.223261-63***

HIN UND ZURÜCK (THERE AND BACK)

- Paul Hindemith. Sketch with music. 1927.
- Libretto by Marcellus Schiffer.
- First performance at the Baden-Baden Festival on 15th July 1927.

The score and plot of the sketch go forward to the end and then return backwards. The piece is in the nature of a satire on operatic practice. Here the jealous tenor Roberto shoots his wife Helene, who has had a letter from her lover. The Professor and Ambulance Man take the body away and Roberto jumps out of the window. A Wise Man now readjusts matters by playing the whole piece backwards. The reversed music, unlike that of the *Epilogue* to the piano interludes and fugues of *Ludus Tonalis*, which simply repeats the *Prologue* backwards and upside down, is taken phrase by phrase, not simply as a literal palindrome.

Hippolyte et Aricie (Hippolytus and Aricia)

- Jean-Philippe Rameau. *Tragédie en musique* in a prologue and five acts. 1733.
- Libretto by Simon-Joseph Pellegrin, after Racine's drama *Phèdre* (Phaedra), Euripides and Seneca.
- First performance at the Paris Opéra on 1st October 1733.

Characters

Aricie (Aricia)	soprano
Hippolyte (Hippolytus)	haute-contre
Phèdre (Phaedra), his step-mother	soprano
Thésée (Theseus), his father, King of Athens	bass
Oenone, confidante of Phaedra	soprano
Arcas, confidant of Theseus	haute-contre
Diane (Diana)	soprano
L'Amour (Cupid)	soprano
Jupiter	baritone
Tisiphone, a Fury	haute-contre
Pluton (Pluto), King of the Underworld	bass
Mercure (Mercury)	tenor
Neptune	bass
High Priestess of Diana	soprano
Three Fates	haute-contre, tenor & bass

Diana promises Jupiter to protect Hippolytus and Aricia. At the temple of Diana there are ceremonies dedicated to the goddess. Aricia, whom Theseus has bound to chastity, is in love with Hippolytus, who is also loved by his jealous step-mother Phaedra, who is angry to learn of Diana's protection for the couple of the title, but liberated by the news that Theseus has descended to the Underworld, whence she does not expect him to return. He is attempting to rescue his friend Peirithous, who has tried to abduct Pluto's wife. Theseus is eventually released, thanks to the intervention of Neptune and Mercury. He returns to the world to find Hippolytus apparently threatening to kill Phaedra, although he has in fact only repelled her advances and prevented her own death. The return of Theseus is celebrated, but Hippolytus must die. Hippolytus is unwilling to tell Theseus of Phaedra's guilty love, but, with Aricia in a grove of Diana near the sea, he is carried away by a sea-monster. Phaedra now admits her guilt, as she dies, while Theseus is forbidden to see again his son, now saved. In a pastoral scene Aricia is united with a husband and king promised by Diana, and this turns out to be Hippolytus.

Hippolyte et Aricie (Hippolytus and Aricia), Rameau's first opera, written at a relatively late stage in his career, when he was already established as a musical theorist, concentrates particular attention on Theseus, with a second act in Hades that dispenses with the two lovers of the title. There is an instrumental suite derived from the work and an instrumental hunting scene in the fourth act.

HMS Pinafore

- Arthur Sullivan. Operetta in two acts. 1878.
- Libretto by W.S.Gilbert.
- First performance at the Opera Comique, London, on 25th May 1878.

Captain Corcoran has high ambitions for his daughter Josephine, who he hopes will marry Sir Joseph Porter, who, through a variety of occupations, has reached the position of First Lord of the Admiralty. She, however, is in love with the sailor Ralph Rackstraw. Matters are put right when Little Buttercup, Ralph's substantial former foster-mother, reveals that, through a common enough mistake in the period, she has mixed up two babies. Ralph is, therefore, of a more elevated social position and eligible to marry Josephine.

Gilbert's satirical treatment of the navy, of place-seekers and of dramas involving the navy and misplaced babies, provided Sullivan with an opportunity for a tuneful score that includes Handelian parody and a well known patter-song in *When I was a lad I served a term*, with, for the large Little Buttercup, *I'm called Little Buttercup*.

Hochzeit des Camacho, Die (Camacho's Wedding)

- Felix Mendelssohn. Opera in two acts. 1825.
- Libretto perhaps by Friedrich Voigt, after the episode in Cervantes' *Don Quixote*.
- First performance at the Schauspielhaus, Berlin, on 29th April 1827.

Carrasco wants his daughter Quiteria to marry the rich Camacho, but she loves the relatively poor Basilio. The latter's pretended suicide at Camacho's wedding-feast persuades Carrasco to allow marriage with the supposedly dying man, who is then restored suddenly to life. The action is complicated by the interventions of Don Quixote and Sancho Panza, in search of the cave of Montesinos.

An innovative work, sixteen-year-old Mendelssohn's opera is unified by its overture, the substance of which is integral to the whole work. The overture itself is occasionally heard in the concert-hall.

Holger Danske (Ogier the Dane)

- Friedrich Ludwig Aemilius Kunzen. Opera in three acts. 1789.
- Libretto by Jens Baggesen.
- First performance at the Royal Theatre, Copenhagen, on 30th March 1789.

Characters

Oberon, King of the Fairies	soprano
Titania, Queen of the Sylphs	soprano
Holger Danske, a Danish prince	tenor
Kerasmin, his squire	baritone
Sultan Buurman	bass
Rezia, his daughter	soprano
The Mufti	baritone
Sultana Almansaris	mezzo-soprano
Sultan Bobul	bass
Langulaffer, Prince of Lebanon	silent rôle

The dissension between Oberon and Titania can only be ended when a couple is found who will remain true one to the other under the most extreme tests. The Danish prince Holger Danske, with his squire Kerasmin, is lost on the way to Baghdad. In reply to Kerasmin's singing, Oberon appears and promises help, giving him a magic horn which will set those against whom its sound is directed to dance. Taken to Babylon, they visit the beautiful Princess Rezia, who seems to dream of Holger Danske, although she must marry the Prince of Lebanon the next day. The magic horn is used at the wedding scene before the Sultan Buurman and the Mufti the next day, setting the company to dance until they drop and allowing Holger Danske and Rezia to escape. Off the coast of Tunis they are ship-wrecked, captured by pirates and sold as slaves to Sultan Bobul. In the garden of the Sultana Almansaris Holger Danske works as a gardener, subject to the attentions of the Sultana, which he rejects. He is threatened with death by burning at the stake, while Rezia, subject to the equally unwelcome attentions of the Sultan, seeks his release. In the end both are to be burned at the stake, when the intervention of Oberon and Titania saves them, now united again, as are Rezia and Holger Danske, in happiness.

Holger Danske marks a step towards national opera in Europe, with its Danish text and Danish hero. The libretto has a debt to Wieland, while the composer Kunzen, born in Lübeck, had to face conflict in the contemporary feud between Danish and German writers and artists. The opera is national in its language and in its hero, a magic opera in its use of Oberon and Titania and exotic in its relatively remote scene of action. At the same time it fulfils something of the demands of the popular *Rettungsoper*, the 'rescue opera' that was becoming popular in these years and that led in the early years of the next century to Beethoven's *Fidelio*. The opera, very much in the international musical idiom of the day, enjoyed very limited success during the life-time of the composer.

Recommended Recording: Holger Danske (2 CDs) ***Marco Polo / Da Capo 8.224036-37***

HORSEMAN, THE (SEE RATSUMIES)

HUGH THE DROVER

- Ralph Vaughan Williams. Romantic ballad opera in two acts. 1914.
- Libretto by Harold Child.
- First performance at the Royal College of Music, London, on 4th July 1924.

In a country town at the time when Napoleonic invasion was expected, Mary is to be married, unwillingly, to John, the butcher, but falls in love with a stranger, Hugh the Drover, who wins a fight with the butcher and is accused of being a French spy, to be put in the stocks. Mary attempts to release him and hides under his cloak, as John returns from drinking, planning to call on her. She is discovered and disowned by her father, but when soldiers arrive to arrest Hugh, he is recognised as their former comrade. Mary and Hugh are united, choosing a life of freedom on the open road.

Hugh the Drover is in the pastoral English tradition fashionable at the time of its composition, perhaps as a reaction to the years of war. Hugh's *Song of the Road*, sometimes heard in isolation from its dramatic context, reflects this fictional romantic view of a life untrammelled by the restraints of the town.

Huguenots, Les (The Huguenots)

- Giacomo Meyerbeer. Grand opera in five acts. 1835.
- Libretto by Eugène Scribe and Emile Deschamps.
- First performance at the Paris Opéra on 29th February 1836.

Characters

Raoul de Nangis, a Huguenot nobleman	tenor
Marcel, his Huguenot servant, a soldier	bass
Bois-Rosé, a Huguenot soldier	tenor
Marguerite de Valois, betrothed to Henry IV of Navarre	soprano
Urbain, her page	mezzo-soprano
Valentine, daughter of the Count de Saint-Bris	soprano
Count de Saint-Bris, a Catholic nobleman	baritone
Count de Nevers, a Catholic nobleman	baritone
Cossé	tenor
Méru	baritone
Thoré Catholic gentlemen	baritone
Tavannes	tenor
de Retz	baritone

At a banquet at the château of the Count de Nevers, Raoul is among the guests, with his staunch Huguenot servant Marcel. He is in love with a girl that he once helped but of whose identity he has no idea. Marcel's Lutheran hymn and Raoul's Huguenot battle-narrative merely amuse the Catholic guests. The Count leaves the company to join a lady in the garden, one whom Raoul recognises at once as the girl he had helped. Urbain, page to Marguerite de Valois, takes Raoul, blindfold, to meet his mistress. She, however, has had the idea of solving religious divisions in France by arranging the marriage of Raoul and Valentine, who, it now seems clear, is engaged to the Count de Nevers. When Valentine is brought in, Raoul refuses any such match, thinking that she already has a liaison with the Count de Nevers. Bloodshed is narrowly averted, when her father, the Count de Saint-Bris, resents the imputation. In the third act Valentine and de Nevers are to marry. Catholic and Huguenot soldiers add to the unease of the situation outside the Paris chapel. Marcel brings a challenge from Raoul to the Count of Saint-Bris, whose friends plan to murder Raoul, but Valentine reveals the plot, and in the event there is open conflict between Catholic and Huguenot supporters. It is only now that Raoul realises that the reason for Valentine's meeting in the garden with de Nevers was to seek release from her engagement. He visits Valentine and, hidden, overhears the

Catholic plan for the massacre of St Bartholomew, a plot in which de Nevers refuses any part, breaking his sword and being taken prisoner. In spite of her open protestations of love, Raoul rushes away to warn his friends of the massacre which has already begun. Taking refuge with Marcel and Valentine, they are all three killed by Saint-Bris, unaware that he is killing his own daughter, now a Huguenot herself.

An important example of French *grand opéra, Les Huguenots* is characteristic of the genre in its grandiose conception and its serious treatment of a historical religious conflict. Raoul's Huguenot account of Catholic discomfiture, *Piff, paff, piff, paff,* sung at the banquet given by the Count de Nevers, has provided a baritone concert item, with the Queen's *O beau pays de la Touraine* (O fair country of Touraine). Valentine and Raoul have a notable love duet in *O ciel, où courez-vous?* (O heaven, where are you running?) after the Consecration of the Swords in the fourth act, as adherents of the Catholic party plan to massacre the Huguenots. The length of the opera has led to various abridgements, notably in the omission of the fifth act and the joining of the second to the first act, making a three-act work.

I

Icebreak, The

- Michael Tippett. Opera in three acts. 1976.
- Libretto by the composer.
- First performance at Covent Garden, London, on 7th July 1977.

Characters

Lev, a teacher and poet	bass
Nadia, his wife	lyric soprano
Yuri, their son	baritone
Gayle, his girl-friend	dramatic soprano
Hannah, her black friend, a nurse	mezzo-soprano
Olympion, her boy-friend, a black champion	tenor
Police Lieutenant	bass
Luke, an intern at Hannah's hospital	tenor
Astron, a psychedelic messenger	lyric mezzo-soprano & countertenor

Lev, after twenty years imprisonment, regains his wife Nadia and their son Yuri in the New World. There is a consequent conflict between father and son, the latter is involved with tendencies typical of this new world and is seriously injured in a race riot. Nadia dies, remembering her own country and the ice breaking in spring, and there is a scene in the Paradise Garden, where the psychedelic messenger is represented by two voices together. Yuri recovers in hospital and is reconciled with his father.

Tippett's opera is unusual in its direct confrontation of contemporary problems, the gap in understanding between generations and the problems of race relations, where an individual may be seen as a racial stereotype. The Paradise Garden suggests another contemporary phenomenon in a work that contains other allusions, ranging from Shakespeare to Goethe.

Idomeneo, re di Creta (*Idomeneo, King of Crete*)

- Wolfgang Amadeus Mozart. *Dramma per musica* in three acts. 1781.
- Libretto by Giovanni Battista Varesco, after Antoine Danchet's libretto of 1712 for André Campra.
- First performance at the Residenztheater, Munich, on 29th January 1781.

Characters

Idomeneo (Idomeneus), King of Crete	tenor
Idamante (Idamantes), his son	male soprano
Ilia, daughter of King Priam of Troy	soprano
Elettra, daughter of King Agamemnon of Argos	soprano
Arbace (Arbaces), Idomeneo's confidant	tenor
High Priest of Neptune	tenor
La Voce, the voice of Neptune	bass

Ilia, a Trojan prisoner in Crete, is in love with Idamantes, son of Idomeneus, who, it seems, may have perished with the Greek fleet. Ilia imagines that the Greek princess Electra may fare better with Idamantes, who enters, bringing news of the sighting of the Greek fleet and the decision to release the Trojan prisoners, while he remains captive to the charms of Ilia. Electra objects to this act of clemency, and Arbaces enters with the news that the fleet has sunk. Idomeneus, however, has survived, thanks to the vow he has made to Neptune to sacrifice the first living being he meets on his return. Idamantes approaches him, neither of them recognising the other. When Idomeneus learns that the other is his son, he rushes away. In the second act Idomeneus confides in Arbaces, who suggests that Idamantes should go away, escorting Electra back to Argos, until some other solution may be found. As they are about to board ship, a storm arises and a sea-monster emerges. Idomeneus admits the vow he has made, but does not give the name of his son. In the third act Ilia and Idamantes are together in the palace gardens, joined there by Idomeneus and Electra, all expressing their conflicting feelings. The sea-monster meanwhile has been causing devastation and Idomeneus admits to the High Priest of Neptune that the sacrificial victim should be his son Idamantes. He, however, has killed the monster and now offers himself as a victim. Ilia tries to take his place, but the voice of Neptune bids Idomeneus abdicate in favour of his son, who should marry Ilia, a command that allows Electra a final expression of jealousy and anger. Idomeneus is grateful for the rest that retirement will bring.

The overture to *Idomeneo, re di Creta* (Idomeneus, King of Crete) is closely reflected in the opera itself, a fine reworking of a traditional *opera seria* subject. The Munich orchestra, formed principally from players who had followed the Elector from Mannheim to his new capital, included a larger string section and a pair of clarinets, an important instrument that was only now finding its proper place in the orchestra. There is ballet music and a chaconne for chorus to end the first act. Ilia, in an additional aria for 1786, opens the second act by seeking reassurance from Idamantes, whose *Non temer, amato bene* (Do not fear, well beloved) later served as a concert aria. Her third act *Zeffiretti lusinghieri* (Pleasant breezes) asks the winds to take her messages of love to Idamantes. Electra has a very notable and dramatic angry aria in her *D'Oreste, d'Ajace* (Of Orestes, of Ajax), a contrast with the resigned *Torna la pace* (Peace returns) of Idomeneus, which follows. The second of the arias of Idomeneus, *Fuor del mar* (Out of the sea) celebrates his survival after ship-wreck in floridly ornamented music that also exists in a simplified version. His first aria, *Vedrommi intorno* (I shall see around me), had expressed his fears at the rashness of his vow to Neptune, whose voice, from his stone statue, prefigures that of the Commendatore's statue in *Don Giovanni*.

Recommended Recording: Overture ***Naxos 8.550185***

Ile de Merlin, L' (Merlin's Island)

- Christoph Willibald von Gluck. *Opéra comique* in one act. 1758.
- Libretto based on *Le monde renversé* (The World Upside-Down) by Alain René Le Sage and d'Orneval in 1718, revised by Louis Anseaume.
- First performance at Schönbrunn Schlosstheater, Vienna, on 3rd October 1758.

L'île de Merlin, ou Le monde renversé (Merlin's Island, or The World Upside-Down) provides a satire on contemporary life, with characters that reverse the popularly supposed characteristics of their mortal counterparts, including an honest lawyer, a woman doctor and others. The work is based on an earlier *vaudeville*.

Im Weissen Rössl (White Horse Inn)

- Ralph Benatzky. *Singspiel* in three acts. 1930. Additional material by Bruno Granichstaedten, Robert Gilbert, Robert Stolz and others.
- Libretto by Hans Müller, with lyrics by Robert Gilbert, based on the comedy by Oskar Blumenthal and Gustav Kadelburg.
- First performance at the Grosses Schauspielhaus, Berlin, on 8th November 1930.

Josepha, owner of The White Horse Inn, is divided in her affections between her head-waiter Leopold and Dr Siedler, a richer man. She chooses the former, after intervention from the Emperor.

Robert Stolz was the composer of the well known duet for Josepha and Leopold, *Mein Liebeslied muss ein Walzer sein* (My love-song must be a waltz) and *Die ganze Welt ist himmelblau* (The whole world is heavenly blue), while Benatzky's *Es muss was wunderbares sein* (It must be quite wonderful) and *Im weissen Rössl am Wolfgangsee* (White Horse Inn on Lake Wolfgang) remain well enough known, from a work that enjoys continued popularity.

Recommended Recording: Mein Liebeslied muss ein Walzer sein ***Naxos 8.550942***

Imeneo (Hymen)

- George Frideric Handel. Opera in three acts. 1740.
- Libretto adapted from the work of Silvio Stampiglia.
- First performance at Lincoln's Inn Fields, London, on 22nd November 1740.

Hymen explains how, disguised as a girl, he had attended the Eleusinian mysteries with Rosmene and Clomiris and rescued the two girls from pirates on the way back. Claiming the hand of the former, he displaces Rosmene's betrothed, after she has resolved through a dream of the Underworld, her own dilemma.

Immortal Hour, The

- Rutland Boughton. Music drama in two acts. 1914.
- Libretto based on the play and poems by Fiona MacLeod.
- First performance at the Assembly Rooms, Glastonbury, on 26th August 1914.

Eochaidh, the king, is searching in the forest for the Immortal Hour. He finds love with a fairy princess, Etain, who is compelled back to the land of heart's desire by her lord, Midir, after a year of happiness with Eochaidh, who is struck dead by Dalua, Lord of the Shadows, not living to experience the sadness of parting and deprivation.

Rutland Boughton's opera won considerable success in the years after 1918, but is now remembered, perhaps, for the *Faery Song* that reminds Etain of her home.

Impresario, The (see Schauspieldirektor, Der)

(see Schauspieldirektor, Der)

Incontro improvviso, L' (The Unexpected Meeting)

- Joseph Haydn. *Dramma giocoso* in three acts. 1775.
- Libretto by Carl Friberth, after the *opéra comique* by L.H.Dancourt, *La rencontre imprévue* (The Unexpected Meeting).
- First performance at Esterháza on 29th August 1775.

In Cairo the impoverished Osmin is recruited by the Calender into a company of begging dervishes, while the Persian Princess Rezia, in the seraglio, thinks of her lover Ali. He has been looking for her and with Osmin accepts an invitation to a house where he meets her again. The Calender is now recruited in a plan for Ali and Rezia to escape. The Sultan, returning, offers a reward for Rezia's recapture, and she and Ali are betrayed by the Calender. The Sultan, however, pardons the lovers, but threatens the Calender with death, before banishing him from Cairo.

As in Mozart's *Die Entführung aus dem Serail* (The Abduction from the Seraglio), *L'incontro improvviso* (The Unexpected Meeting), set in 1764 in its French form by Gluck, makes use of the fashionable Turkish plot and music of the time, the latter particularly in the instrumentation of the overture and in the third act. Musical characteristics include use of triangle, tambourine and drums, with a melody often over an unchanging harmony.

Incoronazione di Poppea, L' (The Coronation of Poppaea)

- Claudio Monteverdi. *Dramma musicale* in a prologue and three acts. 1643.
- Libretto by Giovanni Francesco Busenello, based on the *Annales* of Tacitus, Suetonius, Dio Cassius and the pseudo-Senecan *Octavia.*
- First performance at the Teatro SS Giovanni e Paolo, Venice in 1643.

Characters

La Fortuna (Fortune)	soprano
La Virtù (Virtue)	soprano
Amore (Cupid)	soprano
Nerone (Nero), Emperor of Rome	male soprano
Poppea (Poppaea)	soprano

Ottavia (Octavia), Empress of Rome	soprano
Ottone (Otho)	male alto
Drusilla, a lady of the court	soprano
Seneca, a philosopher, Nero's tutor	bass
Arnalta, old nurse and confidante of Poppea	male alto
Nutrice (Nurse), nurse of Ottavia	male alto
Lucano, poet, friend of Nero, nephew of Seneca	tenor
Valletto, page of the Empress	male(?) soprano
Damigella, lady-in-waiting to the Empress	soprano
Liberto, Captain of the Praetorian Guard	tenor
Two Soldiers of the Praetorian Guard	tenors
Littore (Lictor)	bass
Pallade (Pallas), goddess of wisdom	soprano
Mercurio (Mercury), messenger of the gods	bass
Venere (Venus)	soprano

In the prologue Fortune, Virtue and Cupid argue about their respective powers. Love sets out to demonstrate his supremacy, in what follows. In the street outside Poppaea's house, Otho complains at her infidelity. He was her lover, but now she is sleeping within with Nero, the Emperor, while his two soldiers guard the house. The couple emerge, as dawn breaks, and sing of their love. With her nurse Arnalta Poppaea reveals her ambition to become Empress, while elsewhere Octavia, Empress, wife of Nero, and of the imperial family of Augustus, laments her husband's desertion. Seneca tries to comfort her, mocked by her page, and is warned by Pallas Athene of his coming death. Nevertheless he dares to advise his old pupil, Nero, that he should not cast aside Octavia. Nero insists that he will go his own way. Otho overhears Nero and Poppaea, he promising to make her Empress and she urging the discarding of Seneca, whose death Nero now orders. Otho is definitively rejected by Poppaea and, meeting Drusilla, who loves him, promises fidelity to her. The sentence of death is brought to Seneca, who parts philosophically from his followers, before leaving to take his life in traditional Roman fashion. On the news of his death, Nero and his dissolute friend Lucan, make merry. Octavia tells Otho he must kill Poppaea and he borrows Drusilla's clothes as a disguise. His attempt to kill Poppaea as she sleeps is frustrated by the direct intervention of Cupid. Poppaea wakes and sees one she believes to be Drusilla escaping. The old nurse Arnalta raises the alarm. Arrested, Drusilla tries to shield Otho, but Otho confesses, blaming Octavia, who can now with some justification be sent into exile. Octavia bids a sad farewell to Rome, Arnalta comments on the success of her mistress and Nero and Poppaea celebrate their love and the coronation of the latter as Empress.

Monteverdi's last opera ends with one of the most effective of all love duets, the haunting *Pur ti miro, pur ti godo* (I gaze on you, I delight in you). Of the many riches of a work of particular splendour mention should be made of Seneca's death scene, *Amici è giunta l'hora* (Friends, the hour is at hand) and the pleading of his followers *Non morir Seneca, no* (Do not die, Seneca, no), Nero and Lucan's rejoicing at his death, *Hor che Seneca è morto / cantiam, cantiam, Lucano* (Now that Seneca is dead / Let us sing, let us sing, Lucan) and Arnalta's sound if comic advice to her mistress, *Ben sei pazza, se credi / che ti possano far contenta, e salva / un garzon cieco, et una donna calva* (You are a fool if you think / that they can make you happy and safe / a blind boy and a bald woman). There are also notable scenes for Octavia, in particular her first act *Disprezzata Regina* (Queen humiliated) and her farewell to Rome, *A Dio, Roma, a Dio patria, amici a Dio* (Farewell Rome, farewell my country, farewell friends), with its verbal echoes of the earlier parting of the lovers Nero and Poppaea, after a night together.

Indes galantes, Les (The Gallant Indies)

- Jean-Philippe Rameau. *Opéra-ballet* in a prologue and four entrées. 1735. Later additions in 1736.
- Libretto by Louis Fuzelier.
- First performance at the Paris Opéra on 23rd August 1735.

Cupids, in the prologue, resolve to find out examples of love in exotic climates. *Le turc généreux* (The Generous Turk) allows the generous Osman to set free his captive Emilie, whom he loves, so that she may be re-united with her former lover Valère. *Les Incas du Pérou* (The Incas of Peru) deals with the rivalry in love of the Inca Huascar and the Spaniard Don Carlos, the latter victorious in his pursuit of Princess Phani, in spite of volcanic eruptions. *Les fleurs* (The Flowers) offers a Persian love intrigue, revised after its first performance into a simple tale of suspicions proved false, as the Sultana Fatima finds that her husband Tacmas has no designs on Atalide. *Les sauvages* (The Savages) moves to North America, where a Spaniard and a Frenchman compete for the love of Zima, daughter of a chief, who, not unnaturally, prefers one of her own people.

An orchestral and a harpsichord suite have been derived from *Les Indes galantes* (The Gallant Indies), which continues the French tradition of *opéra-ballet* stemming from Lully, with its diversion away from the mythological and into the contemporary to be found in André Campra's *L'Europe galante* of 1697. The entrée *Les sauvages* includes the earlier harpsichord piece of that name, a work with which the Jesuit missionary Amiot unsuccessfully tried to charm the ears of Mandarins in Peking a little later in the century, leading him to form curious biological theories.

Indian Queen, The

- Henry Purcell. Semi-opera in a prologue and five acts. 1695.
- Text from the play by John Dryden and Robert Howard.
- First performance at the Theatre Royal, Drury Lane, London, in autumn 1695.

Set in Mexico, the Queen Zempoalla defends her kingdom against invading Peruvians, led by Montezuma, who joins the Mexicans, finding that the true Queen, displaced by Zempoalla, is his mother.

Perhaps unfinished at Purcell's death in 1695, *The Indian Queen* continues the mixed genre of semi-opera found in *King Arthur* and other works for which Purcell provided music, with its spoken drama and musical scenes and episodes. There are instrumental introductions and dances, with the well known song *Ye twice ten thousand deities*, a bass song for the magician Ismeron, and the even more familiar *I attempt from love's sickness to fly*.

Recommended Recording: The Indian Queen ***Naxos 8.553752***

Infedeltà delusa, L' (Deceit Outwitted)

- Joseph Haydn. *Burletta per musica* in two acts. 1773.
- Libretto by Marco Coltellini, perhaps revised by Carl Friberth.
- First performance at Esterháza on 26th July 1773.

Vespina, sister of Nanni, loves Nencio, while Sandrina is the object of Nanni's affections. Sandrina's father Filippo forces her to marriage with Nencio, to the dismay of Nanni and Vespina. Nencio serenades Sandrina. Disguised as an old woman, Vespina complains to Filippo that Nencio is already married to her daughter. When Nencio returns to visit Sandrina, he is told to go away, repulsed by Filippo and by Vespina, now disguised as a drunken German servant. In a further disguise she returns as the Marquis of Ripafratta, ready to marry Sandrina, but by various tricks she brings about the marriage of Sandrina and Nanni, while Nencio is united with Vespina.

The opera was the third that Haydn had written for Esterháza, a comedy that seems to have pleased his employer, Prince Nikolaus Esterházy. The work was performed in September of the same year as part of the entertainment provided for a visit to Esterháza of the Empress Maria Theresia.

Inganno felice, L' (The Happy Deception)

- Gioachino Rossini. *Farsa* in one act. 1811.
- Libretto by Giuseppe Foppa.
- First performance at the Teatro S Moisè, Venice, on 8th January 1812.

Isabella, the wronged and banished wife of Duke Bertrando, long supposed dead, has in fact been rescued from the sea by the villager Tarabotto. The Duke, with his wicked confidant Ormondo and the latter's henchman Batone, comes to the village, where the duplicity of the villains is revealed.

The opera, among Rossini's earlier works, is set in a mining village. Foppa also provided the libretto for Rossini's *La scala di seta* (The Silken Ladder) and *Il Signor Bruschino*.

Intermezzo

- Richard Strauss. *Bürgerliche Komödie mit sinfonischen Zwischenspielen* in two acts. 1923.
- Libretto by the composer.
- First performance at the Staatsoper, Dresden, on 4th November 1924.

Characters

Christine	soprano
Hofkapellmeister Robert Storch, her husband	baritone
Franzl, their son	speaking part
Anna, their maid	soprano
Baron Lummer	tenor
The Notary	baritone
His Wife	soprano
Storch's Skat Partners:	
Kapellmeister Stroh	tenor
Commercial Counsellor	baritone
Legal Counsellor	baritone
Singer	bass

Storch and his wife are packing and she continues to nag him, reminding him of her higher social status. She tells her maid that she would prefer it if he stood up to her. She is invited to go skating and there collides with a young man of whom she makes much, when she discovers that he is Baron Lummer. At an inn Christine and Lummer dance. At home again Lummer visits her and tells her of his wish to study natural history, not law, which is what his family wants. She promises her husband's support. An important instrumental interlude, one of twelve interludes in the opera, leads to a scene in the Baron's room, where he complains about Christine's interest and demands on him, but ends by writing to ask for money. At the Storch's Lummer's demand for a thousand marks is rejected by Christine, who again assures him of her husband's help in his proposed studies. She is handed by the maid a letter for her husband from a woman asking for opera tickets and writes to her husband declaring that she is leaving him. The first act ends with Christine in her son's bedroom. Franzl thinks she is to blame, but she again claims to be better than her husband. The second act opens with a game of skat, with Storch's friends discussing his pleasant character and the unfortunate temper of his wife. Christine's telegram is handed to Storch and he goes out. At the notary's Christine demands a divorce on the grounds of her husband's infidelity. Storch wanders about distraught, until Stroh meets him and tells him the original message must have been intended for him, since their names are similar. At home Christine continues her anger with everyone, and Stroh comes to her to explain the confusion. When Storch returns home, his wife continues to nag him, forcing him to stand up to her and to express jealousy of Baron Lummer. All ends in reconciliation.

Strauss based his opera on his own life and marriage. In form it is a series of short scenes, separated by instrumental interludes. In the libretto he paints a picture of himself as gentle and reasonable and of his wife as an unreasonable shrew. Stroh was the conductor Josef Stransky, with Strauss's son and their maid under their own names. This autobiographical creation follows the programmatic *Sinfonia domestica* of 1903. The best known of the twelve instrumental interludes is that which ends the first act.

Recommended Recording: Intermezzo: Symphonic Interludes ***Naxos 8.553379***

IOLANTA

- Pyotr Il'yich Tchaikovsky. Lyric opera in one act. 1891.
- Libretto by Modest Il'yich Tchaikovsky, after the play *Kong Renés Datter* (King René's Daughter) by Henrik Hertz.
- First performance at the Maliy Theatre, St Petersburg, on 18th December 1892.

CHARACTERS

Iolanta, blind daughter of King René	soprano
René, her father, King of Provence	bass
Robert, Duke of Burgundy	bass-baritone
Count Vaudémont, a Burgundian knight	tenor
Ibn-Hakia, a Moorish physician	baritone
Almeric, King René's armour-bearer	tenor
Bertrand, castle gate-keeper	baritone
Martha, his wife, Iolanta's nurse	contralto
Brigitta, a friend of Iolanta	soprano
Laura, a friend of Iolanta	mezzo-soprano

Iolanta is picking fruit with her friends. She does not know that she is different from anyone else, although she is blind. Her nurse and her friends lull her to sleep. The physician Ibn-Hakia insists to the King that no cure is possible unless she is told she is blind and herself wants a cure. Her father will not accept this. Robert, Duke of Burgundy, who is to marry Iolanta, but loves another, comes upon the girl sleeping in the garden. He leaves, while his companion Vaudémont falls in love with Iolanta, to whom he explains the glories of light. The King and Ibn-Hakia return, the former angry that Iolanta now understands her condition, while the doctor sees now some hope for her, particularly when she is determined to regain her sight in order to save Vaudémont from the death that King René has otherwise threatened him. In the end Iolanta recovers her sight and is united with Vaudémont, while Robert is released from his engagement to her.

Iolanta was commissioned with the ballet *Nutcracker*. Stories of medieval knights and ladies did not touch his heart, Tchaikovsky later admitted. The opera was well enough received by the public, but severely criticized in the press, while Rimsky-Korsakov thought it one of Tchaikovsky's weakest works, embittered, perhaps, by the recent lack of success of his own opera *Mlada*, which had received far less official support. Vocal excerpts that may appear in recitals include the Duke of Burgundy's *Who can compare with my Mathilde?* and the love duet between Iolanta and Vaudémont, as well as Iolanta's *arioso* as the work opens.

IPHIGENIA

The daughter of the Greek general Agamemnon, Iphigenia was sacrificed by her father, on the advice of the priests, in order to bring a fair wind to take the Greek fleet to Troy. Versions of the story suggest that Iphigenia was in fact saved by divine intervention. The sacrifice brought from Tennyson the immortal lines: *One drew a sharp knife through my tender throat / Slowly and nothing more.*

Iphigenia's death, opposed by her mother Clytemnestra, led later to Agamemnon's murder by his wife and her lover, followed by the desired revenge of Electra and Orestes, their children, and the consequent difficulties encountered by the latter with the Furies. The subject of Iphigenia was treated dramatically by Euripides and by Racine, and later by Goethe, among others.

Iphigénie en Aulide (Iphigenia in Aulis)

- Christoph Willibald von Gluck. *Tragédie* in three acts. 1773.
- Revised version in 1775.
- Libretto by Marie François Louis Gand Leblanc Roullet, after *Iphigénie en Aulide* by Jean Racine, based on the play by Euripides.
- First performance at the Paris Opéra on 19th April 1774.

Characters

Agamemnon, King of Mycenae and Argos	baritone
Clitemnestre (Clytemnestra), his wife	soprano
Iphigénie (Iphigenia), their daughter	soprano
Achille (Achilles), a Greek hero	tenor
Patrocle (Patroclus), a friend of Achilles	bass
Calchas, High Priest	bass
Arcas, Captain of Agamemnon's guards	bass
Three Greek Women	sopranos
Slave from Lesbos	soprano

Agamemnon has offended the goddess Diana by killing her favourite stag. The oracle tells him he must sacrifice his daughter if he wants a fair wind to take his ships to Troy. He sends for Iphigenia, telling her she should come to marry Achilles. She arrives in Aulis, accompanied by her mother Clytemnestra. Agamemnon has tried to deter Iphigenia from coming, claiming that Achilles has been unfaithful. When the couple meet, this is soon disproved. As they prepare to marry, Arcas reveals Agamemnon's true intentions, and Achilles remonstrates with Agamemnon, who is in a dilemma. The Greeks, however, demand the sacrifice. This is about to take place, in spite of the open opposition of Achilles and his men, when Calchas announces a change of the divine will (represented in the revised version by the intervention of the *dea ex machina* Diana herself). All ends in happiness.

The opera was the first of the seven Gluck wrote for Paris and had the encouragement of the wife of the heir to the throne of France, the Habsburg princess Marie Antoinette, his former pupil. The overture reflects the conflicts of supposed religious duty and paternal love and there is a first act *divertissement*, an ironic celebration of the arrival of Iphigenia in Aulis, and a second *divertissement* in celebration of the courage of Achilles in the second act, with a final *divertissement* at the end of the first version of the opera. Gluck claimed here to have found an international operatic style, a synthesis of the more rhetorical French style and the lyrical Italian, suggesting an end to the quarrels of the century between the two.

Iphigénie en Tauride (Iphigenia in Tauris)

- Christoph Willibald von Gluck. *Tragédie* in four acts. 1779.
- German version, 1781.
- Libretto by Nicolas-François Guillard, after the play of Guymond de la Touche, based on Euripides.
- First performance at the Paris Opéra on 18th May 1779.

Characters

Iphigénie (Iphigenia), priestess of Diana	soprano
Oreste (Orestes), her brother, King of Argos and Mycenae	baritone
Pylades, his friend, King of Phocis	tenor
Thoas, King of Tauris	bass
Diana	soprano

In a storm Iphigenia, now a priestess of the goddess Diana, recalls the misfortunes of her family, the murder of her father Agamemnon by her mother Clytemnestra, later killed by Orestes. Thoas, anxious after the storm, calls for human sacrifice to ward off evil, suggesting as victims two Greeks, stranded on the shore. In the temple of Diana the two are held for sacrifice, Orestes haunted by guilt, while Pylades expresses his friendship. Without revealing his identity, Orestes tells Iphigenia of the fate of Agamemnon and his family, claiming that only one daughter survives, Electra. Iphigenia tries to prevent the sacrifice, detecting in him a resemblance to her brother. She sends a letter to Electra, which Pylades is persuaded to take. She is about to sacrifice Orestes, when she recognises him as her brother, and she and her priestesses acknowledge him as king. Pylades now returns to save the day and Thoas, who has still demanded sacrifice, is killed. The statue of Diana is now restored to the Greeks.

The sixth of Gluck's operas for Paris, *Iphigénie en Tauride*, opens with a remarkable overture, the opening calm leading to a storm and the voice of the priestess Iphigenia in supplication. This follows Gluck's principle of providing an overture that should give audiences an idea of what is to follow. The setting, in Scythia, allows the introduction of 'Turkish' music at the end of the first act, while Orestes has an important mad scene at the beginning of the second act. Iphigenia prays to Diana in *O toi qui prolongeas mes jours* (O you who prolonged my life), while the presentiments of Thoas allow him the aria *De noirs pressentiments* (Dark presentiments). Iphigenia's reaction to the words of Orestes, claiming that he too is dead, in the second act are heard in *O malheureuse Iphigénie* (O unhappy Iphigenia). The declaration of friendship by Pylades offers the second act *Unis dès la plus tendre enfance* (United from tenderest childhood). A rival version of the story, by Niccolò Piccinni, was staged in Paris in 1781 with some success, but has long been eclipsed by Gluck's treatment of the subject.

Iris

- Pietro Mascagni. *Melodramma* in three acts. 1898.
- Libretto by Luigi Illica.
- First performance at the Teatro Costanzi, Rome, on 22nd November 1898.

Characters

Il Cieco, the blind man	bass
Iris, his daughter	soprano
Osaka, a rich young man	tenor
Kyoto, keeper of a house of ill repute	baritone

Iris is the only support of her blind father. She is desired by Osaka and Kyoto plans to obtain her for him. Abducted, she wakens in Kyoto's Green House. There she is wooed by Osaka, but she does not understand him, mistaking him for the sun god. Giving up his pursuit, Osaka leaves the house, and Kyoto tries to lure him back by dressing Iris in fine clothes and letting her be seen on the balcony. Her father, understanding she is there and thinking that this is of her own free will, curses her. In the third act the body of Iris is found by rag-pickers. When she shows signs of life, they stop taking her jewels and run away. The sun rises, and Iris is able, in death, to rise above the selfishness of Osaka, Kyoto and her father.

Set in 19th century Japan, *Iris* provided Mascagni with an opportunity for exoticism, with the introduction of the *shamisen*, the Japanese three-string lute, and appropriate percussion instruments, notably in the theatrical performance that covers the abduction of Iris. The opera may be seen as a precursor of Puccini's *Madama Butterfly* in its attempted combination of realism and the exotic. Well known excerpts from the opera must include the *Hymn to the Sun*, the chorus with which the work opens, and the tenor serenade *Apri la tua finestra* (Open your window), as Osaka, representing the sun god in the marionette show before the abduction of Iris, serenades her. The choice of names of geographical or Greek provenance may seem curious, in this context.

IRMELIN

- Frederick Delius. Opera in three acts. 1892.
- Libretto by the composer.
- First performance at the New Theatre, Oxford, on 4th May 1953.

Irmelin, who has her own dreams, is told by the King, her father, that she must marry after six months and is offered a choice of three noble suitors. In the second act Nils, the swine, as he remarks, his only mates for many a year, has his own dreams of an ideal princess, towards whom the Silver Stream guides him. Rolf, a robber chief and Nils's master, is now prepared to woo Irmelin and calls Nils to the castle. Nils, however, insists on leaving to follow the Silver Stream. Six months later Irmelin is to marry one of the knights proposed by her father. Nils appears and is asked by the King to sing to the company. Afterwards he is able to meet Irmelin by night in the garden and they realise that each is the ideal of the other's dreams. As day breaks, they move away together, while the royal castle vanishes.

The first opera completed by Delius, *Irmelin* was first staged through the agency of Sir Thomas Beecham in 1953, but has never found any permanent place in operatic repertoire. The *Prelude*, derived from the opera in 1931, may be heard in the concert-hall, but the whole work is hampered by a weak libretto.

Recommended Recording: Prelude — ***Naxos 8.553001***

IRRELOHE, DAS

- Franz Schreker. Opera in three acts. 1923.
- Libretto by the composer.
- First performance in Cologne on 27th March 1924.

Characters

Count Heinrich	tenor
Eva	soprano
Peter	baritone
Lola, his mother	contralto
Christobald	tenor

Count Heinrich, in Irrelohe Castle, fears madness, if he gives way to love. His desire, however, for the forester's daughter Eva, inspires the jealousy of her suitor Peter and his marriage to Eva finally brings the vengeance of Christobald, a fiddler, whose betrothed, Peter's mother, had been raped by Count Heinrich's father on her wedding-day. Peter tries to take Eva back from the Count, who does not know that Peter is his brother. They fight and Peter is killed, while Christobald has his revenge, burning down the castle. Count Heinrich is consoled by the love of Eva.

The sixth of Schreker's nine completed operas, *Irrelohe*, provoked some authoritative hostile criticism, in spite of the composer's earlier success that had culminated in *Der Schatzgräber* (The Treasure-Seeker) in 1920 and his appointment as Director of the Berlin Hochschule für Musik.

Isabeau

- Pietro Mascagni. *Leggenda drammatica* in three parts. 1910.
- Libretto by Luigi Illica.
- First performance at the Teatro Coliseo, Buenos Aires, on 2nd June 1911.

The chaste Isabeau, daughter of King Raimondo, is compelled to ride naked through the city, but anyone who looks at her is condemned to be blinded. Folco, a falconer, does not know of the prohibition and looks at her. Isabeau, who has refused all suitors, falls in love with him and joins him in prison, to share his fate.

The passing success of *Isabeau*, a modified version of the story of Lady Godiva, depended on singers who undertook the rôle of Folco. His arias *Ah ha! Tu ch'odi lo mio grido* (Ah ha! You who heard my cry) and *E passerà la viva creatura* (And the living creature will pass) have been in the repertoire of singers of great distinction.

Isola disabitata, L' (The Desert Island)

- Joseph Haydn. *Azione teatrale* in two parts. 1779.
- Libretto by Pietro Metastasio.
- First performance at Esterháza on 6th December 1779.

The sisters Costanza and Silvia have been seemingly abandoned on a desert island by the former's husband, Gernando, himself taken captive thirteen years before by pirates. Freed at last, with his friend Enrico he seeks out the sisters and after various misadventures he and his wife are re-united, while Enrico aptly falls in love with Silvia, who, like Miranda in Shakespeare's *The Tempest*, has never seen men before.

Haydn's opera includes an interesting overture and relatively undemanding arias well suited to the principal characters. The part of Silvia was first performed by Luigia Polzelli, mother of Haydn's son and wife of one of his violinists at Esterháza.

Italiana in Algeri, L' (The Italian Girl in Algiers)

- Gioachino Rossini. *Dramma giocoso* in two acts. 1813.
- Libretto based on a libretto by Angelo Anelli.
- First performance at the Teatro S Benedetto, Venice, on 22nd May 1813.

Characters

Mustafà, Bey of Algiers	bass
Elvira, his wife	soprano
Zulma, her confidante	contralto
Haly, Captain of the Algerian corsairs	bass
Lindoro, young Italian, a favourite slave of the Bey	tenor
Isabella, an Italian, loved by Lindoro	contralto
Taddeo, her elderly companion	baritone

The Bey wishes to rid himself of his wife Elvira, planning to marry her off to Lindoro, and bids Haly find him an Italian girl. Lindoro, meanwhile, is in love with Isabella, who is taken prisoner by Haly, with her companion Taddeo, who now pretends to be her uncle. Lindoro is offered his freedom to return to Italy, if he will take Elvira with him. Isabella and Lindoro recognise each other, and she refuses the advances of the Bey, demanding that Lindoro, as an Italian, should be ordered to stay with her. The Bey tries to persuade Isabella to accept him, promoting Taddeo to a high court position, but Isabella uses trickery, notably the invention of a ceremony of the Order of Pappatici, to which the Bey may be admitted, if he can pass the test of silence. The ceremony is used as a cover for the escape of Isabella and Lindoro, who are finally forgiven by the Bey, now reconciled to his wife, admitting that he has been outwitted by the Italian girl.

The opera, which retains a firm place in international operatic repertoire, has a lively overture. In his first act *cavatina* Lindoro expresses his distress at having been parted from his Isabella, *Languir per una bella* (To languish for a fair one). She laments her fate in *Cruda sorte* (Cruel lot), while the comic figure Taddeo has some reservations about his official appointment in *Viva il grande Kaimakan* (Long live the grand Kaymakam) and *Ho un gran peso* (I have a great weight), a complaint about his offical head-gear. The escape planned by Isabella allows her to command the support of Italian captives in *Pensa alla patria* (Think of your own country).

Recommeded Recordings:

Overture	***Naxos 8.550236***
Cruda sorte / Amici, in ogni evento / Pensa alla patria	***Naxos 8.553543***

Ivrogne corrigé, L' (The Drunkard Reformed)

- Christoph Willibald von Gluck. *Opéra comique* in two acts. 1760.
- Libretto after Louis Anseaume and Jean-Baptiste Lourdet de Santerre, based on La Fontaine.
- First performance at the Burgtheater, Vienna, in April 1760.

Gluck's music replaces that of a French original. The drunkard Mathurin wants his daughter Colette to marry his own drinking-companion Lucas. In this he is frustrated by his wife, with the help of Colette and her lover Cléon.

J

Jacobin, The

- Antonín Dvořák. Opera in three acts. 1888. Revised version in 1897.
- Libretto by Marie Červinková-Riegrová.
- First performance at the National Theatre, Prague, on 12th February 1889.

Bohuš returns to his native town with his wife Julie. He has been disowned by his father, Count Vilém, who thinks him a revolutionary, deceived by his nephew Adolf, now declared his heir. Filip, the Count's steward, has designs on Terinka, daughter of the choirmaster Benda. Terinka is in love with the young huntsman Jiři. The designs of Filip are finally frustrated, as are the machinations of Adolf, when the Count is persuaded by Julie of her husband's innocence.

There is an effective if brief prelude to the first act, a lively waltz. The second act is introduced by music that leads to a school-room scene that allows a love duet between Jiři and Terinka, while the third act ends with a choral ballet. The character of Benda, teacher and choirmaster, is said to have been modelled on the composer's own teacher at Zlonice, where he had spent part of his childhood.

Recommended Recording: Preludes and Ballet Music — ***Marco Polo 8.223272***

Jasager, Der (The One Who Says Yes)

- Kurt Weill. *Schuloper* in two acts. 1930.
- Libretto by Bertold Brecht, after the Japanese noh play *Taniko*.
- First performance at the Zentralinstitut für Erziehung und Unterricht, Berlin, on 23rd June 1930.

Characters

The Boy	treble
The Mother	mezzo-soprano
The Teacher	baritone

First Pupil	treble/tenor
Second Pupil	treble/tenor
Third Pupil	treble/baritone

Visiting the house of a pupil, the teacher learns that the boy's mother is ill. There is to be a school trip which will go over the mountains to a town where there are good doctors, and the boy insists on coming to find medicine for his mother, in spite of the objections of the teacher. On the journey the boy is unwell, and the other boys ask if they should throw him down into the valley below, according to old custom. The teacher points out that there is a custom that demands that the boy who is ill should be asked whether the others should turn back because of him. If he agrees to this, the others will still want to throw him down into the valley. The teacher explains that the answer to the question should be that the others should not turn back. The boy assents to this, and is thrown down to his death, after asking the others to fill a jug with medicine for his mother. The chorus that at the beginning had stressed the importance of consent, now tells how the boys killed the one who was ill, no one more guilty than another.

Weill's opera is didactic in intention and in the possibilities of student performance was part of the current movement of *Gebrauchsmusik*, music of utility. Optional scoring allowed minimal performance with strings, without violas, and two pianos, with a harmonium as an alternative to flute, clarinet and alto saxophone. Brecht's text was based on Elisabeth Hauptmann's translation of Arthur Waley's English version of the Japanese *noh* play *Taniko* (The Casting into the Valley), an account of a pilgrimage to the mountains, where the boy, who has insisted on coming, seeks to pray for a cure for his mother. The boy falls ill and is cast down, but in the Japanese original the pilgrims pray for him and a spirit appears, carrying him in her arms. *Der Jasager* won wide popularity at the time, but some found danger in the possible interpretation that conformity was the supreme virtue. Weill intended to make clear that membership of a community must bring acceptance of the consequences of that membership.

JENŮFA

- Leoš Janáček. Opera in three acts. 1903.
- Libretto by the composer, after the play *Její pastorkyňa* (Not Her Own Daughter) by Gabriela Preissová.
- First performance at the National Theatre, Brno, on 21st January 1904.

CHARACTERS

Grandmother Buryjovka, owner of the mill	contralto
Laca Klemeň, her grandson	tenor
Števa Buryja, his stepbrother	tenor
Kostelnička Buryjovka, her daughter-in-law	soprano
Jenůfa, her stepdaughter	soprano
Mill Foreman	baritone
Village Mayor	bass
His Wife	mezzo-soprano
Karolka, his daughter	mezzo-soprano
Maid	mezzo-soprano
Barena, servant-girl at the mill	soprano
Jano, a shepherd boy	soprano
An Old Woman	contralto

At Grandmother Buryja's mill, Jenůfa is anxious. She is pregnant by Števa Buryja, the old woman's grandson, while Laca, jealous of his half-brother Števa, who, as a direct descendant, is favoured by the old woman, is in love with her. Števa may be conscripted, and if he goes this will cause immediate difficulties for Jenůfa. Freed from the threat of conscription, Števa returns, drunk, and his aunt, Jenůfa's stepmother Kostelnička, forbids his marriage, unless he stays sober for a year. Alone with him, Jenůfa seeks to persuade him to marry her, but he puts her off. Laca overhears this and remonstrates with Jenůfa, accidentally cutting her cheek with his knife, as he tries to kiss her. In the second act, six months later, Jenůfa, hidden in her stepmother's house, has given birth to her child. Števa comes to the house, and Kostelnička begs him to marry Jenůfa. He claims, however, that, with her scarred cheek, she no longer interests him, and he is now engaged to Karolka, the mayor's daughter. Laca, calling at the house, is told part of the truth by Kostelnička, who tells him that Jenůfa's child has died. Fearing now that Laca will not marry Jenůfa, she hurries out with the baby, intending to kill him and leave the body in the frozen river. At home again, she tells Jenůfa that the child has died and persuades her to accept Laca, who has returned, as her husband. Three months later the wedding has been prepared, but, as visitors come to the house, with Števa and Laca now reconciled, the shepherd boy Jano brings the news that a dead child has been found in the river. Kostelnička confesses to the murder, to be forgiven by Jenůfa, who, with Laca's love, will survive, as her stepmother is taken away.

Jenůfa was rejected by the Prague National Theatre and first staged in Janáček's home-town of Brno, only reaching Prague audiences in 1916. Performances followed in German translation, winning the work and its composer a significant reputation. The second title of the opera, *Její pastorkyňa* (Not Her Own Daughter), gives a more accurate indication of the central tragic figure of the piece. This is Kostelnička, stepmother and foster-mother of Jenůfa, whose moral stance against the drunken Števa, in an effort to protect Jenůfa, has such terrible consequences for all those concerned. The opera shows Jenůfa, Laca and even Števa growing in maturity, while Kostelnička is forced into lies and infanticide.

JÉRUSALEM (JERUSALEM)

- Giuseppe Verdi, *Opéra* in four acts. 1847.
- Libretto by Alphonse Royer and Gustave Vaëz, after Verdi's earlier opera *I Lombardi alla prima crociata* (The Lombards at the First Crusade), with a libretto by Temistocle Solera.
- First performance at the Paris Opéra on 26th November 1847.

Gaston, Viscount of Béarn is in love with Hélène, daughter of the Count of Toulouse, who is responsible for the death of Gaston's father. Their marriage is to put an end to earlier conflict, to the dismay of Roger, the Count's brother, who desires Hélène. The Count leads a crusade and Roger plans the murder of Gaston, but it is the Count instead who is attacked by the hired murderer. Gaston is accused of the crime and condemned to exile. Four years later in Palestine, Roger is disguised as a hermit, while Hélène seeks out Gaston, now a prisoner. The Count, who has survived the attack on him, is joined by Roger, still unrecognised, for the coming battle. Hélène is now also a prisoner of the Emir and plans to escape with Gaston. After an extended ballet in the gardens of the Emir's harem, the crusaders win their way through, and the Count forces Hélène to part from Gaston, still regarded as his attempted murderer. Condemned to death, Gaston is to be executed, but the sound of battle leads him and Roger to join the mêlée. From this Gaston emerges as a hero, now revealing his identity to the Count, while Roger, mortally wounded, confesses his guilt.

Verdi recast his earlier opera, the successor to *Nabucco* (Nebuchadnezzar), for Paris, and an Italian version was made, under the title *Gerusalemme*. It is, however, *I Lombardi* that has retained a place in operatic repertoire. The Paris version makes various changes in the plot, which still centres on murderous rivalry, spiced now with suggestions of incest. There is a new prelude and various other additions and readjustments of existing material.

JESSONDA

- Louis Spohr. *Grosse Oper* in three acts. 1822.
- Libretto by Eduard Gehe, after the play *La veuve de Malabar* (The Widow of Malabar) by Antoine-Marin Lemièrre.
- First performance at the Hoftheater, Kassel, on 28th July 1823.

Jessonda, widow of the Rajah, must be burned to death. She, before her marriage, had been in love with a Portuguese general. A young Brahmin, Nadori, is sent from the Hindu temple to bring Jessonda the order for her death, according to custom. He falls in love with her sister, Amazili. The Portuguese forces, now camped outside the city, are led by Tristan d'Acunha, who has sworn that Indian customs will be preserved. Nadori has vowed to save Jessonda and Tristan now discovers that she is his long lost love. The Indian breach of the truce allows Tristan to act and Jessonda is rescued in the nick of time, before Dandau, the chief Brahmin, can carry out the intended sacrifice.

While the overture to *Jessonda* may be heard in concert performance, the opera itself no longer holds the place it once did in theatre repertoire. Spohr, newly appointed Hofkapellmeister (Court Music Director) in Kassel, had reservations about Weber's recently performed *Der Freischütz* (The Marksman), and sought a subject that was poetical and uncomplicated, avoiding, in his setting, any spoken dialogue. He deplored, in particular, the use of speech on mundane subjects in an operatic context. Ballets and spectacle were provided in set pieces that might also attract the many, in a German form of grand opera.

Recommended Recording: Overture ***Marco Polo 8.223122***

JEUNE HENRI, LE (THE YOUNG HENRY)

- Etienne-Nicolas Méhul. *Drame lyrique* in two acts. 1791.
- Libretto by Jean-Nicolas Bouilly.
- First performance by the Paris Opéra-Comique at the Salle Favart on 1st May 1797.

Méhul's opera was ill-timed in its description of the golden youth of Henri IV of France, a subject in which he intended to reflect the Dauphin and the care exercised in his upbringing by his mother, Queen Marie Antoinette. The revolution and subsequent regicide made changes in the work necessary, but it failed to please audiences when it was eventually staged. Its overture, known as *La chasse du jeune Henri* (The Hunt of the Young Henry) is colourfully pictorial.

Job

- Luigi Dallapiccola. *Sacra rappresentazione.* 1950.
- Libretto by the composer, after the Book of Job.
- First performance at the Teatro Eliseo, Rome, on 30th October 1950.

The title *sacra rappresentazione* (sacred representation) suggests the world of the miracle plays, reflecting the interest of a number of 20th century Italian composers, Malipiero, Respighi and Pizzetti among them, in earlier Italian music. Dallapiccola's *Job* uses a twelve-note series and speech in a text that suggests contemporary relevance.

Jolie fille de Perth, La (The Fair Maid of Perth)

- Georges Bizet. *Opéra* in four acts. 1866.
- Libretto by Jules-Henri Vernoy de Saint-Georges and Jules Adenis, after the novel by Walter Scott.
- First performance at the Théâtre Lyrique, Paris, on 26th December 1867.

Characters

Henri (Henry) Smith, a blacksmith	tenor
Catharine Glover	soprano
Simon Glover, her father, a glover	bass
Mab, queen of the gypsies	soprano
Ralph, Glover's apprentice	bass/baritone
Le Duc de Rothsay (Duke of Rothsay)	baritone/tenor
A Lord in his service	tenor
His Major-Domo	bass

Smith is in love with Catharine Glover, inspiring the jealousy of Ralph. The gypsy Mab is given refuge in Smith's workshop and emerges from hiding when the Duke of Rothsay is there, seeking Smith's services and suggesting that Catharine come to his castle. The Duke persuades Mab to help him abduct Catharine and she is clumsily serenaded by Smith that night, followed by a drinking-song from Ralph, who has seen a masked woman who seems to be Catharine being led to the castle. He reports this to Glover and Smith but now sees the real Catharine, leaning from her window, in answer to Smith's serenade. At the castle the Duke entertains the supposed Catharine, in fact Mab, followed there by her anxious father and jealous lover. Smith finds clear proof of infidelity in a flower that has passed from him to Catharine and from her to Mab, thence to the Duke. When St Valentine's Day dawns, there is to be a duel between Smith and Ralph, but this is stopped by the Duke, leading to a happy ending, once Catharine has been restored to her wits, temporarily in abeyance at the thought of the duel.

Bizet avoids Scottish musical references in a weak version of Scott's original novel. Well known excerpts from the score must include Ralph's drunken *Quand la flamme de l'amour* (When the flame of love), Smith's serenade *A la voix d'un amant fidèle* (At the voice of a faithful lover) and Catharine's mad scene ballad, *Echo, viens sur l'air embaumé* (Echo, come over the balmy air).

Jonny spielt auf (Jonny Strikes Up)

- Ernst Krenek. *Oper* in two parts. 1925.
- Libretto by the composer.
- First performance at the Neues Theater, Leipzig, on 10th February 1927.

The intellectual composer Max meets Anita, a singer, during an expedition to the Alps. She has sung a leading rôle in one of his operas and will now undertake a new rôle in Paris, leaving Max in the city where the two have settled together. In a Paris hotel the maid Yvonne is tidying the room of Daniello, a violin virtuoso. Jonny, a black jazz fiddler, shows interest in Daniello's Amati violin, which he takes and hides in the banjo case that Anita has brought, a prop for her performance. In the morning she leaves Daniello, taking the case with her, with Yvonne, dismissed as a suspect in the theft of the violin, and a ring that Daniello gives her for Max. Home again, she gives Max the ring, confirmation to him that she has been unfaithful, while Jonny, helped by Yvonne, takes the violin again. Max contemplates suicide, as he climbs again in the Alps, but is deterred when he hears Anita singing an aria from his opera, broadcast on the hotel radio. There follows Jonny's band, with the violin, recognised by Daniello, who is also at the hotel. Intending to escape to America, Jonny puts the violin in the luggage of Max and Anita, who are also going to America. Max is arrested and Anita and Yvonne are under suspicion. When Daniello tries to stop them leaving, he falls under a train and is killed. Escaping from the police, Max is re-united with Anita and they set out for America, while Jonny plays the violin from above on the station clock.

Krenek's opera is heavily symbolic, with Jonny representing freedom and the future, Daniello and his violin the weight of European culture. *Jonny spielt auf* won immediate and astonishingly wide success in Weimar Germany, of the mood of which it seems typical. It also achieved international success of a similar order. The eclectic mixture of styles within a thoroughly modern context had great contemporary appeal, although this may have faded with time.

Juive, La (The Jewess)

- Fromental Halévy. *Opéra* in five acts. 1835.
- Libretto by Eugène Scribe.
- First performance at the Paris Opéra on 23rd February 1835.

Characters

Eléazar, a Jewish goldsmith	tenor
Rachel, his daughter	soprano
Léopold, prince of the Empire	tenor
Cardinal Brogni, president of the Council	bass
Princess Eudoxie, niece of the Emperor	soprano
Ruggiero, provost of the city of Constance	baritone
Albert, sergeant in the Imperial army	baritone

It is 1414. In the city of Constance there is a festive *Te Deum* to celebrate the defeat of the Hussites by Prince Leopold, the Emperor's nephew. Eleazar evokes popular resentment by working on a holiday, but is released through the intervention of Cardinal Brogni, who had once banished him from Rome. Leopold, under the assumed identity of Samuel, a young Jewish painter, has been wooing Rachel, who is surprised when he deflects the attention of a hostile crowd from her and her father, since he has been recognised by Albert, a sergeant in the Emperor's army. Leopold celebrates Passover with Eleazar's family, although his behaviour arouses some suspicion. Princess Eudoxie, Leopold's wife, comes to buy from Eleazar a gold chain for her husband. Leopold now admits that he is a Christian and that he cannot marry Rachel: indeed any love between Christian and Jew is punishable by death. In the third act Rachel begs Princess Eudoxie for employment, fearing that Leopold has deserted her to follow the princess. When Princess Eudoxie, at an imperial banquet, gives Leopold the chain, Rachel seizes it, revealing the liaison she has enjoyed with him. Eleazar, Rachel and Leopold are arrested. In the following act attempts are made to secure the release of Leopold, and Cardinal Brogni urges Eleazar to recant. In spite of his efforts Eleazar and Rachel are condemned to death and it is only when Rachel is put to death that Eleazar reveals, before he follows her, that Rachel is the long lost daughter of the Cardinal.

La Juive (The Jewess) is the first of Halévy's grand operas and the one by which he is chiefly remembered as a composer. The opera starts with the singing of the *Te Deum*, heard from the church, while the crowd outside murmurs against Eleazar. In *Si la rigueur et la vengeance* (If harshness and revenge) Cardinal Brogni shows mercy to Eleazar and Rachel, and she, in *Il va venir*

(He will come), awaits a secret meeting with Leopold, after Passover. With *Vous qui du Dieu vivant outrager la puissance, soyez maudits* (You who offend against the power of the living God, be accursed) Cardinal Brogni pronounces anathema on the three and in *Rachel, quand du Seigneur la grâce tutélaire.* Rachel, when the Lord's saving grace). Eleazar is tempted for a moment to take the step that might save Rachel from death.

JUNGE LORD, DER (THE YOUNG LORD)

- Hans Werner Henze. *Komische Oper* in two acts. 1964.
- Libretto by Ingeborg Bachmann, after the story *Der Affe als Mensch* (The Ape as Man) from Wilhelm Hauff's *Der Scheik von Alexandria und seine Sklaven* (The Sheikh of Alexandria and His Slaves).
- First performance at the Deutsche Oper, Berlin, on 7th April 1965.

CHARACTERS

Sir Edgar	silent rôle
His Secretary	baritone
Lord Barrat, Sir Edgar's nephew	tenor
Begonia, his Jamaican cook	mezzo-soprano
The Mayor	bass-baritone
Councillor Hasentreffer	baritone
Councillor Scharf	baritone
Professor von Mucker	tenor buffo
Baroness Grünwiesel	mezzo-soprano
Frau von Hufnagel	mezzo-soprano
Frau Hasentreffer	soprano
Luise, ward of Baroness Grünwiesel	soprano
Ida, her friend	soprano
Maid	soprano
Wilhelm, a student	tenor
Amintore La Rocca, a circus director	dramatic tenor
Lamplighter	baritone
Monsieur la Truiare, dancing-master	silent rôle
Meadows, the butler	silent rôle
Jeremy, a Moor	silent rôle

In 1830 in the small German town of Hülsdorf-Gotha preparations are made for the reception of an English nobleman, whose arrival will bring money to the town and even marriage to an eligible local girl. Luise, the most eligible, is in love with the student Wilhelm. Sir Edgar's strange retinue precedes his arrival, animals, a black page, servants and the Jamaican cook Begonia. Sir Edgar appears in a third carriage and makes it clear that he is tired after his journey and does not want to put the townspeople to any trouble. The Baroness gives a reception, inviting Sir Edgar, whose black page brings a refusal that she finds intensely insulting. A circus comes to the town and Sir Edgar comes out to see them, paying their dues to the council and inviting them into his house, to the annoyance of the better class of townspeople whom he has slighted. On a winter night cries are heard from Sir Edgar's house, explained by his secretary as the shouts of Sir Edgar's nephew trying, with some reluctance, to learn German: soon they will be invited to meet him. Preparations are made in the house to entertain the town notables. The room is full of curiosities and Sir Edgar makes his entrance, with the young lord, dressed fashionably, wearing gloves and glasses, and behaving oddly, gulping down the tea Luise offers him and throwing the cup away, among other examples of perceived aristocratic carelessness of convention. The Mayor shows interest in Begonia, while the ladies make much of the young Lord Barrat, his uncouth behaviour admired and imitated. Wilhelm, however, remains apart from this. At the Casino ball-room Luise is now in love with Lord Barrat and Wilhelm looks on with clear disapproval, as the news of their betrothal spreads. As the dance begins, Lord Barrat behaves with ever greater eccentricity, at first imitated and then watched with expressed admiration, until he starts to swing from the chandelier. Eventually he tears off his clothes, revealing himself as a monkey.

Sharply satirical, *Der junge Lord* (The Young Lord) is dramatically in the tradition of *opera buffa*, with an orchestra of classical dimensions augmented by a rather larger array of percussion. The choice of subject and its treatment is a reflection of the composer's residence in Italy, after disillusionment with contemporary German society. The score allows occasional pastiche and witty allusion, with lyrical writing in particular for Luise and Wilhelm.

Kaiser von Atlantis, Der (The Emperor of Atlantis)

- Viktor Ullmann. Legend in four scenes. 1943.
- Libretto by Petr Kien.
- First performance at the Bellevue Theatre, Amsterdam, on 16th December 1975.

Characters

Emperor Überall	baritone
Death	bass-baritone
Pierrot	tenor
A Loudspeaker	bass-baritone
Drummer	mezzo-soprano
Soldier	tenor
Girl	soprano
Two Dancers	silent rôles

Death, finding that the living no longer laugh, the dying no longer die, resigns, so that no-one dies. Pierrot can make no-one laugh, and Death regrets the past, when war was really war. The Drummer proclaims war to the finish, to the sound of *Deutschland über alles* (Germany above all) in a minor key. The Emperor in his palace directs proceedings, but no-one dies, while a soldier and a girl from opposing sides meet but make love not war. In the palace again the Emperor finds the situation intolerable and begs Death to resume his duties. This he will only do if the Emperor is his first victim, a request to which the Emperor finally assents, as the remaining characters sing a version of Luther's *Ein' feste Burg ist unser Gott* (A firm stronghold our God is still)

Written in the concentration camp at Theresienstadt (Terezín), Victor Ullmann's *Der Kaiser von Atlantis, oder Der Tod dankt ab* (The Emperor of Atlantis, or Death Abdicates) reflects the circumstances of its composition. The music retains elements of the composer's past, as a Vienna pupil of Schoenberg and a contemporary of Kurt Weill and Hindemith.

Kashchey the Deathless

- Nikolay Andreyevich Rimsky-Korsakov. Autumn parable in one act. 1902.
- Libretto by the composer and his daughter, after a libretto by Yevgeny Maximovich Petrovsky.
- First performance by Mamontov's Opera Company at the Solodovnikov Theatre, Moscow, on 25th December 1902.

Like Stravinsky's ballet *The Firebird*, Rimsky-Korsakov's seasonal opera treats traditional Russian stories of the wicked sorcerer Kashchey, who holds captive the Princess Unearthly-Beauty, to be rescued by Prince Ivan, who melts the hard heart of the sorcerer's daughter.

Katerina Izmaylova (see Lady Macbeth of the Mtsensk District)

- Dmitry Shostakovich. Opera in four acts. 1934. Revised version of *Lady Macbeth of the Mtsensk District*, reverting to its original title. Libretto by the composer and Alexander Preys, after a short story by Nikolay Leskov.
- First performance of the later revision at the Stanislavsky-Nemirovich-Danchenko Music Theatre, Moscow, on 8th January 1963.

Katya Kabanova

- Leoš Janáček. Opera in three acts. 1921.
- Libretto by the composer, after the play *Groza* (Storm) by Alexander Nikolayevich Ostrovsky.
- First performance at the National Theatre, Brno, on 23rd November 1921.

Characters

Marfa Ignatěvna Kabanová, widow of a rich merchant	contralto
Tichon Ivanyč Kabanov, her son	tenor
Katěrina (Katya), his wife	soprano
Varvara, a foster-child with the Kabanovs	mezzo-soprano
Savël Prokofjevič Dikoj, a rich merchant	bass
Boris Grigorjevič Dikoj, his nephew	tenor

Váňa Kudrjáš, Dikoj's clerk	tenor
Glaša, a servant of the Kabanovs	mezzo-soprano
Fekluša, a servant	mezzo-soprano
Kuligin, a friend of Kudrjáš	baritone

Set in the small Russian town of Kalinov, on the banks of the Volga, in 1860, the opera opens by the riverside, outside the Kabanovs' house. Boris, tied by the terms of his grandmother's will to employment with his unreasonable and tyrannical uncle, complains to Kudrjáš and admits that he is in love with Katya, now returning from church in a party led by her domineering mother-in-law, who abuses her son and Katya. Inside the house Katya tells the servant Varvara of her unhappiness, the latter urging her to look to others, apart from her husband. Tichon announces that he must go to Kazan on business, at his mother's behest. She makes him elicit from Katya a promise not to see any other men, while he is away. Later the same day, Katya is nagged by her mother-in-law. Varvara arranges to let her into the garden, where she may meet another. In the garden Varvara meets Kudrjáš and Katya comes out to meet Boris. In a summer-house by the river bank, some days later, Kudrjáš and his friend Kuligin take shelter from a storm, joined by Dikoj, who regards the storm as an omen. As he goes, Varvara appears, joined by Boris, whom she warns of Tichon's return. Boris hides, as Katya and her husband and mother-in-law come in, Katya now loudly confessing her infidelity. The final scene finds Tichon and the servant Glaša looking for Katya, who has left home. As they move away in their search, Katya appears and now meets Boris for the last time. They bid each other farewell and Katya, now alone, throws herself into the river. Tichon, restrained by his mother, cannot save her, and Dikoj drags her body onto the bank.

Janáček dedicated his opera to the young Kamila Stösslová, with whom he became infatuated during his final years. He seems to have modelled his portrait of Katya on her. Concert excerpts from scores as tightly knit as those of Janáček are virtually impossible, with the close melodic dependence of each melodic figure on the words set, although the emotive prelude to *Kat'a Kabanová*, with its suggestion of Tichon's journey to Kazan and Katya's reflection on her unhappy situation, may occasionally be heard out of its operatic context.

Khovanshchina (The Khovansky Rising)

- Modest Petrovich Mussorgsky. National music drama in six scenes. Completed by Rimsky-Korsakov. 1883. Other versions by Ravel and Stravinsky, 1913; and by Shostakovich, 1960.
- Libretto by the composer and Vladimir Vasil'yevich Stasov.
- First performance of Rimsky-Korsakov version at the Kononov Auditorium, St Petersburg, on 21st February 1886.

Characters

Prince Ivan Khovansky, leader of the Strel'tsï	bass
Prince Andrey Khovansky, his son	tenor
Prince Vasily Golitsïn	tenor
The Boyar Shaklovity	baritone
Dosifey, leader of the Old Believers	bass
Marfa, a young widow, an Old Believer	mezzo-soprano
Susanna, an Old Believer	soprano
Scrivener	tenor
Emma, a girl from the German quarter	soprano
Lutheran Pastor	bass
Varsonof'yev, attendant upon Golitsïn	bass
Kuz'ka, a musketeer	baritone
Streshnev, a young boyar	tenor
Three Strel'tsï (musketeers)	basses

In the Kremlin square in Moscow, the crack militia regiment of musketeers, the Strel'tsï, are on guard. A scrivener enters and is required by the Boyar Shaklovity to write a letter denouncing the Khovansky faction. Prince Khovansky's son Andrey pursues Emma, who is entrusted by the old Prince Khovansky to the care of Marfa. Dosifey, an Old Believer, offers a prayer. In his study Prince Golitsïn reads a love letter from the Tsarevna Sophia. A Pastor pleads for Emma and the Lutherans, while Marfa tells his fortune, foretelling disgrace. Golitsïn orders his people to have her drowned, while Dosifey urges the union of the Khovansky and Golitsïn factions in the cause of the Old Believers. In the Strel'tsï quarter of Moscow, Marfa sadly considers her love for Andrey Khovansky and Shaklovity reflects on the sad past of Russia with its factions and tyrants. The scrivener brings news of an attack by the mercenaries of the young Tsar Peter. At home Khovansky is entertained by his Persian slaves. Summoned to the presence of the Tsarevna he is stabbed by Shaklovity. In the fifth scene Golitsïn has been exiled and the Strel'tsï are to be executed. Marfa offers escape for Andrey and they leave together. A pardon comes for the Strel'tsï. At night by a hermitage in the forest Dosifey laments the result of his own attempt to secure the restoration of the Old Believers, while Marfa and Andrey join in building a pyre for their own immolation.

The historical background of *Khovanshchina* lies in the problems following the death of the young Tsar Fyodor. Power had been shared by the late Tsar's inadequate brother Ivan and his half-brother Peter, later Peter the Great, with their sister Sophia as regent. The three factions in the opera are those of the Strel'tsï, under Prince Khovansky, of the Tsarevna, represented by Prince Golitsïn, and of the Old Believers, anxious to overturn religious reforms. The polymath Vladimir Stasov, mentor of the Mighty Handful, the Five, the group of Russian nationalist composers, helped Mussorgsky in devising the libretto, but at the composer's death in 1881 much of the score was left unfinished and nearly all of it unorchestrated, to be completed for performance by Rimsky-Korsakov, who made various changes and tended, in editing the work of his seemingly less technically proficient colleagues, to smooth out anything he regarded as crude or amateur. Orchestral excerpts from the score include the prelude, depicting dawn over the Moscow River and the *Dance of the Persian Slaves* that entertains Prince Khovansky. Various solutions have been proposed for the ordering of the scenes, as Mussorgsky left them.

KING AND CHARCOAL BURNER

- Antonín Dvořák. Comic opera in three acts. 1871. Revised version, 1874.
- Libretto by B.J.Lobeský.
- First performance of the revised version at the Provisional Theatre, Prague, on 24th November 1874.

The King, lost in the forest, is entertained by the charcoal burner, whose daughter Liduška is in love with a young charcoal burner, Jeník. He is jealous of her association with the stranger, in whom she has confided, and becomes a soldier in the King's army, rising to the position of captain of the Royal Guard. Invited to the royal palace, the old charcoal burner is at first accused of inhospitality to the stranger in the forest, before Liduška and Jeník are joined in a union that her father had earlier forbidden.

The first version of the opera proved beyond the possibilities of the Provisional Theatre in 1871. It was, therefore, a revised version that was first staged there in 1874. The first version was staged at the Prague National Theatre only in 1929. As with the majority of the other operas of Dvořak, the work is seldom heard abroad, although the overture has an occasional place in concert repertoire.

KING ARTHUR

- Henry Purcell. Semi-opera in five acts. 1691.
- Text by John Dryden.
- First performance at the Queen's Theatre, Dorset Garden, London, in early summer 1691.

In *King Arthur* there is again a separation between music and words, although the two are interwoven and the work is not simply a play with incidental music. The principal characters, King Arthur, Emmeline and the Saxon enemy Osmond, have only speaking parts, while the greater part of the music is entrusted to the spirits, good and bad, that complicate the action. Arthur has the task of rescuing his beloved Emmeline, blind until cured by the spirit Philidel, from the power of the Saxons, led by Oswald, abetted by his magician Osmond, the counterpart of Arthur's Merlin. The music includes a scene of Saxon sacrifice to Woden, a battle with the Britons and the misleading of the Saxon enemy, enticed off the beaten track by spirits. A pastoral entertainment is offered to Emmeline and there is a remarkable cold scene, in which Osmond demonstrates his magic powers by summoning up the Cold Genius, whose icy influence is only dissipated eventually by love. The fourth act is dominated by an extended passacaglia, music built on a short repeated ground bass, while the last act finds a place for both the pastoral and the patriotic, as Emmeline is freed and enemies reconciled, perhaps the intended political message of Dryden's original work, written in 1684 for a celebration of the restoration of the monarchy.

KING PRIAM

- Michael Tippett. Opera in three acts. 1961.
- Libretto by the composer, after the *Iliad* of Homer.
- First performance by the Royal Opera at the Belgrade Theatre, Coventry, on 29th May 1962.

CHARACTERS

Priam, King of Troy	bass-baritone
Hecuba, his wife	dramatic soprano
Hector, eldest son of Priam and Hecuba	baritone
Andromache, his wife	lyric dramatic soprano
Paris, second son of Priam, as a boy	treble

Paris, as a man	tenor
Helen, wife of Menelaus of Sparta, then wife in adultery to Paris	mezzo-soprano
Achilles, a Greek hero	heroic tenor
Patroclus, his friend	light baritone
Nurse	mezzo-soprano
Old Man	bass
Young Guard	lyric tenor
Hermes, messenger of the gods	high light tenor

In the royal palace of Troy King Priam and his wife Hecuba are told that the boy born to them, Paris, will cause the death of his father. Hecuba insists that the child be killed but Priam is torn between his duty as a king and his duty as a father, eventually commanding that the baby be put to death. The Nurse, Old Man and Young Guard, the last told to dispose of the child, serve as a Greek chorus, commenting now on the action and its moral implications. Priam and Hector, hunting in the countryside outside Troy, meet a handsome boy, who tells them his name is Paris. Priam accepts him as his son. As a young man, Paris is presented with the choice between the three goddesses, Athene, Hera and Aphrodite, here represented by Hecuba, Andromache and Helen. He chooses the last. War follows, with dispute between Hector and Paris and, on the Greek side, Patroclus's appearance on the battlefield in the armour of his friend Achilles, who has withdrawn from the fight. Patroclus is killed. In the third act the women return, quarrelling then praying to the goddesses. News comes of Hector's death, which Paris brings to his father. Priam makes it clear that he could rather have spared Paris, and bids him kill Achilles. In the darkness of night Priam begs Achilles for the body of his son Hector, now granted him, while Achilles laments the death of Patroclus, whom he had loved. Sitting together at table, drinking wine, Achilles and Priam know that Paris will kill Achilles and that Priam will be killed by Neoptolemus, son of Achilles. Hermes, in an interlude, sings of the healing power of music, leading to the final scene, in which Priam, before the altar, will only speak kindly to Helen, before Neoptolemus bursts in and kills him, while Troy burns.

Tippett's operas have in general had a less immediate appeal than Britten's and there are those who have found Tippett's libretti obscure and his musical language less intelligible. *King Priam*, however, treats a well known subject, although with considerable originality. Underlying the work must be the pacifist principles of the composer, the pity of war. The chorus, represented by the Nurse, Old Man and Young Guard, consider, in a series of interludes, the moral questions raised. Tippett describes his subject to be the mysterious nature of human choice, proper choice demanding self-knowledge, and this is stressed in the first scene and the following interlude. The third interlude, which precedes the last scene, has been arranged by the composer as a separate instrumental piece for flute, oboe and piano or harpsichord.

King Roger

- Karol Szymanowski. Opera in three acts. 1924.
- Libretto by Jaroslaw Iwaskiewicz and the composer, after the *Bacchae* of Euripides.
- First performance at the Wielki Theatre, Warsaw, on 19th June 1926.

Characters

Król Roger II (King Roger), King of Sicily	baritone
Shepherd	tenor
Roxana, Queen of Sicily	soprano
Edrisi, Arab sage	tenor
Archbishop	bass
Deaconess	contralto

In 12th century Sicily, in a richly Byzantine church setting, the Archbishop and Deaconess deplore the influence of a strange doctrine on the people. Edrisi tells King Roger of the Shepherd, who teaches this new faith, and Queen Roxana pleads on his behalf. The formality dissolves with the lyrical appearance of the Shepherd, who exercises even stronger fascination over the Queen. The King orders the Shepherd to stand trial that night. In an inner courtyard of the palace the Shepherd, with his music of tambourine and zither, arrives, to the delight of the Queen, and he and his followers dance in ecstasy. The King vainly tries to seize the Shepherd, who leaves, with Roxana and his followers. In a ruined Greek amphitheatre the King and the Shepherd meet, the former now freed of those inhibitions that had repressed the Dionysian element in his own soul, as he greets the rising sun.

King Roger echoes the harsher Greek tragedy of Euripides, in which there is a conflict between a king, representing formal traditions, and his wife and mother and their followers, who join the cult of Dionysus (Bacchus). King Pentheus spies on the ceremonies and is torn in pieces by the women, who take him for an animal. In Szymanowski's choice of subject, dictated in part by his own antiquarian interests, there is implicit the conflict of the classical order of Apollo and the wilder freedom of Dionysus, as expounded by Nietzsche. Roxana's ecstatic song enjoys an independent existence both vocally and in an arrangement for violin and piano by Pawel Kochański.

Recommended Recording: King Roger (2 CDs) ***Naxos 8.660062-63***

Kiss, The

- Bedřich Smetana. Folk opera in two acts. 1876.
- Libretto by Eliška Krásnohorská, after a short story by Karolina Světlá.
- First performance at the Provisional Theatre, Prague, on 7th November 1876.

Lukáš has long loved Vendulka and now a widower, with a baby, he returns to marry her. In spite of general approval and a tender duet between the two, she repels his attempt to kiss her, explaining that in respect for his first wife, they should wait until they are married. She repels him again and Lukáš goes angrily away, leaving Vendulka to sing lullabies to the baby, sleeping herself, until roused by the drunken return of Lukáš. She runs off. In the forest Lukáš does not know what to do and is advised by Tomeš, his brother-in-law, to ask Vendulka's pardon. She, however, now appears in the forest with her aunt Martinka, who has now involved her in activities as a smuggler. The lovers are united in the final scene, when Vendulka's offer to kiss Lukáš is refused, until she pardon him.

The national style of the opera, in its village setting, has won the work an audience at home. Less frequently staged abroad, the overture may be familiar, with Vendulka's *Cradle Song*.

Kleider machen Leute (Clothes Make the Man)

- Alexander Zemlinsky. *Musikalische Komödie* in a Vorspiel and three acts. 1910. Revised version in 1922.
- Libretto by Leo Feld, after the novelle by Gottfried Keller.
- First performance at the Volksoper, Vienna, on 2nd December 1910.

The poor tailor Strapinski sets out to try his luck in Goldach. There his fashionable dress leads Nettchen, the local magistrate's daughter, to set her cap at him, rejecting her suitor Böhni. Strapinski's efforts to escape are frustrated and in the end he admits to Nettchen his real origins, after which she still announces her intention of marrying him.

Zemlinsky's score finds room for music typical of Vienna, as well as elements more typical of his brother-in-law and one-time pupil Arnold Schoenberg.

Knot Garden, The

- Michael Tippett. Opera in three acts. 1969.
- Libretto by the composer.
- First performance at Covent Garden, London, on 2nd December 1970.

Characters

Faber, a civil engineer	robust baritone
Thea, his wife, a gardener	dramatic mezzo-soprano
Flora, their ward	light high soprano
Denise, her sister, a dedicated freedom-fighter	dramatic soprano
Mel, a black writer	lyric bass-baritone
Dov, his white friend, a musician	lyric tenor
Mangus, an analyst	high tenor baritone

The first act, given the title *Confrontation*, opens with Mangus, a Prospero figure amid the storm, lying on his couch. The characters appear, Faber and Thea approaching middle age and unhappily married, he finding refuge in his work and she in her garden. Thea suspects Faber of designs on their neurotic ward, Flora. Dov and Mel are lovers, the former Ariel to the latter's Caliban in a scene with Flora recalling Lewis Carroll's *Alice in Wonderland*. Flora goes out and Thea exercises some attraction over Mel, leaving Dov isolated, to approach Faber, when he returns from his office. Denise appears, scarred by torture, to offer her own anguish. The second act, *Labyrinth*, opens with Thea and Denise, together but not communicating one with the other. Flora, a lost child, meets Faber, and Thea returns, striking her husband with a whip. Dov finds him and is tempted by Faber, but replaced by Mel, who seeks an end to his relationship with Dov. Mel is joined by Denise, whose fight against injustice strikes a chord with him. Dov and Flora are together. She sings a Schubert song, followed by Dov's first song, during which a rose-garden begins to form. The third act, *Charade*, finds Mangus as Prospero again, with Dov and Mel in their earlier rôles of Ariel and Caliban, Flora as Miranda and Faber as Ferdinand, but Thea and Denise as themselves. The first charade is based on the first exploration of the magic island of Shakespeare's *The Tempest*, with Flora-Miranda admiring the goodness of her father, Mangus-Prospero, as he raises up Mel-Caliban and releases Dov-Ariel from the tree in which he is imprisoned. The second charade has Dov defending Flora from the assault of Mel. In the third Flora and Ferdinand play chess, but Flora runs off, free from Faber. The final charade is a trial scene, with Mangus as judge and Faber as gaoler. Dov is accused and freed, followed by Mel, before Mangus puts an end to the scene, declaring Prospero a fake. With the self-knowledge and understanding acquired, the characters now leave,

Denise and Mel together, Faber and Thea together in greater sympathy, Flora confident by herself, and Dov, a figure of the composer himself, left to develop without Mel as a creative artist.

The Knot Garden is a work of complex symbolism. It opens with a suggestion of serialism, a twelve-note theme, but proceeds in an idiom that is purely Tippett. The parallel drawn with *The Tempest* is echoed verbally and in the music, notably in the quotations from Tippett's earlier *Songs for Ariel*, while the use of the electric guitar, blues, spirituals and other more or less contemporary musical references make the opera an essentially contemporary work. The character of Dov suggested the later *Songs for Dov*, completed in 1970.

König Hirsch (The Stag King)

- Hans Werner Henze. Opera in three acts. 1955. Revised as *Il re cervo, oder Die Irrfahrten der Wahrheit* (The Stag King, or The Wanderings of Truth) in 1962.
- Libretto by Heinz von Cramer, after a fable by Carlo Gozzi.
- First performance of the original version at the Städtische Oper, Berlin on 23rd September 1956.

Characters

Leandro, the King	tenor
Costanza, his beloved	soprano
Tartaglia, the Chancellor	bass-baritone
Scolatella I	coloratura soprano
Scolatella II	soubrette
Scolatella III	mezzo-soprano
Scolatella IV	contralto
Checco, a melancholy musician	tenor buffo
Coltellino, an unsuccessful murderer	tenor buffo
Six Alchemists	silent rôles
Two Statues	contraltos
Cigolotti, a magician	speaking part
The Stag	speaking part

King Leandro, raised in the forest among animals, returns to the more complex human world. As the coronation is prepared, the first candidate for the position of Queen appears, Scolatella I, summoning a double from the mirror, followed by a third and a fourth. Scolatella I hides, as

Tartaglia comes in, complaining bitterly at the crowning of a boy King. Scolatella I makes herself known to him, thinking he must be the King. Costanza is brought in by her guards and Tartaglia tries to persuade her to murder Leandro. The animals bid farewell to Leandro, promising to laugh if anyone tries to deceive him. The four Scolatellas are brought to him, but rejected, followed by Costanza. His preference for her annoys Tartaglia, who reveals her as a potential assassin. The King decides to abdicate and leave for the forest, led by the magician Cigolotti, disguised as a parrot. Tartaglia recruits Coltellino to murder the King. In the forest Tartaglia pursues the King. Through magic Leandro takes refuge in the body of a stag, but Tartaglia overhears the spell that Checco sings and uses it to enter the King's body. Tartaglia as king exercises a tyrannical rule over the people, who are brought to ruin. The Stag King, however, returns and Coltellino now shoots the one he supposes to be the King, Tartaglia, leaving Leandro to assume his original shape and position, with Costanza as his Queen.

König Hirsch (Stag King) was cut very considerably from its original five hours for its first performance. The later version used the Italian names of Gozzi's fable and involved a number of changes, reducing the work to more practical length. The latent political symbolism of the opera is clear enough, while musical influences must include Italy and the operatic traditions from Bellini. The composer wrote the work while living on Ischia, where he had frequent contact with William Walton and met W.H.Auden and Chester Kallman. The forced necessity of shortening the work for its first performance in Berlin led Henze to use material from the score for his *Fourth Symphony* and for the orchestral *La selva incantata* (The Enchanted Wood).

KÖNIGIN VON SABA, DIE (THE QUEEN OF SHEBA)

- Karl Goldmark. Opera in four acts. 1871.
- Libretto by Salomon Hermann Mosenthal.
- First performance at the Hofoperntheater, Vienna, on 10th March 1875.

Assad, Solomon's envoy to the Queen of Sheba, is to marry Sulamith, daughter of the High Priest, but has been fascinated by a strange and beautiful woman he has met. She is revealed as the Queen herself, and the ensuing drama involves the relationship between Assad and the Queen, who sometimes fails to acknowledge him, and Sulamith, who remains loyal to Assad. Blasphemy leads to exile for him and refusing to follow the Queen he dies in the desert, in the arms of Sulamith.

Die Königin von Saba (The Queen of Sheba) won Goldmark a considerable reputation. It was the first and most immediately successful of his six operas. Assad's arietta *Magische Töne* (Magic sounds) provided a lyrical italianate aria for Caruso and other excerpts from the score that may be familiar include the ballet music that entertains the Queen at the opening of the third act.

Königskinder, Die (The King's Children)

- Engelbert Humperdinck. *Märchenoper* in three acts. 1910.
- Expanded from the earlier melodrama of 1897.
- Libretto by Ernst Rosmer (Else Bernstein-Porges).
- First performance at the Metropolitan Opera, New York, on 28th December 1910.

Characters

King's Son	tenor
Goose-Girl	soprano
Fiddler	baritone
Witch	mezzo-soprano
Woodcutter	bass
Broom-Maker	tenor
Senior Councillor	bass
Stable Girl	contralto
Innkeeper's Daughter	mezzo-soprano
Innkeeper	baritone
Tailor	tenor
Gate-Keepers	tenor & baritone

In the forest the goose-girl, a princess under a spell, serves the witch. The prince meets her and they fall in love. A broom-maker and a woodcutter come, with a fiddler, to find out from the Witch who will be King and she tells them the first person to enter the gates of the city after the bells have rung for noon the next day. The fiddler, with whom the other two have not shared their reward from the townspeople, helps the goose-girl break the witch's spell. The next day the townsfolk are excitedly awaiting the arrival of their king. The prince has stayed in the town, engaged as a swineherd by the innkeeper. As the bells ring, the city gates are opened and the goose-girl comes in, greeted by the prince, but the people are angry, thinking they have been cheated, and drive the couple away. In the third act the fiddler is in the forest, living in the witch's hut. The broom-maker, with the children of the town, comes to the hut to persuade the fiddler to return, and he, with the children, sets out to find the prince and princess. Starving, the two approach the witch's hut, begging bread in exchange for the prince's crown. This they are given, but the bread is the magic poisoned bread that the witch had made, and the prince and princess die, to be found there by the children and the fiddler when they return.

Humperdinck's opera differs from *Hänsel und Gretel* (Hansel and Gretel) above all in its sad ending. The play that was the basis of the libretto involves more complex symbolism of alienation and is, therefore, rather more than a fairy-story. Orchestral excerpts must include the preludes to the three acts, the first suggesting the wandering of the prince, the second the dances of the townspeople as they await their king and the third the fiddler's watch for the prince and princess in the forest.

Recommended Recording: Overture ***Naxos 8.550146***

KULLERVO

- Aulis Sallinen. Opera in two acts. 1988.
- Libretto by the composer after the play by Aleksis Kivi.
- First performance at the Los Angeles Music Center on 25th February 1992.

Untamo has destroyed his brother Kalervo's family, only keeping Kullervo as a slave. He sells Kullervo to a smith. When the man's wife tries to seduce him, he kills her. Through his friend Kimmo he finds his parents again, but all is not well between them. A Blind Singer tells how Kullervo had unknowingly seduced his own sister and he must leave his family once more. He takes revenge on Untamo's family, but when he seeks out Kimmo, he finds that his friend has lost his reason. In despair, he seeks death in the flames.

Kivi's play was based on events recounted in the epic *Kalevala*, to which Sallinen partly turns in the libretto. The opera is in generally approachable musical language, colourfully scored and highly dramatic in its subject and treatment.

Lady Macbeth of the Mtsensk District

- Dmitry Shostakovich. Opera in four acts. 1932. Revised version, as *Katerina Izmaylova*, in 1958.
- Libretto by the composer and Alexander Preys, after the story by Nikolay Leskov.
- First performance at the Maliy Operniy Teatr, Leningrad, on 22nd January 1934. Revised version performed at the Stanislavsky-Nemirovich-Danchenko Music Theatre, Moscow, on 8th January 1963.

Characters

Katerina L'vovna Izmaylova, wife of Zinovy Borisovich	soprano
Boris Timofeyevich Izmaylov, a merchant	high bass
Zinovy Borisovich Izmaylov, his son, a merchant	tenor
Sergey, employed by the Izmaylovs	tenor
Aksin'ya, employed by the Izmaylovs	soprano
A Drunk	tenor
Mill Hand	baritone
Steward	bass
Porter	bass
Three Workmen	tenors
Coachman	tenor
Priest	bass
Chief of Police	baritone
Policeman	bass
Teacher	tenor
Drunken Guest	tenor
Sentry	bass
Sonyetka, a convict	contralto
Female Convict	soprano
Old Convict	bass

Katerina L'vovna is bored in a childless marriage, hating her husband Zinovy, who leaves on business, her tyrannical father-in-law forcing her to swear fidelity in his absence. Workmen tease and molest Ak'sinya, in particular Sergey, a new worker in the yard. As Katerina gets ready for bed, Sergey appears, asking to borrow a book. They become lovers. Her father-in-law Boris Timofeyevich sees a light in her room and sees Sergey coming out. He whips him and then demands from Katerina mushrooms to eat. After eating, he falls down dead, poisoned, although there is not yet any suspicion. Sergey and Katerina make love, interrupted by the ghost of Boris Timofeyevich. Zinovy returns and tries to assault his wife, who, with Sergey, strangles him. They hide the body. A peasant sees Katerina going to her cellar, and thinks there may be something to drink there. Here, however, he finds Zinovy's body and calls the police. Bored with nothing more to do than make trouble for a Nihilist teacher, they are happy to interrupt the wedding-feast of Sergey and Katerina, to which they have not been invited. Katerina and Sergey are arrested and sent to a prison colony in Siberia. Sergey finds consolation with another young convict, Sonyetka, and they taunt Katerina, who throws herself into a lake and drowns.

Shostakovich's opera won very considerable success at its first staging. Its subject, a bourgeois crime, and its realism seemed to suit the political requirements of socialist doctrine. The work had been intended as the first of four operas on Russian women. It was, therefore, a shock when Stalin, in 1936, saw the opera and condemned it as chaos rather than music, as the official press immediately informed its readers. The work was not staged again in Russia until the revised version of 1963, ten years after the death of Stalin. An orchestral suite has been derived from the score, which remains powerful, dramatic and demanding.

LAKMÉ

- Léo Delibes. *Opéra* in three acts. 1882.
- Libretto by Edmond Gondinet and Philippe Gille, after the novel *Rarahu* by Pierre Loti.
- First performance by the Paris Opéra-Comique at the Salle Favart on 14th April 1883.

CHARACTERS

Nilakantha, a Brahmin priest	bass-baritone
Lakmé, his daughter	soprano
Mallika, her slave	mezzo-soprano
Hadji, servant of Nikalantha	tenor
Frédéric, an English officer	baritone
Gérald, an English officer	tenor

Miss Ellen, his fiancée	soprano
Rose, her cousin	soprano
Mistress Benson, their governess	mezzo-soprano

In British India the young English officer Gérald falls in love with Lakmé, daughter of the Brahmin priest Nilakantha, who harbours feelings of hatred towards the British. Nilakantha is angry at the pollution of his land by the intruder and sets his daughter to attract the man by her singing. This she does, and when Gérald, in the market-place, rushes forward to help her as she faints, Nilakantha stabs him. Gérald is tended in the forest in secret by Hadji, a servant loyal to Lakmé, who aids him in his task. She goes to bring water from the sacred spring to confirm their love, but Frédéric appears, reminding Gérald of his duty. He resolves to obey and Lakmé poisons herself, leaving Gérald, as she dies, to drink the sacred water that would have united them.

Lakmé incorporates in its story a fashionably exotic element, a reflection of the writing of Pierre Loti. The work enjoyed a popular place in operatic repertoire for many years, while Lakmé's duet with Mallika, *Sous le dôme épais* (Beneath the thick dome) has enjoyed recent disproportionate success, for extraneous reasons. Equally famous is the *Bell Song*, *Où va la jeune indoue?* (Where does the young Indian girl go?), sung by Lakmé in the market-place, as she obeys her father's command to attract the man who has profaned his temple.

Recommended Recordings:

Sous le dôme épais (Flower Duet)	***Naxos 8.551171***
Airs de danse	***Naxos 8.550081***

Land des Lächelns, Das (The Land of Smiles)

- Franz Lehár. *Romantische Operette* in three acts. 1929.
- Libretto by Ludwig Herzer and Fritz Löhner, after the libretto by Victor Léon for Lehár's *Die gelbe Jacke* (The Yellow Jacket).
- First performance at the Metropoltheater, Berlin, on 10th October 1929.

In Vienna the Chinese Prince Sou-Chong admires Lisa, daughter of Count Lichtenfels. He returns to China as prime minister, with Lisa, but she is home-sick and attempts to escape with dragoon officer Count Gustl von Pottenstein. Their plan is foiled, but in the end Sou-Chong reluctantly allows her to return to Vienna.

Das Land des Lächelns (The Land of Smiles), a revision of *Die gelbe Jacke* (The Yellow Jacket), its title a reference to the yellow coat of Chinese office, was among Lehár's most successful operettas, providing a leading rôle for the tenor Richard Tauber. Popular songs from the operetta include Sou-Chong's *Dein ist mein ganzes Herz* (Thine is my heart), as he refuses to follow Chinese custom in taking four wives. In *Wer hat die Liebe uns ins Herz gesenkt* (Who has planted love in our hearts) Lisa and Sou-Chong sing of their love, while Sou-Chong's earlier modesty in Vienna is expressed in *Immer nur lächeln* (Always only smiling), with his description of Chinese customs of wooing in *Von Apfelblüten einen Kranz* (A garland of apple-blossom).

Recommended Recording:
Dein ist mein ganzes Herz / Immer nur lächeln /
Von Apfelblüten / Wer hat die Liebe ***Naxos 8.550941***

LEAR

- Aribert Reimann. Opera in two parts. 1978.
- Libretto by Claus H.Henneberg, after Shakespeare's tragedy *King Lear*.
- First performance at the Nationaltheater, Munich, on 9th July 1978.

King Lear divides his kingdom between his daughters Goneril and Regan, disinheriting Cordelia, whose honesty displeases him. Edmund, bastard son of the Earl of Gloucester, turns his father against his legitimate son, Edgar. The Earl of Kent, who has entered Lear's service in disguise, is put in the stocks and the King himself is humiliated by his two daughters. In a storm on the open heath, Lear, accompanied by the Fool and Kent, goes out of his mind, his madness reflected in the assumed madness of Edgar, disguised as Tom o'Bedlam. In the second part Gloucester is blinded by Regan and Cornwall, the latter killed by a servant. He is turned out of his castle, which Edmund now takes. The blind Gloucester is led by Edgar to what he thinks to be the cliffs of Dover and Lear now meets him, before being taken to meet his daughter Cordelia, wife of the French king. Lear and Cordelia are taken prisoner by Edmund. Regan is poisoned by Goneril, jealous of the love of Edmund, who is now challenged and killed by Edgar, in the guise of an unknown knight. Cordelia has been hanged, on the orders of Edmund, and Lear laments her death before dying himself.

There is a strong serial element in Reimann's *Lear*, a work scored for an elaborate orchestra, while the libretto follows closely enough the scheme of Shakespeare's play. The rôle of King Lear was designed for Dietrich Fischer-Dieskau.

LEGEND OF THE INVISIBLE CITY OF KITEZH AND THE MAIDEN FEVRONIYA, THE

- Nikolay Andreyevich Rimsky-Korsakov. Opera in four acts. 1907.
- Libretto by Vladimir Nikolayevich Bel'sky.
- First performance at the Mariinsky Theatre, St Petersburg, on 20th February 1907.

Living in the forest with her brother, Fevroniya meets a hunter, who has lost his way. He offers her marriage and promises to send a match-maker. One of his huntsmen tells her that the stranger is Prince Vsevolod, son of Prince Yury, ruler of Kitezh. A bard prophesies trouble, as she goes to her wedding. A Tatar attack finds her a prisoner, and while another prisoner, the drunkard Grishka who had mocked her, offers to lead the enemy to Greater Kitezh, she prays for a miracle to make the city invisible. In the city preparations are made for defence against the Tatars and Vsevolod leads his army at the battle of Kerzhenets, to die the death of a hero. Grishka leads the Tatars to the river bank, but the city is invisible, and Grishka is bound and threatened with death. Fevroniya treats him kindly, but he goes mad, while Fevroniya is led by the spirit of her betrothed to the Invisible City, where she marries him, to enjoy there eternal life.

Rimsky-Korsakov's opera treats a traditional Russian subject and belongs to a growing repertoire of Russian operas on national subjects, a trend that had started with Glinka and had been continued by Mussorgsky and Borodin, among others. Orchestral excerpts include the opening *Hymn to Nature*, Fevroniya's *Wedding Procession*, the *Battle of Kerzhenets* and the *Death of Fevroniya and Apotheosis of the Invisible City*.

Recommended Recording: Massacre at Kerzhenets ***Naxos 8.550230***

LIBUŠE

- Bedřich Smetana. Festival opera in three acts. 1872.
- Libretto by Josef Wenzig.
- First performance at the National Theatre, Prague, 1881.

Libuše, Princess of Bohemia, adjudicates in a land dispute between two nephews of Lutobor, but the elder refuses to accept the judgement from a woman. Libuše then chooses a husband, Přemysl. Lutobor's daughter Krasava claims responsibility for the dispute, but is united eventually with the elder nephew, Chrudoš, forgiven by Libuše, now at her court at the castle of Vyšehrad. She foresees the future of the Czech people in a series of patriotic tableaux.

Libuše was written for the opening of the Prague National Theatre. It opens with an impressive overture, sometimes heard in the concert-hall, but as an opera it is less effective than patriotic.

Liden Kirsten (Little Kirsten)

- Johan Peter Emilius Hartmann. Romantic opera in two acts. 1845.
- Libretto by Hans Christian Andersen.
- First performance at the Royal Theatre, Copenhagen, on 12th May 1846.

Little Kirsten is to enter a convent the next day. The peasant woman Ingeborg's son Sverkel, who was brought up with Kirsten, returns from his travels abroad and persuades her to marry him. At this point Kirsten's mother, Lady Malfred declares this impossible, since the two are in fact brother and sister. Ingeborg, however, confesses that the child she had been given by Lady Malfred to rear in secret had died and his place had been taken by her own child, Sverkel. There is, in the end, no objection to the marriage.

The opera *Liden Kirsten*, with a text based on earlier ballads, seemed to capture the spirit of traditional Danish music. The work won considerable favour in Denmark as a truly national opera, a quality that limited its appeal abroad.

Liebe der Danae, Die (The Love of Danae)

- Richard Strauss. *Heitere Mythologie* in three acts. 1940.
- Libretto by Joseph Gregor.
- First performed in a dress rehearsal at the Festspielhaus, Salzburg, on 16th August 1944. The public performance was cancelled. First public performance at the same theatre on 14th August 1952.

Characters

Jupiter	baritone
Merkur (Mercury)	tenor
Pollux, King of Eos	tenor
Danae, his daughter	soprano
Xanthe, her servant	soprano
Midas, King of Lydia	tenor
Four Kings, nephews of Pollux	two tenors & two basses
Semele	soprano
Europa	soprano

Alkmene (Alcmene)	their wives	mezzo-soprano
Leda		contralto
Four Guards		basses

King Pollux, bankrupt, needs a rich husband for his daughter Danae, but she has no time for men, although Midas, King of Lydia, has shown interest in her portrait, carried through the region by the four nephews of Pollux. Danae's interest is in gold, since it is in a shower of gold that Jupiter had been visiting her. The nephews, their wives former mistresses of Jupiter in one form or another, give an account of their journey. Midas arrives and in the guise of a servant Chrysopher comes to an immediate understanding with Danae. Midas had in fact been given his power to transform things to gold at a touch in order to allow Jupiter to approach Danae in this form. In the second act the four Queens prepare the marriage chamber. Jupiter warns Midas of his intentions, but the latter gives way to his feelings and Danae is turned to a gold statue, which, when confronted with the necessity of choice between Jupiter and Midas, chooses the latter. Jupiter, in the third act, resists the approaches of his old mistresses, paying off Pollux and the latter's creditors and nephews, with a shower of golden rain in return for the loss of Danae, now safely away with her Midas, originally a donkey-driver, and happy to bid farewell to Jupiter in a final scene.

The "cheerful mythology" of *Die Liebe der Danae* (The Love of Danae) is Strauss's penultimate opera, to be followed only by the conversation-piece *Capriccio*. The idea of the subject had come originally from von Hofmannsthal. After his death Strauss had collaborated with Stefan Zweig, until the anti-semitic policies of the National Socialist government in Germany made that impossible. Gregor, recommended by Zweig, was a considerable theatre historian, but subjected to severe criticism from Strauss. The opera is demanding in its casting and is characteristic of the composer at his most lavish.

Recommended Recording: Die Liebe der Danae (Suite) ***Naxos 8.550342***

LIEBESVERBOT, DAS (THE BAN ON LOVE)

- Richard Wagner. *Grosse komische Oper* in two acts. 1836.
- Libretto by the composer, after Shakespeare's play *Measure for Measure*.
- First performance at the Stadttheater, Magdeburg, on 29th March 1836.

The Regent Friedrich bans love, but Claudio is found guilty of breaking the law. His sister Isabella, a novice, is persuaded to appeal for mercy, and Friedrich hypocritically demands her favours. She finds it possible, however, to send in her place the discarded wife of Friedrich, Mariana. His duplicity is now revealed, and a measure of free love is restored when the king returns.

Wagner's second opera shows some trace of the idiom that he was to make his own in his later work. The overture is very occasionally heard in the concert-hall, but the opera itself is seldom staged, except as a curiosity.

Life for the Tsar, A

- Mikhail Ivanovich Glinka. Patriotic-Heroic Tragic Opera in five acts. 1836.
- Libretto by Yegor Fyodorovich Rozen, Vladimir Sollogub, Nestor Vasil'yevich Kukol'nik and Vasily Andreyevich Zhukovsky.
- First performance at the Bol'shoy Theatre, St Petersburg, on 9th December 1836.

Characters

Ivan Susanin, a peasant from Domnino	bass
Antonida, his daughter	soprano
Bogdan Sobinin, her betrothed	tenor
Vanya, an orphan, adopted by Susanin	contralto
A Polish Commander	baritone
A Russian Commander	bass
Polish Messenger	tenor

Antonida is eager to marry Sobinin, but her father Susanin refuses permission until there is a true Tsar on the throne of Russia. Sobinin tells him that Mikhail Romanov has been chosen. In the second act a group of supporters of the Polish claimant plans to seize Mikhail. In the third act Vanya expresses his fears for the safety of Mikhail, but Susanin is confident and preparations continue for the wedding of his daughter. A detachment of Polish soldiers bursts in, demanding to be taken to the Tsar. Susanin pretends to agree, planning to lead them off the trail, while sending Vanya with a message to the monastery where Mikhail is hiding. Susanin is killed by his captors, once he tells them of the trick he has played on them, while Vanya has been able to warn the Tsar. The fifth act or epilogue presents the new Tsar's coronation, with Mikhail pledging to remember Susanin's action.

A Life for the Tsar occupies an important position in Russian theatre as the first opera to win a permanent place in repertoire. Ivan Susanin was a patriotic hero of the early 17th century and gave his life for the new Tsar Mikhail, first of the Romanov dynasty, elected to his position in 1613. Glinka and the writers with whom he was associated chose, in Susanin, a hero of Russian nationalism well suited to the mood of the time. The opera uses Russian melodies that become a full part of the musical texture of the work. Orchestral excerpts heard in the concert-hall consist largely of the Polish elements of the second act, *Polonaise*, *Waltz* and *Mazurka*, for the ball given by the Commander of the Polish forces.

Recommended Recording: Overture **_Naxos 8.550085_**

LIGHTHOUSE, THE

- Peter Maxwell Davies. Opera in a prologue and one act. 1979.
- Libretto by the composer.
- First performance at the Moray House Gymnasium, Edinburgh, on 2nd September 1980.

CHARACTERS

Blazes	baritone
Sandy	tenor
Arthur	bass

The opera opens with a court of inquiry into the mysterious discovery in 1900 of the unexplained disappearance of the three lighthouse-keepers of the Flannan Isles lighthouse, in the Outer Hebrides. The single act, under the title *The Cry of the Beast*, suggests how the keepers, storm-bound, might have spent their last night, Arthur a religious zealot, Blazes intolerant of what he sees as hypocrisy and Sandy trying to keep the peace between them. The three sing songs, seemingly straightforward enough, but in fact reflecting aspects of their own hidden problems. Ghosts appear from their pasts and seem to lure Blazes and Sandy out into the fog, while Arthur sees an approaching light as the Beast, the Golden Calf, to fight against which they all go out to their deaths. The light Arthur has seen is that of the relief ship, and as the work draws to a close the three relief lighthouse keepers are seen, but it is not clear whether they have been forced to kill the demented keepers that they have come to relieve or whether they remain mystified by the empty lighthouse.

The Lighthouse, for three singers and twelve instrumentalists, is built on an analogy from the Tower of the Tarot, overtly referred to by Arthur. It is a demanding work for the three singers concerned, the second of the composer's chamber operas, after his earlier *The Martyrdom of St Magnus*.

LINDA DI CHAMONIX (LINDA OF CHAMONIX)

- Gaetano Donizetti. *Melodramma semiserio* in three acts. 1842.
- Libretto by Gaetano Rossi, after the play *La grâce de Dieu* (The Grace of God) by Adolphe-Philippe d'Ennery and Gustave Lemoine.
- First performance at the Kärntnertortheater, Vienna, on 19th May 1842.

Linda's parents are worried at the attentions paid her by the Marquis and think they may have to leave their farm in the Haute Savoie. She is in love with Carlo, and thinks he is a painter, although he is, in fact, the nephew of the Marquis. The Calvinist pastor advises Linda's father to send her away with other young people to Paris, since the Marquis, it seems, has offered to buy her favours in return for the mortgage of her father's farm. In Paris Carlo establishes her in a fine apartment and plans to marry her. She rejects further advances from the Marquis, but is cursed by her father, when he finds her in such luxury, imagining the worst. Meanwhile Carlo is being forced by his mother into an appropriate marriage, news of which sends Linda mad. Matters are put right in the third act, when Carlo is allowed to marry her, a step that brings her to her senses again.

Linda's father Antonio expresses his sadness at the likely forced departure from his native valley in *Ambo nati in questa valle* (Both born in this valley). Linda's entrance, *O luce di quest'anima* (O light of this soul) was added for the Paris staging of the opera. There is a particularly fine love duet for Carlo and Linda in *A consolarmi affrettisi* (Hurry to console me).

Recommended Recording: O luce di quest'anima ***Naxos 8.550605***

LITTLE KIRSTEN (SEE LIDEN KIRSTEN)

LITTLE SWEEP, THE

- Benjamin Britten. An entertainment for young people. 1949.
- Libretto by Eric Crozier.
- First performance at the Jubilee Hall, Aldeburgh, on 14th June 1949.

CHARACTERS

Sam, the new sweep-boy	treble
Gay Brook	treble
Sophie Brook	soprano

John Crome	treble
Tina Crome	soprano
Hugh Crome	treble
Miss Baggot, the housekeeper	contralto
Rowan, the nursery-maid	soprano
Black Bob, the sweep-master	bass
Tom, the coachman	bass
Clem, Black Bob's assistant	tenor
Alfred, the gardener	tenor

Sam, the new sweep-boy, is brought by Black Bob and his assistant Clem to sweep the chimneys. He is rescued by the children of the house and their guests, with the helpful sympathy of the nursery-maid Rowan, but in spite of the powerful Miss Baggot, and smuggled away in the luggage of the visiting children, when they leave.

The Little Sweep forms part of *Let's make an opera*, a work that introduces children to opera and also includes audience songs, interludes that serve to cover Sammy's bath and the passing of night, while Sammy remains hidden, with Sammy's triumphant departure. The songs and ensembles of the characters demonstrate clearly and cleverly the characters and their feelings. The parts of Bob and Tom and of Clem and Alfred are doubled.

Lohengrin

- Richard Wagner. *Romantische Oper* in three acts. 1848.
- Libretto by the composer.
- First performance at the Grossherzogliches Hoftheater, Weimar, on 28th August 1850.

Characters

Heinrich der Vogler (Henry the Fowler)	bass
Lohengrin	tenor
Elsa of Brabant	soprano
Duke Gottfried, her brother	silent rôle
Friedrich von Telramund, a count of Brabant	baritone
Ortrud, his wife	mezzo-soprano
The King's Herald	bass

In 10th century Antwerp King Henry urges the support of Brabant against Hungary. Friedrich von Telramund accuses Elsa of having killed her brother in order to usurp the dukedom that he now claims for himself. The matter is to be settled by combat, and Elsa now prays for her champion to come forward in answer to the Herald's challenge. The mysterious knight Lohengrin appears, in a boat drawn by a swan, and, making Elsa promise never to ask his name or origin, defeats Telramund, sparing his life. Ortrud and Telramund now plan their revenge, planting the seeds of doubt in Elsa's mind. The Herald announces the banishment of Telramund and the assumption of the title Protector by the unnamed knight, who will that day marry Elsa, whose doubts now grow, with Telramund accusing Lohengrin of sorcery. Finally, in the bridal chamber, she asks him the question. Telramund bursts in, and is killed by Lohengrin, who then agrees to answer Elsa's question in the presence of the people. Before the King's judgement seat he reveals his name, Lohengrin, his parentage, as a son of Parsifal, and his rôle as a servant of the Holy Grail, with power that depended on not revealing his name. He tells Elsa that her brother would have come back to her, after a year together, but now he must go, as he came. The swan that draws his boat is revealed, however, as Gottfried, bewitched by Ortrud, and restored to life again as Duke of Brabant. Elsa now falls back dead in her brother's arms.

Lohengrin was first performed at Weimar under the direction of Liszt, after Wagner, having sided with the revolutionaries in Dresden, had taken refuge in Switzerland. The work makes use of the technique Wagner had now more fully developed of leit-motifs, leading motifs associated with ideas or characters in the drama. Here the first act prelude is based on the motif of the Holy Grail, followed, as the work goes on, by some 36 more significant motifs. These include the motif of the forbidden question. Some of the best known music is found in the prelude to the third act, leading to the very familiar *Wedding March*. Familiar vocal excerpts must also include Elsa's dream, *Einsam, in trüben Tagen* (Alone in days of trouble), in which she sees a vision of the knight who will save her, and her later thanks for his championship, *Euch Lüften, die mein Klagen so traurig oft erfüllt* (You breezes who answered my often sad complaints). Lohengrin's answer to the forbidden question is given in the moving *In fernem Land* (In distant land).

Recommended Recording: Prelude / Introduction to Act III ***Naxos 8.550136***

LOMBARDI ALLA PRIMA CROCIATA, I (THE LOMBARDS AT THE FIRST CRUSADE) (SEE ALSO JÉRUSALEM)

- Giuseppe Verdi. *Dramma lirico* in four acts. 1842.
- Libretto by Temistocle Solera, after the poem of the same name by Tommaso Grossi.
- First performance at the Teatro alla Scala, Milan, on 11th February 1843.

Characters

Arvino, son of Folco	tenor
Pagano, son of Folco	bass
Viclinda, wife of Arvino	soprano
Giselda, her daughter	soprano
Pirro, henchman of Arvino	bass
Prior of the city of Milan	tenor
Acciano, tyrant of Antioch	bass
Oronte, son of Acciano	tenor
Sofia, wife of Acciano	soprano

In the first act, *The Vendetta*, Arvino and Pagano are reconciled, but, while the former is to lead a crusade, the latter remembers the cause of their quarrel, Viclinda, and murders his father, a crime for which Arvino would have him put to death, while Giselda counsels mercy. The second act, *The Man of the Cave*, finds Giselda a prisoner of Acciano in Antioch, loved by Oronte, who is urged by his secretly Christian mother Sofia to be converted. Pagano is now a hermit and learns from Pirro, who does not recognise him, the disposition of the enemy forces. He joins the crusading army of Arvino in an attempt to rescue Giselda. She, however, is appalled at the violence of the crusaders when they storm Antioch, killing Acciano and his son, as Sofia tells her. The third act, *The Conversion*, Giselda, with Oronte, who has survived, makes her escape from both parties, to be cursed by Arvino, who now seeks out Pagano, seen nearby. Giselda helps Oronte, wounded by the crusaders, to the hermit's cave, where he is baptized. *The Holy Sepulchre* finds Giselda reconciled to her father. She sees Oronte in a dream, showing her where the crusaders, now dying of thirst, may find water. In the final scene, after the battle to take Jerusalem has been successful, the hermit, badly wounded, reveals his identity to his brother, as he dies.

Verdi's *I Lombardi*, later reworked for performance in Paris under the title *Jérusalem*, won immediate success, following the earlier triumph in Milan with *Nabucco*. After the prelude and introduction, the first act, in its second scene, brings Giselda's prayer *Salve, Maria* (Hail, Mary), while the second allows her the rondo-finale *Se vano è il pregare* (If prayer is in vain). Oronte's death scene offers the famous trio, with Giselda and Pagano and a solo violin obbligato, *Qual voluttà* (What pleasure), and there is a rousing chorus from the crusaders in *O Signore dal tetto natio* (O Lord of our native land), as patriotic in contemporary intention as the earlier *Va pensiero* (Go, my thoughts) in *Nabucco*.

Long Christmas Dinner, The

- Paul Hindemith. Opera in one act. 1960.
- Libretto by Thornton Wilder, after his play of the same name. German libretto by the composer as *Das lange Weihnachtsmahl.*
- First performance at the Nationaltheater, Mannheim, on 17th December 1961.

The opera covers ninety years of the Bayard family, at one Christmas dinner, one generation succeeding another at the table.

Hindemith's opera lasts only an hour and a second work had been planned but was never written. The work is framed by a well known carol, *God rest ye merry, gentlemen*, and makes use of various set forms in its eight sections.

Lotario (Lothario)

- George Frideric Handel. Opera in three acts. 1729.
- Libretto adapted anonymously from Antonio Salvi's *Adelaide*.
- First performance at the King's Theatre, London, on 2nd December 1729.

Idelberto, son of Berengario, loves Adelaida. His father has killed her husband and plans to take by storm the city of Pavia, where she has taken refuge. The German king Lotario comforts Adelaida and she agrees to marry him, once peace is restored. Adelaida is taken prisoner by Berengario and offered the choice of death or marriage to Idelberto, affairs being considerably complicated by the intervention of Berengario's wife Matilda, with her husband a prisoner of Lotario. Matters are finally settled when Lotario takes Pavia and regains Adelaida in safety, with Idelberto granted the kingdom of his parents Berengario and Matilda, to whom proper clemency is shown.

Handel's opera began a new season under new arrangements. He had visited Italy and Rome and recruited new singers, some of whom failed to please. *Lotario* won no great success, but provided material that Handel used again in a number of later works.

Louise

- Gustave Charpentier. *Roman musical* in four acts. 1896.
- Libretto by the composer.
- First performance by the Paris Opéra-Comique at the Salle Favart on 2nd February 1900.

The young artist Julien tries to persuade Louise to elope with him, but her mother intervenes, joined by her father, when he returns from work. In a street scene at the foot of Montmartre, hawkers and passers-by mingle. Julien and his friends seek out the place where Louise works, and she and Julien argue. In a further scene Julien serenades her, as she works with the other seamstresses, now persuading her to choose freedom. In the third act the couple is together, with Louise then crowned muse of Montmartre. She answers now her mother's call to return home, since her father is ill and needs her. Now her parents try to go back on their promise to allow her freedom, but she chooses again to leave them, answering the call of Paris, cursed by her father.

The subject of *Louise* is in accordance with contemporary fashions of realism. Set in working-class Paris, it includes elements characteristic enough of the streets and allows its heroine to choose free love rather than marriage. One of the best known arias from the work is Louise's third act protestation of love, *Depuis le jour où je me suis donnée* (Since the day I gave myself). Rather less frequently heard is her father's final scene with her, urging compliance.

Recommended Recording: Louise (3 CDs) ***Naxos 8.110102-04***

LOVE FOR THREE ORANGES, THE

- Sergey Prokofiev. Opera in a prologue and four acts. 1919.
- Libretto by the composer, after the *fiaba* by Carlo Gozzi *L'amore delle tre melarance* (The Love of the Three Oranges).
- First performance at the Auditorium, Chicago, on 30th December 1921.

CHARACTERS

King of Clubs	bass
The Prince, his son	tenor
Princess Clarice, the King's niece	contralto
Leander, the prime minister, as King of Spades	baritone
Truffaldino, jester	tenor
Pantalone, a courtier, confidant of the King	baritone
Celio, a sorcerer, protector of the King	bass
Fata Morgana, a witch, protectress of Leander	soprano
Linetta	contralto
Nicoletta princesses in the oranges	mezzo-soprano
Ninetta	soprano
Cook	hoarse bass

Farfarello, a devil	bass
Smeraldina, a black slave-girl	mezzo-soprano
Master of Ceremonies	tenor
Herald	bass
Trumpeter	bass trombone
Ten Reasonable Spectators	five tenors & five basses

The prologue brings an argument between those who favour different forms of entertainment, overruled by what follows. The cure of laughter must be found for the Prince's hypochondria. Leander, an enemy of the King, plots with Clarice, his possible successor, to make the Prince's condition worse. Truffaldino tries to amuse him in various ways, but only succeeds by accident when Fata Morgana falls over, exposing herself. She curses him with the love for three oranges that he must now pursue. With the help of Celio and Farfarello the Prince finds the three oranges in the kitchen-garden of the witch Creonta. The oranges must only be opened in the presence of water. The first two reveal princesses, who emerge only to die of thirst. The third, Ninetta, comes out when the Prince himself opens the last orange, saved from death by the intervention of those watching. Ninetta demands proper clothes, before accompanying the Prince, and in his absence is changed by Fata Morgana into a rat, her place taken by the slave-girl Smeraldina. A happy ending is secured when Celio changes Ninetta back into her original form, with Smeraldina, Fata Morgana, Clarice and Leander disappearing through a trap-door.

Gozzi's fable makes use of *commedia dell'arte* figures, the result of a wager with Goldoni. The work was adapted by Vsevolod Meyerhold, founder of the Russian Society of New Drama, Vladimir Solov'yov and Konstant Vogak. The aesthetic quarrel between proponents of different forms of entertainment is allotted to the prologue, much as, in the operas of Monteverdi and his contemporaries, the gods may dispute in a prologue and watch or even interfere in the action that follows. The instrumental suite derived by Prokofiev from the opera enjoys continuing popularity, with the *March*, a recurrent feature in the work, the best known excerpt.

Recommended Recording: The Love for Three Oranges (Suite) ***Naxos 8.550381***

Lucia di Lammermoor (Lucy of Lammermoor)

- Gaetano Donizetti. *Dramma tragico* in three acts. 1835.
- Libretto by Salvadore Cammarano, after Walter Scott's novel *The Bride of Lammermoor*.
- First performance at the Teatro S Carlo, Naples, on 26th September 1835.

CHARACTERS

Lucia	soprano
Enrico Ashton, her brother, laird of Lammermoor	baritone
Edgardo, laird of Ravenswood	tenor
Lord Arturo Bucklaw	tenor
Raimondo Bidebent, chaplain at Lammermoor	bass
Alisa, companion to Lucia	mezzo-soprano
Normanno, huntsman, Enrico's retainer	tenor

The Ashtons need Lucia to marry well, in order to save the family fortunes. Normanno reveals to Enrico that Lucia has long been in love with his mortal enemy Edgardo, laird of Ravenswood. In the Lammermoor Castle grounds Lucia recalls the enmity between the two families, thinking she has seen the ghost of a Lammermoor girl killed by a Ravenswood. Edgardo, who is to leave for France to support the Stuarts, wants to heal the long-standing breach with the Ashtons. The couple exchange rings. Enrico arranges a marriage for Lucia with Arturo Bucklaw, forging a letter in proof of Edgardo's infidelity. Raimondo adds his persuasion. At the wedding Edgardo returns, bursting in after Lucia has signed the marriage contract with Arturo. While Enrico demands his withdrawal, Edgardo expresses his anger and despair in forcible terms, to the increased agitation of Lucia. By a ruined tower of Ravenswood Edgardo and Enrico meet, the latter challenging Edgardo to a duel. At Lammermoor Castle the wedding is celebrated. Raimondo enters with the news that Lucia has killed Arturo and is asking for her bridegroom. She comes in, now in madness, exciting the contrition of her brother, as he returns from his meeting with Edgardo. In the Ravenswood graveyard Edgardo is to meet Enrico's challenge. Learning that Lucia is dead, he stabs himself.

Lucia di Lammermoor has traditionally provided leading sopranos with an important vehicle for dramatic and vocal display, notably in the mad scene of the third act, *Alfin son tua* (At last I am yours). At the start Enrico expresses his anger, when Normanno tells him of Lucia's dalliance with Edgardo, in *Cruda, funesta smania* (Cruel, dreadful longing). Lucia tells her friend Alisa of her forebodings in *Regnava nel silenzio* (Night reigned in silence). She is later, in madness, to recall the love duet with Edgardo, *Verranno a te* (My sighs will come to you). Edgardo has a moving final scene, with *Fra poco a me ricovero* (Soon death will be my refuge) and his outburst when he learns of Lucia's death, *Tu che a Dio spiegasti l'ali* (You who have taken wing to God).

Recommended Recording: Il dolce suono (Mad Scene) — ***Naxos 8.550605***

Lucio Silla (Lucius Sulla)

- Wolfgang Amadeus Mozart. *Dramma per musica*. 1772.
- Libretto by Giovanni de Gamerra.
- First performance at the Regio Ducal Teatro, Milan, on 26th December 1772.

Characters

Lucio Silla (Lucius Sulla), dictator of Rome	tenor
Giunia (Junia), daughter of Caius Marius	soprano
Cecilio (Caecilius), exiled Roman senator	male soprano
Lucio Cinna (Lucius Cinna), his friend	soprano
Celia, sister of Sulla	soprano
Aufidio (Aufidius), tribune, friend of Sulla	tenor

Caecilius has returned in secret from exile to Rome and learns that Sulla intends to marry Junia, to whom he himself was betrothed. Junia, daughter of Sulla's defeated enemy Marius, rejects Sulla's advances, even when faced with death for herself or for Caecilius, who has made an unsuccessful attempt on Sulla's life. All ends in forgiveness, when Junia and Caecilius are allowed to marry, and Cinna, who has sided against Sulla, can marry the dictator's sister Celia.

Mozart's opera was written for performance in Milan before the Archduke Ferdinand, third son of the Empress Maria Theresia, and his wife. It was first staged as part of an entertainment that also included three ballets, the start delayed by the necessity the Archduke found himself under of writing New Year greetings to his family in Vienna. The libretto was later set by Johann Christian Bach for performance in Mannheim in 1775.

Recommended Recording: Overture ***Naxos 8.550185***

Lucrezia

- Ottorino Respighi. Opera in one act and three moments. 1935.
- Libretto by Claudio Guastalla after Shakespeare's *The Rape of Lucretia*, Livy's *Ab urbe condita* and André Obey's play *Le viol de Lucrèce*.
- First performance at the Teatro alla Scala, Milan, on 24th February 1937.

Characters

La Voce	mezzo-soprano
Lucrezia, wife of Collatinus	soprano
Venilia, her maid	soprano
Servia, second maid	mezzo-soprano
Collatino, nephew of the King	tenor
Bruto, nephew of the King	tenor
Tarquinio, prince of Rome	baritone
Tito, his brother	baritone
Valerio, a friend of Spurius	baritone
Arunte, brother of Tarquinius	bass
Spurio Lucrezio, father of Lucrezia	bass

In the first part of the opera the men drink together in the Praetorian tent of Tarquinius. Collatinus boasts of Lucretia's beauty and virtue. They set out to ride to Rome, to test the virtue of Lucretia, of which Collatinus is certain. Tarquinius visits the house of Lucretia, who receives him with due decorum. He tries to woo her, then rapes her. In the third section Lucretia sends for her father and her husband and kills herself.

Respighi left the full scoring of his opera incomplete, to be finished, after his death, by his wife, with the help of the composer Ennio Porrino.

Recommended Recording: Lucrezia — ***Marco Polo 8.223717***

Luisa Miller

- Giuseppe Verdi. *Melodramma tragico* in three acts. 1849.
- Libretto by Salvadore Cammarano, after Friedrich Schiller's play *Kabale und Liebe* (Cabal and Love).
- First performance at the Teatro S Carlo, Naples, on 8th December 1849.

Characters

Count Walter	bass
Rodolfo, his son	tenor
Federica, Duchess of Ostheim, Walter's niece	contralto
Wurm, Walter's steward	bass
Miller, a retired soldier	baritone

Luisa, his daughter	soprano
Laura, a peasant girl	mezzo-soprano
A Peasant	tenor

In a village of the Tyrol, in the early 17th century, Luisa is in love with Carlo, in fact Rodolfo in disguise, who has come there with the new Count. Her father is suspicious of the young man and is angry when Wurm, who has asked for her hand, reveals the identity of Carlo. In the castle Count Walter tells his son to marry the widowed Duchess Federica, but he admits to her that he loves another. Miller, at home, tells Luisa of Carlo's true identity, and Rodolfo enters, assuring Luisa of his love for her. The Count now has Miller and his daughter arrested. Rodolfo threatens to reveal a terrible secret, forcing the Count to release Luisa. The first act had the title *Love*. The second bears the title *Intrigue*, and now Wurm comes to Luisa, demanding that she renounce Rodolfo and elope with him, if she wishes to have her father released. In the castle again Wurm and the Count discuss the plot against Luisa and make it clear that they have murdered the old Count and that Rodolfo has discovered their secret. Luisa is now made to renounce Rodolfo, before Federica, and claim that she loves Wurm. In the castle gardens Rodolfo reads Luisa's letter of renunciation, that Wurm had dictated to her. He challenges Wurm to a duel, but this is avoided, and his father persuades him to marry Federica. In the third act, *Poison*, Miller understands what Luisa has really done, as she writes a letter to Rodolfo suggesting a suicide pact, but then tears it up. Rodolfo arrives, forcing Luisa to admit the circumstances in which her earlier letter had been written. They drink together wine that Rodolfo has poisoned, and die together, but not before Luisa has explained what happened and Rodolfo has killed Wurm.

With the success of *Nabucco* in Milan in 1842, Verdi began a period he later described as his years in the galley, with fourteen more operas in a period of nine years. *Luisa Miller* was the second of the two operas he wrote for the Teatro S Carlo in Naples. *La battaglia di Legnano* had been staged in Rome in January 1849, with the new opera eleven months later, to be followed by *Stiffelio* in Trieste in November 1850 and *Rigoletto* at La Fenice in Venice in March 1851. *Luisa Miller* opens with a symphonic overture, based on a single theme, and not a medley of tunes from what is to follow. Luisa offers her well known prayer in the second act, when confronted by Wurm, *Tu puniscimi, o Signore* (Punish me, O Lord), followed by her later *cabaletta* in which she contemplates her death, after her act of renunciation, *A brani, a brani, o perfido* (Torn in shreds, traitor). With *La tomba è un letto* (The tomb is a bed) she tells her father that death is only a sleep and in *Padre, ricevi l'estremo addio* (Father, receive this last farewell) she dies, in the presence of her father and Rodolfo, so soon to die himself. Rodolfo has notable moments in the third scene of the second act, when he recalls his earlier happiness in *Cuando le sere al placido* (In those evenings).

Recommended Recording: Overture ***Naxos 8.553018***

Lulu

- Alban Berg. Opera in a prologue and three acts. 1935.
  Third act completed by Friedrich Cerha in 1978.
- Libretto by the composer, after the plays *Erdgeist* (Earth-Spirit) and *Die Büchse der Pandora* (Pandora's Box) by Franz Wedekind.
- First performance of the first two acts at the Stadttheater, Zürich, on 2nd June 1937. First complete performance with the third act at the Paris Opéra on 24th February 1979.

Characters

Lulu	high soprano
Gräfin Geschwitz	dramatic mezzo-soprano
Theatrical Dresser	contralto
Schoolboy	contralto
Groom	contralto
Professor of Medicine	speaking part
Banker	high bass
Professor	silent rôle
Painter	lyric tenor
Negro	lyric tenor
Dr Schön, a newspaper editor	heroic baritone
Jack the Ripper	heroic baritone
Alwa, son of Dr Schön, a composer	heroic tenor
Schigolch, an old man	high character bass
Animal-Tamer	bass
Rodrigo, an athlete	bass
The Prince, a traveller in Africa	tenor
Manservant	tenor
The Marquis	tenor
Theatre Manager	buffo bass
Clown	silent rôle
Stagehand	silent rôle
Police Commissioner	speaking part
Young Girl	opera soubrette

Her Mother	contralto
Woman Artist	mezzo-soprano
Journalist	high baritone
Manservant	lower baritone

In a prologue the animal-tamer introduces his menagerie, with the snake and Lulu the last to appear. The first act opens in the Painter's studio, where Lulu is having her portrait painted, watched by Dr Schön, who is taken by his son Alwa to see a new ballet. Lulu is seduced by the Painter and when her husband, the Professor of Medicine, arrives he suffers a heart attack and dies. In the second scene Lulu and the Painter are prosperously married. Old Schigolch calls, a figure from Lulu's past, perhaps her father. He goes and Dr Schön comes in. He tells the Painter of Lulu's past, causing him to cut his throat. The police are called and Lulu promises to marry Dr Schön. The third scene is set in a theatre dressing-room. Alwa is with Lulu, as she changes for her performance, and she tells him of the proposal she has had from the Prince, who wants to take her to Africa. She is angry when she sees Dr Schön in the audience with his fiancée. She forces him to break off his engagement. Now married to Dr Schön, she still has lovers, including the lesbian Countess Geschwitz. In her husband's absence she entertains the Athlete, a Schoolboy and Schigolch, all of whom declare their love for her, followed by Alwa. Dr Schön has returned and brandishes a gun, but Lulu, claiming that he always knew what she was, shoots him. In an interlude she is arrested, tried, imprisoned, to be released through the agency of Countess Geschwitz and now the object of Alwa's declarations of love. Lulu's downfall begins in Paris, where she is blackmailed by the Athlete and by the Marquis. The failure of Jungfrau Railway shares brings financial ruin to everyone. Lulu persuades Geschwitz to spend the night with the Athlete. In London Lulu works as a prostitute, awaited by Alwa and Schigolch, as she returns with her first customer, the Professor. Countess Geschwitz appears, with Lulu's portrait from the first scene of the opera, a symbol of her beauty and its effect on all of them. Lulu's second customer is the Negro, who kills Alwa in an argument over money. Her third is Jack the Ripper, to the sound of material connected with Dr Schön. He kills Lulu and then stabs the Countess to death.

Berg's opera makes use of twelve-note serial technique, shaped to his own purposes, in a number of more or less conventional forms, sonata, rondo, variation and so on. Lulu herself is seen differently by the various people with whom she has contact, and the opera traces her rise and fall in more or less symmetrical halves. Berg died in 1935, leaving the third act sketched but not completed. Various early attempts to finish the work came to nothing, leading Berg's widow to forbid any use of the remaining sketches. It was not until 1979, three years after her death, that it proved possible to stage the whole work, completed by Friedrich Cerha. The work as a whole lacks the clear formal unity of Berg's earlier opera *Wozzeck*, its episodic structure dictated by the dramatic material on which it is based. For Wedekind and for Berg Lulu embodies amoral female sexuality.

The first play, *Erdgeist* (Earth Spirit), takes Lulu's progress up to the killing of Dr Schön, while the second, *Die Büchse der Pandora* (Pandora's Box) traces her relationship with Countess Geschwitz, her work as a prostitute and her death. Dramatically *Lulu* is powerful and demanding.

Lustige Witwe, Die (The Merry Widow)

- Franz Lehár. *Operette* in three acts. 1905.
- Libretto by Victor Léon and Leo Stein, after the play *L'attaché d'ambassade* (The Embassy Attaché) by Henri Meilhac.
- First performance at the Theater an der Wien, Vienna, on 30th December 1905.

Characters

Baron Mirko Zeta, Pontevedrin ambassador in Paris	baritone
Valencienne, his wife	soprano
Count Danilo Danilowitsch, cavalry officer, legation secretary	tenor
Hanna Glawari, a rich widow	soprano
Camille de Rosillon	tenor
Vicomte Cascada	baritone
Raoul de St Brioche	baritone
Bogdanowitsch, Pontevedrin consul	baritone
Sylviane, his wife	soprano
Kromow, counsellor at the Pontevedrin legation	baritone
Olga, his wife	mezzo-soprano
Pritschitsch, retired Pontevedrin colonel	baritone
Praskowia, his wife	mezzo-soprano
Njegus, clerk at the legation	speaking part
Lolo, Dodo, Jou-Jou, Frou-Frou, Clo-Clo Margot, girls from Maxim's	sopranos

Baron Mirko is anxious that the fortune left to the Pontevedrin widow Hanna Glawari by her banker husband should not be lost to their country. He therefore tries to force Count Danilo to marry her. Danilo resists the suggestion and there is, in any case, a rumour that she may marry the French Camille de Rosillon, who is in fact conducting a flirtation with the Pontevedrin envoy's wife. Hanna, whatever misunderstandings may take place, secretly loves Danilo, and he, in spite of his scruples against fortune-hunters, loves her, a love realised as the operetta comes to an end.

Die lustige Witwe (The Merry Widow) is probably the best known of all Lehár's operettas. Danilo expresses his resistance to any infringement of his liberty as a bachelor in Paris in *O Vaterland* (O fatherland), giving an outline of his busy day out of the office, with nights spent at Maxim's. Hanna Glawari evokes the spirit of her country in her famous *Vilja-Lied* (There was once a forest maiden). Camille woos Valencienne with *Wie eine Rosenknospe* (Like a rose-bud), transferring his addresses to Hanna, when they have been spied by Baron Mirko. The difficulties between Hanna and Danilo disappear in the third act waltz duet *Lippen schweigen* (Lips are silent).

Recommended Recordings:

Lippen schweigen	***Naxos 8.550941***
O Vaterland / Vilja-Lied	***Naxos 8.550942***

LUSTIGEN WEIBER VON WINDSOR, DIE (THE MERRY WIVES OF WINDSOR)

- Otto Nicolai. *Komische-fantastische Oper* in three acts. 1849.
- Libretto by Salomon Hermann Mosenthal, after the play by Shakespeare.
- First performance at the Königliches Opernhaus, Berlin, on 9th March 1849.

Nicolai's opera follows Shakespeare's play closely enough, with some changes of names. The Fords become Fluth, the Pages Reich and Slender Junker Spärlich. Falstaff's retainers are omitted, but the libretto follows his inept attempts to seduce the two Merry Wives, here Frau Fluth and Frau Reich, and his gulling, first escaping in a basket of dirty linen and then mocked by pretended fairies in Windsor Forest. The love affair between the young Anna Reich (Anne Page) and Fenton provides a lyrical contrast.

The opera opens with a popular overture and in the first act Mrs Ford and Mrs Page compare the identical love-letters that Falstaff has sent them, in the duet *Nein, das ist wirklich doch zu keck!* (No, that is really just too cheeky). The second act allows Fenton a *Romanze* as he waits for Anne in their family garden, *Horch, die lerche singt im Hain* (Hark, the lark sings in the grove) and something of the magic of Windsor Great Park at night is conjured up in the chorus *O süsser Mond* (O sweet moon).

Recommended Recordings:

Overture	***Naxos 8.550146***
O süsser Mond	***Naxos 8.550507***

Macbeth

- Giuseppe Verdi. Opera in four acts. 1847.
- Libretto by Francesco Maria Piave, after the play by Shakespeare.
- First performance at the Teatro della Pergola, Florence, on 14th March 1847.

Characters

Macbeth	baritone
Banco (Banquo), his fellow-general	bass
Duncano (Duncan),King of Scotland	silent rôle
Lady Macbeth, Macbeth's wife	soprano
Lady-in-waiting to Lady Macbeth	mezzo-soprano
Macduff, lord of Fife	tenor
Malcolm, Duncan's son	tenor
Fleanzio (Fleance), Banquo's son	silent rôle
Servant	bass
Doctor	bass
Murderer	bass
Ghost of Banco (Banquo)	silent rôle
Herald	bass

Shakespeare's three witches become a chorus of witches who greet Macbeth and Banquo with their prophecies. Lady Macbeth reads the letter from her husband that announces the coming of Duncan, who is murdered as he sleeps. The first act ends with Macduff's announcement of the murder. In the second act Macbeth, jealous of the future prophesied for Banquo's posterity, goes on to procure the murder of Banquo, whose ghost appears to haunt him. The third act brings the witches back, with an additional ballet for the French version of the opera given in Paris in 1865. The witches summon up apparitions that tell Macbeth what lies in store for him. The fourth act opens on the English border, where Malcolm leads a force against Macbeth. This is followed by the sleep-walking scene for Lady Macbeth, herself a prey, like her husband, to conscience. Malcolm's soldiers, camouflaged under branches, bring Birnam Wood to Dunsinane, as the witches had foretold. A cry of women marks the death of Lady Macbeth and her husband is killed in single combat with Macduff.

Verdi made a number of changes in *Macbeth*, the first of his Shakespearean operas, for the French version of 1865, in particular the necessary addition of a ballet at the start of the third act. In general the action follows Shakespeare, with the obvious necessary abridgements and omissions. The prelude makes use of material from the opera, in particular that associated with the witches in the third act and the famous sleep-walking scene of the fourth. Lady Macbeth's letter scene, *Nel dì della vittoria* (In the day of success) presents her as an immediately powerful figure. The exiled Scots under Malcolm echo patriotic sentiment in Italy in their *Patria oppressa* (Our country oppressed), while Macduff laments the reported murder of his wife and children in *Ah, la paterna mano* (Ah, a father's hand). Lady Macbeth appears in the first great sleep-walking scene of Italian opera, *Una macchia* (A spot), observed by her lady-in-waiting and the doctor. In the last scene, Macbeth, nearing his end, regrets his lack of those accompaniments of age, *Pietà, rispetto, amore* (Kindness, respect, love). The French version of the work ends with a hymn of victory, instead of Macbeth's final despair and death.

Recommended Recordings:

Overture	***Naxos 8.553089***
Patria oppressa	***Naxos 8.550241***
Ah la paterna mano	***Naxos 8.550497***

MACBETH

- Ernest Bloch. Lyric drama in a prologue and three acts. 1909.
- French libretto by Edmond Fleg, after the play by Shakespeare, with other versions in Italian and in English for later performances.
- First performance by the Paris Opéra-Comique at the Salle Favart on 2nd November 1910.

Bloch's opera follows Shakespeare in a treatment as much dramatic as operatic.

MADAMA BUTTERFLY

- Giacomo Puccini. *Tragedia giapponese* in two acts. 1903.
- Libretto by Giuseppe Giacosa and Luigi Illica, after the play *Madame Butterfly* by David Belasco, based on John Luther Long's story, a work indebted to Pierre Loti's *Madame Chrysanthème*.
- First performance at the Teatro alla Scala, Milan, on 28th May 1904.

CHARACTERS

Cio-Cio-San (Madame Butterfly)	soprano
Suzuki, her maid	mezzo-soprano
F.B.Pinkerton, Lieutenant in the American navy	tenor
Sharpless, American consul in Nagasaki	baritone
Goro, a marriage-broker	tenor
Prince Yamadori	tenor
The Bonze, Cio-Cio-San's uncle	bass
Yakuside, Cio-Cio-San's uncle	bass
Imperial Commissioner	bass
Official Registrar	bass
Cio-Cio-San's Mother	mezzo-soprano
Cio-Cio-San's Aunt	soprano
Cio-Cio-San's Cousin	soprano
Kate Pinkerton	mezzo-soprano
Dolore, Cio-Cio-San's child	silent rôle

Goro, the marriage-broker, shows Lieutenant Pinkerton the house where he will live with Cio-Cio-San, after their marriage, and introduces the servants. Pinkerton explains to the consul Sharpless, who has joined him, that he has the house on a long lease, to be terminated at a month's notice: his coming marriage is to be undertaken on similar terms, since he has no intention of continuing the relationship. Cio-Cio-San and her family arrive and the wedding takes place, interrupted by the Bonze, who curses her as a renegade. The company disperses, leaving Cio-Cio-San and Pinkerton alone together, as evening draws on. Three years later she awaits still the return of Pinkerton, who has never seen the son she has born him. Attempts are made by Goro to bring about another marriage, to Prince Yamadori. Eventually Pinkerton does return, having prepared Sharpless by a letter. He brings with him his American wife, and Cio-Cio-San kills herself with the knife that her father had used for his own death by imperial command.

Madama Butterfly is one of Puccini's most moving operas, its drama centred on Cio-Cio-San, whose childish innocence at her marriage and continued ingenuous faith are contrasted with the callousness of Pinkerton. Japanese melodies are used to provide an element of authenticity, with American musical references to mark Pinkerton's primary loyalties. There is a fine extended love duet for Cio-Cio-San and Pinkerton at the end of the first act, *Viene la sera* (Evening approaches), with her later *Un bel dì vedremo* (One fine day we shall see) among the best known of all Italian operatic arias. As Pinkerton's ship returns, she and Suzuki decorate the house with cherry-blossom, *Scuoti quella fronda di ciliegio* (Shake that cherry-tree branch), while the *Humming Chorus* provides an interlude before Pinkerton's delayed appearance, for which she has waited so long. He feels a touch of sorrow at what he has done, as he bids the little house farewell in *Addio, fiorito asil* (Farewell, happy home).

Recommended Recordings:

Madama Butterfly (2 CDs)	***Naxos 8.660015-16***
Highlights	***Naxos 8.553152***

MADAME SANS-GÊNE (MADAME CAREFREE)

- Umberto Giordano. Opera in three acts. 1915.
- Libretto by Renato Simoni, after the comedy by Victorien Sardou and Emile Moreau.
- First performance at the Metropolitan Opera, New York, on 25th January 1915.

Giordano's opera opens in Paris in 1792, where the laundress Caterina, the carefree Madame Sans-Gêne of the title, shelters a fugitive Austrian nobleman, the Count of Neipperg, and provides laundry for Napoleon, as the revolution continues. The second act, in 1811, finds Napoleon at the height of his power, with Caterina's husband, formerly Sergeant Lefèbvre, now Duke of Danzig. Caterina incurs general displeasure by her failure to adapt to new circumstances of elegance. The third act puts an end to suspicions of intrigue between the Empress and Neipperg, and to the difficulties of Caterina and her husband.

Like *Andrea Chénier* the opera makes use of appropriate revolutionary musical material in the first act. Giordano's realistic comedy was conducted by Toscanini at its first performance, but has won no lasting place in repertoire.

Maddalena

- Sergey Prokofiev. Opera in one act. 1913. Completed by Edward Downes for concert performance in 1978.
- Libretto by the composer, after the play by Baron Liven (Magda Gustavovna Liven-Orlova).
- First staged performance at the Opernhaus, Graz, on 28th November 1981.

Set in 15th century Venice, the opera deals with the rivalry in love of the painter Genaro and the alchemist Stenio, who kill each other over the former's wife, Maddalena.

Prokofiev wrote his one act opera quickly in 1911, while still a student at the Conservatory in St Petersburg, hoping for a performance there. He orchestrated only one of the four scenes and rewrote much of the music in 1913.

Magic Flute, The (see Zauberflöte, Die)

Magic Fountain, The

- Frederick Delius. Lyric drama in three acts. 1895.
- Libretto by the composer.
- First broadcast performance by the BBC, London, on 20th November 1977.

The Spanish nobleman Solano seeks the magic fountain of eternal youth and ship-wrecked on the coast of Florida is tended by the Indian princess Watawa. She seeks revenge for Spanish cruelty to her people and leads him to the fountain, the water of which proves fatal both to her and to Solano, whom she has come to love.

The second of the operas of Delius, *The Magic Fountain,* was to form part of a trilogy dealing with Florida, where he had been sent by his father to manage a plantation of oranges. *Koanga*, completed in 1897, proved the most successful of these projected works.

Mahagonny

- Kurt Weill. *Songspiel* in three parts. 1927.
- Text from Bertolt Brecht's *Hauspostille* (House Mag).
- First performance in the Grosser Bühnensaal of the Kurhaus, Baden-Baden, on 17th July 1927.

Mahagonny formed the basis of the opera *Aufstieg und Fall der Stadt Mahagonny* (Rise and Fall of the City of Mahagonny), which expanded and replaced it. In a series of "songs" the decadence of contemporary capitalist society is shown, with whisky, women and gambling the chief preoccupations of the imaginary city of Mahagonny. The work, for which Weill coined the idiosyncratic descriptive title *Songspiel*, is scored for a jazz ensemble to which two violins are added. Brecht's title *Mahagonny*, his own coinage from the German *Mahagoni* (mahogany), seems to have come to his mind at the sight of Hitler's Brown Shirts at the time of the abortive 1923 Putsch.

Maid of Orleans, The

- Pyotr Il'yich Tchaikovsky. Opera in four acts. 1879.
- Libretto by the composer, after Vasily Andreyevich Zhukovsky's translation of Friedrich von Schiller's tragedy, Jules Barbier's *Jeanne d'Arc* (Joan of Arc) and a libretto by Auguste Mermet.
- First performance at the Mariinsky Theatre, St Petersburg, on 25th February 1881.

Characters

Joan of Arc	mezzo-soprano (later modified for soprano)
Charles VII, King of France	tenor
Agnès Sorel, his mistress	soprano
Dunois, a French knight	baritone
Lionel, a Burgundian knight	baritone
Thibaut, Joan's father	bass
Raymond, Joan's betrothed	tenor
Bertrand, an old peasant	bass
Archbishop	bass
Lauret	bass
Soldier	bass
Angel Voice	soprano

At a village festival near Domrémy, Thibaut urges his daughter Joan to marry Raymond. News comes of a threatened English attack, but Joan prophesies the death of the English commander, which is immediately confirmed by a soldier. She embarks on her mission to save France. Charles, at the castle of Chinon, is entertained, while his mistress Agnès Sorel offers to help raise money for the empty royal treasury. The knight Dunois leaves him in disgust, when the King chooses retreat rather than do battle with the English. The Archbishop brings news of victory, with the French led by a young woman. Joan is brought in and convinces the King of her genuine powers. In battle near Rheims Joan fights the Burgundian Lionel, whom she defeats, falling in love with him and sparing his life. Lionel deserts to the French side. At the coronation of the King, Joan is denounced as a sorceress by her father and secretly admits the charge, looking at Lionel. In a dense forest she meets Lionel, guilty now at betraying her divine mission. English soldiers kill Lionel and take her prisoner. In the final scene Joan is burned at the stake.

The sixth of Tchaikovsky's operas, *The Maid of Orleans*, was written after the completion of *Eugene Onegin* and in the difficult months that followed the break-down of his short-lived marriage. Probably the best known excerpt from the opera is Joan's farewell to her native village, known in French as *Adieu, fôrets* (Farewell, forests).

MAID OF PSKOV, THE

- Nikolay Andreyevich Rimsky-Korsakov. Opera in a prologue and three acts. 1872. Revised for productions in 1895 and in 1901.
- Libretto by the composer, after a play by Lev Alexandorvich Mey.
- First performance at the Mariinsky Theatre, St Petersburg, on 13th January 1873.

Princess Olga, reputed daughter of Prince Yury Ivanovich Tokmakov, viceroy in Pskov, is promised in marriage to Matuta, a friend and contemporary of Prince Yury, as she tells Tucha, a bailiff's son, before overhearing the revelation from her supposed father that she is the daughter of another. The forces of Tsar Ivan the Terrible approach Pskov and Tucha organizes resistance. The Tsar's attack ends when he finds out that Olga is really his own daughter, but she is killed when Tucha attacks the Tsar's armies, unaware that hostilities have been ended.

Rimsky-Korsakov's first opera, *The Maid of Pskov*, presents a dilemma for the heroine Olga, in love with the leader of republican opposition to the Tsar and loving, too, her father, the Tsar. Capital of the Pskov region, the city of Pskov was an outpost of Novgorod, destroyed by Ivan the Terrible, who spared Pskov, for whatever reason. The unhistorical story on which the opera is based sought to explain the Tsar's unexpected decision.

MAKROPULOS AFFAIR, THE

- Leoš Janáček. Opera in three acts. 1925.
- Libretto by the composer, after Karel Čapek's comedy.
- First performance at the National Theatre, Brno, on 18th December 1926.

Characters

Emilia Marty, a famous opera singer	dramatic soprano
Albert Gregor	tenor
Dr Kolenatý, his lawyer	bass-baritone
Vítek, his clerk	tenor
Kristina, Vítek's daughter, a young singer	soprano
Baron Jaroslav Prus, a lawyer	baritone
Janek, his son	tenor
Cleaning Woman	contralto
Stage Technician	bass
Hauk-Šendorf	operetta tenor
Chambermaid	contralto
Doctor	silent rôle

The alchemist Hieronymus Makropulos had provided the Habsburg Emperor Rudolf with an elixir, that was first to be tested on the alchemist's own daughter. She became ill and the alchemist was put to death, but later the elixir began to work. Emilia Marty has now lived some three hundred years, using different names, but always with the initials of her original name, Elina Makropulos. The opera at first is concerned with a law-suit that has lasted a hundred years over the property left by Baron Prus, who had had an illegitimate son with Elian MacGregor. The first act opens in Dr Kolenatý's office, where the case between Albert Gregor and the present Baron Prus is being discussed. The clerk Vítek's daughter Kristina is an admirer of the great opera singer Emilia Marty, who is ushered in by Dr Kolenatý and shows considerable knowledge of the case, telling him where the former Baron Prus's will may be found. She is overheard by Albert Gregor, who is fascinated by her. The lawyer returns with the will and Emilia Marty is still interested in regaining certain Greek papers that must still be in the possession of the present Baron Prus. In the theatre after Emilia Marty's performance, various admirers wait for her, including Kristina, with her lover Janek, and Gregor, who offers flowers and jewels to Marty. Old Hauk-Šendorf recalls times in Spain with Eugenia Montez, whom, it seems, Marty closely resembles. She persuades Prus to bring her the documents she wants and he tells her of his discovery of a birth registration for Elina Makropulos, the E.M., perhaps, of the letters in his possession. In the third act Prus has made love to Marty, finding her cold and unresponsive. He gives her the paper she wants, the formula of the old alchemist's elixir. Prus is called out, to learn that his son Janek, infatuated with Marty, has killed himself. Hauk-Šendorf comes in, with his wife's jewels, proposing that he and Marty should elope to Spain. He is followed by Gregor, Dr Kolenatý, Vítek, Kristina, Prus and a doctor. A study of the handwriting on various documents has suggested to them that Marty is a forger. She confesses to them the truth, which they finally believe, and offers the formula to Kristina, who burns it, as Emilia Marty dies.

Janáček's opera is dominated by the character of Emilia Marty, the object of fascination to those she encounters, but finally cold and disillusioned in a meaningless existence of over three hundred years. The opera lacks any element of the spectacular, and this inevitably concentrates all attention on the powerful musical treatment of the drama and the protagonist.

Malheurs d'Orphée, Les (The Misfortunes of Orpheus)

- Darius Milhaud. Chamber opera in three acts. 1924.
- Libretto by Armand Lunel.
- First performance at the Théâtre de la Monnaie, Brussels, on 7th May 1926.

The peasant Orpheus resolves to marry the gypsy Eurydice. To avoid her relatives, they escape to the mountains, where she succumbs to a mysterious disease, to be carried away by the animals that mourn her. Orpheus returns to his village, where Eurydice's gypsy sisters accuse him of her death and kill him, later realising their mistake.

Milhaud's short chamber opera is scored for thirteen instruments, with music that he described as stripped to its bare essentials. The mourning chorus and funeral cortège of Eurydice are sometimes performed out of their dramatic context.

Mamelles de Tirésias, Les (The Breasts of Tiresias)

- Francis Poulenc. *Opéra bouffe* in a prologue and two acts. 1944.
- Libretto by the composer, after the play by Guillaume Apollinaire.
- First performance by the Paris Opéra-Comique at the Salle Favart on 3rd June 1947.

Characters

Theatre Director	baritone
Thérèse	soprano
Her Husband	tenor
Monsieur Lacouf	tenor
Monsieur Presto	baritone
Gendarme	baritone
Newspaper Vendor	mezzo-soprano

Reporter from Paris	tenor
Son	baritone
Audience:	
An Elegant Lady	mezzo-soprano
A Woman	mezzo-soprano
A Bearded Gentleman	bass

Set in Zanzibar, an imaginary town somewhere on the French riviera, between Nice and Monte Carlo, the opera opens with a prologue in which the Theatre Director addresses the audience in an extended aria. Thérèse, a feminist with military ambitions, appears, denying her husband. Her breasts, represented by balloons, escape from her blouse and float upwards and she starts to grow a beard. Her husband, coming out of the house, thinks that the stranger that he sees has killed his wife and donned her clothes, until she explains to him that she is no longer Thérèse, but now Tirésias. Thin Lacouf and fat Presto emerge from a café, quarrelling and finally shooting each other, mourned by Thérèse-Tirésias in elegant male clothing and her husband dressed as a housewife, now courted by the Gendarme and proclaiming the fertility of men. In the second part the husband has achieved remarkable success, with forty thousand babies in a day, and is interviewed by a journalist. The husband boasts that one of his children has already written a best-seller. When the journalist asks for a small loan, he is quickly sent packing. It seems that the more children you have, the richer you will be, but the creation of a journalist he tries to make works out badly. The Gendarme complains about the sudden increase in population, to be fed, the husband suggests, by taking ration cards from the fortune-teller's. When the fortune-teller appears she advises further children, reproaching the Gendarme with sterility and finally strangling him, before revealing herself as Thérèse in person. Her husband is pleased, the Gendarme comes to life again, and she and her husband waltz together. He buys some balloons, but to no perceptible effect.

An allusive and witty score matches Apollinaire's text, with comic music and often traditional forms to accompany its absurdities. Poulenc also prepared a version of the work for accompaniment by two pianos. He aptly described the work as crammed with music and madly scenic, each event on the stage connected with the music.

Manon

- Jules Massenet. *Opéra comique* in five acts. 1883.
- Libretto by Henri Meilhac and Philippe Gille, after the novel *L'histoire du chevalier des Grieux et de Manon Lescaut* by the Abbé Prévost.
- First performance by the Paris Opéra-Comique at the Salle Favart on 19th January 1884.

Characters

Manon Lescaut	soprano
Chevalier des Grieux	tenor
Comte des Grieux, his father	bass
Poussette	mezzo-soprano
Javotte actresses	mezzo-soprano
Rosette	mezzo-soprano
Lescaut, Manon's cousin	baritone
Guillot de Morfontaine, an elderly roué	tenor
De Brétigny, a nobleman	baritone
Innkeeper	baritone
Two Guardsmen	tenor & baritone
Maid	mezzo-soprano

In the courtyard of an inn at Amiens the coach from Arras arrives, bringing the fifteen-year-old Manon, to be met by her cousin, on her way to a convent, where her father is sending her. Guillot, who has been waiting for his dinner at the inn with de Brétigny and the three actresses, Poussette, Javotte and Rosette, approaches her, offering her, among other things, the use of his coach. She is reproached by her cousin, but dazzled by the apparent luxury in which others seem to live. Des Grieux, who is travelling to see his father, catches sight of Manon and falls in love with her and the two take Guillot's coach and escape together to Paris. Living together there, des Grieux seeks permission from his father to marry, but Lescaut and de Brétigny arrive, suggesting to Manon a more luxurious existence and telling her that des Grieux is to be carried off, on his father's orders. In the Cours-la-Reine in Paris the three actresses have escaped, for a moment, the vigiliance of Guillot. Manon enters escorted by her new protector, de Brétigny, and learns from the Comte des Grieux that his son is to be ordained priest. She orders her coach to take her to St Sulpice, where des Grieux is to preach, leaving Guillot humiliated again, having obeyed her whim of inviting the opera ballet for her entertainment, something denied her by de Brétigny. At the seminary of St Sulpice Manon meets des Grieux, who now gives up his intention to enter the priesthood, his love re-awakened. In the fourth act, at the Hôtel Transylvanie, Lescaut and the actresses are gambling, joined by Guillot. Manon and des Grieux enter and he is induced to gamble as well, now his fortune is almost exhausted. He wins, but Guillot accuses him of cheating and has him arrested, supported by the Comte des Grieux, who hopes to bring his son to his senses. Manon is arrested as his accomplice, and while des Grieux is quickly released, she is condemned, for her immoral way of life, to transportation. Attempts to secure her release fail, but Lescaut bribes the sergeant and she is allowed a final moment with des Grieux in which they recall their earlier happiness. Broken, she dies, begging his forgiveness.

Massenet's opera, probably his best known, contains a remarkable portrait of Manon, as she grows from wide-eyed innocence to a guilty womanhood. There are some ambiguities in the character of Lescaut, her brother in the original novel, but now her cousin, combining in himself the character of guardian of the family honour, bragging soldier and loyal friend of des Grieux. In Paris Manon reads back to des Grieux the letter he has written to his father, seeking permission to marry her, *On l'appelle Manon* (She is called Manon). By the end of the second act she is bidding farewell to her relatively humble existence with des Grieux in *Adieu, petite table* (Farewell, little table). In a moment of dramatic irony, des Grieux returns to tell her of the country retreat where they will live, *En fermant les yeux* (Closing our eyes), followed, as the scene ends, by his abduction. At the Cours-la-Reine Manon is enjoying the luxury that association with de Brétigny has brought her, expressing her satisfaction in *Je marche sur tous les chemins* (I step proudly every way). Des Grieux has music of particular poignancy in the last act, where he is parted from Manon for ever.

Manon Lescaut

- Giacomo Puccini. *Dramma lirico* in four acts. 1892. Revised for Milan in 1894.
- Libretto by Domenico Oliva and Luigi Illica, after the novel *L'histoire du chevalier des Grieux et de Manon Lescaut* by the Abbé Prévost.
- First performance at the Teatro Regio, Turin, on 1st February 1893.

Characters

Manon Lescaut	soprano
Lescaut, her brother, Sergeant of the Royal Guards	baritone
Il cavaliere des Grieux, a student	tenor
Geronte di Ravoir, Treasurer-General	bass
Edmondo, a student	tenor
Innkeeper	bass
Singer	mezzo-soprano
Dancing-Master	tenor
Lamplighter	tenor
Sergeant of the Royal Archers	bass
Naval Captain	bass

In a square in Amiens Edmond and other students tease the girls, as they go home. Des Grieux, also a student, does not join in their banter. The Arras coach arrives, bringing Géronte, the Treasurer-General, Lescaut, a soldier, and his sister Manon. Des Grieux falls in love with her and seeks some way of preventing her entry into a convent, where her father is sending her. Géronte, with Lescaut's connivance, plans to abduct Manon, but is overheard by Edmond. Des Grieux and Manon escape in Géronte's coach. In the second act Manon has already been tempted to leave des Grieux and is living a dull if relatively luxurious life with Géronte. Lescaut arranges for des Grieux, now introduced by him to gambling, to visit her and she seeks his forgiveness. They are interrupted by Géronte and Lescaut now enters, warning them that the old man has denounced Manon to the authorities. She tries to collect her jewellery and other belongings, but is caught and arrested before she can escape. Imprisoned, she is sentenced to be transported, events covered in an orchestral interlude. At Le Havre Lescaut tries to bribe the guards to allow his sister to escape, but fails. Des Grieux, however, is able to exchange words with her, at the window of her prison. He persuades the captain of the ship that will take her and the other convicts to America to allow him to sail with them as a cabin-boy. In the fourth act des Grieux has had a duel with the son of the French governor of the province and he and Manon have escaped, hoping to cross the desert to British territory. He leaves her, searching for water, and when he returns she is already dying, pledging him her love in her last breath.

Puccini's libretto is far more succinct than that used by Massenet and makes for a more satisfactory, shorter and more coherent opera. The text for Puccini, however, caused a number of difficulties, making use of the services first of the playwright Marco Praga and the poet Domenico Praga, then of Leoncavallo and finally of Luigi Illica. Des Grieux expresses his search for love in the first scene, with *Tra voi, belle* (Amongst you, fair ones), finding what he has sought in *Donna non vidi mai* (Never saw I such a lady). With *In quelle trine morbide* (In those dull hangings), Manon regrets the boredom of her life with Géronte, greeting with rapture des Grieux, in *Tu, tu, amore? Tu?!* (You, you, my love? You?). He senses her weakness in *Ah! Manon, mi tradisce il tuo folle pensier* (Ah! Manon, your foolish thoughts betray me), as she seeks to take with her the jewels Géronte has given her. There is a moving *Intermezzo*, a recollection of past joys, as Manon is tried and condemned and as she lies dying in the desert waste she sings her final *Sola, perduta, abbandonata* (Alone, lost, forsaken).

Recommended Recording:
Manon Lescaut (2 CDs) ***Naxos 8.660019-20***

MANON LESCAUT

- Daniel-François-Esprit Auber. *Opéra comique* in three acts. 1856.
- Libretto by Eugène Scribe, after the novel *L'histoire du chevalier des Grieux et de Manon Lescaut* by the Abbé Prévost.
- First performance by the Paris Opéra Comique at the Salle Favart on 23rd February 1856.

Scribe's libretto makes a number of changes in the story of Manon Lescaut, retaining the essential relationship between Manon and des Grieux, with the former's love of luxury but with a more complicated fate for des Grieux, obliged to enlist in her protector's regiment, to settle a debt arising from the dishonesty of her cousin Lescaut. *C'est l'histoire amoureuse* (It is the story of love) remains a popular excerpt from the first act, where Manon seeks to earn money as a café singer. As in Puccini's opera, Manon dies in the arms of des Grieux in the Louisiana desert.

MAOMETTO II (MEHMED II)

- Gioachino Rossini. *Dramma* in two acts. 1820.
- Libretto by Cesare della Valle, after his verse drama *Anna Erizo*, perhaps influenced by Byron's *The Siege of Corinth*.
- First performance at the Teatro S Carlo, Naples, on 3rd December 1820.

CHARACTERS

General Condulmiero	tenor
Paolo Erisso, governor of Negroponte	tenor
Anna, his daughter	soprano
Maometto II	bass
General Calbo	contralto
Selimo	tenor

The opera is set in the historical context of the fall of the Venetian colony of Negroponte to the Turks in 1476. The Venetian governor Paolo Erisso intends his daughter Anna to marry Calbo, but she loves Uberto, whom she had met in Corinth. Uberto turns out to be Mehmed II in disguise. Anna suffers a conflict between duty and love, choosing the former in marriage to Calbo and final death by her own hand as the Turkish forces storm Negroponte. For performance in Venice Rossini substituted a happy ending, with victory for the Venetian soldiers.

Maometto II was reworked by Rossini as *Le siège de Corinthe* (The Siege of Corinth), the action shifted to a Greek city to fit contemporary circumstances of the Greek War of Independence. The first act contains the famous *terzettone* or grand trio, for Anna, Erisso and Calbo, *Ohimè! qual fulmine* (Alas! What a thunderbolt), when Uberto is revealed to her as an impostor. This has been preceded by Anna's *cavatina*, *Ah! che invan su questo ciglio* (Ah! That in vain on these eyes), in which she dreads what is to come. The trio is followed by her prayer *Giusto Cielo, in tal periglio* (Just Heaven, in such danger) as the Turkish forces break into the town. Calbo comforts Erisso by praise of Anna's virtue in the aria *Non temer: d'un basso affetto* (Do not fear: of a base feeling that heart was incapable).55

Recommended Recording: Non temer ***Naxos 8.553543***

MARIA DE ROHAN (MARIA OF ROHAN)

- Gaetano Donizetti. *Melodramma tragico* in three acts. 1843.
- Libretto by Salvadore Cammarano, after the play *Un duel sous le Cardinal de Richelieu* (A Duel under Cardinal Richelieu).
- First performed at the Kärntnertortheater, Vienna, on 5th June 1843.

Maria, married to the Duc de Chevreuse, imprisoned for killing the nephew of Cardinal Richelieu in a duel, asks her former lover Riccardo, Comte de Chalais, for help and he, hearing Maria insulted, challenges her enemy to a duel. Chevreuse, now released, promises to be his second. Maria tries to prevent the duel, confessing her renewed love for Riccardo, who writes a letter of farewell to her, to be delivered if he dies. Chevreuse fights the duel in his place and is slightly hurt, but meanwhile documents have been seized from Riccardo's rooms by the Cardinal's men. Chevreuse shows Riccardo a secret passage through which he can escape, and Riccardo urges Maria to follow him. He returns to fetch her, but Chevreuse now has the letter and Maria admits her guilt. Chevreuse challenges Riccardo, who kills himself and Maria is left to mourn him.

There is a fine scene for the baritone Chevreuse in the third act *Bella e di sol vestita* (Fair and robed in the sun). Maria has her own moving first act entrance aria in *Cupa, fatal mestizia* (Dark, fatal sadness), while Riccardo has his moment in his second act aria *Alma soave e cara* (Gentle and dear soul), as he thinks of his likely death in his duel with the man who has insulted Maria.

MARIA DE RUDENZ (MARIA OF RUDENZ)

- Gaetano Donizetti. *Dramma tragico* in three acts. 1838.

- Libretto by Salvadore Cammarano, after the play *La nonne sanglante* (The Blood-Stained Nun) by Bourgeois, Cuvelier and de Mallian, based on *The Monk* by Matthew Lewis.
- First performance at the Teatro La Fenice, Venice, on 30th January 1838.

Donizetti's opera allows the heroine of the title to have two death scenes, the second one final. Corrado elopes with Maria and deserts her, plotting to marry her sister, the heiress Matilde, loved by his brother Enrico. Taking her revenge, she shows Corrado Matilde's tomb. He stabs her and she seems to die. Enrico challenges Corrado to a duel and is killed by him, while Maria, coming to life again, stabs Matilde and then dies again in front of Corrado, the sole survivor.

In spite of its lurid plot, with its Gothic secret passages and trap-doors, *Maria de Rudenz* contains some fine music, including Maria's *larghetto, Sì, del chiostro penitente* (Yes, penitent in the cloister).

Maria egiziaca (The Egyptian Mary)

- Ottorino Respighi. *Mistero* (*Trittico per concerto*). 1932.
- Libretto by Claudio Guastalla, after *Le vite dei santi padri* (The Lives of the Holy Fathers) by Fra Domenico Cavalca.
- First staged performance at the Teatro Goldoni, Venice, on 10th August 1932.

Originally semi-staged, *Maria egiziaca* follows the 14th century life of St Mary, originally a prostitute, who continued her old profession in order to pay for a pilgrimage to Jerusalem, followed by years of repentance as a desert hermit.

In his score for this mystery play Respighi made full use of earlier forms of music, as he had elsewhere in his work. *Maria egiziaca* is in three episodes, a concert triptych in original intention.

Maria Padilla

- Gaetano Donizetti. *Melodramma* in three acts. 1841.
- Libretto by Gaetano Rossi and the composer, after the play by François Ancelot.
- First performance at the Teatro alla Scala, Milan, on 26th December 1841.

Abducted by King Pedro the Cruel, Maria Padilla accepts her situation, on the understanding that she will become Queen. Her father, punished for his objections, goes mad, and Maria kills herself when King Pedro finds himself obliged to marry a French princess.

Donizetti's opera for La Scala in Milan was eclipsed by the success of Verdi's *Nabucco*. The demanding nature of the title rôle may have contributed to its subsequent neglect.

Maria Stuarda (Mary Stuart)

- Gaetano Donizetti. *Tragedia lirica* in two acts. 1835.
- Libretto by Giuseppe Bardari, after the play *Maria Stuart* by Friedrich von Schiller.
- First performance at the Teatro alla Scala, Milan, on 30th December 1835.

Characters

Elisabetta (Elizabeth), Queen of England	soprano
Maria Stuarda (Mary Stuart), Queen of Scots	soprano
Anna (Hannah Kennedy), her lady-in-waiting	mezzo-soprano
Leicester (Robert Dudley), Earl of Leicester)	tenor
Talbot, Earl of Shrewsbury	baritone
Cecil, Lord Burleigh	bass
Herald	bass

Queen Elizabeth considers marriage to the Dauphin, but is in love with Leicester, who is persuaded by Talbot to arrange a meeting between Queen Mary and the English Queen. Elizabeth is now jealous of Leicester's attachment to her cousin. She visits Mary at Fotheringay, where she has been held prisoner, but the meeting brings conflict between the two, with Mary eventually stung into reproaching Elizabeth for her illegitimacy. At Westminster Cecil urges Mary's execution, while Leicester pleads for her life, arousing Elizabeth's jealousy once more. The death warrant is taken to Fotheringay, where Mary makes her confession to Talbot, now revealed as a priest, and goes to her execution, witnessed, as the English Queen had commanded, by Leicester.

Leicester's love for Mary is re-awakened when Talbot hands him a miniature of her. This he expresses in the first act *Ah! rimiro il bel sembiante* (Ah! I see again the fair likeness). The scene between the two Queens is a remarkable one, with Elizabeth angry at a woman she sees as *sempre la stessa, superba, orgogliosa* (always the same, haughty, proud), while Mary is provoked into reminding her of her parentage, *figlia impura di Bolena* (tainted daughter of Anne Boleyn). Most moving of all is the final scene, in which Mary utters her final prayer and faces death with noble serenity.

Marino Faliero

- Gaetano Donizetti. *Tragedia lirica* in three acts. 1835.
- Libretto by Giovanni Emanuele Bidera, revised by Agustino Ruffini, after the tragedy by Casimir Delavigne.
- First performance at the Théâtre Italien, Paris, on 12th March 1835.

Marino Faliero, Doge of Venice, is involved in a plot against the Council. His wife Elena has been unfaithful to him with his nephew Fernando, to whom she gives her scarf as a token. Fernando is mortally wounded in a duel with Elena's accuser, Steno, and asks to be buried with the scarf. The plot against the Council is discovered and Marino Faliero is executed, after forgiving his wife for her behaviour and asking that the scarf be used too for his burial.

Marino Faliero was Donizetti's first opera for Paris, at the invitation of Rossini. It brought to a final head the rivalry between him and Bellini, who had been in Paris since 1833 but died in September 1835. Rossini helped Bellini with practical advice and may well have performed the same service for Donizetti.

Maritana

- Vincent Wallace. Grand opera in three acts. 1845.
- Libretto by Edward Fitzball, after the play *Don César de Bazan* by Adolphe Philippe d'Ennery and Philippe François Pinel Dumanoir.
- First performance at Drury Lane, London, on 15th November 1845.

Characters

Maritana, a handsome gypsy girl	soprano
Don Caesar de Bazan, an impoverished nobleman	tenor
Don José de Santarem, a courtier	baritone
Lazarillo, a poor boy	mezzo-soprano
The Marchioness of Montefiore	mezzo-soprano
Captain of the Guard	baritone
Marquis of Montefiore	bass
Charles II, King of Spain	bass
The Alcalde	bass

Don José seeks to further his designs on the Queen of Spain by helping the King in his pursuit of the gypsy street-singer Maritana. Don Caesar returns to Madrid and, although duelling is now a capital offence to be rewarded by hanging, challenges a Captain of the Guard to a duel, in order to help the escape of an apprentice boy, Lazarillo. In prison Don José offers Don Caesar the chance of being shot rather than hanged, if he will marry a veiled woman, before his execution. He hopes by this to give the King access to Maritana. In the event Lazarillo has taken the bullets out of the guns of the firing-squad and Don Caesar escapes, now eager to find his mysterious bride. He had, in fact, been pardoned by the King, but Don José had prevented the delivery of the message. Maritana has been taken to the Marquis of Montefiore's castle, but will not hear the King's protestations, having fallen in love with Don Caesar. He now appears and would sign away his rights, when confronted by the aging Marchioness, who has taken Maritana's place, but soon recognises his true bride. The third act brings Don Caesar face to face with the King and allows misunderstandings to be put right. Don José is killed, when he brings the Queen to see the infidelity of the King that he has abetted, and Don Caesar is now united with Maritana.

Maritana won wide success, both in English and in an Italian translation. Don Caesar's *Yes, let me like a soldier fall*, in which he welcomes shooting rather than hanging, was once in popular drawing-room repertoire and the opera has recently been revived.

Recommended Recording:
Maritana (2 CDs) ***Marco Polo 8.223406-07***

Marriage of Figaro, The (see Nozze di Figaro, Le)

Martha

- Friedrich Flotow. Romantic comic opera in four acts. 1847.
- Libretto by W. Friedrich, after the ballet-pantomime *Lady Henriette, ou La servante de Greenwich* (Lady Harriet, or The Servant of Greenwich) by Jules Henri Vernoy de Saint-Georges.
- First performance at the Kärntnertortheater, Vienna, on 25th November 1847.

Characters

Lady Harriet Durham, maid of honour to Queen Anne	soprano
Sir Tristan Mickleford, her cousin	bass
Plumkett, a young farmer	bass

Lyonel, his foster-brother, later Earl of Derby	tenor
Nancy, waiting-maid to Lady Harriet	mezzo-soprano
Sheriff	bass
Three Manservants	tenor & basses
Three Maidservants	soprano & mezzo-sopranos

Lady Harriet is bored with life, particularly with the attentions of her elderly cousin, Sir Tristan Mickleford. With her maid Nancy, she decides to go to Richmond Fair, where girls hire themselves out each year as servants. In spite of Sir Tristan's efforts, the two are hired, Lady Harriet, now disguised as Martha, by Lyonel and Nancy by Plumkett, and had hoped at this point to end the prank, but Sir Tristan had been driven away by the hostile crowd. As servants the girls are useless, as Nancy is careful to demonstrate, while Lyonel falls in love with the disguised Lady Harriet. In the night the two escape and return to their old life. Lyonel, entrusted as a baby to the care of Plumkett's mother, is revealed in the fourth act as the rightful Earl of Derby, while Nancy is in love with Plumkett. Both couples are finally united.

In the second act Lady Harriet sings to her new master the Irish folk-song *The Last Rose of Summer*, a song that is recalled in the final scene. There is a tuneful duet for Lyonel and Plumkett in *Ja, seit früher Kindheit Tagen* (Yes, since the days of early childhood). The third act brings the tenor Lyonel's *Ach so fromm* (Ah so good) in a score that has a wealth of melody to commend it. It remains the best known opera by Flotow.

Recommended Recording: M'appari tutt'amor (Ach, so fromm) ***Naxos 8.551172***

MARTYRDOM OF ST MAGNUS, THE

- Peter Maxwell Davies. Chamber opera in nine scenes. 1976.
- Libretto by the composer, after the novel by George Mackay Brown.
- First performance at St Magnus Cathedral, Kirkwall, on 17th June 1977.

The death of St Magnus at the hands of Hakon, Earl of Orkney, and his henchman Lifolf, presents the martyr as a universal victim, from the Battle of Menai Straits between Welsh and Vikings, through temptation, to the final murder, a death that was needed. Blind Mary, who serves as a chorus, is finally cured through the saint's intercession, leaving her to ask how long sacrifices such as this should continue.

The opera calls for five singers in 26 rôles, with a small instrumental group of eleven players. It was written for the first St Magnus Festival in Orkney and starting from plainchant develops musical material to fit the dramatic material, as it moves to the present day, with its possibilities of the sacrifice of an individual to an ideology.

Martyrs, Les (see Poliuto)

Mask of Orpheus, The

- Harrison Birtwistle. Lyric tragedy in three acts. 1984.
- Libretto by Peter Zinovieff.
- First performance at the Coliseum, London, on 21st May 1986.

Various myths of Orpheus, some contradictory, are presented in a complex work in which Orpheus, Eurydice and Aristaeus are represented in three ways, as Man or Woman, as Hero or Heroine, and as Myth, as singer, mime and puppet. The complicated and intricate symbolism of the work is matched by the score, with its use of pre-recorded electronic tapes, in particular for mimed interludes, and its dramatic time distortions that offer alternative versions of the myths.

Maskarade (Masquerade)

- Carl Nielsen. Comic opera in three acts. 1906
- Libretto by Vilhelm Anderson after the play by Ludwig Holberg.
- First performance at the Royal Theatre, Copenhagen, on 11th November 1906.

Set in 1723, the opera open in the house of Jeronimus, whose son Leander is in love and has exchanged rings with a girl he had met at a dance the evening before. His servant Henrik points out that this may bring complications, since his father has arranged a match for him with a neighbour's daughter. Leander's mother, Magdelone, plans also to go the masquerade, but the scene is interrupted by Jeronimus, who forbids them from any such entertainment. His neighbour Leonard enters, complaining that his daughter has fallen in love. Henrik, by a trick, helps Leander to make his way to the masquerade, where he meets his beloved Leonora. Magdelone and Leonard join the entertainment, followed finally by Jeronimus. It is only when the masks are finally removed that all is revealed. Leonora is Leonard's daughter, the girl that Jeronmius had intended his son to marry.

The overture to *Maskarade* is well enough known in concert performance, as is the *Dance of the Cockerels* from the masquerade from the third act.

Masnadieri, I (The Bandits)

- Giuseppe Verdi. *Melodramma* in four parts. 1847.
- Libretto by Andrea Maffei, based on the play *Die Räuber* (The Bandits) by Friedrich von Schiller.
- First performance at Her Majesty's Theatre, London, on 22nd July 1847.

Characters

Massimiliano, Count Moor	bass
Carlo, his son	tenor
Francesco, Carlo's brother	baritone
Amalia, an orphan, the Count's niece	soprano
Arminio, the Count's treasurer	tenor
Moser, a pastor	bass
Rolla, Carlo Moor's companion	tenor

Carlo reflects on his love for Amalia. He learns that he is forbidden to return home and decides to become a bandit. In Count Moor's castle, Francesco plans to cause the Count's death by announcing Carlo's death in battle. Amalia watches over the Count and hears his complaint that he will not see Carlo again. Francesco announces Carlo's supposed death, adding the falsehood that Carlo had cursed his father, as he died, and asked that Francesco should marry Amalia. In the second act Amalia mourns the Count and Carlo, when Arminio announces their survival. Francesco attempts to force his attentions on Amalia but is repulsed. The bandits, meanwhile, are near the castle, and Amalia, who has fled from Francesco, meets Carlo, who in turn discovers his father, imprisoned in a lonely tower by Francesco, but the latter does not recognise him. Amalia is taken prisoner by other bandits, while Carlo, eventually regretting his life of crime, but unable now to avoid its consequences, stabs her to the heart.

I Masnadieri (The Bandits) failed to please audiences, for whatever reason. The opening prelude is in the form of a miniature concerto for the principal cellist at Her Majesty's Theatre, Alfredo Piatti. As Amalia sees Massimiliano fading, about to die to join his son Carlo, she sings, prematurely, it transpires, *Tu del mio Carlo al seno volasti* (You have flown to the bosom of my Carlo). There is excitement in the final trio for Carlo, Amalia and Massimiliano, before the closing catastrophe.

Recommended Recording: Overture — ***Naxos 8.553089***

Master of Clamecy, The (see Colas Breugnon)

Mastersingers of Nuremberg, The (see Meistersinger von Nürnberg, Die)

Mathis der Maler (Mathis the Painter)

- Paul Hindemith. Opera in seven scenes. 1935.
- Libretto by the composer.
- First performance at the Stadttheater, Zürich, on 28th May 1938.

Characters

Albrecht von Brandenburg, Cardinal Archbishop of Mainz	tenor
Mathis, painter in his service	baritone
Lorenz von Pommersfelden, Dean of Mainz	bass
Wolfgang Capito, counsellor to the Cardinal	tenor
Riedinger, a rich burgher of Mainz	bass
Hans Schwalb, peasant leader	tenor
Truchsess von Waldburg, Prefect of Waldburg	bass
Sylvester von Schaumberg, one of his officers	tenor
Ursula, daughter of Riedinger	soprano
Regina, daughter of Schwalb	soprano
Graf von Helfenstein	silent rôle
Gräfin Helfenstein	contralto

The painter Mathis helps the rebel peasant leader Schwalb and his daughter Regina escape from pursuing soldiers. Mathis is in love with Ursula, daughter of the rich Protestant citizen Riedinger, whose financial support the Cardinal needs but who is protesting about the burning of Lutheran books. The Cardinal warns Mathis not to meddle in politics, when the officer Sylvester complains of his action in helping Schwalb and his daughter to escape. Mathis seeks release from the Cardinal's service. Meanwhile Lutheran books are being burned, seized from Riedinger's house by Capito, the Cardinal's counsellor, who has a letter from Luther suggesting that the Cardinal marry a Protestant, to heal the religious breach in the city. Ursula is approached and begs Mathis to take her away. In the following scene Mathis rescues the Countess Helfenstein from the peasants and escapes arrest through her intercession. Capito urges the Cardinal to marry Ursula, whose father is rich, but he refuses to sacrifice principles to expediency. Mathis flees from the fighting, taking with him Regina, whose father has been killed. As St Anthony, he sees in a dream the figure of Luxury (the Countess), Beggar, Prostitute and Martyr (Ursula), Warlord (Schwalb) and Merchant (Pommersfelden) and is tempted by the demons of the Isenheim altarpiece. On another panel of the altarpiece he sees the meeting of St Anthony and St Paul (the Cardinal), the latter urging him to return to painting. In his studio again Mathis is among his paintings, while Ursula tends the dying Regina. After her death, the same studio is seen, now empty, apart from a few possessions. Mathis, alone, is visited by the Cardinal and tells him his work is now done. He prepares to go, ready now to leave the world.

Hindemith's opera was condemned by the National Socialist government of Germany, through the personal intervention of Hermann Göring, a ban that led to the resignation of Furtwängler from the Berlin Staatsoper and the Berlin Philharmonic Orchestra and to the emigration of Hindemith himself. Hindemith's *Mathis der Maler Symphony* was derived from the work, which deals with the relationship between the artist and society, questions raised by Schwalb when he meets Mathis in the first scene. Mathis himself is modelled on the painter Mathias Grünewald, with the sixth of the seven scenes referring explicitly to the Isenheim altarpiece.

Matilde de Shabran (Matilde of Shabran)

- Gioachino Rossini. *Melodramma giocoso* in two acts. 1821.
- Libretto by Jacopo Ferretti, after the libretto for Méhul's opera *Euphrosine* by F.-B.Hoffman and the play *Mathilde* by J.M.Boutet de Monvel.
- First performance at the Teatro Apollo, Rome, on 24th February 1821.

Matilde succeeds in dominating the misogynist Duke Corradino, entrusted with her care after the death of her father. Corradino's autocratic behaviour, with the machinations of the Contessa d'Arco, who has designs on him, create complications, which are surmounted once he realises what has really been happening. This leads him to contemplate suicide, from which he is saved by the intervention of the heroine and her companions.

Matrimonio segreto, Il (The Clandestine Marriage)

- Domenico Cimarosa. *Melodramma giocoso* in two acts. 1792.
- Libretto by Giovanni Bertati, after the play *The Clandestine Marriage* by George Colman and David Garrick.
- First performance at the Burgtheater, Vienna, on 7th February 1792.

Characters

Geronimo, a rich merchant	bass
Carolina, his daughter	soprano
Elisetta, her sister	mezzo-soprano
Paolino, Geronimo's clerk	tenor
Fidalma, Geronimo's sister	contralto
Count Robinson	bass

Carolina and Paolino have been secretly married and hope that Geronimo can be mollified by the marriage of her elder sister Elisetta into the aristocracy, satisfying her father's social aspirations. Geronimo, in spite of his deafness, is given the news of Elisetta's coming marriage to Count Robinson and is duly delighted. Elisetta, however, now gives herself all the airs of a countess, while Geronimo's sister Fidalma, a widow, has her eye on Paolino. The Count is disappointed to find that his bride is to be Elisetta, the least attractive of the women, and he offers to take a smaller dowry, if he may marry Carolina. She and Paolino plan to elope together, but are caught by the others and are forced to reveal their secret marriage. Count Robinson is willing to content himself with Elisetta, and Geronimo forgives Carolina and Paolino.

Mozart had been two months dead, when Cimarosa's opera was staged in Vienna, to the satisfaction of the Emperor Leopold II, who had taken much less delight in Mozart's work. There is a sparkling overture and music that is witty and elegant in its portrayal of the characters and situations of the opera, with the comic *bourgeois gentilhomme* Geronimo and the ridiculous Count.

Mavra

- Igor Stravinsky. *Opéra bouffe* in one act. 1922.
- Libretto by Boris Yevgen'yevich Kochno, after Pushkin's verse-tale *Domik v Kolomne* (The Little House at Kolomna).
- First staged performance at the Paris Opéra on 3rd June 1922.

Characters

Parasha	soprano
Her Mother	contralto
A Neighbour	mezzo-soprano
Vasily, a hussar	tenor

Parasha is in love with Vasily and after the cook's death plans to introduce him into her family household in the guise of a new servant, Mavra. Her mother, to her alarm, finds Mavra shaving and he escapes through the window.

Mavra was first staged by Dyagilev and was eclipsed by the spectacular Russian ballets with which it was programmed. A Russian *opera buffa*, it continues what Stravinsky knew as the 'town' tradition of Glinka and Tchaikovsky, in which the Russian element was combined in a synthesis with Western European musical techniques, as opposed to the compulsory doctrinaire nationalism of the Five, with their suspicions of "German" influence. *Mavra* marks the beginning of Stravinsky's neo-classicism with its parodies of the Russian-Italian tradition of the earlier 19th century. Parasha's Russian song *Drug moy milÿy* (Darling heart, sun of my life) is the best known element of the score, later arranged for violin and for cello.

MAY NIGHT

- Nikolay Andreyevich Rimsky-Korsakov. Opera in three acts. 1879.
- Libretto by the composer, after the story by Gogol.
- First performance at the Mariinsky Theatre, St Petersburg, on 21st January 1880.

Levko, son of the village mayor , is determined to marry Hanna and tells her the story of the girl who had been turned out of the Big House by her step-mother and drowned herself, being transformed into a water-nymph, who then dragged her step-mother into the water, to join her. Levko's father tries to woo Hanna. At the mayor's house, to which the drunken charcoal-burner has been directed as his own, a stone is thrown through the window and Levko and his friends, outside, sing a ribald song. Levko, disguised as a blackened devil, comes in and when his father seeks to imprison him in the store-room, Levko's friends rescue him and put the mayor's sister-in-law there in his place. She is released, only to be put back there again by Levko and his friends, making her even angrier when the door is opened again, as the mayor and his friends try to deal with the devil they imagine they have caught. Levko's marriage to Hanna is eventually arranged through the intervention of the literate water-nymph, the drowned maiden of Gogol's story, in return for his help in identifying her step-mother among the other nymphs.

May Night makes full use of traditional folk-songs in its treatment of a well known story that had found its way to the Ukraine from an earlier German source. Rimsky-Korsakov's friends among the Five were modified in their praise of the work, suspecting, perhaps, the composer's use of counterpoint, while the first staging of the third act, with its dancing water-nymphs, seems to have been inadequate, failing in its intended effect.

Recommended Recording: Overture ***Naxos 8.553858***

MAZEPPA

- Pyotr Il'yich Tchaikovsky. Opera in three acts. 1883.
- Libretto by Victor Burenin and the composer, after Pushkin's poem *Poltava*.
- First performance at the Bolshoy Theatre, Moscow, on 15th February 1884.

The Ukrainian hetman Mazeppa is entertained in the house of the Cossack judge Kochubey and although he is not young demands the hand of the judge's daughter Mariya in marriage. Kochubey is compelled to comply, through force of arms, and now plans revenge by sending Mariya's young lover Andrey to report to the Tsar Mazeppa's separatist plans. Incredulous, the Tsar hands Kochubey over to Mazeppa to be imprisoned and executed, the sentence carried out in spite of Mariya's attempted intervention. Mazeppa, in collusion with Sweden, attempts revolt but is defeated at the battle of Poltava. In flight he finds himself in Kochubey's garden again and here is confronted by Andrey, whom he mortally wounds. Mariya comes to him, but in madness, cradling the dying Andrey's head in her arms. Mazeppa makes his escape.

Two orchestral excerpts from *Mazeppa* that may be heard in the concert-hall are the *Cossack Dance* that entertains Mazeppa at the house of Kochubey in the first act and the music that accompanies the tableau representing the battle of Poltava. The imprisoned and tortured Kochubey's *Three treasures* gives his moving reply to the brutal Orlik, who seeks to find where his captive's money is hidden. Kochubey tells him that his three treasures are his honour and his daughter, both stolen from him, and his vengeance, which still remains.

MEDEA

Medea was the daughter of the King of Colchis and materially assisted Jason and his Argonauts in the theft from her father of the golden fleece, deterring paternal pursuit by chopping her brother into pieces and dropping them in the sea. In Corinth Jason sought to replace her by marrying the daughter of the King and she took revenge by sending a poisoned robe to the bride, which killed her, and murdering her own two sons by Jason, before taking her departure in a dragon-drawn chariot. She appears as an early feminist in the play *Medea* by Euripides and her exploits are the subject of a play by Seneca, an influence on the French dramatist Pierre Corneille for his *Médée*. Operas on the subject of Medea include works by Giovanni Pacini, Simon Mayr, Marc-Antoine Charpentier, Joseph-François Salomon, Luigi Cherubini, Darius Milhaud and, with a touch of the absurd, Ernst Krenek, in addition to Francesco Cavalli's kinder portrait of her in his *Giasone*.

Medea

- Jiři Antoní (Georg) Benda. Melodrama in one act. 1775.
- Text by Friedrich Wilhelm Gotter.
- First performance at the Theater am Rannstädter Tor, Leipzig, on 1st May 1775.

Medea, in Corinth, takes her revenge on Jason, by securing the death of his intended bride Kreusa and killing her own two sons by him.

Georg Benda followed his melodrama *Ariadne auf Naxos* with a second such work, on the subject of Medea, intended now for Sophie Seyler, wife of Abel Seyler, a distinguished actor-manager. Mozart saw Benda's *Medea* in Mannheim in 1778 and at one time planned to write a melodrama of his own, a spoken dramatic text with musical accompaniment, on the subject of Semiramide.

Recommended Recording: Medea — ***Naxos 8.553346***

Médée (Medea)

- Marc-Antoine Charpentier. *Tragédie mise en musique* in a prologue and five acts. 1693.
- Libretto by Thomas Corneille.
- First performance at the Paris Opéra on 4th December 1693.

Characters

Médée (Medea), princess of Colchis	soprano
Nérine, her confidante	soprano
Jason, prince of Thessaly	haute-contre
Arcas, his confidant	tenor
Créon (Creon), King of Corinth	bass
Oronte (Orontes), prince of Argos	baritone
Créuse (Creusa), daughter of Creon	soprano
Cléone, her confidante	soprano

Shepherds praise the King, Louis XIV, and call down Victory, Bellona and Glory. In the first act Medea complains that Jason is deserting her for Creusa but offers a fine robe for the princess. Jason himself must decide whether his gratitude to Medea in the matter of the golden fleece and their later attempt against Pelias, Jason's uncle, should outweigh his love for Creusa. Creon pledges help against her enemies to Medea, who must be exiled, while Jason and Orontes, united in love of Creusa, will be of use to him in Corinth. Orontes promises to help Medea, who now plans revenge on Jason and Creusa. Through witchcraft she makes Creon mad and he kills Orontes and himself. Creusa dies in the poisoned robes Medea had given her, and she now confesses that she has killed her two children by Jason.

Charpentier's opera contains stock ingredients in a mad scene for Creon, a magic scene for Medea and ballets for Love's prisoners and for spirits and demons. Medea is given arias that range from sorrow to fury. The libretto is by Thomas Corneille, brother of Pierre Corneille, who also wrote a tragedy on the same subject.

Médée (Medea)

- Luigi Cherubini. *Opéra comique* in three acts. 1797.
- Libretto by François-Benoît Hoffman.
- First performance at the Théâtre Feydeau, Paris, on 13th March 1797.

Characters

Jason, leader of the Argonauts	tenor
Médée (Medea), his wife	soprano
Néris (Neris), her confidante	mezzo-soprano
Créon (Creon), King of Corinth	bass
Dircé (Dirce), his daughter	soprano
Two Attendants	soprano & mezzo-soprano

Dirce seeks Hymen's blessing on her marriage to Jason and the Argonauts bring gifts to her. Creon promises to protect Jason's children and Jason himself tells Dirce that Medea is probably dead. A stranger appears, revealed as Medea, threatening and arguing with Jason, and deploring the effect of the golden fleece on their fortunes. In the second act she meets Creon's anger, seeking from Jason a last meeting with her children. She sends them to Dirce with a poisoned robe. While Dirce, off-stage, dies in agony, Medea steels herself to kill her children. Jason tries to stop her, but he is too late and now sees her, accompanied by the Furies, standing with blood-stained knife at the doors of the temple, which then bursts into flames, as she takes flight.

Cherubini's very demanding opera has enjoyed mixed success, but is now re-established in current repertoire, largely thanks to Maria Callas, who sang the rôle in 1952 and later appeared in Pasolini's film on the same subject. Notable excerpts from the score include the second act *Ah! nos peines seront communes* (Ah! Our sufferings will be shared), as Neris sympathizes with Medea. In the first act Medea appeals to Jason in *Vous voyez de vos fils la mère infortunée* (You see the unlucky mother of your sons) and in the third she screws her courage to the sticking-place in *Eh quoi, je suis Médée* (What, I am Medea). The opera is sometimes performed in Italian translation and various productions have chosen either to shorten the spoken dialogue or to replace it with recitative.

Medium, The

- Gian Carlo Menotti. Tragic opera in two acts. 1945.
- Libretto by the composer.
- First performance at the Brander Matthews Theater, Columbia University, New York, on 8th May 1946.

Characters

Madame Flora, called Baba, a medium	contralto
Monica, her daughter	soprano
Toby, a mute gypsy boy	silent rôle
Mr Gobineau	baritone
Mrs Gobineau	soprano
Mrs Nolan	mezzo-soprano

Madam Flora scolds Toby for touching her things and then receives the clients attending her séance. She calls up the spirit of Mrs Nolan's dead child, which is now impersonated by Monica in a white dress, but suddenly screams that something touched her. Mrs Nolan and the Gobineaus leave, while Madam Flora accuses Toby, defended by Monica, who tries to console her mother. A voice is heard singing the song that Monica had sung as the spirit of the child. In the second act Toby has been using the puppet theatre to show something of his unexpressed love for Monica, and she now speaks for him. Madam Flora continues to drink, scolding and attacking Toby again, and sending the people away, when they arrive for another séance, telling them she is a fraud. She falls into a drunken sleep, from which she is aroused by a noise from Toby. He hides behind the curtain of the puppet theatre, and Madam Flora takes a gun and shoots him, killing the ghost that has haunted her.

The Medium is a powerful dramatic piece, with music for Monica that is both poignant and memorable. These songs include her child-like fairy-story song, as she combs her hair, *Where, oh, where is my new golden spindle and thread?*, the simple and moving *Oh black swan, where, oh, where is my lover gone?* and her song for Toby *Monica, Monica, can't you see?*. Madam Flora, an avowed swindler, is increasingly haunted by the spirits she has pretended to conjure up, her self-control disintegrating under the influence of drink and forces that she cannot understand. She is set against the two innocent children, Toby and Monica, in a taut tragedy. For later performances Menotti wrote the curtain-raiser, *The Telephone*.

MEFISTOFELE (MEPHISTOPHELES)

- Arrigo Boito. Opera in a prologue, five acts and an epilogue. Revised for performances in 1875 and 1876.
- Libretto by the composer, after Goethe's play *Faust*.
- First performance at the Teatro alla Scala, Milan, on 5th March 1858.

CHARACTERS

Mefistofele (Mephistopheles)	bass
Faust, a scholar	tenor
Wagner, his pupil	tenor
Margherita	soprano
Marta, her neighbour	mezzo-soprano
Elena (Helen of Troy)	soprano
Pantalis, her companion	mezzo-soprano
Nereo, a Greek elder	tenor

Amid the choirs of Heaven, Mephistopheles wagers that he can gain the soul of Faust. As Easter is celebrated in a square in Frankfurt, Faust notices a mysterious friar, who appears later in his study, revealing himself as Mephistopheles, the spirit that denies everything, and striking a bargain for Faust's soul. In the second act Faust, now young again, seduces Margherita and in a second scene is taken up into the Harz mountains to witness a Witches' Sabbath, where he sees a vision of Margherita with the mark of blood round her neck. In prison, accused of the murder of her mother and of her own baby, Margherita is visited by Faust, who urges her to escape. When Mephistopheles appears she recognises him as the Devil, and turns away from Faust as she dies, penitent and saved. In the Vale of Tempe Faust sees Helen of Troy, who tells of the destruction of Priam's city. Faust kneels before her, as his ideal of beauty, pledging his love. In the epilogue Faust, now old again, realises the futility of what he has experienced and prays for salvation, in spite of the urging of Mephistopheles, eager to lead him away. Finally Faust is saved, as the choirs of Heaven confirm.

Boito's opera provides a notable bass title rôle, particularly in the opening aria *Ave Signor!* (Hail, Lord) and his revelation of himself as the spirit of denial *Son lo spirito che nega sempre* (I am the spirit that always denies). Faust in his study in the first act thinks of God in *Dai campi, dai prati* (From the fields, from the meadows), while Margherita, in prison, tells of how she drowned her child in *L'altra notte in fondo al mare* (One night to the sea in sadness). The opera was unsuccessful at its first performance and was considerably modified for its later stagings in Bologna and then, in the now generally accepted version, in Venice.

Meistersinger von Nürnberg, Die (The Mastersingers of Nuremberg)

- Richard Wagner. Music drama in three acts. 1867.
- Libretto by the composer.
- First performance at the Königliches Hof- und Nationaltheater, Munich, on 21st June 1868.

Characters

Hans Sachs, cobbler	bass-baritone
Veit Pogner, goldsmith	bass
Kunz Vogelgesang, furrier	tenor
Konrad Nachtigal, tinsmith	bass
Sixtus Beckmesser, town clerk	bass
Fritz Kothner, baker	bass
Balthasar Zorn, pewterer	tenor
Ulrich Eisslinger, grocer	tenor
Augustin Moser, tailor	tenor
Hermann Ortel, soapmaker	bass
Hans Schwarz, stocking weaver	bass
Hans Foltz, coppersmith	bass
Walther von Stolzing, a young knight from Franconia	tenor
David, Sachs' apprentice	tenor
Eva, Pogner's daughter	soprano
Magdalene, her nurse	soprano
Nightwatchman	bass

In St Katharine's Church Walther tries to attract the attention of Eva and learns finally from Magdalene that she is to marry the winner of the mastersingers' contest the next day. Magdalene's lover David, Sach's apprentice, starts to teach Walther the rules of the contest. Pogner welcomes Walther's entry to the contest and makes it clear that he is offering his goods and his only daughter as a prize to the winner, provided that Eva approves of the man who wins. Hans Sachs proposes that the winner should be chosen by the people but the suggestion is rejected. Asked about his teacher, Walther claims the poet Walther von der Vogelweide and nature and proceeds to sing his trial song for entry to the guild, while Beckmesser, in the marker's booth, scratches on a slate a record of Walther's mistakes. Sachs alone approves the song, and Walther is rejected. The second act shows midsummer eve in Nuremberg, where Sachs sings of the joys of spring, recalling Walther's trial song. Walther himself now urges Eva to elope with him and she changes clothes with Magdalene, but they wait, while Beckmesser comes to serenade Eva, now Magdalene in disguise, and Sachs punctuates the serenade with his own singing and cobbling. A riot follows, with David attacking Beckmesser, who he thinks has been serenading his Magdalene. The nightwatchman's horn puts an end to the disturbance. In the opening of the third act Sachs, in his workshop, considers human delusions. Walther comes to him, telling of a dream he has had and singing what is to be his prize song. Beckmesser now enters the workshop, alone, and takes the song that Walther has left there, accusing Sachs of intending to enter the contest himself. Sachs denies this and lets Beckmesser take the song. Eva now seeks consolation from Sachs, who tells her he will not be King Mark to Tristan and Isolde. David, joining Sachs, is promoted from apprentice to journeyman. At the contest Beckmesser sings to his own melody the song he has taken from Sachs, producing a travesty of it. Walther now comes forward and makes sense of the poem in a winning performance. Walther at first refuses the Master's chain that Pogner offers him, but it is Sachs who has the last word in praise of holy German art.

Wagner's only mature comedy is a remarkable example of holy German art. Leitmotifs are now interwoven, over forty of them, with a dozen or so used in the famous prelude. Further orchestral excerpts may be heard in the *Dance of the Apprentices* and *Entry of the Masters* from the third act. While it must always be difficult to isolate concert excerpts from a through-composed score, the prize song itself, *Morgenlich leuchtend in rosigem Schein* (Bathed in the rosy light of day) has also been extracted for instrumental arrangement, for violin by August Wilhelmj and by Fritz Kreisler and for cello by Pablo Casals. Sachs has two well known monologues, the so-called Flieder Monologue, *Was duftet doch der Flieder* (What scent the lilac brings) and the Wahn Monologue, *Wahn! Wahn! Überall Wahn!* (Delusion! Delusion! Delusion above all!). The ridicule accorded Beckmesser, with his misplaced musical accents and pedantry, thinly hides an attack on the critic Eduard Hanslick, a leading figure in the field of musical aesthetics, and Wagner's anti-semitism openly expressed in his writings, notably in *Das Judenthum in der Musik* (The Jews in Music). This attack was much more than a jibe at Hanslick's Jewish maternal descent.

Recommended Recording: Overture ***Naxos 8.550498***

MERRIE ENGLAND

- Edward German. Operetta in two acts. 1902.
- Libretto by Basil Hood.
- First performance at the Savoy Theatre, London, on 2nd April 1902.

Edward German's patriotic pageant deals with love and rivalries at the court of Queen Elizabeth I, a monarch jealous of Sir Walter Raleigh's affection for Bessie Throckmorton, revealed to her by the Earl of Essex. It perpetuates the fiction that the England of Good Queen Bess was actually merry and includes the well known song for the Queen *O peaceful England, while I my watch am keeping* and the stirring *Yeomen of England.* The work established German as a possible successor to Arthur Sullivan in the world of English operetta.

Recommended Recording:
Merrie England (Ballet Music) — ***Marco Polo 8.223677***

MERRY WIDOW, THE (SEE LUSTIGE WITWE, DIE)

MERRY WIVES OF WINDSOR, DIE (SEE LUSTIGEN WEIBER VON WINDSOR, DIE)

MIDSUMMER MARRIAGE, THE

- Michael Tippett. Opera in three acts. 1952.
- Libretto by the composer.
- First performance at Covent Garden, London, on 27th January 1955.

CHARACTERS

Mark, a young man of unknown parentage	tenor
Jenifer, his betrothed, a young girl	soprano
King Fisher, Jenifer's father, a business-man	baritone
Bella, his secretary	soprano
Jack, her boy-friend, a mechanic	tenor
Sosostris, a clairvoyante	contralto
He-Ancient, Priest of the Temple	bass

She-Ancient, Priestess of the Temple	mezzo-soprano
Strephon, one of the dancers	dancer

Mark has hoped to elope with Jenifer, whose father opposes their marriage. They meet after dawn on midsummer morning, the mists clearing to reveal a temple. Mark and Jenifer's friends arrive, expecting the wedding and sing a hymn to the sun, after which dancers emerge from the temple. Mark, who has now arrived, asks the Ancients for a new dance. Jenifer now arrives and mounts the steps towards the temple, while Mark descends through gates to a cave below, as if descending to Hell. King Fisher appears, with his secretary, meets the Ancients and demands that the gates be opened. Bella suggests calling her boy-friend Jack to open the gates, but any attempt to open them is met by a voice that warns them against this. The rising tension between King Fisher and the warning voice leads to the re-appearance of Jenifer at the top of the steps, now transformed, recounting her spiritual experiences above, matched by Mark's below. The second act, 'Afternoon', finds Jack and Bella expressing their comfortable love for each other. There follow three ritual dances, 'The Earth in Autumn'. 'The Waters in Winter' and 'The Air in Spring'. These represent the conflict between male and female, the former represented by the dancer Strephon, in the first a hare hunted by a hound, in the second a fish hunted by an otter and in the third a bird hunted by a hawk. The third act, 'Evening and Night', brings back King Fisher to challenge the powers of the unseen. He is warned not to meddle with things beyond him. Madame Sosostris, a clairvoyante, at first Jack in disguise and then a being of oracular powers, has an aria that is at the heart of the act. King Fisher seeks to tear away the veils of the mysterious oracular figure, revealing Mark and Jenifer, in the heart of a lotus, now transfigured. King Fisher is blinded by the light and tries to kill Mark, but dies, while Strephon, a sacrifical victim, dances the final ritual dance 'The Fire in Summer'.

Tippett's opera, his first major attempt at the form, occupied him for some six years. The work has an obvious parallel in Mozart's *Die Zauberflöte* (The Magic Flute), where Tamino and Pamina, like Mark and Jenifer, must undergo trials before being joined in transfigured union. Jack and Bella, more mundane characters, have their counterpart in Papageno and Papagena. The *Ritual Dances* have occasionally been extracted from the score for separate performance.

Recommended Recording: Ritual Dances — ***Naxos 8.553591***

MIDSUMMER NIGHT'S DREAM, A

- Benjamin Britten. Opera in three acts. 1960.
- Libretto by the composer and Peter Pears, after the play by Shakespeare.
- First performance at the Jubilee Hall, Aldeburgh, on 11th June 1960.

CHARACTERS

Oberon, King of the Fairies	countertenor
Tytania, Queen of the Fairies	coloratura soprano
Puck	speaking part
Theseus, Duke of Athens	bass
Hippolyta, betrothed to Theseus	contralto
Lysander	tenor
Demetrius	baritone
Hermia	mezzo-soprano
Helena	soprano
Bottom, a weaver	bass-baritone
Quince, a carpenter	bass
Flute, a bellows-mender	tenor
Snug, a joiner	bass
Snout, a tinker	tenor
Starveling, a tailor	baritone
Fairies:	
Cobweb, Peaseblossom, Mustardseed & Moth	trebles

In the wood at twilight the fairies and Puck set the scene for the meeting of Oberon and Tytania, quarrelling over the possession of an Indian boy. When Tytania has gone, Oberon tells Puck to pluck the magic herb that will help him succeed. The mortal Athenian lovers then enter, Hermia and Lysander in love and Helena hoping to win the unwilling love of Demetrius, who loves Hermia. Oberon tells Puck to use the magic herb on the eyes of Demetrius, so that he will love Helena. The Rustics appear, preparing their play for the Duke's wedding. They are followed by a weary Lysander and Hermia. As they rest, Puck puts the magic love-herb on Lysander's eyes. Waking, he first sees Helena, and now falls in love, following after her. Hermia wakes alone. Oberon approaches Tytania as she sleeps, and squeezes the magic herb on her eyes. In the second act the Rustics rehearse their play, *Pyramus and Thisbe*. Puck puts an ass's head on Bottom and his friends scatter in fear, thinking him bewitched. Tytania wakes and falls in love with him, ordering her fairies to entertain him. Oberon endeavours to put matters right between Demetrius and Helena, as they sleep, and squeezes the magic herb onto the eyes of Demetrius, who now falls in love with Helena. Lysander and Demetrius quarrel, but, lulled to sleep, Lysander is given the remedy for his misplaced affection. The third act releases Bottom from his ass's head and Tytania from her enchantment, while the mortal lovers are properly paired and Oberon has his Indian boy again. At the Duke's palace Theseus decrees a triple wedding, for himself and the two pairs of lovers, while the wedding entertainment is to be *Pyramus and Thisbe*. At midnight the mortals disperse, leaving Oberon, Tytania and their fairies to bless the house.

Britten's *A Midsummer Night's Dream* uses a well judged abridgement of Shakespeare's text, setting the piece in a mysterious night world of magic, represented by Oberon, Tytania, Puck and the fairies. The mortal lovers provide another stratum, with a third element in the music of the mechanicals, Britten's Rustics, heard at their best in the subtle operatic parody of *Pyramus and Thisbe*, mad scene and all. The opera has enjoyed continued success since its first performance at the Aldeburgh Festival in 1960.

Mignon

- Ambroise Thomas. *Opéra comique* in three acts. 1866.
- Libretto by Jules Barbier and Michel Carré, after episodes in Goethe's *Wilhelm Meisters Lehrjahre* (Wilhelm Meister's Apprenticeship).
- First performance by the Paris Opéra-Comique at the Salle Favart on 17th November 1866.

Characters

Mignon	mezzo-soprano
Wilhelm Meister, a student	tenor
Philine, an actress	soprano
Lothario, a wandering minstrel	bass
Laerte, an actor	tenor
Jarno, a gypsy	bass
Frédéric, a young nobleman	tenor or contralto
Antonio, a servant	bass

In the courtyard of a German inn Lothario, the old harper of Goethe's novel, sings, Philine and Laerte are seen, and Mignon is protected from Jarno, who wants to make her dance, by Wilhelm Meister and the minstrel. Mignon gives them both wild flowers. Wilhelm questions Mignon about her childhood and buys her freedom. She is in love with her saviour, but uneasy that the flowers that she gave him have been given, in fact by Laerte, to Philine, with whom Frédéric is in love. Philine, however, considers Wilhelm a better catch. In the castle where the actors are to perform, Wilhelm assists Philine as she makes ready, watched jealously by Mignon. When the two have gone out, Mignon dons one of Philine's costumes and separates Frédéric and Wilhelm when a serious quarrel breaks out. Wilhelm warns Mignon that they must part. In the castle grounds Mignon is in despair, comforted by Lothario, who sets the castle on fire in response to Mignon's angry wish that the place might burn, when she hears the applause for Philine's performance. Wilhelm rescues Mignon from the building, where Philine had sent her for the wild flowers given to Wilhelm the day before. The third act is set in an Italian castle that Wilhelm plans to buy for Mignon, who has been seriously ill. The surroundings awaken Lothario's memories and he now comes to his senses, recognising the castle as his own and Mignon as his long lost daughter, in search of whom he had wandered as a minstrel.

Among the best known melodies from *Mignon* is that of the gavotte, used to open the second act, and recurring in Frédéric's song of pleasure at being in Philine's dressing-room at the castle. Mignon's famous *Kennst du das Land*, set by so many of the greatest composers, is her reply to Wilhelm Meister's first questions about her childhood, *Connais-tu le pays?* (Do you know the land where the lemon-trees bloom?). Lothario, setting out for the south again, sings with Mignon the *Swallow Duet*, *Légères hirondelles* (Graceful swallows). In *Je connais un pauvre enfant* (I know a poor gypsy boy), Mignon, wearing one of Philine's costumes, sings a *styrienne*, a form of song attributed to the Styria region of Austria and with *Adieu, Mignon! Courage!* (Farewell, Mignon! Courage!) Wilhelm Meister tells her they must part. In *As-tu souffert? As-tu pleuré?* (Have you suffered? Have you wept?) Lothario and Mignon sing of their sad lives. Philine, as Titania in Shakespeare's *A Midsummer Night's Dream*, sings a *polonaise*, *Je suis Titania* (I am Titania), followed by a choral *barcarolle*. In the third act Lothario has a moving *berceuse* (lullaby) as Mignon rests, *De son cœur j'ai calmé la fièvre* (I have calmed the fever of her heart).

MIKADO, THE

- Arthur Sullivan. Operetta in two acts. 1885.
- Libretto by W.S.Gilbert.
- First performance at the Savoy Theatre, London, on 14th March 1885.

In *The Mikado, or The Town of Titipu* Nanki-Poo wanders as a minstrel, to escape marriage to Katisha. His beloved Yum-Yum is to marry the Lord High Executioner Ko-Ko, himself condemned to death. By a subterfuge the Emperor is satisfied by the mock execution of Nanki-Poo, the disguised son of the Emperor, the price exacted for marriage to Yum-Yum, secured with the assistance of Pooh-Bah.

Possibly the best known of the Gilbert and Sullivan operettas, *The Mikado* opens with a lively overture. Nanki-Poo introduces himself in *A wandering minstrel I* in a score that contains a number of songs well known to enthusiasts, *Behold the Lord High Executioner*, *Taken from a country jail*, *Three little maids from school are we*, *The sun, whose rays are all ablaze* and *There is beauty in the bellow of the blast*.

Mines of Sulphur, The

- Richard Rodney Bennett. Opera in three acts. 1963.
- Libretto by Beverley Cross.
- First performance at Sadler's Wells, London, on 24th February 1965.

In the 18th century in a remote house in the west of England, a deserter, a tramp and a gypsy woman have murdered the rich owner of the house, which they have taken over. A company of actors seeks refuge in the house and stages there a play that reflects the murderers' situation. The deserter and his accomplices plan to imprison the actors in the cellar and burn the house down, but before this can happen it is revealed that one of the actresses is infected with the plague.

The Mines of Sulphur is an impressively dramatic opera, written in a musical language that makes use of the twelve-note series of Schoenberg in writing that is essentially vocal and effective.

Mireille

- Charles-François Gounod. *Opéra* in five acts. 1864.
- Libretto by Michel Carré, after Frédéric Mistral's Provençal poem *Mirèio*.
- First performance at the Théâtre Lyrique, Paris, on 19th March 1864.

In a mulberry orchard, where girls are picking leaves, Taven, a sorceress, tells their futures, some to meet sadness in love. Clémence is confident that she will marry a handsome prince, but Mireille would be happy with much less, since she is in love with Vincent, who now enters, reciprocating her admiration. At the entrance to the bull-ring in Arles the people dance a *farandole* and Mireille and Vincent sing a love-song. Taven warns Mireille of other suitors and she is approached by and rejects the bull-tender Ourrias. Her father forbids any relationship with Vincent, to the anger of Vincent's father. At Taven's cave Ourrias seeks revenge on Vincent, striking and wounding him when he appears, only to be cursed by Taven and in the following ghostly scene to drown in the Rhône. Mireille is sad, while her father and his men celebrate midsummer eve, and resolves, when she hears of Vincent's fate, to travel to the shrine of the Saintes-Maries. This she does through the heat and thirst of the Crau desert. At the shrine Vincent comes to her, but she dies in his arms, to be welcomed in Heaven.

In a lyrical opera, set in Mistral's Provence and dominated dramatically and vocally by Mireille, the *Chanson de Magali* (Song of Magali), *La brise est douce* (The breeze is gentle) that she sings in happiness with Vincent is the best known. From the first act comes her waltz-song *O légère hirondelle* (O graceful swallow), while Vincent, as the work draws to a close, prays for Mireille in *Anges du paradis* (Angels of Paradise).

Mitridate, re di Ponto (Mithridates, King of Pontus)

- Wolfgang Amadeus Mozart. *Dramma per musica* in three acts. 1770.
- Libretto by Vittorio Amedeo Cigna-Santi, after a translation of Racine's *Mithridate* by Giuseppe Parini.
- First performance at the Regio Ducal Teatro, Milan, on 26th December 1770.

Characters

Mitridate (Mithridates), King of Pontus	tenor
Aspasia, his betrothed	soprano
Farnace (Pharnaces), son of Mithridates	male alto
Sifare (Xiphares), son of Mithridates	male soprano
Marzio (Marcius), a Roman tribune	tenor
Ismene, a Parthian princess, betrothed to Pharnaces	soprano
Arbate (Arbates), Governor of Nymphea	male soprano

Aspasia, betrothed to Mithridates, is loved by his two sons, Pharnaces and Xiphares and reciprocates the love of the latter. Pharnaces conspires with the Roman Marcius against his father, but Mithridates, rumoured dead in his struggle against the Romans, returns, fearing the disloyalty of both of his sons, but reassured by Arbates of the loyalty of Xiphares. Pharnaces is betrothed to the Parthian Ismene, whom he rejects, and Mithridates, now about to renew his warfare against Pompey, distrusts Aspasia and imprisons both his sons when Pharnaces reveals the love of Xiphares for Aspasia, although Xiphares had honourably decided to leave Aspasia and Pontus. Aspasia now rejects Mithridates, who sends her poison, which Xiphares stops her drinking. In battle the King is victorious but wounds himself mortally, returning to unite Aspasia and Xiphares and to forgive Pharnaces, who has acted against the Romans, and join him in marriage to Ismene.

Among some eighteen operas based on Racine's play, from the 1707 work of Alessandro Scarlatti onwards, Mozart's *Mitridate, re di Ponto* (Mithridates, King of Pontus) remains the best known, if because of the composer's later achievement and distinction. Mozart's age, fourteen in 1770, caused opposition in Milan, but in the event the opera won an enthusiastic reception from a usually critical public. The work starts with an overture in the three-movement Italian *sinfonia* tradition. The score includes a moving farewell for Xiphares, now intending to leave Aspasia and

Pontus, in *Lungi da te, mio bene* (Far from you, my beloved). In the scene that opens the second act Pharnaces rejects Ismene in *Va, l'error mio palesa* (Go, my mistake is clear) and he later admits to his father his guilt and treachery in *Son reo: l'error confesso* (I am guilty: I admit my mistake).

Recommended Recording: Overture — ***Naxos 8.550185***

MLADA

- Nikolay Andreyevich Rimsky-Korsakov. Magic opera-ballet in four acts. 1890.
- Libretto by the composer, based on the earlier libretto by Viktor Alexandrovich Krilov.
- First performance at the Mariinsky Theatre, St Petersburg, on 1st November 1892.

Voyslava, daughter of Mstivoy, Prince of Retra, has killed Mlada, for love of Prince Yaromir. With the help of the goddess of the underworld she captivates Yaromir, who sees the murder in his dreams. At the midsummer festival the people dance, with the spirit of Mlada always intervening between Yaromir and Voyslava. By night Mlada leads Yaromir up Mount Triglav, where the dead gather, before the Witches' Sabbath in which Yaromir is shown a vision of Cleopatra. In the last act Yaromir, at the Temple of Radegast, is shown by the spirits that Voyslava is guilty. She confesses her sin and he kills her. The goddess of the underworld, with whom Voyslava had made a compact, destroys the temple and the city of Retra, but Yaromir is finally seen on high, united with Mlada.

In 1872 the Mariinsky Theatre had commissioned an opera on Krilov's libretto, a composite work with a first act by César Cui, a second and third by Rimsky-Korsakov and a fourth by Borodin. Ballet music was to be provided by Ludwig Minkus. Rimsky-Korsakov was persuaded to set the whole work himself some seventeen years later, but *Mlada*, with its mixture of opera and ballet, its title rôle taken by a dancer, was in general coolly received. From the third act the composer derived the orchestral work *A Night on Mount Triglav*.

Recmmended Recordings:
Mlada (Suite) — ***Naxos 8.550486***
Night on Mount Triglav (Mlada Act 3) — ***Naxos 8.553789***

MOÏSE ET PHARAON (MOSES AND PHARAOH) (SEE ALSO MOSÈ IN EGITTO)

- Gioachino Rossini. *Opéra* in four acts. 1827.
- Libretto by Luigi Balocchi and Etienne de Jouy.
- First performance at the Paris Opéra on 26th March 1827.

Moses promises to lead the Israelites out of captivity in Egypt. Anaïs and her mother have been released by Pharoah on the intervention of Queen Sinaïs, who is sympathetic to the Israelites. Anaïs loves Pharoah's son, but intends to leave with her people, while her lover Amenophis has decided she must stay. Moses brings upon Egypt the plague of darkness. This is raised, with freedom again promised, while Pharoah has arranged a marriage for his son Amenophis with an Assyrian princess, to his distress. The High Priest Osiris demands that Moses pay reverence to Isis before the Israelites leave. Moses refuses and the Israelites are sent away in chains. Amenophis and Anaïs meet, he still hoping that their love may be permitted. He warns her that Pharoah's army is pursuing the Israelites, who are now triumphantly led by Moses across the Red Sea, while Pharoah's men are drowned.

Rossini adapted his earlier opera *Mosè in Egitto* (Moses in Egypt) as *Moïse et Pharaon, ou Le passage de la Mer Rouge* (Moses and Pharoah, or The Passage of the Red Sea) for Paris, with a new libretto, creating the necessary grand opera spectacle that France demanded. Staging of the French version of the work makes obviously heavier demands on resources. This second opera for Paris marks a further step by Rossini towards his fourth and final opera for the French capital, *Guillaume Tell* (William Tell).

Mond, Der (The Moon)

- Carl Orff. *Kleines Welttheater* in one act. 1939.
- Libretto by the composer, after the tale collected by the Brothers Grimm.
- First performance at the Staatsoper, Munich, on 5th February 1939.

In two countries, the moon provides light in only one, to be stolen by four rascally characters of the other country. When they die, they share the moon between them and stick it together again in the underworld, where the light provided rouses the dead. St Peter sorts matters out and takes the moon up to the sky, where it now is.

Der Mond (The Moon) followed the success of the staged *Carmina burana* seen in Frankfurt in 1937, couched in a musical idiom familiar from that work.

Mondo della luna, Il (The World of the Moon)

- Joseph Haydn. *Dramma giocoso* in three acts. 1777.
- Libretto by Carlo Goldoni.
- First performance at Esterháza perhaps on 3rd August 1777.

The false astrologer Ecclitico seeks to fool the protective Buonafede into allowing his daughters Clarice and Flaminia, and their maid Lisetta, to marry the husbands they choose, Ecclitico, the cavalier Ernesto and his servant Cecco respectively. Drugged, Buonafede is taken into Ecclitico's garden, which he thinks is the moon. There he sees Cecco as Emperor and Ernesto as Hesperus. They are joined by the girls, who are duly betrothed to the appropriate partners, before Buonafede realises he has been duped. In the third act he assents to the marriages.

Haydn re-used material from the first of his operas for the new seasons established at the theatre of the palace of Esterháza. The overture is occasionally heard in the concert-hall, but, as with other operas by Haydn, *Il mondo della luna* (The World of the Moon) has never found an established place in continuing operatic repertoire.

Montag aus Licht (Monday from Light)

- Karlheinz Stockhausen. Opera in three acts, a greeting and a farewell. 1988.
- Libretto by the composer.
- First performance at the Teatro alla Scala, Milan, on 7th May 1988.

In Eve's first birth, a massive statue of Eve is prepared for birth, producing fourteen offspring, seven boys already aging and seven boys with the heads of animals. Lucifer appears, mocking, and is buried in the sand, to emerge commanding the creatures back into the womb again. In Eve's second birth women break the ice on the frozen waters and a procession of girls carrying lilies heralds the forthcoming birth, now of seven boys and of Eve as Coeur, represented by a basset-horn, and three other basset-horn players. She teaches the children the songs of the days of the week, before abducting or seducing them. In Eve's magic, the third act, the boys are now men, praising Eve, now loved by and loving the palindromic Ave, a flautist, who leads the offspring away to higher things, while the statue now becomes a richly vegetated mountain landscape.

Montag (Monday), the third of the Licht cycle to be written, preceded by *Donnerstag* (Thursday) and *Samstag* (Saturday) but itself the beginning of the week, celebrates Eve as universal Mother. The work, heavily symbolic, makes use again of instruments on stage, notably here the basset-horn and flute, with scoring for an electronic prerecorded score for synthesizers, six solo instrumentalists and fourteen solo singers.

Mörder, Hoffnung der Frauen (Murderer, Hope of Women)

- Paul Hindemith. Opera in one act. 1919.
- Libretto by Oscar Kokoschka.

◆ First performance at the Landestheater, Stuttgart, on 4th June 1921.

Kokoschka's expressionist play of 1907 that had provoked a riot at its first performance the following year deals with a sadistic meeting between a Man and a Woman, watched by ancient warriors and serving-women, the action taking place before a tower which ends ablaze.

Hindemith's first opera was later coupled with the relatively light-hearted *Das Nusch-Nuschi* (Nuts-Nuts), in which a philanderer is castrated, and *Sancta Susanna*, to make an evening's triple-bill entertainment, the three works presented together first in 1922.

Mosè in Egitto (Moses in Egypt) (see *Moïse et Pharaon*)

◆ Gioachino Rossini. *Azione tragico-sacra* in three acts. 1818. Revised in 1819.

◆ Libretto by Andrea Leone Tottola, based on events in the Old Testament and *L'Osiride* (Osiris) by Francesco Ringhieri.

◆ First performance at the Teatro S Carlo, Naples, on 5th March 1818.

Characters

Mosè	bass
Elcia (Anaïs),	soprano
Amaltea (Sinaïs), Queen of Egypt	soprano
Amenosi (Miriam), sister of Moses	mezzo-soprano
Aronne (Aaron),brother of Moses	tenor
Osiride (Amenophis), son of Pharoah	tenor
Mambre (Auphis), a disaffected Egyptian	tenor
Faraone (Pharoah)	bass

Egypt suffers the plague of darkness with light restored by Moses in return for the promise of freedom for the Israelites. Pharoah's son Amenophis plans to prevent their departure, since he loves the Israelite Anaïs. When Pharoah tries to break his promise, Moses engineers a plague of hail and fire. Pharoah suggests an arranged marriage with an Armenian princess for Amenophis, while the latter plans to elope with Anaïs. Moses now calls for the death of the first-born, and Pharoah, making his son joint ruler with himself, tells him to have Moses executed. When Amenophis condemns Moses to death, the latter strikes him dead, to the distress of Anaïs. Leading his people away, Moses prays for the Red Sea to open and the Israelites cross safely to the other side, while Pharoah's pursuing troops are drowned with their master.

The prayer of Moses at the Red Sea, *Dal tuo stellato soglio* (From your starry throne), written for the 1819 staging of the work in Naples, enjoys a concert existence, with the impressive *Eterno! immenso! incomprensibil Dio!* (Eternal! Immense! Incomprehensible God!), with which he puts an end to the plague of darkness with which the Italian version of the opera opens.

Moses und Aron (Moses and Aaron)

- Arnold Schoenberg. Opera in three acts (of which two were completed). 1932.
- Libretto by the composer.
- First staged performance of the incomplete work at the Stadttheater, Zürich, on 6th June 1957.

Moses is called as a prophet, hearing the voice of God in the Burning Bush, which tells him that Aaron will speak for him. Aaron, however, has simpler views of a deity to be swayed by sacrifice and conceived in more tangible terms. Moses and Aaron approach the Israelites, whose reactions are varied, but they cannot accept the notion of bowing down before a God that is invisible. Moses blames Aaron for this lack of acceptance and Aaron takes his rod and changes it into a serpent, followed by the miracle of the leper's hand and of the turning of the Nile waters to blood. Convinced, the people march forward into the desert. An interlude covers the period of forty days spent by Moses on Mount Sinai. To calm the impatient people, Aaron orders gold to be brought and the Golden Calf is made, worshipped with sacrifices and mounting ecstasy, increasing to the orgiastic, before the re-appearance of Moses with the tablets of the law. The Golden Calf disintegrates and Aaron, alone with Moses, defends his decision to allow the people a visible and tangible deity. A pillar of fire leads the Israelites onward in their march, and Moses is left alone in despair.

Schoenberg never gave up the hope of finishing his opera *Moses und Aron* (Moses and Aaron), although the third act, as he had conceived it, seems to offer dramatic problems. It deals with the imprisonment of Aaron, his defence, release and death. The elaborately orchestrated *Dance before the Golden Calf* was performed in the concert-hall in 1951, the year of the composer's death, and it was suggested, and sanctioned by Schoenberg, that the third act should be read, after a performance of the first two acts. This has, in general, proved impracticable. Dramatically, the spectacular scene of the Golden Calf, whatever limitations must be placed on the orgiastic nature of the action, forms a climax. The contrast between Moses and Aaron, between the abstract and the concrete, is seen in the casting of Moses as a spoken rôle and Aaron as a tenor, the first expressed in notated speech, *Sprechgesang*, and therefore integrated with the rest of the score.

Mozart and Salieri

- Nikolay Andreyevich Rimsky-Korsakov. Dramatic scenes. 1897.
- Libretto abridged from Pushkin's verse-play.
- First performance at the Solodovnikov Theatre, Moscow, on 7th December 1898.

Rimsky-Korsakov set Pushkin's verse-drama of the jealousy of the composer Salieri, who had acquired his ability by hard work and the careless insouciance of Mozart, to whom everything had been given naturally. The work offers two tableaux, with prominence given simply to the two voices, the baritone Salieri and the light tenor Mozart, and offers an allusive score, a tribute in part to Dargomizhsky and his opera *The Stone Guest* and providing direct references to works by Mozart. It has been suggested that the composer saw himself as a Salieri, by the side of the natural inspiration he attributed to his nationalist friends Borodin and Mussorgsky.

Muette de Portici, La (The Mute Girl of Portici)

- Daniel-François-Esprit Auber. *Grand opéra* in five acts. 1828.
- Libretto by Eugène Scribe and Germain Delavigne.
- First performance at the Paris Opéra on 29th February 1828.

Characters

Alphonse (Alfonso d'Arcos), son of the Spanish Viceroy of Naples	tenor
Elvire (Elvira), a Spanish princess, his betrothed	soprano
Masaniello, a Naples fisherman	tenor
Fenella, his sister	dancer
Pietro, Borella & Moreno, friends of Masaniello	basses
Lorenzo, confidant of Alfonso	tenor
Selva, an officer of the Viceroy's guard	bass
Lady-in-Waiting to the Princess	soprano

Alfonso has seduced and deserted Fenella and now must marry Elvira. Fenella, who is dumb, seeks Elvira's protection, and when the couple emerge from the chapel, married, Fenella is able to indicate to Elvira her seducer. Masaniello and his friends, fishermen, complain about the tyranny of their overlords. Fenella seeks the aid of Masaniello, showing him that her seducer is married and refusing to give his name. Masaniello swears vengeance. Alfonso's attempt to bring Fenella before Elvira leads to an insurrection led by Masaniello, bringing mob violence that he would rather curb.

Alfonso and Elvira seek shelter from the crowd in Masaniello's hut and are promised safety, in spite of Fenella's initial hesitations. Pietro, coming to the hut, offers Masaniello the position of governor of Naples but demands the death of the two Spaniards, whom he recognises. Masaniello refuses to harm them, allowing them to leave in safety, but is threatened with death now by Pietro and his followers. In the last act, before the Viceroy's palace, Masaniello has been poisoned by Pietro and is now out of his mind. Alfonso, meanwhile, is leading his guards against the rebels, and the eruption of Mount Vesuvius is a sign that the rebellion will be put down. Masaniello marches away with his followers. Elvira now returns with the news that Masaniello has saved her life but has been killed in revenge by one of his own people. Distraught at the news, Fenella kills herself in the lava flowing from the volcano.

La muette de Portici (The Mute Girl of Portici) marks the beginning of French grand opera, with its spectacular effects, here reaching a climax in the eruption of Mount Vesuvius. The revolutionary songs of Masaniello and his companions came to have particular appeal in places where revolution threatened, as in Belgium in 1830, or where the sentiments expressed struck a recognisable chord.

Recommended Recording: Overture (Masaniello) ***Naxos 8.550473***

Nabucco (Nebuchadnezzar)

- Giuseppe Verdi. *Dramma lirico* in four parts. 1842.
- Libretto by Temistocle Solera, after the ballet *Nabuccodonosor* by Antonio Cortesi and the play *Nabuchodonosor* by Auguste Anicet-Bourgeois and Francis Cornu.
- First performance at the Teatro alla Scala, Milan, on 9th March 1842.

Characters

Nabucco (Nebuchadnezzar), King of Babylon	baritone
Ismaele, nephew of the King of Jerusalem	tenor
Zaccaria, High Priest of the Hebrews	bass
Abigaille, slave, presumed the first daughter of Nebuchadnezzar	soprano
Fenena, daughter of Nebuchadnezzar	soprano
High Priest of Baal	bass
Abdallo, an old officer of Nebuchadnezzar	tenor
Anna, sister of Zaccaria	soprano

The first part of the opera, *Jerusalem*, is set in the Temple of Solomon, where the Israelites are encouraged by the High Priest to resist the armies of Babylon. Fenena, daughter of Nebuchadnezzar, had helped Ismaele to escape from Babylon and is now with him, but Abigaille, also in love with him, leads in a band of Assyrians, disguised as Israelites, capturing the Temple, which Nebuchadnezzar orders to be destroyed. The second part, *The Ungodly One*, opens in the palace of Nebuchadnezzar where Abigaille thirsts for revenge on Ismaele. The High Priest of Baal urges her to seize power in Babylon as regent, since Fenena has set the Israelites free. Elsewhere in the palace Zaccaria prays, with Ismaele shunned by the Levites, until it is clear that he has converted Fenena. She is now proclaimed queen, after rumours of her father's death. Abigaille intervenes, acclaimed as queen, but interrupted by the return of Nebuchadnezzar to seize the crown and declare himself both king and god. At this blasphemy he is struck down by a thunderbolt and loses his wits, leaving Abigaille to triumph. The third part, *The Prophecy,* in the hanging gardens of Babylon, finds Abigaille inducing her father to sign Fenena's death warrant. By the banks of the Euphrates the Hebrews lament their exile, but Zaccaria prophesies the destruction of Babylon. The fourth part, *The Broken Idol*, finds Nebuchadnezzar, distracted, but anxious to save Fenena, who is being taken to execution. He prays to the God of Israel and his sanity and powers return, enabling him to rescue Fenena, and converted to resume his reign. Abigaille takes poison, begging for forgiveness as she dies.

Nabucco was Verdi's first great success, marking the real start of his career, after which commission after commission came his way. In addition to the strong impression given in its music, the choice of subject itself fitted well enough the political circumstances of contemporary Italy, largely under foreign domination. The overture, composed principally of material from the opera itself, suggests the firmness of purpose of the oppressed. This is strengthened by the opening chorus of Levites, in *Gli arredi festivi* (The festive vessels now fall), answered by the virgins and other groups, establishing the importance of the chorus in the whole opera. Zaccaria's exhortation follows, designed for a rich deep bass voice, *Sperate, o figli* (Hope, my sons) and the following *D'Egitto là sui lidi* (From Egypt's shores). The rôle of Abigaille is a challenging one, and she makes her first entrance as she captures the Temple, sees Fenena and Ismaele together and pours scorn on them in *Prode guerrier!* (Bold warrior! Is it only the weapons of love that you know?). The best known chorus ever written by Verdi must be *Va, pensiero* (Fly, thought, on golden wings), the chorus of Hebrews lamenting their exile by the waters of Babylon.

Recommended Recordings:
Overture ***Naxos 8.553089***
Va pensiero / Gli arredi festivi ***Naxos 8.550241***

Nacht in Venedig, Eine (A Night in Venice)

- Johann Strauss. *Komische Oper* in three acts. 1883.
- Libretto by F.Zell and Richard Genée, after the libretto *Château Trompette* (Trumpet Castle) by Eugène Cormon and Michel Carré.
- First performance at the Friedrich Wilhelmstädtisches Theater, Berlin, on 3rd October 1883.

It is carnival time and Barbara, the young wife of an elderly Venetian senator, is to be taken by gondola to her aunt's at Murano, out of harm's way. Caramello, barber to the Duke of Urbino and disguised as a gondolier, plans to take her to his master, but she has another assignation and has sent in her place the fisher-girl Annina, the object of Caramello's own affections. At the Duke's palace Caramello realises his mistake and does his best to keep Annina and his master apart. All ends well enough when the Duke returns Annina to him and appoints him steward in his household.

The ninth of Strauss's operettas, *Eine Nacht in Venedig* (A Night in Venice), was first staged, disastrously, in Berlin, to avoid the Vienna Theater an der Wien, where his wife Lili was rumoured to be having an affair with the manager Franz Steiner, or with Steiner's father. In Berlin the famous *Lagunen-Walzer* (Lagoon Waltz) aroused a cats' serenade from the gallery, reflecting the original words, changed for a triumphant Vienna performance. There is an attractive overture to the work, which also allows Caramello the seductive *Komm in die Gondel* (Come into the gondola).

Recommended Recordings:

Overture	***Naxos 8.553936***
Lagunen-Walzer	***Naxos 8.550943***
Komm in die Gondel	***Naxos 8.550941***

NAÏS

- ◆ Jean-Philippe Rameau. *Pastorale-héroique* in a prologue and three acts. 1749.
- ◆ Libretto by Louis de Cahusac.
- ◆ First performance at the Paris Opéra on 22nd April 1749.

Naïs, described in its full title as *opéra pour la Paix* (opera for the Peace), celebrates the Peace of Aix-la-Chapelle that ended the War of the Austrian Succession. The political compromise is reflected in a work that represents Louis XIV as a magnanimous Jupiter and proposes George II of England as Neptune, who successfully woos the nymph Naïs, daughter of Tiresias, defeating other suitors.

NAISSANCE D'OSIRIS, LA (THE BIRTH OF OSIRIS)

- ◆ Jean-Philippe Rameau. *Acte de ballet*. 1754.
- ◆ Libretto by Louis de Cahusac.
- ◆ First performance at Fontainebleau on 12th October 1754.

Described as an allegorical ballet, *La naissance d'Osiris* (The Birth of Osiris) was written in celebration of the birth of the future Louis XVI.

Recommended Recording:

La Naissance d'Osiris (Suite)	***Naxos 8.553388***

Navarraise, La (The Girl from Navarre)

- Jules Massenet. *Episode lyrique* in two acts. 1894.
- Libretto by Jules Claretie and Henri Cain, after the story *La Cigarette* by the former.
- First performance at Covent Garden, London, on 20th June 1894.

The poor orphan from Navarre, Anita, prays with other women in the square of a Basque village, as the Carlist forces under Zuccaraga seem victorious in the war. Her betrothed, the sergeant Araquil, returns from battle, but his father, a rich farmer, expects a dowry with his son's wife. Araquil's captain, Ramon, suggests that Anita has been seeking out the handsome young Zuccaraga, but she returns from the Carlist encampment having killed him, to be rewarded by General Garrido with the sum needed for her dowry. Araquil, however, has followed Anita to the enemy positions and has been mortally wounded. He dies cursing her, and she goes out of her mind.

In *La Navarraise* (The Girl from Navarre) Massenet attempts a fashionable degree of realism and there were obvious comparisons to be drawn with *Cavalleria rusticana* (Rustic Chivalry). As in that work, there is an *Intermezzo*, a nocturne, as Anita makes her way to the enemy lines, before returning, blood-stained but triumphant.

Nelson

- Lennox Berkeley. Opera in three acts. 1954.
- Libretto by Alan Pryce-Jones.
- First performance at Sadler's Wells Theatre, London, on 22nd September 1954.

Lord Nelson is received by Sir William Hamilton and his wife Emma in their Palazzo in Naples. Nelson and Emma Hamilton fall in love. In a London drawing-room Lady Nelson laments her loneliness and when the Hamiltons call, Emma Hamilton is provoked into declaring her love for Nelson. At Merton, outside London, Nelson is confronted with a choice between love and duty, and when word comes that he is needed, chooses the latter. At Portsmouth Emma bids him farewell and in a second scene on board ship he meets his death at the battle of Trafalgar.

Lennox Berkeley's opera deserves more attention than it has received and contains moving music for the neglected Lady Nelson and a fine parting scene for the lovers.

NERONE (NERO)

- Arrigo Boito. *Tragedia* in four acts. 1915.
- Libretto by the composer.
- First performance at the Teatro alla Scala, Milan, on 1st May 1924.

Nero fears the Furies, pursuing him, he imagines, because of his murder of his mother. Simon Magus promises to cure his obsession, and, in a meeting with the Christian Fanuèl, attempts to buy part of the magic power of the new religion. He is refused, the beginning of enmity between the two. In Simon's temple Asteria is enthroned on the altar and worshipped as a goddess by Nero, until he discovers that she is a woman and that he has been tricked by Simon Magus. Simon now reveals to the authorities the whereabouts of the Christians and Fanuèl is arrested, having refused to give Simon the power of flight that Nero has demanded as proof of the authenticity of his magic. Rome burns, with a fire arranged by an assistant of Simon. This will cover Simon's attempts at flight, while for Asteria it may allow Christians to escape and for Nero a chance for new city planning. The Christians are led into the arena, while Simon, thrown down from above, fails to fly. The final scene brings the death of Rubria, a Vestal virgin, once raped by Nero, but a convert to the new faith. Her incipient conversion had moved Asteria in the first act and she had pleaded for the Christians in the arena, only to be thrown down to join them.

Boito's original libretto for *Nerone*, published in 1901, contains a fifth act, cut in the final version for practical reasons. Here Nero is seen in the rôle of Orestes, while Rome burns round him. The work occupied him intermittently from 1877 until 1915, with the opera only staged finally in a four-act version six years after his death. It presents grandiose spectacle and a moving death scene for the Christian convert Rubria, but is better in its libretto than in music of varying effectiveness.

NEUES VOM TAGE (NEWS OF THE DAY)

- Paul Hindemith. *Lustige Oper* in three parts. 1929. Revised in two acts, with a libretto of his own, in 1953.
- Libretto by Marcellus Schiffer.
- First performance at the Kroll Theater, Berlin, on 8th June 1929.

Laura and Eduard plan to divorce and, taking the advice of Herr and Frau M., engage a co-respondent, Hermann, who is to compromise Laura in a meeting in a museum. Eduard's jealousy is aroused, when he sees Laura and Hermann together, and he breaks a valuable statue of Venus over Hermann's head. For this he is imprisoned. Hermann has fallen in love with Laura and surprises her in her hotel bath, seen by staff of the hotel. These events become news of the day and the participants are employed to re-enact their quarrel in nightly cabaret. This effectively resolves their differences, which, nevertheless, must be repeated in public.

Hindemith offers a satire of contemporary life and of some operatic conventions, as in the opening crockery-throwing hate scene at the outset and the sentimentality of the scene for Hermann and Laura. The bath scene scandalized more conventional audiences, including Adolf Hitler and Dr Goebbels, who walked out.

New Year

- Michael Tippett. Opera in three acts. 1988.
- Libretto by the composer.
- First performance at the Wortham Theater Center, Houston, on 27th October 1989.

Characters

Jo Ann, a child psychologist	lyric soprano
Donny, her brother	baritone
Nan, their foster-mother	dramatic mezzo-soprano
Regan	dramatic soprano
Pelegrin, space-ship pilot	lyric tenor
Merlin, a computer wizard	dramatic baritone

Jo Ann cannot cope with Somewhere Today but is seen on computer screen by Pelegrin in his space-ship, travelling from Nowhere Tomorrow with the powerful ruler Regan, who is horrified when she finds that the ship has travelled back in time. Jo Ann, however, discovered by Pelegrin in a crowd celebrating the new year, learns from her contact with him, although they must part.

Tippett originally conceived *New Year* rather as a musical than as an opera and in the score makes use of saxophones and electric guitars, with their obvious popular associations. The work links the communal and the personal, the eternal and the individual, as the composer has explained, adding final words heard from a pop concert in Wembley Stadium in honour of Nelson Mandela, 'One humanity, one justice'.

Night at the Chinese Opera, A

- Judith Weir. Opera in three acts. 1987.
- Libretto by the composer, using, in part, the Yuen Dynasty *Little Orphan of the House of Chao.*
- First performance at the Everyman Theatre, Cheltenham, on 8th July 1987.

The opera traces the story of Chao Lin, explorer and canal-builder, exiled at the accession of Kublai Khan. He attends a performance of *The Chao Family Orphan* which is interrupted by an earthquake. After that his own life is intermingled with the events of the Chinese opera, with imprisonment, threatened execution and final justification before the Emperor.

The opera generally lacks obvious pseudo-Chinese effects and takes as its alleged basis the first of the plays collected in the Yuen Dynasty to reach Europe, translated into French in Du Halde's history of China in the 1730s and imitated by Voltaire, Arthur Murphy, Metastasio and others, while some deplored the original play's failure to observe the dramatic unities of Aristotle.

Nightingale, The

- Igor Stravinsky. Lyric tale in three scenes. 1914.
- Libretto by Stepan Mitusov, after the tale by Hans Christian Andersen.
- First performance at the Paris Opéra on 26th May 1914.

Characters

The Nightingale	soprano
The Cook	soprano
The Fisherman	tenor
The Emperor of China	baritone
The Chamberlain	bass
The Bonze	bass
Death	mezzo-soprano
Three Japanese Envoys	two tenors & bass

The Fisherman welcomes the evening song of the Nightingale, which is now invited by courtiers to sing for the Emperor. It demands as its only reward the tears of listeners. In the palace preparations are made for the entry of the Emperor. The Nightingale sings and is rewarded and the

Japanese envoys present the Emperor with a mechanical clock-work nightingale. The Nightingale flies away. In the third act the Emperor is ill and Death sits by his bed, while ghosts rehearse his evil deeds. The Nightingale flies in and with its song wins back what Death has taken. The Emperor is restored to life, and in the distance the Fisherman's song is heard.

Stravinsky described the staging, with costumes and sets by Alexandre Benois, as one of the most beautiful of all his early works for Dyagilev. The singers were off-stage and the action was carried out by dancers. The composer had started the work in Russia and Rimsky-Korsakov, before his death in 1908, had given his approval of some of the music, redolent, Stravinsky said, of Mussorgsky. The second and third acts were written in the aftermath of *The Rite of Spring*, with the orchestral possibilities that that now involved. With this in mind, he considered the first act as a form of prologue to what follows. The *Chant du rossignol* (Song of the Nightingale), intended as an orchestral work, although later choreographed for Dyagilev, was derived from the second and third acts.

Nixon in China

- John Adams. Opera in two acts. 1987.
- Libretto by Alice Goodman.
- First performance at the Grand Opera, Houston, on 22nd October 1987.

The opera is based on the American president Richard Nixon's visit to China in 1972, contrasting the Nixons and Henry Kissinger, this last caricatured, with the Chinese statesmen, including Mao Tse-tung and his wife Chiang Ch'ing, the latter portrayed unsympathetically.

Post-minimalist in its musical language, the vocal writing of *Nixon in China* captures American intonations, if not Chinese, and offers, in its final act, a thoughful scene, in which the leaders, in private, utter their own thoughts on their achievements, such as they may be.

Norma

- Vincenzo Bellini. *Tragedia lirica* in two acts. 1831.
- Libretto by Felice Romani, after the verse tragedy by Alexandre Soumet.
- First performance at the Teatro alla Scala, Milan, on 26th December 1831.

Characters

Oroveso, Archdruid	bass
Norma, his daughter, Druid high priestess	soprano
Clotilda, her confidante	mezzo-soprano
Adalgisa, a young priestess of the temple	soprano
Pollione, Roman pro-consul in Gaul	tenor
Flavio, a Roman centurion	tenor
Two Children of Norma and Pollione	silent rôles

Oroveso seeks to rouse his countrymen to rebellion against the Romans. Pollione now confides in Flavio that he no longer loves Norma, in spite of the fact that, unknown to everyone, she has born him two sons. Norma tries to prevent rebellion, to protect Pollione, prophesying the fall of Rome through its own internal weaknesses. Pollione persuades Adalgisa to run away to Rome with him. Norma, at home, knows that Pollione plans to leave her, but does not know the name of her rival. Adalgisa admits her infidelity to her people to Norma, who eventually understands that Adalgisa is the new object of Pollione's affections. When Adalgisa realises the situation, she rejects Pollione. Norma considers killing her sons and then asking Adalgisa to go with Pollione and be a mother to her children in her place. Adalgisa refuses to be disloyal to Norma, but goes to Pollione to recall him to his duty. He will not hear her, and Norma now calls for open revolt. Meanwhile Pollione, attempting to abduct Adalgisa, has been taken prisoner, and will be put to death. Norma offers in his place one who has broken faith with her people, herself. A funeral pyre is erected, which she mounts, joined in her final moments by Pollione.

Norma occupies a very particular place in operatic repertoire, a dramatic work of lyrical beauty, not least in the most fanous of Norma's arias, *Casta diva* (Chaste goddess), her first-act prayer to the moon. Oroveso calls the Druids to watch for the new moon in *Ite sul colle, o Druidi* (Go to the hills, O Druids) and in the second act he warns of Pollione's possible successor, inveighing against Roman tyranny in *Ah! del Tebro al giogo indegno* (Ah! To the disgraceful yoke of Rome). Norma has notable duets with Adalgisa and with Pollione, revealing different aspects of her tragic character.

Nose, The

- Dmitry Shostakovich. Opera in three acts. 1928.
- Libretto by the composer, Yevgeny Zamyatin, Georgy Ionin and Alexander Preys, after the story by Gogol.
- First performance at the Maliy Opera Theatre, Leningrad, on 18th January 1930.

The barber Ivan Yakovlevich finds a nose in his freshly baked breakfast bread and is sent out by his shrewish wife to dispose of it. Throwing it into the river, he is challenged by the Police Inspector. Major Kovalyov wakes up to find his nose gone and leaves to see the Chief of Police. In Kazan Cathedral the Nose, in the uniform of a State Councillor, is at prayer, recognised by Kovalyov, who fears to approach anyone in such a high position. In a newspaper office people place advertisements, but Kovalyov's intended advertisement for a lost nose is rejected as beneath the paper's dignity. The Police Inspector now has orders to stop the Nose leaving St Petersburg. As a coach leaves the city, the Nose runs after it, frightens the horses and is caught and beaten down to normal size. The Police Inspector returns the Nose to Kovalyov and after a number of hints is duly rewarded. Kovalyov cannot get it back on again and a doctor tells him it is impossible. Kovalyov suspects the sorcery of Madame Podtochina, who wants him to marry her daughter, and letters are exchanged. Meanwhile people gather in the streets, hoping to see the Nose. In the epilogue Kovalyov wakes up with his nose in place, is shaved by Yakovlevich, and goes out to call on Madame Podtochina, greeting friends and acquaintances on the way.

There is considerable use of parody in Shostakovich's score for the absurd story of *The Nose*. Even with doubling, the need to cast 78 acting or singing rôles offers problems. The composer arranged a seven part *Suite* from the opera, for tenor, bass and orchestra.

Nozze di Figaro, Le (The Marriage of Figaro)

- Wolfgang Amadeus Mozart. *Opera buffa* in four acts. 1786.
- Libretto by Lorenzo Da Ponte, after the play *La folle journée, ou Le mariage de Figaro* (The Mad Day, or The Marriage of Figaro) by Pierre-Augustin Beaumarchais.
- First performance at the Burgtheater, Vienna, on 1st May 1786.

Characters

Count Almaviva	baritone
Countess Almaviva	soprano

Susanna, her maid, betrothed to Figaro	soprano
Figaro, valet to the Count	bass
Cherubino, the Count's page	mezzo-soprano
Bartolo, a doctor from Seville	bass
Marcellina, his housekeeper	soprano
Don Basilio, a music-master	tenor
Don Curzio, a magistrate	tenor
Antonio, a gardener, Susanna's uncle	bass
Barbarina, his daughter	soprano

Figaro and Susanna are to marry, but the Count has given them rooms near to his own, which will be convenient if he needs access to Susanna. Bartolo wants to take revenge on Figaro, who had helped the Count to marry his ward Rosina, now the Countess. His housekeeper Marcellina has lent money to Figaro, who has promised to marry her, if he cannot repay it. Cherubino tells Susanna that he loves all women, and Susanna hides him, as the Count is heard approaching. His proposals to Susanna are interrupted by the sound of Don Basilio coming near, and he too hides behind the chair, allowing Cherubino to hide himself sitting on it, under a dress thrown over him by Susanna. Basilio now refers to Cherubino's love for the Countess, and the Count emerges to find out more. Susanna tries to distract them by fainting, but Cherubino is discovered. Figaro brings in a group of peasants, singing praise of the Count, who has surrendered, it is suggested, his *droit de seigneur* as far as Susanna is concerned, but the Count delays their marriage and packs Cherubino off to the army. Figaro, however, detains Cherubino, since he has plans for him. In the second act the Countess, in her room, is sad, neglected by her husband. She listens to Figaro's plan to dress Cherubino as a girl and put him in Susanna's place in an attempt to trap the Count. Cherubino is singing of his love for the Countess, when the Count returns from hunting, eager to pursue matters divulged to him in an anonymous letter accusing the Countess. Cherubino hides in the closet and Susanna, unseen by the others, comes in. The Countess tells her husband that Susanna is in the closet but the door cannot be opened. The Count, suspicious, goes to fetch tools to open the door, taking the Countess with him. This allows Cherubino to jump out of the window and Susanna to take his place. The Count returns and the closet is opened, revealing Susanna. Antonio, the gardener, adds complications when he comes in to complain of someone jumping out of the window, and Figaro now claims that it was him. The act ends with the appearance of Don Basilio, Bartolo and Marcellina, seeking justice. As the wedding is prepared, in the third act, Susanna, at the suggestion of the Countess, agrees to an assignation with the Count. Marcellina's complaint against Figaro is heard and he claims that he needs parental consent for his marriage to her, if it is to take place. It then transpires that Marcellina is in fact his mother and Bartolo his father. In the fourth act, in the garden at night, Figaro is given cause for jealousy of Susanna, but she is now disguised as the Countess and the

Countess as Susanna. The Count unknowingly woos his own wife, while Figaro deliberately provokes his jealousy by his own approaches to the supposed Countess, in fact Susanna. The opera ends with the Count humbled but penitent, reconciled now with his wife, Figaro with Susanna, Cherubino with Barbarina and Marcellina with Bartolo.

The complexities and symmetries of situation in *Le nozze di Figaro* (The Marriage of Figaro) make up one of the most perfect of Mozart's operas, with a score that offers music of great variety, admirably suited to each situation and character. There is a brilliantly devised overture, followed by the scene in which Figaro measures the room that is to be his and Susanna's. Resolving to get the better of the Count, Figaro sings his well known *Se vuol ballare, signor contino* (If you want to dance, little master count). Revenge of another kind is envisaged by Bartolo in his patter-song *La vendetta* (Vengeance). Cherubino opens his heart to Susanna in *Non sò più cosa son, cosa faccio* (I no longer know who I am or what I am doing), and when Cherubino is duly banished with an army commission, Figaro mocks him with *Non più andrai farfallone amoroso* (You are no longer an amorous butterfly). There is great poignancy in the Countess's second act aria *Porgi amor* (Love, grant me comfort), to which perhaps Cherubino's adolescent *Voi che sapete* (You who know what love is) might provide consolation. The opera continues with a wealth of musical invention and apt dramatic sense, shown to perfection in the comic finales, those final ensembles which offer either a problem to be solved or, in the end, a final reconciliation.

Recommended Recordings:

Overture	***Naxos 8.550185***
Non più andrai / Crudel! Perchè finora / Deh, vieni non tardar	***Naxos 8.550435***
Highlights	***Naxos 8.554172***

Nozze di Teti e di Peleo, Le (The Marriage of Thetis and Peleus)

- Francesco Cavalli. *Opera scenica* (*Festa teatrale*) in three acts. 1639.
- Libretto by Orazio Persiani.
- First performance at the Teatro S Cassiano on 24th January 1639.

Aeolus wishes to prevent the marriage of his son Peleus to Thetis, fearing her to have been compromised by Jupiter. Pluto comes to his aid by sending Discordia to part the two. Hymen eventually puts matters right and the couple marry.

Cavalli's spectacular opera, his first, is the first score to survive of the operas written for theatres in Venice, where the first commercial opera-house had opened in 1637.

Nusch-Nuschi, Das (The Nuts-Nuts)

- Paul Hindemith. Opera in one act. 1921.
- Libretto by Franz Blei.
- First performance at the Landestheater, Stuttgart, on 4th June 1921.

Described as a play for Burmese marionettes, *Nusch-Nuschi* centres not on the creature of the title, half rat, half cayman, but on the seduction by Zatwai of four of the Emperor's wives. Blame is deflected from Zatwai by his servant Tum-Tum, who turns attention to the army chief, Kyce Waing, who is, as it happens, incapable of any such thing. The testicular pun of the title, echoed in its suggested English translation, refers to the powers of Nusch-Nuschi as a castrator.

Das Nusch-Nuschi formed part of a triple bill, with Hindemith's *Mörder, Hoffnung der Frauen* (Murderer, Hope of Women) and *Sancta Susanna.* It created a scandal at its early performances, particularly by quoting Wagner's King Mark, whose words at Tristan's betrayal are echoed in the Emperor's reproach to his army chief.

Oberon

- Carl Maria von Weber. *Romantische Oper* in three acts. 1826.
- Libretto by James Robinson Planché, after the poem *Oberon* by Christoph Martin Wieland.
- First performance at Covent Garden, London, on 12th April 1826.

Characters

Oberon, King of the Elves	tenor
Puck	mezzo-soprano
Sir Huon of Bordeaux	tenor
Sherasmin, his squire	baritone
Reiza, daughter of Haroun al Raschid	soprano
Fatima, her attendant	mezzo-soprano
Two Mermaids	mezzo-sopranos
Charlemagne, Emperor of the Franks	speaking part
Haroun al Raschid, Caliph	speaking part
Babekan, a Saracen prince	speaking part
Almanzor, Emir of Tunis	speaking part
Abdullah, a corsair	speaking part
Titania, Oberon's wife	speaking part
Roshana, wife of Almanzor	speaking part
Namouna, Fatima's grandmother	speaking part
Nadina, a woman in Almanzor's harem	speaking part

Oberon and Titania have quarrelled over the matter of male or female inconstancy and will be reconciled when a couple constant through misfortune can be found. The Emperor Charlemagne has ordered Sir Huon of Bordeaux to travel to Baghdad. There he must kill the man on the right hand of the Caliph and kiss and marry the Caliph's daughter. Sir Huon sees the Caliph's daughter, Reiza, in a dream, and is given by Oberon a magic horn to summon necessary aid and a magic goblet, that will burn the lips of the impure. By the Tigris Sir Huon saves the Saracen prince Babekan, betrothed to Reiza, from a lion. Babekan drinks from the goblet, his lips are burned and he attacks and is repelled by Sir Huon. In Haroun al Raschid's palace Reiza wants to avoid marriage to Babekan and has seen her rescuer in a dream. Sir Huon arrives. In the second act, in the Caliph's palace, Reiza is saved from marriage to Babekan, who is killed, while the court is paralysed by the sound of the magic horn. Sir Huon and Sherasmin, with Reiza and Fatima, escape by ship, which is wrecked. Reiza is abducted by pirates and Oberon tells Puck to take Huon, bound and unconscious, to the house of Ibrahim in Tunis, where the third act opens. Now Sir Huon, escaping from imminent execution through the blowing of the magic horn by his squire, rescues Reiza from the harem of the Emir. Their trials now over, the couple is transported to the palace of Charlemagne by Oberon and Titania and the opera ends with praise of the constant Sir Huon and Reiza.

The mixture of speech and music in *Oberon, or The Elf King's Oath* offered Weber a task that he would willingly have avoided. The work was composed very quickly, under pressure that contributed to the composer's death in London two months after the successful first performance of the opera. The overture, a well known concert opener, makes use of material from the opera and starts with the sound of the magic horn and suggestions of the fairy kingdom of Oberon. It also includes part of Reiza's song *Ocean, thou mighty monster*, in German translation *Ozean du ungeheuer*.

Recommended Recording: Overture — ***Naxos 8.550146***

Oberto, conte di San Bonifacio (Oberto, County of St Boniface)

- Giuseppe Verdi. *Dramma* in two acts. 1839.
- Libretto by Antonio Piazza and Temistocle Solera.
- First performance at the Teatro alla Scala, Milan, on 17th November 1839.

Riccardo, Count of Salinguerra, has seduced Leonora, daughter of Count Oberto, but is to marry Cuniza, sister of Ezzelino da Romano. Leonora and Count Oberto, the latter an enemy of Ezzelino, seek Cuniza's help. There is a duel between Riccardo and Oberto, in which the latter is killed. Riccardo leaves, guilty at his action, and Leonora goes into a convent.

Verdi's first published opera was originally *Rocester*. Rejected by various opera-houses, the libretto was revised by Temistocle Solera for production at La Scala, Milan, where it won moderate success.

Recommended Recording: Overture — ***Naxos 8.553018***

Oca del Cairo, L' (The Goose of Cairo)

- Wolfgang Amadeus Mozart. *Opera buffa* in two acts. 1784.
- Libretto by Giovanni Battista Varesco.
- Unfinished.

Mozart's unfinished comic opera, for which some music survives, had an uninspiring story and libretto by the Salzburg chaplain Giovanni Battista Varesco, who had put together the libretto of *Idomeneo* in 1780. The plot involves the autocratic Don Pippo and his attempts, having banished his wife, to marry a younger girl himself and marry his daughter off to a husband of his choosing, against her will. The goose of the title is a mechanical toy, to be used as a Trojan horse, for the purpose of smuggling into his fortress Biondello, Don Pippo's daughter's young lover. There have been various arrangements of the surviving drafts for performance, from the first known staging in Paris in 1867 onwards.

Occasione fa il ladro (Opportunity Makes the Thief)

- Gioachino Rossini. *Burletta per musica* in one act. 1812.
- Libretto by Luigi Prividali, after the play *Le prétendu par basard, ou L'occasion fait le non* (The Chance Intended, or Opportunity Makes No) by Eugène Scribe.
- First performance at the Teatro S Moisè, Venice, on 24th November 1812.

A chance meeting at an inn between Don Parmenione and Count Alberto provides the occasion for an accidental exchange of luggage. Alberto is on his way to Berenice, whom he is to marry, but she has resolved to test her proposed husband by changing places with her maid. Parmenione tries his luck with Alberto's papers and identity, wooing the disguised maid, Ernestina, while Alberto behaves with correctness towards the supposed maid, the disguised Berenice. Eventually problems are solved, with Alberto and Berenice united.

Occasion fa il ladro (Opportunity Makes the Thief), subtitled *Il cambio della vaglia* (The Exchange of Luggage), follows *La pietra del paragone* (The Touchstone), staged two months earlier in Florence. The new light opera was followed by the *farsa Il Signor Bruschino*, the last such work that Rossini wrote for Venice.

Oedipe (Oedipus)

- George Enescu. *Tragédie lyrique* in four acts. 1932.
- Libretto by Edmond Fleg, after the plays by Sophocles.
- First performance at the Paris Opéra on 13th March 1936.

The first act, a prologue, deals with the birth of Oedipus, the joy of his parents, Jocasta and Laius, and the foreboding of the prophet Tiresias, who foretells that the child will kill his father and marry his mother. The boy is given to a shepherd to take away and kill. Kept alive and brought up as the son of the King and Queen of Corinth, Oedipus is told by the oracle that he will kill his father and marry his mother. Assured that he is their son, he leaves Corinth, killing Laius on his way and solving the riddle proposed by the Sphinx, which has preyed on the people of Thebes. He is rewarded by the hand of the widowed Queen, his mother Jocasta. In the third act Thebes is suffering from a plague, caused by the presence in the city of a polluting figure, identified by Tiresias as Oedipus himself. The King blinds himself, after Jocasta has killed herself. He now goes away into perpetual exile, led by his daughter Antigone. The fourth act takes Oedipus to Athens, where he appears finally as triumphant over Fate, justifying his answer to the riddle of the Sphinx, 'What is greater than Fate?', to which he had replied 'Man', an alteration of the traditional story.

In general Enescu's opera follows the tragedy *Oedipus tyrannus* (King Oedipus) by Sophocles, with a final act derived from *Oedipus at Colonus*. A major work of the Romanian composer, it has found no firm place in operatic repertoire.

Oedipus rex (King Oedipus)

- Igor Stravinsky. Opera-oratorio in two acts. 1927.
- Libretto by Jean Cocteau, after Sophocles.
- First performance at the Théâtre Sarah Bernhardt, Paris, on 30th May 1927.

Characters

Oedipe (Oedipus)	tenor
Jocaste (Jocasta)	mezzo-soprano
Créon (Creon)	bass-baritone
Tirésias (Tiresias)	bass
Shepherd	tenor

Messenger	bass-baritone
Speaker (Narrator)	speaking part

The Speaker, in French, frames the action, declaring at the beginning that a trap has been set for Oedipus. There follow, in the first act, three episodes. In the first the people of Thebes call on Oedipus to save them from plague, in the second Creon returns from the oracle, which has told him of the presence in the city of the murderer of the old king and in the third Tiresias is induced to hint at the identity of the killer, whom Oedipus is resolved to root out, now suspecting some conspiracy between Creon and Tiresias. The second act brings three further episodes. In the fourth episode in the work, Jocasta, the Queen, doubts the truth of the oracle, recalling the place where her former husband had died. Oedipus now starts to wonder, since this corresponds to the place where he had once killed an old man that obstructed his way. The fifth episode reveals, through a messenger and a shepherd, the truth, that Oedipus has killed his father and married his mother. The final episode brings the messenger to announce the death of Jocasta and the blinding of Oedipus, now driven away from Thebes.

Stravinsky chose to use a Latin sung text for his ritual drama, with Cocteau's words translated into Latin by Jean Daniélou. The strict restraints of a language set in stone suggested a formal staging, with masked figures singing to the audience rather than to each other. The music, neo-classical in idiom, yet encompassing a variety of styles, is impressive, while the whole work, deliberately avoiding drama, stage action, remains a clear and precisely chiselled monument. Stravinsky in later years retained his affection for the music, but never seems to have set much store by the French narration provided by Cocteau.

Olympians, The

- Arthur Bliss. Opera in three acts. 1949.
- Libretto by J.B.Priestley.
- First performance at Covent Garden, London, on 29th September 1949.

The gods of Olympus now travel the world as a troupe of wandering actors, resuming their former powers for a few hours on Midsummer Eve. Their intervention in a Provençal village in 1836 allows two young lovers to marry, in spite of the plans of the girl's father.

The Olympians has enjoyed little success in the theatre, in spite of the contemporary distinction of both composer and librettist.

Oprichnik

- Pyotr Il'yich Tchaikovsky. Opera in four acts. 1872.
- Libretto by the composer, after the tragedy by Ivan Lazhechnikov.
- First performance at the Mariinsky Theatre, St Petersburg, on 24th April 1874.

Prince Zhemchuznïy's daughter Natalya is betrothed to the elderly Molchan Mitkov. Her lover, Andrey Morozov, plans to join the *oprichniki*, the Tsar's bodyguards, who have undoubted privileges of money and women. He confides to the *oprichnik* Basmanov that Zhemchuznïy has taken all his family's land and possessions. Natalya hears the men, but they have gone before she can reach them. She sits in sadness, comforted by her nurse and the women of the household. Andrey's mother, in spite of her troubles, disapproves of the *oprichniki* and the Tsar's favourite Basmanov. Without telling her of his intention, he joins the *oprichniki*, inducted by his father's enemy, the commander Prince Vyazminsky. In the third act Andrey's mother and then Natalya are appalled to find Andrey an *oprichnik*, and Basmanov urges him to seek dispensation from his vows from the Tsar. At the wedding of Andrey and Natalya, the Tsar calls for Natalya to be brought to him. Andrey opposes this, but in vain. Cursing the Tsar, he is arrested and executed in the sight of his mother, through the agency of Vyazminsky, who thus has his own revenge.

Tchaikovsky, always critical of his own work, positively disliked his opera *The Oprichnik*. Use is made of Russian folk-song in a score that re-used music from his first opera *The Voyevoda* (The Provincial Governor).

Oreste (Orestes)

- George Frideric Handel. Opera in three acts. 1734.
- Libretto adapted from *L'Oreste* (Orestes) by Giangualberto Barlocci, after *Iphigenia in Tauris* by Euripides.
- First performance at Covent Garden Theatre, London, on 18th December 1734.

Handel's *Oreste* follows the same plot as Gluck, 65 years later, in his *Iphigénie en Tauride*, in which Iphigenia, saved miraculously from sacrifice by her father at Aulis, later finds her brother Orestes, when the latter is wrecked on the coast of Tauris, and is instrumental in saving him from death and in the overthrow of the superstitious and despotic Scythian king Thoas.

Handel borrowed extensively from earlier works for the *pasticcio Oreste*, which won relatively little success at its first performance and was not revived in the composer's life-time.

ORFEO (ORPHEUS)

- Claudio Monteverdi. *Favola in musica* in a prologue and five acts. 1607.
- Libretto by Alessandro Striggio, based on Ovid's *Metamorphoses* and Virgil's *Georgics*.
- First performance at the ducal palace, Mantua, on 24th February 1607.

CHARACTERS

La Musica (Music)	male soprano
Orfeo (Orpheus)	tenor
Euridice (Eurydice)	(male?) soprano
Silvia (Sylvia)	soprano
Speranza (Hope)	(male?) soprano
Caronte (Charon)	bass
Proserpina	soprano
Plutone (Pluto)	bass
Apollo	tenor

In a prologue the figure of Music introduces the piece, a demonstration of the power of music. Orpheus and Eurydice are at last to marry, an event celebrated in dance and song by the shepherd company. The second act continues the celebration of the happiness of Orpheus, interrupted by the appearance of the messenger Sylvia, who breaks the news of the death of Eurydice, before leaving to shun human company, marked by the bad news she has brought. Orpheus, accompanied by Hope, sets out for the Underworld. She leaves him as he approaches the Styx, eventually overpowering the boatman of the dead, Charon, with his music, and crossing the river. In the kingdom of Pluto, Proserpina pleads with her husband for the release of Eurydice, and she is allowed to leave, following Orpheus, provided that he does not look round. As he walks away, doubts assail him and he looks round, only to lose Eurydice, who must now remain in the Underworld. The fifth act finds Orpheus alone in the fields of Thrace, comforted by Echo. In the published libretto and, presumably, in the first performance in the palace of the Duke of Mantua, Orpheus is then set upon by Bacchantes, who tear him in pieces. In Monteverdi's score this is replaced by a final apotheosis, when Apollo appears as a *deus ex machina*, descending on a cloud machine to raise Orpheus to the stars, whence he can see for ever Eurydice, similarly transported.

Monteverdi's opera occupies a supremely important position in the history of music and of opera as one of the earliest examples of the form and certainly the earliest to retain or to have regained a place in present repertoire. With pastoral and madrigal elements in its pastoral setting, it provides music of great power, notably in *Possente spirto* (Powerful spirit), the aria with which Orpheus seeks to sway Charon. There is much to delight and to move in a work that remains dramatically effective and moving. The published score brings the added advantage of a list of instruments used at the performance in Mantua, a valuable indication of contemporary practice for a lavish celebratory court staging.

Recommended Recording:
Orfeo (2 CDs) — ***Naxos 8.554094-95***

Orfeo ed Euridice (Orpheus and Eurydice)

- Christoph Willibald von Gluck. *Azione teatrale* in three acts. 1762.
- Libretto by Ranieri de'Calzabigi.
- First performance at the Burgtheater, Vienna, on 5th October 1762.

Characters

Orfeo (Orpheus)	male alto
Euridice (Eurydice), his wife	soprano
Amore (Cupid)	soprano

Nymphs and shepherds celebrate the funeral rites of Eurydice, assisted by Orpheus, who laments her loss and reproaches the gods with cruelty. Cupid tells him that he may, if he can, bring her back from the dead by the power of music, but must not look at her until she is in the land of the living again. He encounters demons and Furies as he descends, calming them with his music, before entering the Elysian fields, where the blessed spirits dance. Eurydice questions him and faints, as they try to leave, causing him to look round, at which she dies once more. He laments this turn of events, comforted by Cupid, who, rewarding his obvious fidelity, restores Eurydice to life once more. The opera ends in a celebration at the temple of Cupid.

Orfeo ed Euridice (Orpheus and Eurydice) is the first of Gluck's reform operas, collaborations with Ranieri de'Calzabigi, in which composer and poet aimed at a noble classical simplicity, avoiding what Gluck described in his preface to *Alceste* as the abuses of excessive ornamentation and other elements that pandered to the vanity of singers. Instrumental excerpts from the opera, which have appeared over the years in a variety of other arrangements, must include the famous *Dance of the Blessed Spirits*, which is preceded in the opera by the contrasting *Dance of the Furies*. Most moving is the lament of Orpheus when Eurydice has died a second time, *Che farò senza Euridice* (What am I to do without Eurydice).

Recommended Recording: Orfeo ed Euridice (2 CDs) — ***Naxos 8.660064-65***

Oristeo

- Francesco Cavalli. *Drama per musica* in a prologue and three acts. 1651.
- Libretto by Giovanni Faustini.
- First performance at the Teatro S Apollinare, Venice, in 1651.

Diomeda is to marry Oristeo, King of Epirus, but an encounter with his men leads to the death of her father and her consequent vow of chastity. Later she falls in love with Trasimede, who is loved by Corinta, Princess of Locri, while Oristeo in disguise has taken employment in her gardens. Difficulties are finally resolved between Oristeo and Diomeda and between Trasimede and Corinta.

Cavalli's opera also includes an allegorical prologue and interludes, providing the traditional frame for the action. *Oristeo* is the first of his operas for the Teatro S Apollinare, where two more operas of his were staged in the same year, 1651.

Orlando

- George Frideric Handel. Opera in three acts. 1733.
- Libretto adapted from *L'Orlando* of Carlo Sigismondo Capece.
- First performance at the King's Theatre, London, on 27th January 1733.

Characters

Orlando, a knight	male alto
Angelica, Queen of Cathay	soprano
Medoro, an African prince, her lover	male alto
Dorinda, a shepherdess	soprano
Zoroastro, a magician	bass
Isabella, a princess	silent rôle

Orlando is torn between love and glory, urged to the latter by the magician Zoroastro. Orlando rescues the princess Isabella, while the object of his affections, Angelica, loves and is loved by Medoro, who is loved also by Dorinda. Zoroastro successfully prevents a hostile encounter between Orlando and Medoro, but the latter's love for Angelica inevitably becomes known to Dorinda and then, in the second act, to Orlando, who loses his wits. Zoroastro, who has done much to prevent open trouble, flies away with Orlando. In the third act, now mad, Orlando expresses love for Dorinda, addressing her as Venus. All is eventually put right by Zoroastro, with Angelica and Medoro restored to each other and Orlando again in his right mind.

Orlando paladino (The Paladin Roland)

- Joseph Haydn. *Dramma eroicomico* in three acts. 1782.
- Libretto by Nunziato Porta, after Ariosto's *Orlando furioso* (Roland in Madness)
- First performance at Esterháza on 6th December 1782.

Rodomonte, King of Barbaria, seeks Orlando, threatening the shepherd and shepherdess Licone and Eurilla. Medoro, lover of Angelica, Queen of Cathay, is alarmed at the approach of Orlando in madness. Orlando and the boastful Rodomonte meet and fight, while Medoro and Angelica are re-united. The sorceress Alcina has helped the couple and now deals with Orlando, petrifying and unpetrifying him, before immuring him in her cave. He is finally cured, through the good offices of Charon, and beholds with some equanimity the union of Angelica and Medoro, the latter restored to health after being mortally wounded.

Haydn's opera includes a comic element, notably for Orlando's squire, Pasquale, but also finds some humour in the madness of his hero.

Ormindo

- Francesco Cavalli. *Favola regia per musica* in three acts. 1644.
- Libretto by Giovanni Faustini.
- First performance at the Teatro S Cassiano, Venice, in 1644.

Prince Ormindo loves Erisbe, wife of Hariadeno, who is also Ormindo's long-lost father. Amida, prince of Trasimede, also loves Erisbe, but was before this the lover of Princess Sicle, who comes to him, at first in disguise, and revives his former affection for her. Ormindo and Erisbe, escaping from Hariadeno's kingdom, are captured, imprisoned and poisoned, on Hariadeno's orders, by his captain, Osman, who has replaced the poison with a sleeping draught. When the old king regrets his action, he finds Erisbe and Ormindo restored to life, the latter now re-discovered as his son. Cavalli's *Ormindo* has won favour in the present century in a revival by Raymond Leppard.

Orontea

- Antonio Cesti. *Dramma musicale* in a prologue and three acts. 1656.
- Libretto by Giacinto Andrea Cicognini, revised by Giovanni Filippo Apolloni.
- First performance at the Teatro di Sala, Innsbruck, on 19th February 1656.

In the prologue Philosophy and Cupid argue, the latter determined to make Orontea, Queen of Egypt, fall in love. Although declaring herself proof against love, Orontea falls for the young painter Alidoro, who is also loved by the court lady Silandra, who herself is loved by the young courtier Corindo. After a series of intricate complications, Orontea is united with Alidoro, who turns out to be Prince Floridano of Phoenicia, and therefore a suitable match for the Queen, while matters between Silandra and Corindo are put to rights.

Cesti's opera has a continuing comic element in the character of the drunken servant Gelone, with a measure of Senecan wisdom from the court philosopher Creonte. The opera was among the most successful of its time and Orontea's aria *Intorno all'idol mio* (Around my beloved), over the form of her unconscious lover Alidoro, remains in popular vocal repertoire.

Orphée aux enfers (Orpheus in the Underworld)

- Jacques Offenbach. *Opéra bouffon* in two acts. 1858. Revised in four acts in 1874.
- Libretto by Hector-Jonathan Crémieux and Ludovic Halévy.
- First performance by the Théâtre des Bouffes-Parisiens at the Salle Choiseul, Paris, on 21st October 1858.

Public Opinion makes herself known at the outset. Eurydice, unhappily married to Orpheus, whose violin-playing she cannot stand, has a lover, the farmer Aristaeus. Orpheus has laid a trap for him by putting snakes in a cornfield, but Aristaeus lets Eurydice walk there, where she is bitten and dies. Aristaeus turns out to be Pluto, God of the Underworld, so that she is not unhappy to go with him. Orpheus, well rid of her, would be happy enough, were it not for Public Opinion, who insists that he should bring her back from Hades. On Mount Olympus, Venus, Cupid and Mars have been out for the night. They are just home, when Diana's hunting-horn rouses them. Jupiter is displeased at their behaviour and summons Pluto, complaining of his abduction of a mortal. The gods now rebel against Jupiter's hypocrisy, and his own escapades are recalled. Public Opinion arrives, with Orpheus, and Jupiter tells Pluto to give him Eurydice back. Pluto returns to Hades with Jupiter and the latter, in the guise suggested by Cupid of a fly, makes his way through the key-hole into the room where Eurydice is kept under guard. He suggests that they should escape together to Olympus. There is a party in Hades and Jupiter hopes to take Eurydice away with him. Cupid reminds him that Orpheus is on his way, with strait-laced Public Opinion. Cupid suggests the answer. He must allow Orpheus to take Eurydice back with him, provided he does not look round as she follows him. Orpheus does not look round until Jupiter hurls a thunderbolt and shocks him into it. He happily loses Eurydice, who becomes a priestess of Bacchus, god of wine.

Orphée aux enfers (Orpheus in the Underworld) is one of the best known of Offenbach's comic operas, particularly famous for the can-can of the spirits below, a wicked parody of Gluck's sedate *Dance of the Blessed Spirits*. The overture to the work that is now heard was compiled largely by Carl Binder, making use of the original Introduction, Minuet and Canon, to which he added the Can-Can and the violin solo of Orpheus, with which he troubles his wife in the first act.

Recommended Recordings:

Overture	***Naxos 8.550468***
Can-can	***Naxos 8.550924***

Orphée et Eurydice (Orpheus and Eurydice) *(see Orfeo ed Euridice)*

- Christoph Willibald von Gluck. *Tragédie opéra* in three acts. 1774.
- Libretto by Pierre Louis Moline, after the Italian libretto by Calzabigi.
- First performance at the Paris Opéra on 2nd August 1774.

Characters

Orphée (Orpheus)	tenor
Eurydice, his wife	soprano
Amour (Cupid)	soprano

Gluck's version of *Orfeo ed Euridice* (Orpheus and Eurydice) for Paris expanded and re-arranged the work on a larger scale. In the first act Orpheus is allowed an extended and relatively ornate aria and with other changes there is an enlarged *Ballet des ombres heureuses* (Dance of the Blessed Spirits). *J'ai perdu mon Eurydice* (I have lost my Eurydice) enjoys the fame of its Italian counterpart *Che farò senza Euridice* (What shall I do without Eurydice).

Orpheus

The legend of Orpheus has enjoyed obvious favour as a subject for opera. Above all it demonstrates the power of music, and with a pastoral setting had a double appeal to composers and poets. Orpheus was the son of the Muse Calliope, either by a Thracian king or by Apollo, who gave him the power to move rocks and trees and charm wild animals by the power of his lute. After the death of his wife Eurydice, he attempted to bring her back from the Underworld, placating the boatman of the dead, Charon, and the three-headed dog that guards the entrance to Hades, Cerberus, and persuading the King of the Underworld, Pluto (Dis), and his wife Proserpina (Persephone), to allow Eurydice to return to the world above, following her husband, but on condition that he did not look round, as she followed him. He looked round and lost Eurydice, thereafter wandering the fields of Thrace singing of his lost love, until torn apart by jealous women or followers of Dionysus. The Muses were said to have buried his remains, except for his head, which floated, with his lyre, to Lesbos, establishing lyric poetry on that island. The name of Orpheus was also associated with a mystery religion in which the Underworld became a form of purgatory.

Operas based on Orpheus range from the work of Peri, Caccini and Monteverdi to Marc-Antoine Charpentier and Lully, Luigi Rossi, who wrote his second opera on the subject for the French court in 1647, Gluck and Haydn, with, in the present century, Roger-Ducasse, Milhaud, Alfredo Casella, Malipiero and Harrison Birtwistle. The opera on the subject projected by Claude Debussy was never tackled. Literary references to Orpheus are, of course, manifold, from Homer to Rilke and beyond.

Osud (Fate)

- Leoš Janáček. Three novelesque scenes. 1904.
- Libretto by the composer and Fedora Bartošová.
- First staged performance at the National Theatre, Brno, on 25th October 1958.

Characters

Živný, a composer	tenor
Míla Válková	soprano
Doubek, their son, as a child	treble
Doubek, as a student	tenor
Lhotský, a painter	bass
Konečný, an old friend of Živný	baritone
Míla Válková's Mother	contralto
Dr Suda, a lawyer	tenor
Miss Stuhlá, a teacher	soprano
Žán & Nána, servants	silent rôles
Verva, a student	baritone
Součková, a student	soprano
Košinká, a student	contralto

At a spa town the sun is shining and Míla, mother of Živný's child, is walking sadly. She meets him and asks if he has come for their child, but he tells her he has come for both of them. The teacher Miss Stuhlá rehearses her choir and the students prepare for an outing. Míla's mother has prevented her daughter marrying Živný and still objects, because of his poverty and his position as a composer. In the second act Živný works in his study on his autobiographical but unfinished opera. He and Míla are now together. Doubek asks Míla what love is, a question she cannot properly answer. Míla's mother, now insane, scolds her daughter, still complaining that Živný has married her for her money. Míla tries to restrain her, as she goes onto the balcony and both of them fall to their deaths. The final act, set in a room at the Conservatory, finds Živný's students singing the final chorus of the second act of the unfinished opera. In a sudden storm that breaks, Živný sees a vision of Míla and falls down unconscious. One of his students suggests that this may be the end of the opera, but he angrily answers that the last act must be in the hands of God.

Janáček's opera *Fate* is based on the experience of a woman he met at the spa town of Luhačovice. The libretto and the plot have dramatic weaknesses, in that the death of Míla might have been expected to provide an ending. For the first staged performance in 1958 the third act was put first, with the following acts in the form of a flash-back. Adjustments were also made to the text. This has proved as unsatisfactory as Janáček's original plan, with its element of the ridiculous in Míla's death and the apparent anticlimax of the last act.

Otello (Othello)

- Gioachino Rossini. *Dramma* in three acts. 1816.
- Libretto by Francesco Berio di Salsa, after Shakespeare's play *Othello*.
- First performance at the Teatro del Fondo, Naples, on 4th December 1816.

Characters

Otello (Othello), a Moor, commander of the Venetian fleet	tenor
Desdemona	soprano
Elmiro, her father, a Venetian senator	bass
Iago, Othello's lieutenant	tenor
The Doge of Venice	tenor
Rodrigo, his son	tenor
Emilia, Desdemona's confidante	soprano
Officer	tenor

Othello, given Venetian citizenship by the Doge in recognition of his services against the Turks, has married Desdemona secretly, forced to this by the hostility of her father to the match. Rodrigo is in love with Desdemona and Iago is jealous of Othello's success. A politically advantageous marriage is arranged between Desdemona and Rodrigo, and she is now forced to admit her union with Othello. Her father curses her. Rodrigo is now jealous, as is Othello, each suspecting the other and finally joining in a duel. Othello's jealousy is fed by Iago, in particular with a letter from Desdemona that he has intercepted. In her bed-room Desdemona confides in Emilia, singing her Willow Song. Othello becomes angrier at her protestations of innocence and kills her, while the death of Rodrigo that he has ordered Iago to effect has ended with the dying confession and death of Iago. Othello stabs himself.

Rossini's *Otello* used a preponderance of Neapolitan tenors in its treatment of a text provided by the dilettante Marchese Francesco Berio di Salsa, who, in the words of Byron, crucified the original play. The drama is considerably weakened by emasculation if not crucifixion, although the third act continues to have its effect, in particular in the irony of a gondolier's song, with its echo of the sad memories of Dante's ill-fated lovers Paolo and Francesca, Desdemona's Willow Song, *Assisa a piè d'un salice* (Seated by a willow-tree) and her prayer *Deh calma, o Ciel, nel sonno* (Ah calm, O Heaven, in sleep). Inevitably Rossini's treatment of the subject has been overshadowed by Verdi's *Otello*.

Otello (Othello)

- Giuseppe Verdi. *Dramma lirico* in four acts. 1887.
- Libretto by Arrigo Boito, after Shakespeare's play *Othello*.
- First performance at the Teatro alla Scala, Milan, on 5th February 1887.

Characters

Otello, a Moor, general of the Venetian army	tenor
Iago, his ensign	baritone
Cassio, his lieutenant	tenor
Roderigo, a Venetian gentleman	tenor
Lodovico, an ambassador of the Venetian Republic	bass
Montano, Othello's predecessor as Governor of Cyprus	bass
Herald	baritone
Desdemona, wife of Othello	soprano
Emilia, wife of Iago	mezzo-soprano

The crowd awaits the arrival of Othello's ship from the storm. He reaches the harbour of Cyprus triumphant, victorious in battle and is greeted by the people. Iago suggests to Roderigo that he may soon have Desdemona, now wife of Othello, and, through jealousy, plots against Cassio, whom he makes drunk. A fight breaks out with Roderigo, in which Montano becomes involved. Othello is summoned by the general alarm and dismisses Cassio from his service. Othello and Desdemona sing of their love, as he takes her back again into their chamber. In the second act Iago persuades Cassio to seek reinstatement through Desdemona and kindles and feeds Othello's jealousy, producing as final proof of her infidelity his report of what Cassio has said in his sleep and the handkerchief that she has dropped and that has been taken from Emilia by Iago. In the third act Desdemona unwittingly fuels Othello's anger and jealousy by continuing to plead for Cassio. Ambassadors from Venice recall Othello, with Cassio to be left in his place. Othello treats Desdemona cruelly, before the company, and Iago continues to play on his jealousy, the handkerchief now planted in Cassio's lodging. The last act is set in Desdemona's bedroom, where she seeks some comfort from Emilia. Woken from sleep by Othello, she again pleads her innocence, as he suffocates her. She can still murmur words to Emilia, when the latter brings news of Cassio's killing of Roderigo, seeking to excuse Othello. Lodovico gives a report of Roderigo's dying confession and Emilia tells of the handkerchief, convincing Othello of his tragic mistake. Seizing his sword, he kills himself.

Verdi's *Otello* is a major achievement, regarded by many as the greatest of his operas, completed sixteen years after his *Aida* and to be followed only by his second Shakespearean collaboration with Boito, *Falstaff*. The opening storm brings the cry of the chorus *Una vela* (A sail), as Othello's ship is seen, before he lands in triumph, with his victorious *Esultate!* (Rejoice). At the bonfire lit in celebration the people rejoice in another impressive chorus, *Fuoco di gioia* (Fire of joy). The great love duet that ends the first act, *Già nella notte densa s'estingue ogni clamor* (Already in dark night every sound is stilled) has its own inevitable irony, coming after the plotting of Iago and Roderigo and with a knowledge of what is to happen. In Iago's evil creed, *Credo in un Dio crudel* (I believe in a cruel God) he admits in a soliloquy his villainy and he later works on Othello's jealousy in his story of Cassio's dreaming, *Era la notte* (It was night). Othello, provoked by his ensign, resolves on his new course of action in *Ora e per sempre addio, sante memorie* (Now and for ever farewell, sacred memories) and with Iago sings the Oath Duet *Sì, pel ciel marmoreo giuro!* (Yes, by the marble heaven I swear). Othello reveals his feelings in a long soliloquy in the third act, *Dio! mi potevi scagliar tutti i mali della miserià* (God! You could hurl against me all the evils of wretchedness). The last act brings Desdemona's poignant Willow Song and prayer, with Othello's final death speech. Verdi reluctantly provided a ballet for the third act for performance in Paris in 1894.

Recommended Recordings:

Otello (2 CDs)	*Naxos 8.110056-57*
Fuoco di gioia	*Naxos 8.550241*
Willow Song	*Naxos 8.550606*
Desdemona rea	*Naxos 8.553030*

Ottone (Otto)

- George Frideric Handel. Opera in three acts. 1723.
- Libretto adapted by Nicola Francesco Haym from *Teofane* (Theophanes) by Stefano Benedetti Pallavicino.
- First performance at the King's Theatre, London, on 12th January 1723.

Otto, King of Germany, is travelling to Rome to marry Theophanes, Princess of the Eastern Roman Empire. Gismonda, widow of the usurper Berengar, and her son Adalberto make use of a delay in Otto's arrival, caused by conflict with and capture of Emireno, by letting Adalberto impersonate Otto. The resulting political and marital complications, increased by the participation of Otto's cousin Matilda, who is betrothed to Adalberto, are solved when Otto regains his bride and his position, with his prisoner Emireno revealed as Teofane's brother and rightful ruler of the Eastern Empire. Adalberto is forgiven, Gismonda satisfied and all ends well.

The gavotte from the overture enjoyed contemporary popularity, as did Gismonda's *La speranza è giunta* (Hope is with us) and *Vieni, o figlio* (Come, my son). Ottone's own arias include the despairing *Tanti affanni* (Such troubles).

Owen Wingrave

- Benjamin Britten. Opera in two acts. 1970.
- Libretto by Myfanwy Piper, after the short story by Henry James.
- First performance for BBC television on 16th May 1971.

Characters

Owen Wingrave, the last of the Wingraves	baritone
Spencer Coyle, running a military crammer	bass-baritone
Lechmere, a student at Coyle's crammer	tenor
Miss Wingrave, Owen's aunt	dramatic soprano

Mrs Coyle	soprano
Mrs Julian, a widow and dependant at Paramore	soprano
Kate, her daughter	mezzo-soprano
General Sir Philip Wingrave, Owen's grandfather	tenor
Narrator, a ballad-singer	tenor

In Coyle's study Lechmere is enthusiastic about his military studies, but Owen Wingrave now feels unable to follow his family's military traditions. In Hyde Park Owen is glad to have told Coyle, but at the same time Coyle is telling Owen's aunt of her nephew's decision, to her anger. The Coyles, at home, try to persuade Owen to change his mind, but his aunt has summoned him to the family home, Paramore. Owen arrives there to face general hostility. The Coyles and Lechmere arrive, in the hope that something may be done to change Owen's mind, but he remains adamant, now declaring that to declare or wage war should be made a criminal offence. In the second act the Narrator sings the ballad of an earlier Wingrave boy who disgraced his family, was taken to his room and was killed by a blow from his father, later found dead in the same room. Their ghosts still haunt Paramore. Owen, in an interview with his grandfather, is disinherited. He addresses the family portraits, now having found peace himself, and confronts the ghosts. Kate taunts him with the bravery of Lechmere, who would sleep in the haunted room for her, and Owen declares himself willing to rebut the charge of cowardice by spending the night there. In the final scene Lechmere expresses his anxieties about Owen. Kate goes into the haunted room, and finds Owen there dead.

Owen Wingrave was written as a television opera, but can be and has been staged in the theatre. The choice of story reflects Britten's own pacifist principles. The opera opens with a view of the Wingraves, their traditions and their family portraits, stressing the Wingrave military background in an instrumental illustration of each of the eleven portraits, leading finally to Owen himself. The twelve notes of the chromatic scale, sounded together in chords, open the work, and the accompanying chord for each portrait adds one note, until the twelfth is reached, for Owen. The writing, like that of *The Turn of the Screw*, with its twelve-note theme, is not serial but generally tonal and diatonic. Comparison has been drawn between *Owen Wingrave* and *Billy Budd*, since both operas are essentially concerned with the evil of violence and the cause of peace.

Padmâvatî (Padmavati)

- Albert Roussel. *Opéra-ballet* in two acts. 1918.
- Libretto by Louis Laloy.
- First performance at the Paris Opéra on 1st June 1923.

Roussel based his opera on the story of Padmavati, Queen of Chitor, and Alouddin, the Moghul Sultan. Alouddin, who has planned to capture Chitor, is entertained on friendly terms and shown the beauty of Queen Padmavati. He then demands that she be handed over to him, in return for peace. Her husband, who has tried to defend the city, begs her to do as the Sultan has asked. She kills him and is herself burned on her husband's funeral pyre, as the Sultan enters the city.

Roussel had had experience of India, during the course of a long tour of the country and of South-East Asia. This led him to the choice of the Hindu legend of Padmavati as a subject for his opera. In the score he makes use of Hindu scale forms and irregular rhythms.

Pagliacci (Actors)

- Ruggero Leoncavallo. *Dramma* in a prologue and two acts. 1892.
- Libretto by the composer.
- First performance at the Teatro Dal Verme, Milan, on 21st May 1892.

Characters

Canio (Pagliaccio), leader of the players	tenor
Nedda (Columbina), his wife	soprano
Tonio (Taddeo), a clown	baritone
Beppe (Arlecchino)	tenor
Silvio, a villager	baritone
Two Villagers	tenor & baritone

Tonio appears in the prologue, followed by the first act, in which the people of a Calabrian village celebrate the Feast of the Assumption and the arrival of the players. Canio, dressed, as are the other players, in the costumes of the play they will act, tells the people the story they will show, how Pagliaccio will take jealous revenge on the clown, his wife's lover. Canio shows jealousy of Nedda, resenting Tonio's attentions to her. Canio and Beppe leave, and Tonio now makes advances to Nedda. She seizes a whip and strikes him, to his anger. He threatens revenge. Silvio now calls to Nedda and reminds her of her promise to elope with him after the play. Tonio overhears them and brings Canio back, but Silvio has made his escape. Nedda refuses to tell her husband the name of her lover, but he is prepared to wait. Canio now makes ready for the play, although his feelings, which he must hide, are in turmoil. The second act finds the play about to start. Tonio bangs the drum, Nedda goes among the audience collecting money and takes the opportunity to warn Silvio. In the play Nedda, as Columbine, awaits her lover Harlequin, who serenades her. The clown Taddeo returns from the market, makes advances to Columbine and is decisively rejected, turned out of the room by Harlequin, who has now made his appearance. Taddeo brings news of Pagliaccio's imminent return, and Harlequin makes his escape, reminding Columbine to use drugged wine he has brought to put her husband to sleep. Canio's jealousy takes over, as he seeks to force Nedda to reveal the name of her lover. The audience is now alarmed, since it is clear that Canio is no longer acting and that Nedda is terrified for her life. She tries to escape him, but he stabs her in the back and kills Silvio, who has leaped up, trying to intervene.

Leoncavallo based his realistic opera on an incident in the Calabrian village of Montalto, where the subsequent trial had been before his father as magistrate. Often given in a double bill with Mascagni's *verismo* opera *Cavalleria rusticana* (Rustic Chivalry), another story of love and jealousy, *Pagliacci* remains one of the best known operas in the repertory. Tonio's *Prologue* serves at times as a dramatic concert piece, outdone in popularity only by Canio's moving and dramatic *Vesti la giubba* (On with the motley), before the play, followed by an instrumental *Intermezzo*. Harlequin's serenade *O Columbina* offers an element of irony, while Canio's *No, Pagliaccio non son* (No, I am not Pagliaccio) brings the drama to its climax.

Recommended Recording:
Pagliacci ***Naxos 8.660021***

PALADINS, LES (THE PALADINS)

- Jean-Philippe Rameau. *Comédie-lyrique* in three acts. 1760.
- Libretto attributed to Duplat de Monticourt, among others.
- First performance at the Paris Opéra on 12th February 1760.

The knight Atis seeks to marry Argie, a girl guarded closely, on the orders of her guardian Anselme, by Orcan. The elderly Anselme, who had hoped to marry Argie himself, is eventually outwitted.

Based on a story by La Fontaine, itself taken from Ariosto, *Les Paladins* (The Paladins) treats its characters light-heartedly and finds room for musical parody of one sort or another in the process. It includes a number of instrumental episodes, dances and *symphonies*, but as an opera suffers from a weak libretto.

Palazzo incantato, Il (The Enchanted Palace)

- Luigi Rossi. *Attione in musica* in a prologue and three acts. 1642.
- Libretto by Giulio Rospigliosi, after Ariosto's *Orlando furioso* (Roland in Madness).
- First performance at the Palazzo Barberini alle Quattro Fontane, Rome, on 22nd February 1642.

In the sorcerer Atlante's magic palace pagan and Christian knights and ladies seek their lost lovers and companions. Orlando seeks there his Angelica, abducted by the sorcerer, while Bradamante seeks her captive lover Ruggiero. He, however, has met Angelica and thus aroused Bradamante's jealousy. Matters are further complicated by the appearance of the English Astolfo, impervious to love, and, at Atlante's instigation, the object of general hostility. Finally there is an encounter between Atlante, disguised as a false Ruggiero and Ruggiero himself, leading to the destruction of Atlante's magic powers and palace.

Luigi Rossi's *Il palazzo incantato, ovvero La guerriera amante* (The Enchanted Palace, or The Warrior Maid) was written for Cardinal Antonio Barberini and staged at the Palazzo Barberini in Rome. The work made a strong impression and led to Rossi's second opera, *Orfeo*, written for Cardinal Mazarin and the French court, after the exile to France of the Barberini.

Palestrina

- Hans Pfitzner. *Musikalische Legende* in three acts. 1915.
- Libretto by the composer.
- First performance at the Prinzregententheater, Munich, on 12th June 1917.

Characters

Pope Pius IV	bass
Cardinal Giovanni Morone, Papal Legate	baritone
Cardinal Bernardo Novagerio, Papal Legate	tenor
Cardinal Christoph Madruscht, Prince Bishop of Trent	bass
Cardinal Carlo Borromeo	baritone
The Cardinal of Lorraine	bass
Abdisu, Patriarch of Assyria	tenor
Anton Brus of Müglitz, Archbishop of Prague	bass
Count Luna, ambassador of the King of Spain	baritone
Bishop of Budoja	tenor
Theophilus, Bishop of Imola	tenor
Avosmediano, Bishop of Cadiz	bass-baritone
Giovanni Pierluigi da Palestrina, maestro di cappella at Sta Maria Maggiore	tenor
Ighino, his son, aged fifteen	soprano
Silla, his pupil, aged seventeen	mezzo-soprano
Bishop Ercole Severolus, Master of Ceremonies to the Council of Trent	bass-baritone
Five Choristers of S Maria Maggiore	2 tenors & 3 basses
Apparitions:	
Lucrezia, Palestrina's dead wife	contralto
Nine Dead Masters of the Art of Music	3 tenors, 3 baritones & 3 basses
Three Angelic Voices	high sopranos
Silent Rôles:	
Two Papal Nuncios, Jesuits	
Massarelli, Bishop of Thelesia, Secretary to the Council	
Giuseppe, old servant of Palestrina	

In Rome Cardinal Borromeo approaches Palestrina, sad at the death of his wife and weary of the world, urging him to compose a Mass that will prove to the Council of Trent, where it has been proposed that polyphony should be replaced by Gregorian chant, that such a step is unnecessary: Palestrina alone has the ability to compose a Mass that may be a model to future composers. Palestrina is reluctant, in spite of Cardinal Borromeo's anger, but apparitions of former composers encourage him, and his dead wife brings a message of peace, as an angelic voice dictates the new Mass to him. At a meeting of the Council in Trent national differences and petty jealousies appear.

Cardinal Borromeo assures the Council that Palestrina is writing a new Mass. Disturbances between the servants of the delegates are put down by the soldiers of the Prince Bishop of Trent. In the third act Palestrina, in Rome, is told of the success of his Mass, its acceptance confirmed by the Pope himself. The opera ends with Palestrina alone in his room, while the crowds outside praise his achievement.

Pfitzner's most important work, the opera *Palestrina*, completed two years after the first performance of Stravinsky's *Rite of Spring*, is musically and philosophically conservative in an age that had brought a great deal of musical experiment and innovation. It may be regarded as continuing in the spirit of Wagner, with *Palestrina* the obverse of *Die Meistersinger*, where innovation wins the contest, against the conservatism of Beckmesser. Here it is the relatively conservative that is preserved.

Pan Voyevoda

- Nikolay Andreyevich Rimsky-Korsakov. Opera in four acts. 1904.
- Libretto by Il'ya Fyodorovich Tyumenev.
- First performance at St Petersburg Conservatory on 16th October 1904.

Set in 16th or 17th century Poland, *Pan Voyevoda* is among the least satisfactory of Rimsky-Korsakov's operas, with its story of love, jealousy, poisoning and magic. It contains, however, distinctive Polish elements, some of which were used to make up an orchestral suite. The composer took the opportunity to re-use here his earlier *Souvenir de trois chants polonais* (Memory of Three Polish Songs). Rimsky-Korsakov attributed the relative failure of the work to the political uncertainties of the time, which led to the suppression of demonstrations in 1905 and his own resignation from the St Petersburg Conservatory.

Recommended Recording: Pan Voyevoda (Suite) ***Naxos 8.553858***

Paride ed Elena (Paris and Helen)

- Christoph Willibald von Gluck. *Dramma per musica* in five acts. 1770.
- Libretto by Ranieri de'Calzabigi.
- First performance at the Burgtheater, Vienna, on 3rd November 1770.

Characters

Paride (Paris), son of King Priam of Troy	male soprano
Elena (Helen), Queen of Sparta	soprano
Amore (Cupid), under the name of Erasto, confidant of Paris	soprano
Pallas Athene (Minerva), goddess, daughter of Jupiter	soprano
A Trojan	soprano

Paris, having chosen Venus above Juno and Minerva, is in Sparta, sacrificing to Venus and seeking, now with the encouragement of Erasto, the love of Helen. Paris and Helen meet at her royal palace and each is struck by the other's beauty. She calls on him to judge an athletic contest and when asked to sing he does so in praise of her beauty, admitting the purpose of his visit is to win her love. She dismisses him. In despair Paris now pleads with her, and she begins to give way. Eventually, through the intervention of Erasto, who now reveals himself as Cupid, she gives way, but Pallas Athene (Minerva) now warns them of sorrow to come. In the final scene Paris and Helen make ready to embark for Troy.

Paride ed Elena (Paris and Helen) is the third of Gluck's so-called reform operas for Vienna, following *Alceste* (Alcestis) and *Orfeo ed Euridice* (Orpheus and Eurydice), and the least often performed of the three. Arias from the opera that enjoy an independent concert existence include Paris's minor-key declaration of love, *O del mio dolce ardor* (O of my gentle love), in the first act. His second aria is *Spiagge amate* (Beloved shores). In the second act, again in a minor key, Paris fears that he may lose Helen in *Le belle imagini* (The fair semblance) and in the fourth would prefer death to life without Helen, *Di te scordarmi, e vivere* (To forget you and to live). The rôle of Paris offers difficulties of casting, written, as it was, for a relatively high castrato voice. Arias of Paris have been purloined by tenors, with transposition an octave lower, or appropriated by sopranos and mezzo-sopranos.

Parisina

- Gaetano Donizetti. *Melodramma* in three acts. 1833.
- Libretto by Felice Romani, after Byron.
- First performance at the Teatro alla Pergola, Florence, on 17th March 1833.

In 15th century Ferrara, Parisina, wife of the Duke, is in love with Ugo, reputed son of Ernesto, a courtier, but in fact the son of the Duke by an earlier marriage. Ugo returns from exile to win victory in a tournament, receiving his reward from Parisina herself. In her sleep she murmurs Ugo's name and her husband, although he now knows Ugo is his son, has him killed.

Donizetti's opera, written in the space of a few weeks, includes the demanding tenor rôle of Ugo, written for the French singer Gilbert Duprez, who perfected the tenor chest-voice top C, a challenge to later singers. The opera reaches a climax as Parisina dreams of Ugo, her words causing an outburst of jealous anger from the Duke.

PARISINA

- Pietro Mascagni. *Tragedia lirica* in four acts. 1913.
- Libretto by Gabriele d'Annunzio.
- First performance at the Teatro alla Scala, Milan, on 15th December 1913.

Rejected by her husband, Niccolò d'Este, Stella de'Tolomei urges her son Ugo to action against her husband's new wife, Parisina Malatesta. Ugo and Parisina fall in love and are both put to death by Niccolò d'Este.

Mascagni's collaboration with Gabriele d'Annunzio won him no friends, and his opera *Parisina* failed to please contemporary critics, lacking the power of the two *verismo* operas, *L'amico Fritz* (Friend Fritz) and *Cavalleria rusticana* (Rustic Chivalry).

PARSIFAL

- Richard Wagner. *Bühnenweihfestspiel* in three acts. 1882.
- Libretto by the composer.
- First performance at the Festspielhaus, Bayreuth, on 26th July 1882.

CHARACTERS

Amfortas, son of Titurel, ruler of the Kingdom of the Grail	bass-baritone
Titurel, his father, former ruler	bass
Gurnemanz, a veteran Knight of the Grail	bass
Klingsor, a magician	bass
Parsifal	tenor
Kundry	soprano
First & Second Knights of the Grail	tenor & bass
Four Esquires	sopranos & tenors
Klingsor's Flower Maidens	sopranos

The prelude uses motifs of the Last Supper, the Holy Grail and Faith, interwoven with a sorrow motif and part of a motif associated with the torment of sin. Gurnemanz and four esquires, sleeping in a clearing in the woods, waken and make ready for the bath of the sick King Amfortas, balm for whose pain can only come from one person, a blameless fool. Kundry, who now arrives, exhausted, brings balm for the King. The mysterious nature of Kundry is discussed, the good fortune she brings. Gurnemanz explains the entrusting to Titurel of the Grail, the cup used at Christ's last supper, a vessel that caught his blood, with the spear that caused the wound in his side. The magician Klingsor was refused admission to the temple Titurel built and in revenge created a garden with maidens of seductive beauty, a lure and temptation that has led to the downfall of many knights. Amfortas had been wounded attacking Klingsor's castle and had lost to him the Holy Spear. Parsifal enters, having shot a swan, a deed he now regrets. He knows little of his past, except that his mother was Herzeleide, Sorrowful Heart. Kundry explains further that his mother had died when he deserted her. Kundry sinks to the ground, her task fulfilled. The scene changes to the temple of the Grail. Titurel, now too weak to officiate, asks Amfortas to display the Grail, but he refuses, since the sight of the holy vessel makes his wounds bleed the more, as a sinner. Eventually he carries out his allotted task and the sacred bread and wine are given to the assembled knights. Parsifal stands fascinated at what he sees, but says and does nothing to alleviate the suffering of Amfortas. In his castle the magician Klingsor sees in his magic glass the fool approaching. He calls up Kundry, an unwilling instrument of his desire to destroy Parsifal, the blameless fool, whom he now sees attacking his knights. The scene is transformed to that of a magic garden, where the flower maidens attempt to charm Parsifal. Kundry, now in more seductive guise, sends them away and tells Parsifal of his mother. As their lips are about to meet, Parsifal comes to his senses and breaks away, feeling the pain of the wound of Amfortas, which he now understands. Kundry begs him to save her from the curse under which she has laboured since she laughed at the crucifixion of Christ. He understands her wiles and her possible salvation, rejecting her advances. Klingsor hurls the Holy Spear at him, but it remains suspended above his head. He seizes it and makes the sign of the cross with it, at which the garden and castle disappear. By the third act the Kingdom of the Grail is in desolation, the knights living on roots and herbs. Gurnemanz finds Kundry, dishevelled and weary, as in the first act, but her face is transformed. A knight approaches, Parsifal, holding the Holy Spear, which he venerates. It is Good Friday and Kundry and Gurnemanz bathe and anoint Parsifal, who baptizes Kundry. The scene changes to that of the temple, where Amfortas will perform the ceremony of the Grail for the last time, to atone for the death of his father Titurel. Parsifal enters the temple, with Gurnemanz and Kundry, and heals the wound of Amfortas with the touch of the Holy Spear, which he presents to the company. It is Parsifal who now must perform the ceremony of the Grail, which he does as a Holy Dove appears above his head and Amfortas and Gurnemanz acknowledge their new king.

Various interpretations have been put on Wagner's last opera, *Parsifal*, a work specifically and for some time exclusively designed for the consecration of the festival theatre at Bayreuth. At the most obvious level Parsifal may be taken to represent Christianity and Klingsor the pagan world. The mysterious Kundry, to be identified with Herodias in one of Wagner's sources, the *Mabinogion*, serves as a messenger to the servants of the Grail, but is forced at times to do Klingsor's will, until redeemed by one who will resist her lures, as Parsifal triumphantly does. Other aspects of Wagner's thought have been associated with *Parsifal* and the work has given rise to much speculation and investigation. Orchestral excerpts from the score include the preludes to the acts and scenes and the Good Friday music. The knights' chorale *Zum letzten Liebesmahle* (Prepared for the Last Supper) celebrates the ceremony of the Grail and there are relatively extended explanatory narratives for Gurnemanz in *Titurel, der fromme Held* (Titurel, the pious hero), for Amfortas in his lament, *Wehvolles Erbe* (Woeful birthright) and for Kundry in *Ich sah das Kind an seiner Mutter Brust* (I saw the child at its mother's breast).

Recommended Recordings:

Parsifal	***Naxos 8.110049-50***
Prelude to Act I	***Naxos 8.550498***

PARTENOPE

- George Frideric Handel. Opera in three acts. 1730.
- Libretto adapted from Silvio Stampiglia's opera of the same name.
- First performance at the King's Theatre, London, on 24th February 1730.

CHARACTERS

Arsace, Prince of Corinth	male alto
Armindo, Prince of Rhodes	contralto
Partenope, foundress of Naples	soprano
Rosmira, disguised as the Armenian Prince Eurimene	contralto
Ormonte	bass
Emilio, Prince of Cuma	tenor

Arsace and Armindo are rivals for the love of Partenope, who loves the former. He, however, was formerly the lover of Rosmira, whom he recognises but whose identity he is pledged not to reveal. Rosmira, as Eurimene, also claims to be in love with Partenope. Emilio, under threat of war, joins the contest, but is rejected and attacks the city, defended under the command of Partenope, to settle potential jealousies among the princes. In battle with Emilio, Armindo saves Partenope and Arsace saves Rosmira, who creates further complications in her pursuit of Arsace, challenged to single combat. Matters are finally resolved, with Partenope united with Armindo, Rosmira, now revealed as a woman, united with Arsace and Emilio released to rule over Cuma as an ally of Partenope.

Handel's *Partenope* is rich in musical interest, handling in traditional form a plot that has elements of comedy in it. Arsace's aria from the end of the second act, *Furibondo spira il vento* (Furiously breathes the wind), is sometimes heard in the concert-hall.

PASTOR FIDO, IL (THE FAITHFUL SHEPHERD)

- George Frideric Handel. Opera in three acts. 1712.
  Revised for two productions in 1734.
- Libretto by Giacomo Rossi, after the play by Battista Guarini.
- First performance at the Queen's Theatre, London, on 22nd November 1712.

In Arcadia Diana, goddess of the hunt, is displeased, only to be pacified by the union of a couple of heavenly ancestry. These are thought to be the huntsman Silvio, whose interests lie only in hunting, and the shepherdess Amarilli, who is in love with the shepherd Mirtillo. Other shepherdesses intervene to add further intrigue, Eurilla in devious pursuit of Mirtillo and Dorinda aiming at Silvio's love, which she wins. Matters are settled in the temple of Diana, where it is declared that Mirtillo's ancestry allows him to marry Amarilli, previously, through the trickery of Eurilla, condemned to death for breaking her vows to Silvio.

Based on one of the best known Italian pastoral plays of the late 16th century, *Il pastor fido* (The Faithful Shepherd) did not at first meet the expectations of London audiences, after the success of Handel's first opera for London, *Rinaldo*. A revival in 1734, with a much revised and newly composed score, won greater success. The ballet music incorporated in the version of the opera staged in November 1734 is sometimes heard in concert, as is the overture.

PATIENCE

- Arthur Sullivan. Operetta in two acts. 1881.
- Libretto by W.S.Gilbert.
- First performance at the Opéra Comique, London, on 23rd April 1881.

The poets Bunthorne and Grosvenor woo girls of aesthetic pretentions and Patience, the milk-maid, while Colonel Calverley and his dragoons find themselves obliged to follow the same fashions, if they are to interest the girls. Eventually all come to their senses, except Bunthorne, who remains loyal to the principles and affectations that he has espoused.

Gilbert's libretto to *Patience, or Bunthorne's Bride* satirises the aesthetic movement of the time, as well as the more robust sentiments of Colonel Calverley and his men. The poet Bunthorne's philosophy is summarised in the patter-song *If you're anxious for to shine*, while Lady Jane, substantial in figure and no longer young, arouses sympathy for her predicament in *Silver'd is the raven hair*.

Paul Bunyan

- Benjamin Britten. Operetta in a prologue and two acts. 1941. Adjusted for performance in 1974.
- Libretto by W.H.Auden.
- First performance at Brander Mathews Hall, Columbia University, New York, on 5th May 1941.

Characters

Old Trees	soprano, alto, tenor & bass
Four Young Trees	2 sopranos & 2 tenors
Three Wild Geese	2 mezzo-sopranos & soprano
Narrator	baritone/tenor
Voice of Paul Bunyan	speaking part
Johnny Inkslinger, book-keeper	tenor
Tiny, Paul Bunyan's daughter	soprano
Hot Biscuit Slim, a good cook	tenor
Sam Sharkey, a bad cook	tenor
Ben Benny, a bad cook	bass
Hel Helson, foreman	baritone
Four Swedes:	
Andy Anderson	tenor
Pete Peterson	tenor
Jen Jenson	bass
Cross Crosshaulson	bass

John Shears, a farmer	baritone
Western Union Boy	tenor
Fido, a dog	high soprano
Moppet, a cat	mezzo-soprano
Poppet, a cat	mezzo-soprano
Quartet of the Defeated	contralto, tenor, baritone & bass
Four Cronies of Hel Helson	4 baritones
Heron	speaking part
Moon	speaking part
Wind	speaking part
Beetle	speaking part
Squirrel	speaking part

After a prologue for young and old trees and wild geese, the first act opens, after a ballad from the narrator, with the unseen giant, Paul Bunyan, calling together lumberjacks, to be led by Hel Helson. Complaints about food, put into words by Johnny Inkslinger, a poet and book-keeper, and intermediary with the unseen Paul Bunyan, lead to the departure of two bad cooks and the arrival of Slim, a good cook. Bunyan finds a wife his own size and his daughter, Tiny, is introduced, sad at the death of her mother. Hel Helson becomes involved in subversion of Paul Bunyan's benign guidance, when there is a call for farmers, but an off-stage fight finds Helson worsted, then to be reconciled with Paul Bunyan. At a Christmas Eve party the engagement of Slim and Tiny is announced, the latter to run a Manhattan hotel, Helson's practical help in realising the lumberjacks' prospects is acknowledged and Inkslinger is summoned to Hollywood, before Paul Bunyan's final words of farewell.

Britten's early collaboration with W.H.Auden, abandoned for some 35 years after its first staging, was written when the composer was living in the United States of America. The relatively modern legend of Paul Bunyan, the giant who takes the lead in the American conquest of nature, carried a particular appeal to Britten at the time and the form of the work, its narrative elucidated in a series of three ballads sung by the narrator, with the verse of Auden, offered a work of considerable originality that deserved its later revival.

Pêcheurs de perles, Les (The Pearl-Fishers)

- Georges Bizet. *Opéra* in three acts. 1863.
- Libretto by Eugène Cormon and Michel Carré.
- First performance at the Théâtre Lyrique, Paris, on 30th September 1863.

Characters

Zurga, head fisherman	baritone
Nadir, a fisherman	tenor
Leïla, a priestess of Brahma	soprano
Nourabad, high priest of Brahma	bass

In Ceylon Zurga is chosen leader of the fishermen and resumes his friendship with the young Nadir, who has been wandering in the forest, recalling their love for a girl they had once seen in Candy. A veiled woman arrives, to pray for the pearl-fishers, accompanied by the priest Nourabad. She is recognised by Nadir as Leïla, the girl he had once seen, but not by Zurga. Leïla and Nourabad enter the Hindu temple, leaving Nadir, now alone, to admit his love for Leïla, whom he has followed. As she sings her temple prayer, she hears his voice and her song turns to a song of love. Nadir and Leïla meet at night in the temple where she is watching, but their discovery leads to popular anger and threats of death. Zurga intervenes to help Nadir and Leïla escape, but when Nourabad reveals the identity of Leïla, Zurga changes to anger, and condemns the couple to death once more. Leïla pleads with Zurga for his friend Nadir's life, but in vain. It is, however, Zurga who saves them, as they are about to be killed, diverting the attention of the people by setting fire to their camp, thus allowing them to escape.

Fashionably exotic in its story, *Les pêcheurs de perles* (The Pearl-Fishers) reflects various musical influences, including those of Verdi, Meyerbeer and, inevitably, Gounod. The best known music from the opera is found in the duet for Zurga and Nadir, when they recall their friendship and the girl they had once seen, *Au fond du temple saint* (Within the sacred temple). Nadir's soliloquy, overheard by Leïla, *Je crois entendre encore* (I think I hear again), has a firm place in tenor repertoire, while sopranos may find their own sustenance in Leïla's moving *cavatina*, *Comme autrefois dans la nuit sombre* (As once in the dark forest), as she awaits her nocturnal meeting with Nadir.

Recommended Recording: Au fond du temple saint — ***Naxos 8.553030***

Pelléas et Mélisande (Pelleas and Melisande)

- Claude Debussy. Opera in five acts. 1902.
- Libretto after the play by Maurice Maeterlinck.
- First performance by the Paris Opéra-Comique at the Salle Favart on 30th April 1902.

Characters

Arkel, King of Allemonde	bass
Geneviève, mother of Pelléas and Golaud	contralto
Pelléas, grandson of Arkel	baritone
Golaud, his half-brother	baritone
Mélisande	soprano
Yniold, Golaud's son by a former marriage	treble
Doctor	baritone
Shepherd	baritone

Golaud, out hunting in the forest, loses his way. Hearing the sound of weeping, he finds Mélisande and persuades her to come home with him. In Arkel's castle, Geneviève reads a letter from Golaud, confessing his marriage to Mélisande and seeking forgiveness. Pelléas is refused permission to join his dying friend Marcellus, since his father is also near to death. In the third scene Pelléas and Mélisande meet outside the castle. In the second act Pelléas is showing Mélisande the castle grounds. They sit by the side of a shady fountain, where, as the clock strikes midday, she drops the ring that Golaud had given her. In the castle Golaud is resting. At midday his horse had thrown him. He notices that Mélisande no longer wears the ring he gave her, and angrily tells her that she must find it, with the help of Pelléas. In the following scene Pelléas and Mélisande enter the cave where she has told Golaud she had lost the ring. They find paupers sleeping there, and quietly leave. In the third act Mélisande, at the window of a tower in the castle, is combing her hair for the night. Pelléas comes to the foot of the tower, from where he can fondle her hair. Golaud emerges, to upbraid them for their childishness. He leads Pelléas down to a disused well in the castle vaults, where a slip would be fatal. When they emerge he openly tells Pelléas to avoid the company of Mélisande. At night in front of the castle, Golaud makes his son Yniold stand on his shoulders and tell him what he sees in Mélisande's chamber. He sees her there with Pelléas. Pelléas, in the fourth act, has been warned that he must leave. Before he goes, he seeks to meet Mélisande by the Fountain of the Blind. Arkel is moved by the beauty of Mélisande and is shocked when Golaud, in his presence, speaks angrily to her. In the park, Yniold questions a shepherd, before running off. Pelléas and Mélisande meet and avow their love for each other, observed by Golaud, who kills Pelléas and wounds Mélisande. In the final act Mélisande, in a chamber in the castle, is recovering from her wounds. She gives birth to a baby girl, but dies, leaving the child to live in her place.

Set in a medieval dream-world, *Pelléas et Mélisande* (Pelleas and Melisande), which had firmly established Maeterlinck's international reputation, provided an apt frame-work for Debussy's evocative opera, in which Mélisande occupies the central position, the drama studying her in relationship with others, with Golaud, with Pelléas and with Arkel. While remote from Wagner in

its pre-Raphaelite world, the opera makes use of Wagnerian techniques of leitmotifs and of some Wagnerian harmonic elements. In other respects, however, it remains thoroughly characteristic of Debussy, with a modal opening that sets the period, scene and mood.

Recommended Recording:
Pelléas et Mélisande (3 CDs) ***Naxos 8.660047-49***

PÉNÉLOPE (PENELOPE)

- Gabriel Fauré. *Poème lyrique* in three acts. 1913.
- Libretto by René Fauchois.
- First performance at the Opéra, Monte Carlo, on 4th March 1913.

Penelope, awaiting the much delayed return of her husband Ulysses, fends off her suitors by promising to marry one of them when her weaving is complete. She gives hospitality to a beggar, Ulysses in disguise, and seen by the suitors unravelling her weaving, is forced to agree to make a choice the next day. By the sea, where she has waited for Ulysses, she questions the visitor, who suggests that only the man who can bend the great bow of Ulysses should be her husband. The next day Ulysses alone bends the bow, the suitors are killed and there is general rejoicing at his homecoming.

Fauré returned to purely classical tradition in his choice of subject and libretto for the opera *Pénélope* (Penelope) with music that often recalls that of his songs. He makes use of leitmotifs for Penelope, her sadness and her love, with motifs for the suitors and for Ulysses as king and as beggar.

PERFECT FOOL, THE

- Gustav Holst. Opera in one act. 1922.
- Libretto by the composer.
- First performance at Covent Garden, London, on 14th May 1923.

The Wizard summons a ballet of Spirits of Earth, Fire and Water, introducing a ballet that aims at a parody of Wagner's *Parsifal*. A mother successfully marries her son, the Fool of the title, to a princess, by taking a magic potion that the Wizard had proposed to use himself. The Fool is too weak and uninterested to take advantage of the situation offered him.

It is principally the ballet music from Holst's *The Perfect Fool* that has remained in occasional concert repertoire. In other respects the opera achieved no very great success, either in its parody or as a whole.

Périchole, La

- Jacques Offenbach. *Opéra bouffe* in two acts. 1868.
- Libretto by Henri Meilhac and Ludovic Halévy, after the comedy *Le carrosse du Saint-Sacrement* (The Carriage of the Holy Sacrament) by Prosper Mérimée.
- First performance at the Théâtre des Variétés, Paris, on 6th October 1868.

La Périchole and her companion Piquillo are street-singers in Lima, where the Viceroy is attracted to her and offers her a position as lady-in-waiting. Favourites of the Viceroy must be married and Piquillo volunteers his services as a husband to any of them, too drunk to notice that he is marrying an equally intoxicated La Périchole. The Viceroy eventually frees them, after Piquillo has suffered imprisonment as an unwilling husband.

Among Offenbach's most successful and charming works, *La Périchole* includes delightful music in an effective comic opera.

Persée (Perseus)

- Jean-Baptiste Lully, *Tragédie en musique* in a prologue and five acts. 1682.
- Libretto by Philippe Quinault, after Ovid's *Metamorphoses*.
- First performance at the Paris Opéra on 17th or 18th April 1682.

Persée (Perseus) treats the story of Perseus in human terms, his love for Andromeda, who loves him but is betrothed to Phineus, abetted by Merope, who loves Perseus. Medusa is duly killed, and her monstrous progeny appear, before Andromeda is rescued and a happy ending secured.

Lully's opera provided much that was spectacular in a work that makes full use of the orchestra, now employed also in the accompaniment of solo voices.

Perséphone (Persephone)

- Igor Stravinsky. *Mélodrame* in three scenes. 1934.
- Text by André Gide.
- First performance at the Paris Opéra on 30th April 1934.

Persephone, daughter of Demeter, against the warning of the high priest Eumolpus, inhales the scent of the narcissus and plucks it, seeing the shades of the dead, to whose region she now goes. In a second scene she is found in the Elysian Fields, where she sees in the narcissus her bereaved mother and is told by Eumolpus that she is to marry Triptolemos, the one who will teach men to cultivate the soil and who will bring her back to the light. In the third scene she is reborn, wife both to Triptolemos and to Pluto in the Underworld.

Persephone represents the cycle of the seasons and crops. Stravinsky's work is scored for *récitant*, tenor (Eumolpus), children's chorus, mixed chorus and orchestra, with *Oedipus rex* (King Oedipus) and *Apollon musagète* (Apollo, Leader of the Muses) forming his so-called Greek trilogy. Gide had strong enough objections to the setting of his words, which already had, he maintained, their own rhythm. The part of Persephone, written for Ida Rubinstein, was mimed and recited, while the tenor, Eumolpus, provides much of the necessary narrative element.

Pescatrici, Le (The Fisher-Women)

- Joseph Haydn. *Dramma giocoso* in three acts. 1770.
- Libretto by Carlo Goldoni, with possible revisions by Carl Friberth.
- First performance at Esterháza on 16th September 1770.

The fisherwomen Nerina and Lesbina vie for rediscovery as the long lost Princess of Benevento sought by Prince Lindoro, their claims furthered by one another's lovers. Their attempts are unsuccessful and the rightful princess is revealed as Eurilda.

Written for the wedding celebrations of Prince Nikolaus Esterházy, Haydn's opera has only survived in part, although attempts have been made at reconstruction of the complete work.

Peter Grimes

- Benjamin Britten. Opera in a prologue and three acts. 1945.
- Libretto by Montagu Slater, after George Crabbe's poem *The Borough*.
- First performance at Sadler's Wells, London, on 7th June 1945.

Characters

Peter Grimes, a fisherman	tenor
Boy (John), his apprentice	silent rôle
Ellen Orford, a widow, schoolmistress	soprano
Captain Balstrode, a retired merchant skipper	baritone
Auntie, landlady of The Boar	contralto
Auntie's Two Nieces, main attractions of The Boar	sopranos

Bob Boles, fisherman and Methodist	tenor
Swallow, a lawyer	bass
Mrs Sedley, widow of an East India Company factor	mezzo-soprano
Rev. Horace Adams, the rector	tenor
Ned Keene, apothecary and quack	baritone
Dr Thorp	silent rôle
Hobson, the carrier	bass

In the prologue, with the inquest on his apprentice, Peter Grimes is warned by the coroner, Swallow, not to take another boy apprentice. Popular prejudice is strong, but Ellen Orford shows sympathy. In the first act various inhabitants of the borough appear, while the fishermen and their wives go about their daily tasks. Ned Keene has found Grimes another apprentice, and Hobson agrees to bring him the boy, when Ellen Orford volunteers to look after him. While hostility is general, Balstrode too offers friendly advice to Grimes, suggesting that he leave the town to seek work on a merchant-ship. The second scene is set in The Boar, while a storm rages outside. Mrs Sedley comes to collect the laudanum Keene will bring her, Balstrode jokingly complains of the noise the frightened nieces are making and Boles, drunk, makes advances to them. Grimes comes in from the storm, intending to collect his new apprentice. His position as an outsider increases tension that is dissolved when Auntie calls for a song. Hobson comes in, with Ellen and the boy, and Grimes takes the latter away at once to what he calls home. The second act opens with Sunday morning. The people are in church, while outside Ellen questions the new apprentice about his life. She sees the boy's jersey is torn and that he has a bruise and pleads with Grimes to keep the day of rest, when he comes to take the boy off to work. In anger Grimes strikes her, the scene overheard by others, who now agree to set off in a party to Grimes's hut to see what is going on. The men march off together, intent on dealing with Grimes. A passacaglia, at the centre of the opera, leads to a new scene set in Grimes's hut. As the party of vindictive townspeople approaches, Grimes urges the boy to hurry down the cliff to the boat. The boy slips and falls to his death and Grimes follows down the cliff, leaving the hut empty, to the evident surprise of the men who now enter and find nothing amiss. The third act is set outside the Moot Hall, where a dance is taking place. Various people of the borough are seen, but Grimes is not there. Balstrode has found the jersey that Ellen had made for the boy, washed up on the shore. Mrs Sedley overhears and before long a band of angry men has formed, eager to hunt down Peter Grimes, the outsider. Grimes is now distraught at the disasters of his life and the failure of his ambitions. Balstrode advises him to take his boat out into the bay and sink it. The opera ends as Swallow confirms the coastguards' report that a boat has been seen out at sea, sinking. The life of the borough resumes.

A remarkable and pertinent study of the outsider Peter Grimes, his situation reflecting in one sense the position of Britten and his friend, the tenor Peter Pears, as pacifists and homosexuals in an intolerant and prejudiced society, and a still wider preoccupation with the rôle of the outsider, the opera *Peter Grimes* began a true revival of English opera as part of international operatic repertoire. The *Four Sea Interludes*, *Dawn, Sunday Morning, Moonlight* and *Storm*, with the *Passacaglia* are often heard in concert. Moving moments in the opera must include Ellen Orford's plea *Let her among you without fault* and her *Embroidery Song* in the third act. Peter Grimes expresses something of his aspirations in the second scene of the first act, with his *Now the Great Bear and Pleiades* and reveals his disturbed state of mind in his final scene. The fishermen have their own contribution to the second scene in The Boar when they sing the round *Old Joe has gone fishing* and it is the people of the borough, in their hypocrisy and incomprehension, who constitute the villain of an immensely theatrical work.

Recommended Recording:
Peter Grimes (Four Sea Interludes) — ***Naxos 8.553107***

Peter Schmoll und seine Nachbarn (Peter Schmoll and His Neighbours)

- Carl Maria von Weber. Opera in two acts. 1802.
- Libretto by Joseph Türk, after a novel by Carl Gottlob Cramer.
- First performance at Augsburg, possibly in March 1803.

Characters

Peter Schmoll, a rich banker	baritone
Martin Schmoll, his brother	bass
Minette, Martin Schmoll's daughter	soprano
Karl Prirkner	tenor
Hans Bast, a servant	bass
Niklas, a peasant	baritone

Peter Schmoll, a sixty-year-old banker, lives with his nineteen-year-old niece Minette and his old factotum Hans Bast in a country-house. Peter Schmoll has fallen in love with Minette and eventually proposes marriage, but she is in love with the young Karl Prirkner. One day there appear with the peasant Niklas, who is selling vegetables, an old man and a young man, claiming to be father and son. They are, in fact, Martin Schmoll and Karl, who, after years of searching, have found where Peter Schmoll, uprooted by the French revolution, has settled. Various misundertandings are resolved, with the help of Hans Bast, and Minette and Karl Prirkner are happily united.

Weber wrote his opera at the age of fifteen, providing twenty numbers for a work of which the full text has been lost. The achievement is remarkable enough and satisfied one of Weber's teachers, Michael Haydn, who had supervised the composition of the work.

Recommended Recording:
Peter Schmoll (2 CDs) ***Marco Polo 8.223592-93***

PHAËTON (PHAETHON)

- Jean-Baptiste Lully. *Tragédie en musique* in a prologue and five acts. 1683.
- Libretto by Philippe Quinault, after Ovid's *Metamorphoses*.
- First performance at Versailles on 6th January 1683.

Phaethon, son of Clymene and the Sun, drives his father's chariot through the sky, to be brought to earth disastrously by a thunderbolt of Jupiter.

Lully's opera gives the expected opportunity for spectacle, in Phaethon's flight and fall and, elsewhere, in the metamorphoses of Proteus. The *Chaconne* from the opera, with other airs and dances, was transcribed for harpsichord by Jean-Henri d'Anglebert, who performed the same service for a number of other instrumental excerpts from Lully's operas.

PHILÉMON ET BAUCIS (PHILEMON AND BAUCIS)

- Charles-François Gounod. *Opéra* in three acts. 1860.
- Libretto by Jules Barbier and Michel Carré.
- First performance by the Théâtre Lyrique, Paris, on 18th February 1860.

The old Philemon and Baucis are restored to youth by Jupiter, grateful for their hospitality, something their neighbours have not shown. Jupiter then falls in love with the young Baucis, who solves this difficulty by requesting and receiving old age again.

Vulcan's bass aria *Au bruit des lourds marteaux* (To the sound of heavy hammers) and the soprano *O riante nature* (O laughing nature) of Baucis, with her *Ah! si je redevenais belle* (Ah! If I were beautiful again) may be heard occasionally in recital.

Philemon und Baucis (Philemon and Baucis)

- Joseph Haydn. Singspiel marionette opera. 1773.
- Libretto by Gottlieb Konrad Pfeffel.
- First performance at Esterháza on 2nd September 1773.

Jupiter and Mercury take shelter with Philemon and Baucis, whose dead son is restored to life, with his betrothed, as a reward for a hospitality not shown by others. A temple is built, with Philemon and Baucis as priests, being raised to heaven in a chariot.

The gods have speaking rôles in a work that has never achieved any lasting success. It opens with an energetic overture, but some parts of the work are now lost.

Pia de'Tolomei (Pia of Tolomei)

- Gaetano Donizetti. *Tragedia lirica* in two acts. 1837.
- Libretto by Salvadore Cammarano, after the novella by Bartolomeo Sestini, based on an episode in Dante's *Divina Commedia: Purgatorio*.
- First performance at the Teatro Apollo, Venice, on 18th February 1837.

Pia is pursued by her brother-in-law Ghino, who convinces her husband that she is unfaithful to him, a false charge that results in her death by poison. Ghino, mortally wounded in battle, tells his brother of his deception, but it is too late.

Pia de'Tolomei is not among Donizetti's more important works, although Ghino provides an effective study of a man in conflict with himself.

Piccolo Marat, Il (The Little Marat)

- Pietro Mascagni. *Dramma lirico* in three acts. 1921.
- Libretto by Giovacchino Forzato.
- First performance at the Teatro Costanzi, Rome, on 2nd May 1921.

The Prince of Fleury, in the French revolution, saves himself and his mother by assuming the name of the Little Marat and enlisting in the revolutionary forces.

The opera mingles an element of realism (*verismo*) with the improbabilities of a fairy-story, but offered contemporary singers some chance to shine.

Pietra del paragone, La (The Touchstone)

- Gioachino Rossini. *Melodramma giocoso* in two acts. 1812.
- Libretto by Luigi Romanelli.
- First performance at the Teatro alla Scala, Milan, on 26th September 1812.

Count Asdrubale, a rich young bachelor, is giving a party, attended by a number of pretentious fortune-hunters. He pretends to have lost all his money, proving thus the loyalty of the Marchesina Clarice, who poses as her own brother, to test the strength of the Count's affection in her turn.

The opera includes a parody of critics in the affected Pacuvio's pretentious *Ombretta sdegnosa del Missipipi* (Disdainful shadow of the Missipipi), with its ridiculous repetitions of the last syllables and the poet Giocondo's address to Clarice *Quell'alme pupille* (Those gentle eyes).

Pilgrim's Progress, The

- Ralph Vaughan Williams. Morality in a prologue, four acts and an epilogue. 1951.
- Libretto by the composer, after John Bunyan, with additions from various sources by Ursula Vaughan Williams.
- First performance at Covent Garden, London, on 26th April 1951.

After a prologue in which the writer John Bunyan, in Bedford Goal, finishes his book, Pilgrim sets out on his journey through life, to the wicket gate, the King's highway, the Valley of Humiliation, Vanity Fair, thence to the Delectable Mountains and finally to the Celestial City.

Vaughan Williams intended his opera, on which he had started to work in 1925, after earlier settings of parts of the work, to avoid the overtly Christian. Watchful the Porter's song has an occasional place in vocal concert repertoire. In its context it bridges the gap between the first and second acts.

Pimpinone

- Georg Philipp Telemann. Intermezzo in three scenes. 1725.
- Libretto by Johann Philipp Praetorius, after Pietro Pariati.
- First performance at the Theater am Gänsemarkt, Hamburg, on 27th September 1725.

Vespetta plans a careful campaign against the rich Pimpinone, who engages her as a servant, persuades him to marry her, to avoid gossip, and to provide her with the necessary dowry. She finally wins freedom to do much as she likes, thanks to the marriage contract she has devised with Pimpinone.

Pariati's libretto, given in German as *Pimpinone, oder Die ungleiche Heirat, oder Die herrschsüchtige Cammer-Mädgen* (Pimpinone, or The Unequal Marriage, or The Despotic Chambermaid), had been set earlier in the century by Albinoni. Telemann's idiomatic treatment of the work won immediate popularity.

PIRATA, IL (THE PIRATE)

- Vincenzo Bellini. *Melodramma* in two acts. 1827.
- Libretto by Felice Romani, after Isidore J.S.Taylor's play *Bertram, ou Le pirate* (Bertram, or The Pirate), itself based on the play *Bertram, or The Castle of St Aldobrando* by Charles Maturin.
- First performance at the Teatro alla Scala, Milan, on 27th October 1827.

CHARACTERS

Ernesto, Duke of Caldora	bass
Imogene, his wife	soprano
Adele, her companion	soprano
Gualtiero, former Count of Montalto	tenor
Itulbo, Gualtiero's lieutenant	tenor
Goffredo, a hermit, former tutor to Gualtiero	bass
Son of Ernesto and Imogene	treble

Imogene, in order to save her father, has been forced to marry Ernesto, although she loves Gualtiero. A storm wrecks Gualtiero's pirate ship on the shores near Caldora, where Imogene meets him again and explains what has happened. He seeks revenge on Duke Ernesto, which he achieves by killing him in single combat. Gualtiero is condemned to death.

Bellini's first opera for Milan established his reputation and marked a further stage in the development of romantic opera. From the opera comes the soprano *Col sorriso d'innocenza* (With the smile of innocence) in which Imogene, now out of her mind, hopes that her son can persuade Duke Ernesto, who is now dead, to forgive Gualtiero.

Pirates of Penzance, The

- Arthur Sullivan. Operetta in two acts. 1879.
- Libretto by W.S.Gilbert.
- First performance at the Royal Bijou Theatre, Paignton, on 30th December 1879.

An unfortunate mistake finds Frederic apprenticed to a pirate instead of a pilot. With the help of his beloved Mabel, daughter of the very model of a modern major-general, he tries to bring the pirates to justice, but as a Leap Year baby born on 29th February, he is still an infant and therefore apprenticed. Matters are put right when it is discovered that the pirates themselves are really noblemen who have gone astray.

The operetta contains a well known patter-song for Mabel's father, *I am the very model of a modern Major-General* and an equally familiar song of police complicity with the criminal in *When a felon's not engaged*. The score contains the expected elements of operatic parody.

Platée (Plataea)

- Jean-Philippe Rameau. *Comédie lyrique* in a prologue and three acts. 1745.
- Libretto by Adrien-Joseph Le Valois d'Orville, after the play *Platée, ou Junon jalouse* (Plataea, or Juno Jealous) by Jacques Autreau.
- First performance at La Grande Ecurie, Versailles, on 31st March 1745.

King Cithaeron suggests to Mercury that Jupiter may teach his jealous wife Juno a lesson if he woos the unattractive and conceited marsh-nymph Plataea. She has set her cap at Cithaeron, but responds favourably, to the accompaniment of frogs. Jupiter appears to Plataea in a variety of shapes, as a donkey, then as an owl, and finally as himself, to be entertained in a mock divertissement. Juno, in hiding, observes the mock-wedding ceremony, eventually emerging to unveil the bride and realise the ridiculous nature of the proceedings. Plataea is left to the mockery of the country-people.

Platée, which includes opportunities for parody and for onomatopoiea in its frog and donkey noises, was written for performance at the wedding of the Dauphin and a Spanish princess in 1745. Described also as a *ballet bouffon*, it includes elements of broad musical and dramatic comedy.

Poliuto

- Gaetano Donizetti. *Tragedia lirica* in three acts. 1838.
- Libretto by Salvadore Cammarano, after Pierre Corneille's drama *Polyeucte*.

- First performance at the Teatro S Carlo, Naples, on 30th November 1848.

In Armenia, in the 3rd century, Poliuto is secretly baptized by Nearco. His wife Paolina, once betrothed to Severo, has rejected the high priest Callistene, who arouses Poliuto's jealousy by allowing him to overhear a conversation between her and Severo. The Christian Nearco is captured and condemned to death, refusing to name his most recent convert. Poliuto comes forward and is also imprisoned. In death he is joined by his wife Paolina, herself now embracing the new faith.

Donizetti reworked *Poliuto* for Paris as *Les martyrs* (The Martyrs), with a French libretto by Eugène Scribe. The French version won little success, even when translated into Italian for opera-houses in Italy, and the first performance of the original opera was given after Donizetti's death. In the tenor aria *D'un alma troppo fervida* (Of a soul that is too fervent), Poliuto prays for calmness of spirit, while the soprano Paolina, moved by the Christian rites, sings *Di quai soavi lagrime* (From these sweet tears). The baritone Severo is introduced by *Di tua beltade immagine* (The image of your beauty). In a final duet Paolina begs Poliuto to recant in *Ah! fuggi da morte* (Ah! Escape death), but soon they both declare their faith.

Pomo d'oro, Il (The Golden Apple)

- Antonio Cesti. *Festa teatrale* in a prologue and five acts. 1666.
- Libretto by Francesco Sbarra.
- First performance at the Hoftheater auf der Cortina, Vienna, on 12th and 14th July 1668.

The prologue celebrates the glory of Austria and the Emperor Leopold I. Opening scenes at the court of Pluto in the Underworld are followed by scenes set in the palace of Jupiter, where the golden apple provokes discord between Venus, Athena and Juno. On Mount Ida Paris, in love with the nymph Oenone, resolves the conflict by adjudging Venus the fairest, after she has bribed him by the promise of Helen. Athena and Juno seek their revenge, while matters are complicated by the relationship between Paris and Oenone. The endless discord between the goddesses is finally brought to an end when the apple itself is awarded to the Empress Margherita.

Cesti's opera was originally written for the wedding of Leopold I and Margherita of Spain, although its first performance was delayed for two years. The score of the third and fifth acts is incomplete and there are interpolated elements from the Emperor and from Johann Heinrich Schmelzer, who provided ballet music. The work calls for elaborate spectacular effects and its performance extends to some eight hours, the reason for its first performance in two parts.

Porgy and Bess

- George Gershwin. Folk opera in three acts. 1935.
- Libretto by DuBose Heyward, with lyrics by Heyward and Ira Gershwin, based on Heyward's novel *Porgy*.
- First performance at the Alvin Theatre, New York, on 10th October 1935.

Characters

Porgy, a crippled beggar	bass-baritone
Bess	soprano
Crown, her lover, a stevedore	baritone
Serena, Robbins's wife	soprano
Clara, Jake's wife	soprano
Maria, keeper of the cook-shop	contralto
Jake, a fisherman	baritone
Sportin' Life, a dope peddler	tenor
Mingo	tenor
Robbins, living on Catfish Row	tenor
Peter, the honeyman	tenor
Frazier, a 'lawyer'	baritone
Annie	mezzo-soprano
Lily, Peter's wife, strawberry woman	mezzo-soprano
Jim, a cotton-picker	baritone
Undertaker	baritone
Nelson	tenor
Crab Man	tenor
Mr Archdale, a white man	speaking part

In a tenement on Catfish Row Clara sings a lullaby to her baby, while elsewhere there is a crap game. The cripple Porgy is teased about his affection for Bess, who comes in with her drunken man, Crown, with whom violence breaks out. Crown, drunk and having lost in the game, kills Robbins, and is given money by Bess to make his escape, while she eventually finds shelter with Porgy. There is a wake for Robbins, with Peter seized by the police as a witness. A month later the fishermen prepare to put to sea, while Frazier arranges a 'legal' divorce for Bess from Crown. She repulses Sportin' Life, who continues to press her to go away with him. At a picnic on Kittiwah Island from which Porgy is excluded, Crown re-appears and claims Bess again. A storm drowns the fisherman

Jake, with, it seems, Clara, and Crown, who had gone to their help. Crown returns and is murdered by Porgy, although his guilt is not detected. While he is held as a witness, Sportin' Life gives Bess some dope, and when Porgy returns, Bess has gone away with him, now followed by Porgy.

Gershwin's opera has a particular importance of its own, set, as it is, in black America. Clara's lullaby *Summertime*, repeated by Bess, when she looks after Clara's baby, is among the best known songs from the opera. Other well known songs include Jake's *A woman is a sometime thing*, Serena's lament for Robbins *My man's gone now*, and Bess's wake spiritual *Headin' for the Promise' Land*. The second act brings Porgy's Banjo Song *Oh I got plenty o'nuttin* and his duet with Bess, *Bess, you is my woman now*. At the picnic Sportin' Life sings *It ain't necessarily so*, while Porgy expresses his final determination to follow Bess in *Oh, Lord, I'm on my way*. The symphonic suite *Catfish Row* was derived from the opera.

Poro (Porus)

- George Frideric Handel. Opera in three acts. 1731.
- Libretto adapted from Pietro Metastasio's *Alessandro nell'Indie*.
- First performance at the King's Theatre, London, on 2nd February 1731.

The Indian King Porus, defeated and at first captured by Alexander, although he does not reveal his identity, is jealous of his beloved Cleophis. After a variety of intrigues, prompted largely by Alexander's treacherous general Timagenes, Porus and Cleophis are united, through the generosity of Alexander, who surrenders his own claims to her.

Poro, re dell'Indie (Porus, King of India) won considerable success in London. The opera was revised for revival later in 1731 and again in 1736.

Prima la musica e poi le parole (First the Music and then the Words)

- Antonio Salieri. *Divertimento teatrale* in one act. 1786.
- Libretto by Giovanni Battista Casti.
- First performance at the Orangerie, Schönbrunn, Vienna, on 7th February 1786.

A Music Director and a Poet argue about a new work, for which the music has been written and which now only needs words. A prima donna of serious opera and a singer of comic opera vie for supremacy and in the end sing together, joined by the Poet and Music Director.

Salieri's jeu d'esprit includes witty parody of a popular opera of the time, *Giulio Sabino*, by Giuseppe Sarti. It was performed for the Emperor together with Mozart's parody of theatrical life, *Der Schauspieldirektor* (The Impresario).

PRINCE IGOR

- Alexander Porfir'yevich Borodin. Opera in a prologue and four acts. Unfinished at the composer's death in 1887 and completed by Nikolay Andreyevich Rimsky-Korsakov and Alexander Konstantinovich Glazunov.
- Libretto by the composer, after a scenario by Vladimir Vasil'yevich Stasov.
- First performance at the Mariinsky Theatre, St Petersburg, on 4th November 1890.

CHARACTERS

Igor Svyatoslavich, Prince of Seversk	baritone
Yaroslavna, his second wife	soprano
Vladimir Igorevich, Prince Igor's son by his first marriage	tenor
Vladimir Yaroslavich, Prince Galitzky, brother of Princess Yaroslavna	high bass
Khan Konchak, a Polovtsian leader	bass
Khan Gzak, a Polovtsian leader	silent rôle
Konchakovna, daughter of Khan Konchak	contralto
Ovlur, a baptized Polovtsian	tenor
Skula, a gudok-player	bass
Yeroshka, a gudok-player	tenor
Yaroslavna's Nurse	soprano
Polovtsian Maiden	soprano

In Putivl' Prince Galitzky rules in place of Prince Igor, who has marched out against the Polovtsians. While the deserters Skula and Yeroshka sing the praises of Galitzky, urging the deposing of Igor, Princess Yaroslavna laments her husband's departure. Prince Igor and his son are captured by Khan Konchak, and Vladimir falls in love with the Khan's daughter Konchakovna. Prince Igor is offered freedom and an alliance and is entertained as an honoured guest. Khan Gzak is also victorious against the Russians. Igor himself escapes, but Vladimir remains behind, accepted as a husband for Konchakovna. The opera ends with the return of Prince Igor to his own city, welcomed by Princess Yaroslavna, and, with less certainty, by the duplicitous Skula and Yeroshka, who spread the good news of their prince's return.

Various versions of *Prince Igor* have been made, since the first completion of the work by Rimsky-Korsakov and Glazunov cut a large part of what Borodin had already written. Best known of everything in the score are the exotic *Polovtsian Dances*, which entertain the captive Russian prince and his son, and the overture, reconstructed from memory, it was alleged, by Glazunov.

Recommended Recordings:

Overture	***Naxos 8.550085***
Polovtsian Dances	***Naxos 8.550501***

PRINCESS IDA

- Arthur Sullivan. Operetta in three acts. 1883.
- Libretto by W.S. Gilbert, after Tennyson's poem *The Princess*.
- First performance at the Savoy Theatre, London, on 5th January 1884.

The planned marriage of Prince Hilarion and Princess Ida is imperilled by the latter's educational ambitions, when she sets up a women's university. Difficulties are resolved when the princess hands over the administration to the substantial contralto Lady Blanch and agrees to marry her betrothed.

Gilbert satirises women's education in *Princess Ida, or Castle Adamant*, which won less immediate success than the music, at least, deserved.

PRINZ VON HOMBURG, DER (THE PRINCE OF HOMBURG)

- Hans Werner Henze. Opera in three acts. 1958.
- Libretto by Ingeborg Bachmann, after the play *Prinz Friedrich von Homburg* by Heinrich von Kleist.
- First performance at the Staatsoper, Hamburg, on 22nd May 1960.

CHARACTERS

Friedrich Wilhelm, Elector of Brandenburg	tenor
The Electress, his wife	contralto
Princess Natalie of Orange, her niece, Colonel-in-Chief of Dragoons	soprano
Field Marshal Dörfling	baritone
Friedrich Artur, Prince of Homburg, General of Cavalry	high baritone
Colonel Kottwitz, in the Prince's regiment	bass

Count Hohenzollern, attached to the Elector	lyric tenor
Three Officers	tenor, baritone & bass
Three Ladies of the Court	soprano, mezzo-soprano & contralto
Sergeant	baritone
Two Orderlies	tenor & baritone

In the castle garden Prince Friedrich sits dreaming, twining a wreath of flowers. The Elector takes the wreath from him, hangs a silver medallion round his neck and gives him the hand of Princess Natalie. He is roused by Count Hohenzollern, still holding the glove of the Princess. In the castle Field Marshal Dörfling outlines the plan of battle, while the Prince day-dreams, assenting but thinking that the Princess must be looking for her glove, which he now drops. On the battle-field the Prince still thinks of the Princess, not having taken in the orders he was given. He attacks, against orders, and after the battle there are rumours of the death of the Elector. These are false, however, and the Elector re-appears, threatening to court-martial the man responsible for disobeying orders and commanding the premature cavalry charge. The Prince is imprisoned. In his cell he learns from Count Hohenzollern of the expected ratification by the Elector of the sentence of death. The Electress cannot intercede for him, but the Princess does and is told that the decision of the fairness of the verdict must rest with the Prince himself. The Prince must agree with the decision of the court, but the Princess decides to follow the dictates of her heart and use her Dragoons to set him free. The Elector realises that he has gained his point with the Prince and tears up the death warrant. In the final scene Friedrich is led into the garden, blindfold, as if for execution, but when the blindfold is removed he is rewarded by the Elector with a garland of victory and the hand of the Princess.

Suggested by Visconti, *Der Prinz von Homburg* (The Prince of Homburg) appealed also to Henze in its treatment of the conflict between individual freedom and the state. The score is in some respects less purely innovative and therefore demanding on audiences than some of Henze's operatic work. The composer makes use of traditional forms and a large chamber orchestra, with contrasting instrumentation for each scene.

PRODIGAL SON, THE

- Benjamin Britten. Church parable. 1968.
- Libretto by William Plomer.
- First performance in Orford Church, Suffolk, on 10th June 1968.

Performed by a group of monks, the parable of the Prodigal Son, after the opening hymn, reveals the Abbot as Tempter, enticing the Younger Son to seek his inheritance, while his Father and Elder Brother continue their life of hard work and piety. The Younger Son wastes his substance in riotous living and returns in penitence, to be welcomed by his Father and eventually reconciled with his Elder Brother, after which the Abbot points the moral of the story.

The Prodigal Son opens and closes with the plainchant hymn *Jam lucis orto sidere*, for the Office of Prime, and, as with the earlier church parables, draws on this material. Once again, as in *Curlew River* and *The Burning Fiery Furnace*, singers and instrumentalists appear initially as monks, the singers donning their masks and costumes during an opening instrumental interlude.

Prophète, Le (The Prophet)

- Giacomo Meyebeer. Grand opera in five acts. 1840.
- Libretto by Eugène Scribe.
- First performance at the Paris Opéra on 16th April 1849.

Characters

Jean de Leyde (John of Leyden)	tenor
Fidès, his mother	mezzo-soprano
Berthe, his betrothed	soprano
Jonas, an Anabaptist	tenor
Mathisen, an Anabaptist	bass/baritone
Zacharie, an Anabaptist	bass
Count Oberthal	bass

Berthe, outside the castle of Count Oberthal, is to seek permission to marry John, son of Fidès. The Anabaptists provoke the peasantry to rise against their overlord, but the Count emerges to restore them to order by his presence. He refuses Berthe permission and orders her and Fidès to be taken prisoner. In his inn in Leyden John has dreamed that he was greeted as Messiah and then taken to Hell by Satan. The Anabaptists plan to use him, telling him of his resemblance to a picture of King David in Münster. Berthe rushes in, seeking his help, but the Count demands her surrender, in return for the freedom of Fidès. Now provoked, John joins the Anabaptists. In their camp prisoners are taken and the Count, who has made his way in, is soon recognised and condemned, to be spared on John's orders, when he learns that Berthe is in Münster. John calms disaffected Anabaptist troops before battle. In the city Fidès, now begging, meets Berthe. John, the prophet, is crowned Emperor in the cathedral and Fidès realises that the prophet is her son, who now disowns her. In a cellar under the palace, the three Anabaptists plan to hand John over to the armies of the Emperor. Fidès, brought in as a prisoner, urges him to give up power, and Berthe, who now for the first time learns that John is the so-called prophet, kills herself. In a great hall of the palace, where the prophet is the centre of adulation, the three Anabaptists and Oberthal enter, as John drinks. Fidès comes to her son, but at this moment there is an explosion and the walls of the palace collapse in ruins, destroyed by the charge of gunpowder that John had prepared.

The production of *Le Prophète* (The Prophet) was delayed until circumstances at the Paris Opéra were propitious. In 1849 it served also a political purpose, after the suppression of popular disaffection that had recently arisen in Paris, as elsewhere in Europe. The opera provides obvious opportunities for grand spectacle. Berthe, in the pastoral opening of the work, has a cavatina *Mon cœur s'élance* (My heart leaps up), expressing her love for John, who, in the second act, sings of his own love for her in *Pour Berthe, moi je soupire* (For Berthe I sigh). His mother Fidès plays a part of great dramatic and musical importance, grateful for her release in *Ah, mon fils* (Ah, my son) in the second act. There is ballet music for those skating, as they approach the camp of the Anabaptists, by the frozen lake. This music served Frederick Ashton for his ballet *Les patineurs* (The Skaters). There is a hymn of triumph for John and the chorus, *Roi du ciel et des anges* (King of Heaven and of the Angels) and the famous *Coronation March*, with a fifth act solo for Fidès, *O prêtres de Baal* (O priests of Baal).

Protagonist, Der (The Protagonist)

- Kurt Weill. Opera in one act. 1925.
- Libretto by Georg Kaiser, after his play.
- First performance at the Staatsoper, Dresden, on 27th March 1926.

In a country inn in Elizabethan England, a troupe of players rehearses a play to be given before the Duke that evening. Catherine, sister of the Protagonist, confesses to him that she has a lover, exciting his jealousy. News of the sudden arrival of a bishop causes the Duke to demand a tragedy instead of the original bawdy comedy, and the new play, with the Protagonist as a deceived husband, is rehearsed. At the point where the Protagonist is about to take his revenge, Catherine happily comes in, with her lover, to be killed in earnest by her brother.

Kaiser's play, with its two mime scenes, allowed particular musical opportunities. Georg Kaiser and his wife had been kind to Weill after the death of his mentor Ferruccio Busoni, whose place they seemed to take. Weill's opera is more or less contemporaneous with Alban Berg's *Wozzeck*, which he regarded as the end of a development from Wagner's *Tristan und Isolde* through Richard Strauss. Weill saw his own work as suggesting a new course, itself an example of *Neue Sachlichkeit* (New Objectivity), that nevertheless draws, at least in its text, on Expressionism, a movement with which Kaiser is generally associated.

Prozess, Der (The Trial)

- Gottfried von Einem. Opera in nine scenes. 1952.
- Libretto by Boris Blacher and Heinz von Cramer, after the novel by Franz Kafka.
- First performance at the Festspielhaus, Salzburg, on 17th August 1953.

Scenes are taken from Kafka's novel, in which Josef K. is arrested, allowed to go to work, tried in his own house. He insults the court and runs away, and then is arrested once more, beaten up, and provided with a lawyer who knows more than Josef K. of the case. Application to a painter for help is useless and he is eventually taken to his execution.

The problems of the conflict between the individual and the state continued to be relevant, when the opera was written, as now. Astringent music is used for Kafka's bitter fantasy.

Punainen viiva (The Red Line)

- Aulis Sallinen. Opera in two acts. 1978.
- Libretto by the composer after a novel by Ilmari Kianto.
- First performance at the Finnish National Opera, Helsinki, on 30th November 1978.

A poor peasant in the backwoods struggles, with his wife and children, to make a living, after a bear has killed the last of their sheep and the church, to which he appeals, will offer no help. He goes to sell game and while he is away a pedlar appears, entertaining the children with his balled. A socialist activist persuades the peasants and their wives to vote: if they mark a red line on the ballot slip, all their difficulties will be at and end. The peasant goes to work in a logging camp, but when he returns he finds his children dead from disease and starvation and his wife mourning. The bear attacks again and the peasant is killed, found by his wife with a red line across his throat.

Sallinen's second opera is set in 1907, the year of universal suffrage in Finland. The bitterness of the satire and the melancholy of the final scene may be contrasted with the lighter mood of the pedlar's folk-song.

Punch and Judy

- Harrison Birtwistle. Tragicomedy or comitragedy. 1967.
- Libretto by Stephen Pruslin.
- First performance at the Jubilee Hall, Aldeburgh, on 8th June 1968.

Punch sings a lullaby and then throws the baby on the fire. He stabs Judy, who is led to execution, before setting out to find Pretty Polly. The Choregos, who has introduced the piece, with Judy, the Doctor and the Lawyer, comments on the murder. Punch travels and finds Polly, who is not impressed. The Doctor and Lawyer reason with Punch, who kills them with appropriate weapons. Punch again seeks Polly, who again rejects him. Punch now saws the Choregos in half. Punch is tormented in a nightmare and then seeks but fails to find Polly. In prison he tricks the Choregos, who appears as the hangman Jack Ketch, and hangs him. There is a love duet for Punch and Polly, while the gibbet becomes a maypole, with all revived. The Choregos provides an epilogue to what is now a comedy.

A remarkable work, *Punch and Judy* offers a stylized and ritualistic piece, scored for a chamber ensemble of fifteen instruments that often explore the highest registers. It has something of the ritual of Greek drama, something of early Baroque operatic form and an essential English element in its choice of the traditional puppets and their story as a basis. The symmetrical organization of the piece, framed by a prologue and epilogue, offers a series of Melodramas, Passion Chorales and Quests for Polly.

Puritani, I (The Puritans)

- Vincenzo Bellini. *Melodramma serio* in three parts. 1835.
- Libretto by Carlo Pepoli, after the play *Têtes rondes et cavaliers* (Roundheads and Cavaliers) by J.-A. F.-P. Ancelot and Jean Xavier Boniface, dit Saintine.
- First performance at the Théâtre Italien, Paris, on 24th January 1835.

Characters

Lord Gualtiero Walton, Governor General of the fortress	bass
Sir Giorgio Walton, his brother, also a Puritan	bass
Lord Arturo Talbo, a Cavalier	tenor
Sir Riccardo Forth, a Puritan colonel	baritone
Sir Bruno Robertson, a Puritan officer	tenor
Enrichetta di Francia, (Queen Henrietta Maria, widow of King Charles I)	mezzo-soprano
Elvira, daughter of Lord Walton	soprano

Elvira is in love with Lord Arthur Talbot, but her father wants her to marry Sir Richard Forth, eventually giving in to her wishes. The Queen, imprisoned in the same fortress and under threat of execution, is saved by Lord Arthur, who leads her out under Elvira's bridal veil, outwitting Sir Richard, who sees that the woman is not Elvira. She, thinking herself deserted, goes mad. Sir George and Sir Richard resolve to seek revenge for Elvira's madness in battle against Lord Arthur, who, in the third act, finds Elvira again, in spite of the danger to himself. Captured, he is about to be executed, when news of Puritan victory brings with it a general pardon. Elvira recovers her sanity and her lover.

Bellini's last opera provides an opportunity for tenors in the rôle of Arturo, with his *cavatina*, when allowed to claim her as his bride, *A te, o cara* (To you, my dear one), and for sopranos in Elvira's joyful *Son vergin vezzosa* (I am a pretty girl) and her mad scene, *Qui la voce sua soave* (Here his sweet voice).

Recommended Recording: Qui la voce sua soave ***Naxos 8.550605***

PYGMALION

- Jiři Antonín (Georg) Benda. *Melodramma* (Monodrama) in one act. 1779.
- Libretto by Friedrich Wilhelm Gotter, after Jean-Jacques Rousseau.
- First performance at the Hoftheater, Gotha, on 20th September 1779.

Pygmalion, having renounced women, is in love with the statue he has made, his Galatea. Venus allows her to come to life, giving him final happiness.

Benda's melodramas make interesting and influential use of speech and accompanying music, a practice that impressed Mozart and found its place in later opera, and, to some extent, in the 20th century cinema, where music has been used to accompany and heighten speech and dramatic action.

Recommended Recording:
Pygmalion ***Naxos 8.553345***

Quattro rusteghi, I (The School for Fathers)

- Ermanno Wolf-Ferrari. Comic opera in three acts. 1906
- Libretto by Luigi Sugana and Giuseppe Pizzolato, after the play *I rusteghi* by Carlo Goldoni.
- First performance at the Hoftheater, Munich, on 19th March 1906.

The pedantic and conventional Lunardo and Maurizio have arranged the marriage of Lucieta, daughter of the former, to the latter's son Filipeto, but the couple are not to see one another before the wedding. Filipeto, disguised as a woman, contrives to see Lucieta and the couple fall in love, only to find that the rigid conventions followed by their fathers now demand the cancellation of the wedding. Matters are finally resolved through the saner activities of the men's wives and by Felice, wife to the *rustego* Cancian, and her friend Count Riccardo.

Goldoni's Venetian dialect is largely preserved in what some have regarded as Wolf-Ferrari's best comic opera, with its prelude and intermezzo well enough known in concert performance.

Queen of Spades, The

- Pyotr Il'yich Tchaikovsky. Opera in three acts. 1890.
- Libretto by Modest Il'yich Tchaikovsky and the composer, after the novella by Pushkin.
- First performance at the Mariinsky Theatre, St Peterburg on 19th December 1890.

Characters

Hermann	tenor
Count Tomsky	baritone
Prince Yeletsky	baritone
The Countess	mezzo-soprano
Lisa, her grand-daughter	soprano
Pauline, Lisa's companion	contralto

Chekalinsky	tenor
Surin	bass
Chaplitsky	tenor
Narumov	bass
Master of Ceremonies	tenor
Catherine the Great	silent rôle
Governess	mezzo-soprano
Masha, Lisa's maid	soprano
In the interlude (Acts 2)	
Chloë	soprano
Daphnis (Pauline)	contralto
Plutus (Tomsky)	baritone

In the Summer Garden in St. Petersburg Hermann's friends discuss his strange behaviour, how he watches others gambling, but never takes part. Hermann, entering with Count Tomsky, explains his sadness by his love for a girl whose name he does not know. They congratulate Prince Yeletsky on his engagement, but Hermann is horrified to find that Yeletsky's betrothed is the girl with whom he has fallen in love, Lisa, grand-daughter of the old Countess. Count Tomsky tells his friends the story of the Countess and why she never gambles. When she was young in Paris, she had been given the secret of winning at cards and had used this to recoup her fortunes. She has been, thereafter, pledged never to play again, and, having revealed her secret to two others, is to die at the hands of the third to whom she confides it. Hermann is agitated at the story, and now left alone resolves to win the hand of Lisa from Prince Yeletsky by means of the Countess's secret. In Lisa's room she and Pauline, with their friends, entertain one another with songs. They are told to restrain themselves by the Governess, sent to them by the Countess. On her balcony, now alone, Lisa thinks of her betrothed. Hermann appears below and the two declare their love for each other, their meeting interrupted by the Countess telling Lisa to go to bed. At a ball, Yeletsky sings to Lisa of his love for her. Hermann is teased by his friends, who suggest that he will be the third man, the one to learn the secret of the Countess. The Master of Ceremonies introduces a pastoral interlude and Lisa tells Hermann how to reach the Countess's room. There the Countess regrets modern fashions, remembering the past. Hermann breaks in, demanding to learn her secret of winning and threatening her with his revolver. The Countess dies and Lisa, disturbed by the noise, comes in to find that Hermann has apparently used her to learn of the gambler's secret. In his army quarters Hermann is distraught. The ghost of the Countess appears to him and tells him the secret, three, seven, ace. By the banks of the Neva, Lisa waits for Hermann, who appears, as the clock strikes nidnight. Their meeting is interrupted, however, when Hermann insists on leaving at once for the gaming-house, where he may use what he has learned. Lisa realises Hermann's obsession and throws herself into the river. In the gaming-house Hermann plays against Yeletsky, staking everthing on the last of the three cards, the expected ace. Instead it is the queen of spades that appears, seeming to look at him with the face of the Countess. In final madness he kills himself.

There is much subtlety in the symbolism employed in *The Queen of Spades*. Well known elements from the score include Yeletsky's aria, which he sings to Lisa in the second act, a declaration of love, and Lisa's musing towards the end of the first act, when she has doubts about her coming marriage. All in all, there are many remarkable features in the opera, with its second act *divertissement* a foil to what follows, and motivic, textual and rhythmic connections between parts of the work.

Radamisto

- George Frideric Handel. Opera in three acts. 1720.
- Libretto adapted from 1712 version of Domenico Lalli's *L'amor tirannico, o Zenobia.*
- First performance at the King's Theatre, London, on 27th April 1720.

Characters

Radamisto, son of Farasmane	(male) soprano
Zenobia, his wife	contralto
Farasmane, King of Thrace	bass
Tiridate, King of Armenia	tenor
Polissena, his wife, daughter of Farasmane	soprano
Tigrane, Prince of Pontus	(male) soprano
Fraarte, brother of Tiridate	male soprano

Tiridate falls in love with his sister-in-law Zenobia and makes war against Farasmane, assisted by Tigrane, who makes advances to Polissena. Farasmane is taken prisoner and his kingdom seized, while Radamisto and Zenobia take refuge in the capital city, where they resist attack, escaping, in spite of the threats made against the life of the captive Farasmane. After various confusions of disguise, capture and re-capture, Tiridate is defeated but magnanimously pardoned by Radamisto, content now to be re-united with his Zenobia.

Radamisto won success with the London public in 1720 and was first revised in the same year, with the title-rôle transposed down for the alto castrato Senesino and the part of Tiridate given to a bass. The rôles of Radamisto and Tigrane were originally taken by women, but in December 1720 were allotted to castrati, with further revisions for 1728, when the redoubtable prime donne Faustina Bordoni and Francesca Cuzzoni competed for attention as Zenobia and Polissena respectively. The aria *Ombra cara di mia sposa* (Dear shade of my wife) was a particular favourite of Handel himself.

- Igor Stravinsky. Opera in three acts. 1951.
- Libretto by W.H.Auden and Chester Kallman, after Hogarth.
- First performance at the Teatro La Fenice, Venice, on 11th September 1951.

CHARACTERS

Tom Rakewell	tenor
Nick Shadow	baritone
Trulove	bass
Anne Trulove, his daughter	soprano
Mother Goose	mezzo-soprano
Baba the Turk	mezzo-soprano
Sellem, an auctioneer	tenor
Keeper of the Madhouse	bass

Tom Rakewell and Anne, together in her father's garden, sing of their love, and her father suggests honest employment in a city counting-house for his future son-in-law. Tom, however, has other ends in view, about to be realised, when Nick Shadow suddenly appears, claiming to have been the servant of an uncle of Tom's who has died and left his nephew an unexpected fortune. Tom engages Shadow as his servant, with wages to be settled after a year and a day, and the two of them set out at once for London. Here Shadow introduces Tom to extravagant and licentious company, drinking together with whores and roaring-boys at the brothel of Mother Goose, who claims the company of Tom for the night. Meanwhile Anne resolves to seek Tom out, having heard no news of him. In London, life for Tom seems empty, but Shadow suggests that he should marry Baba the Turk, a bearded lady whose appearance at St Giles's Fair has caused a sensation. Tom accepts the proposal, which will surely win him fame. Anne arrives before Tom's house, as he returns with Baba the Turk and all her strange paraphernalia, and leaves in dismay. The garrulous bearded lady makes life difficult for Tom and he silences her by putting a wig back-to-front over her head. Shadow proposes another scheme, a machine to turn stones into bread, which Tom can win fame by manufacturing. The third act brings Tom's ruin, his possessions sold at auction, and Baba now urging Anne to save him. Shadow, with Tom at night in a graveyard, now claims his wages, offering him a choice of death by rope, poison, knife or gun. A chance remains for Tom if he can guess three cards correctly, as they are dealt. Inspired by thoughts of Anne, Tom correctly guesses the Queen of Hearts, then, as a spade falls on a nearby grave, the deuce of spades, followed again, frustrating Shadow's attempted trickery, by the Queen of Hearts. Shadow is defeated, but Tom loses his reason, now imagining himself to be Adonis, visited in Bedlam by Anne, his Venus. As she leaves, he calls out and dies, leaving the cast to point the moral of the work in an epilogue.

Stravinsky's opera was inspired by the series of paintings by Hogarth of the same name, illustrations of the road to ruin. Auden collaborated with his friend Chester Kallman on the libretto, which they completed early in 1948. The music was completed by April 1951, to be produced in Venice the following September. The composer follows classical Mozartian forms, with due allusion to operatic developments of the 19th century, but writes music that is always recognisably his own in its melodies, harmonies and instrumentation, the whole the acme of 20th century neo-classicism. The libretto combines the subject of Hogarth's satire with Mephistophelean legend, as the Devil, Nick Shadow, leads Tom, like some latter-day Faust, into cynical excess.

Rape of Lucretia, The

- Benjamin Britten. Opera in two acts. 1946.
- Libretto by Ronald Duncan, after the play *Le viol de Lucrèce* of André Obey.
- First performance at Glyndebourne on 12th July 1946.

Characters

Male Chorus	tenor
Female Chorus	mezzo-soprano
Collatinus	bass
Junius	baritone
Tarquinius	baritone
Lucretia	contralto
Bianca	mezzo-soprano
Lucia	soprano

The male and female chorus lament the state of Rome under the Etruscan upstart Tarquinius. At an army camp outside Rome Collatinus, Junius and Tarquinius drink and discuss the trustworthiness of women, and it seems that Lucretia alone, wife of Collatinus, is of perfect virtue. This is seen as a challenge by Tarquinius, who rides to Rome, eager to test Lucretia's virtue. There he is received as a guest into her house and escorted to his chamber. As Lucretia sleeps, Tarquinius approaches and violates her chastity. The morning dawns brightly, but Lucretia sends now for her husband and kills herself in his presence. The male and female chorus point the Christian moral and message of hope.

Based on the play by André Obey and on Shakespeare, Livy, Nathaniel Lee, Thomas Heywood and F. Ponsard, *The Rape of Lucretia* places the story of Lucretia, a martyr to chastity, in a Christian setting, to which the male and female chorus draw attention. The work was written for Glyndebourne and followed the success of *Peter Grimes* in 1945. It marks the beginning of Britten's interest in chamber opera, to be followed by *Albert Herring*, staged at Glyndebourne in the following season.

Rapimento di Cefalo, Il (The Abduction of Cephalus)

- ◆ Giulio Caccini. Opera in a prologue, five scenes and an epilogue. 1600.
- ◆ Libretto by Gabriello Chiabrera.
- ◆ First performance at the Palazzo Uffizi, Florence, on 9th October 1600.

Cephalus is seduced by Aurora, the Dawn, who leaves Notte (Night) to reign, until Jupiter orders Mercury to see that Cupid brings Aurora and her lover back together, so that the light of day may be restored.

The greater part of the music written by Caccini for this spectacle to celebrate the marriage of Maria de' Medici and Henri IV of France is lost, but a description of the event survives, with two excerpts published by Caccini in his *Nuove musiche*, itself an important document for styles of contemporary vocal performance.

Rappresentatione di Anima et di Corpo (Play of Soul and of Body)

- ◆ Emilio de' Cavalieri. Sacred opera in a prologue and three acts.1600.
- ◆ Text attributed to Agostino Manni.
- ◆ First performance at the Oratorio di S Maria in Vallicella, Rome, in February 1600.

In a musical morality play Soul and Body dispute, with the participation of other allegorical characters, angels and souls in Heaven or in Hell.

The work combines attempts to restore something of ancient classical drama with traditional and Counter-reformation religious dramatic traditions, here associated with the Oratorian movement in contemporary Rome. Although colourfully staged in 1600, it points towards the new genre of oratorio, without staging.

Recommended Recording: Rappresentatione di Anima et di Corpo (2 CDs) Naxos 8.554096-97

Ratsumies (The Horseman)

- Aulis Sallinen. Opera in three acts. 1974.
- Libretto by Paavo Haavikko.
- First performance at the Savonlinna Festival on 17th July 1975.

Set in a period when Finland was at the mercy of her powerful neighbours, Russia and Sweden, The Horseman opens in Novgorod, where Antti, the horseman, and his wife Anna are bonded servants. Anna is forced to sleep with the Merchant, her master, while Antti, at the insistence of the Merchant's Wife, dresses in a bear-skin, according to Easter custom, seeking a maiden for himself and questioning the Merchant. He eventually succeeds in binding the Merchant and killing him and his Wife by burning theur house down. In Ovanlinna Anna petitions the Judge to declare her a widow, but this he will not do until her husband has failed to return for a year and a night. Antti returns, disguised as an old man, but is recognised by a Woman he has seduced, by Yeoman as a horse-thief and by the Judge as one who had old sold him the horse. Antti, Anna, the Yeoman and the seduced Woman are imprisoned in a cell, but when the Judge seeks the Woman's favours they overpower him and make their escape. Sheltering with an outlaw, they eventually agree on a plan to mount an assault on the castle, hoping to establish a new state, between Russia and Sweden. Antti leads an unsuccessful attack, in which he is killed.

Sallinen's opera is political allegory and at the same time a study of individuals and their interaction. It enjoyed considerable success at its first performance and led to a further commission for a second opera, *Punainen viiva* (The Red Line).

Re Cervo, Il (King Stag) (see König Hirsch*)*

Re in ascolto, Un (A King Listening)

- Luciano Berio. *Azione musicale* in two parts. 1984.
- Libretto arranged by the composer from texts by Italo Calvino, W.H.Auden, Friedrich Einsiedel and Friedrich Wilhelm Gotter.
- First performance at the Kleines Festspielhaus, Salzburg, on 7th August 1984.

Un re in ascolto is derived primarily from Shakespeare's play *The Tempest*, with Prospero now master of a theatre, his island, searching for the means to bring his plans to fruition, his auditions for a singer and his quest eventually realised, before his final death, in music.

Re pastore, Il (The Shepherd King)

- Wolfgang Amadeus Mozart. *Serenata* in two acts. 1775.
- Libretto by Pietro Metastasio.
- First performance at the Archbishop's Palace, Salzburg, on 23rd April 1775.

Characters

Aminta, really Abdolonimo, heir to the King of Sidon	male soprano
Elisa, a noble Phoenician, descended from Cadmus	soprano
Alessandro, King of Macedonia	tenor
Tamiri, daughter of Straton, deposed by Alessandro	soprano
Agenore, a nobleman of Sidon	tenor

Alexander in disguise and accompanied by Agenor hears from Amyntas of the merits of a simple life and is resolved to restore him to his proper position. He seeks to arrange a marriage between Amyntas and Tamiri, who is loved by Agenor, while Amyntas himself loves Elisa. Alexander, when he learns the true situation, magnanimously agrees to the marriages of the pairs of lovers.

Metastasio's *Il re pastore* is based on Torquato Tasso's play *Aminta.* The overture was used again by Mozart as the first movement of a symphony, with a following aria serving as a slow movement and with an added movement. The aria of Amyntas *L'amerò* (I shall love her) continued to enjoy considerable popularity in the concert-hall, as did his earlier aria *Aer tranquillo* (Calm air).

Recommended Recording: Overture ***Naxos 8.550185***

Red Line, The (see Punainen Viiva)

Reine de Saba, La (The Queen of Sheba)

- Charles-François Gounod. *Opéra* in five acts. 1862.
- Libretto by Jules Barbier and Michel Carré after *Le voyage en Orient* by Gérard de Nerval.
- First performance at the Paris Opéra on 18th February 1862.

King Solomon wants to marry the Queen of Sheba, who herself is associated with the sculptor and architect Adoniram, descended like her from Tubalkaïn. Plans of elopement together are foiled, when workers who had earlier destroyed a great bronze vessel by Adoniram murder the artist.

Gounod's opera was initially unsuccessful, but fared marginally better in revival outside Paris. It has provided tenors with Adoniram's aria *Faiblesse de la race humaine . . . Inspirez-moi, race divine* (Weakness of the human race . . . . Inspire me, divine race) and the Queen's *Plus grand dans son obscurité* (Greater in his obscurity).

Rheingold, Das (The Rhinegold)

- Richard Wagner. *Vorabend* (Prologue) to *Der Ring des Nibelungen* (The Ring of the Nibelung) in four scenes. 1854.
- Libretto by the composer.
- First performance at the Königliches und Nationaltheater, Munich, on 22nd September 1869.

Characters

Wotan, ruler of Heaven and Earth	bass-baritone
Fricka, his wife, goddess of married bliss	mezzo-soprano
Freia, her sister, goddess of youth	soprano
Donner, her brother, god of thunder	bass-baritone
Froh, his brother	tenor
Erda, goddess of fate	contralto
Loge, demigod of fire	tenor
Fasolt, a giant	bass-baritone
Fafner, his brother	bass
Alberich, a Nibelung	bass-baritone
Mime, his brother	tenor
Woglinde, a Rhinemaiden	soprano
Wellgunde, her sister	soprano
Flosshilde, her sister	mezzo-soprano

The Rhinemaidens, guardians of the Rhinegold, swim in the waters, teasing the Nibelung Alberich and revealing the secret of the gold that he who forges a ring from it will rule the world, but the one who forges the ring must abjure love. Alberich seizes the gold and makes off. Wotan and Fricka awake from their sleep and see the new castle completed: now its builders Fasolt and Fafner must be rewarded with Fricka's sister, Freia, who seeks escape from the bargain. Her brothers Donner and Froh try to protect her, but the two giants insist on their reward, Fasolt hoping thus to

deprive the gods of youth, imparted by the apples that Freia has in her possession. Loge had hoped to find fault with the castle in order to secure Freia's release. He tells the other gods of Alberich's forging of the ring and renunciation of love, which will bring him power over the world and suggests that it can easily be stolen from the Nibelung. The giants decide that they would accept the ring instead of Freia, but take her away with them as a hostage, until this can be accomplished. Wotan decides that he will go with Loge to the home of the Nibelungs.

There is hammering in the realm of Alberich, where Mime has been made to forge a gold net, the Tarncap, which Alberich dons, making himself thereby invisible. Wotan and Loge arrive and learn from Mime of Alberich's cruel tyranny over the Nibelungs. When Alberich returns, Loge tricks him into transforming himself into a toad, which they then seize, snatching the Tarncap from his head and restoring him as a captive to his original shape. In the realm of the gods Alberich is forced to surrender the ring, on which he puts a curse. With Alberich's gold and eventually with the ring itself, Wotan buys back Freia's freedom. Fafner quarrels with his brother over the division of the spoil and kills him. Wotan names his new castle Valhalla and leads the others into it, while Loge contemplates return to his original form, as fire to consume Valhalla, as fate has decreed.

The first of the four dramas of Wagner's tetralogy sets the scene for what is to follow. The music brings together a series of motifs that will re-appear in the later parts of the cycle in a work that follows the principles laid down in his own writings, rules to which he does not elsewhere strictly adhere, in view of the musical difficulties they present. Excerpts from the opera that may be heard in concert recital include Erda's warning to Wotan, *Weiche, Wotan, weiche!* (Yield it, Wotan, yield it!), as she urges him to give up the ring and the treasure he has taken from Alberich, Wotan's greeting to Valhalla *Abendlich strahlt der Sonne Auge* (At evening the eye of the sun shines) and the entrance of the gods into Valhalla, this last often in an orchestral version.

Recommended Recording: Entrance of the Gods into Valhalla — ***Naxos 8.550211***

RICCARDO PRIMO (RICHARD THE FIRST)

- George Frideric Handel. Opera in three acts. 1727.
- Libretto by Paolo Antonio Rolli, adapted from a libretto by Francesco Briani for *Isacio tiranno.*
- First performance at the King's Theatre, London, on 11th November 1727.

Costanza awaits the arrival in Cyprus of her future husband, Richard, King of England, his ship now delayed by a storm. The governor of Cyprus, Isaac Comnenus, seeks to substitute his own daughter Pulcheria for Costanza, whom Richard has never met. The plot is foiled, Pulcheria is united with her own lover Oronte and Richard with Costanza. Isaac is pardoned, but replaced as governor by Oronte.

Handel was able to employ the alto castrato Senesino in the title-rôle of his opera, with the two principal women in the plot, Costanza and Pulcheria, sung by Francesca Cuzzoni and Faustina Bordoni respectively, who had earlier in the season resorted to hair-pulling and screaming at one another, encouraged by their rival supporters in the audience.

Ricciardo e Zoraide (Ricciardo and Zoraide)

- Gioachino Rossini. *Dramma* in two acts. 1818.
- Libretto by Francesco Berio di Salsa, after the poem *Il Ricciardetto* by Niccolò Forteguerri.
- First performance at the Teatro S Carlo, Naples, on 3rd December 1818.

Agorante, angry at the refusal of Ircano to give him his daughter Zoraide in marriage, ousts Ircano from his kingdom of Nubia and later takes prisoner Zoraide, who has meanwhile fallen love with the knight Ricciardo. Ricciardo, in disguise, tricks Agorante into allowing a combat between himself and Ircano in which he is victorious, but when Ircano, Zoraide and Ricciardo find themselves prisoners of Agorante, they are saved by the intervention of the Christian knights of Ricciardo's company, led by Ernesto. Agorante is pardoned and Ricciardo duly united in marriage with Zoraide.

Rossini's opera starts with an overture that suggests later styles of composition in its latent romanticism. In spite of the stock characters of the plot, the tyrannical King Agorante, with his jealous wife Zomira, the noble Christian Ricciardo and the unfortunate father of Zoraide, a long-suffering bass, there are moments of musical interest in an important element in Rossini's further development of operatic style and form.

Richard Coeur-de-Lion (Richard the Lionheart)

- André Ernest-Modeste Grétry. *Comédie mise en musique* in three (later four) acts. 1784.
- Libretto by Michel-Jean Sedaine.
- First performance by the Paris Comédie-Italienne at the Salle Favart on 21st October 1784.

The troubadour Blondel, feigning blindness, seeks to find his imprisoned master, King Richard, who is rescued with the help of a Welsh knight, Williams, and united with Marguerite of Flanders.

Blondel's song, as he searches for King Richard, *Ô Richard! Ô mon roi!* (O Richard! O my king!) was once a well enough known part of Grétry's opera, a work that looks forward to styles of French opera of the next century, thematically united by the song that Richard had composed for Marguerite and that is recalled by the violin-playing Blondel, from below the walls of the castle where Richard is held prisoner.

Riders to the Sea

- Ralph Vaughan Williams. Opera in one act. 1931.
- Libretto by the composer, after the play by John Millington Synge.
- First performance at the Royal College of Music, London, on 1st December 1937.

Nora's father, her four brothers and now a fifth, Michael, whose clothes have been brought in, have been drowned. Maurya, her mother, so far ignorant of Michael's fate, is troubled when her remaining son Bartley plans to take horses by boat to Galway Fair. She follows him, sees Michael on the pony Bartley is leading, and returns to hear now of Michael's death, understanding that Bartley too will die, an event that is now reported to her.

A chamber opera, *Riders to the Sea* follows closely enough Synge's words, with their own folk echoes. The music is starkly simple and the whole work lasts little more than half an hour in performance, culminating in Maurya's lament *They are all gone now*.

Rienzi, der Letzte der Tribunen (Rienzi, the Last of the Tribunes)

- Richard Wagner. *Grosse tragische Oper* in five acts. 1840.
- Libretto by the composer, after the novel by Edward Bulwer-Lytton.
- First performance at the Königlich Sächsisches Hoftheater, Dresden, on 20th October 1842.

Characters

Cola Rienzi, a Roman tribune	tenor
Irene, his sister	soprano
Steffano Colonna, a nobleman	bass
Adriano, his son	mezzo-soprano
Paolo Orsini, a nobleman	bass
Cardinal Raimondo, Papal Legate	bass

Baroncelli, a Roman citizen	tenor
Cecco del Vecchio, a Roman citizen	bass
Messenger of Peace	soprano

The Pope has fled from Rome and open conflict has broken out between the two noble families, the Colonna and the Orsini. One of the latter seeks to abduct Rienzi's sister Irene, who is rescued by Adriano Colonna. Order is restored in the city by Rienzi, supported by fellow-citizens. Cardinal Raimondo pledges Rienzi the support of the Church in curbing the powers of the feuding nobles and Adriano eventually agrees to act with him. In spite of the public support seemingly offered to Rienzi, the nobles scheme against him, as Adriano warns him. An attempt at assassination is foiled but the guilty members of the nobility are spared at the urging of Irene and Adriano. Further attempt at insurrection is made, and Orsini and Colonna are killed, but the loss of life has led the citizens now to plot against their tribune, while the Church, with the Holy Roman Emperor, joins in his condemnation. Adriano tries to persuade Irene to desert her brother, but she is resolute and she and Rienzi retreat to the Capitol, where they die as the building burns.

Rienzi was Wagner's first significant operatic success, following the earlier *Die Feen* and *Das Liebesverbot*. The plot, with its championship of the citizens against the nobility, political partisanship with which the composer concurred, was calculated to appeal to Paris, but when no performance there proved possible, Wagner offered it to Dresden, where it at first proved impossibly long with a first performance that lasted some six hours. Later cuts reduced the work to more manageable proportions. The overture remains particularly well known, while vocal excerpts that may be heard in the concert-hall include Rienzi's declaration to the people of Rome *Erstehe, hohe Roma, neu!* (Arise, great Rome, anew!), Adriano's divided loyalties in *Gerechter Gott!* (God of justice!) and, best known of all, Rienzi's prayer *Allmächt'ger Vater!* (Almighty Father!), the theme of which is heard in the overture.

Rigoletto

- Giuseppe Verdi. *Melodramma* in three acts. 1851.
- Libretto by Francesco Maria Piave, after Victor Hugo's play *Le roi s'amuse.*
- First performance at the Teatro La Fenice, Venice, on 11th March 1851.

Characters

The Duke of Mantua	tenor
Rigoletto, his court jester	baritone

Gilda, his daughter	soprano
Giovanna, her duenna	mezzo-soprano
Count Ceprano, a noble	bass
Countess Ceprano	mezzo-soprano
Count Monterone, a noble	baritone
Matteo Borsa, a courtier	tenor
Cavaliere Marullo, a courtier	baritone
Sparafucile, a hired assassin	bass
Maddalena, his sister	contralto
Court Usher	bass
Page	mezzo-soprano

Rigoletto is happy to abet the Duke in his amorous exploits and his bitter tongue earns him the hatred of the courtiers, of Count Ceprano, openly cuckolded by the Duke and of Count Monterone, whose daughter the Duke has dishonoured. Monterone vents his anger at the Duke and curses Rigoletto. Meanwhile the courtiers suspect that Rigoletto himself has a mistress and plot their revenge. The bravo Sparafucile offers his services to Rigoletto, should he require them, and Rigoletto sees a similarity between their functions, before he goes into his house, where he warns his daughter Gilda, recently returned from her convent schooling, to be careful not to leave the house. Gilda, however, has been wooed by one she believes to be a young student, whom she has seen in church. This is, in fact, the Duke. The courtiers take their revenge on Rigoletto by abducting Gilda and taking her to the Duke, assisted by a blindfold Rigoletto, who thinks he is helping the abduction of Countess Ceprano. At court again, he turns on those who have tricked him, and plans his own revenge on the Duke through the agency of Sparafucile. Rigoletto then seeks to disillusion Gilda, who still loves the Duke, by showing her his depravity. He takes her to witness an assignation with Maddalena, Sparafucile's sister, having arranged that Sparafucile will murder him. Maddalena, however, pleads for the young man's life, and Sparafucile agrees that if any other man should come before midnight, he will kill them in place of the young man, and give Rigoletto the body in a sack, as agreed. Gilda determines to sacrifice herself for the Duke, and, dressed as a man as she is, enters the room and is murdered. Her body, in a sack, is delivered to Rigoletto outside, but his delight is destroyed when he hears the voice of the Duke inside the house, and opens the sack to reveal the body of his daughter.

Rigoletto is one of the best known of Verdi's operas, with the Duke's *La donna è mobile* (Woman is fickle) the most famous of its arias and one that has a particular function in the opera, as it returns at the end to reveal to Rigoletto the fact that the Duke is still alive. The theme of Monterone's curse, an element that recurs in the opera, is first heard in the opening prelude, while the Duke's character is first established with the carefree *Questa o quella* (This or that woman). Rigoletto's first meeting with Sparafucile gives rise to his monologue *Pari siamo* (We are alike), as he considers the weapons of the dagger and the tongue. Disguised as a student, the Duke protests his love for Gilda, telling her his supposed name, which she fondly recalls in *Caro nome* (Dear name). At court, after the abduction of his daughter, Rigoletto turns on his tormentors in *Cortigiani, vil razza dannata* (Courtiers, vile cursed race), later consoling Gilda with *Piangi, fanciulla* (Weep, child). The third act quartet takes the drama to a height of tension, as Rigoletto and Gilda secretly observe the meeting between Maddalena and the Duke, who addresses her as *Bella figlia d'amore* (Fair daughter of love), a scene that Liszt recaptures in his piano concert paraphrase of the opera.

Recommended Recordings:

Rigoletto (2 CDs)	***Naxos 8.660013-14***
Highlights	***Naxos 8.553042***

RINALDO

- George Frideric Handel. Opera in three acts. 1711.
- Libretto by Giacomo Rossi, on a scenario by Aaron Hill.
- First performance at the King's Theatre, London, on 24th February 1711.

CHARACTERS

Goffredo, Captain General of the Christian army	(male) alto
Almirena, his daughter, betrothed to Rinaldo	soprano
Rinaldo, a Christian hero	(male) mezzo-soprano
Eustazio, Goffredo's brother	(male) alto
Argante, Saracen King of Jerusalem, lover of Armida	bass
Armida, a sorceress, Queen of Damascus	soprano
A Christian Magician	bass
A Herald	tenor
A Siren	soprano
Two Mermaids	soprano

With his crusaders, Goffredo, who has promised Rinaldo the hand of his daughter Almirena, is attacking Jerusalem. Argante seeks a truce during which Armida, through her magic, abducts Rinaldo's beloved Almirena. Rinaldo resolves to find Almirena, now a prisoner in Argante's palace, but he is intercepted by Armida, now in the guise of Almirena, whom he rejects. Armida's anger is further aroused when Argante, thinking he is addressing Almirena, protests his love for her. Goffredo, in the third act, reaches Armida's magic mountain, helped by a magic wand, given him by a Christian magician, an aid in warding off the monsters that guard the place. In Armida's garden Rinaldo is prevented from killing the sorceress, from whose murderous intentions he has just saved Almirena, by the intervention of the Furies. The arrival of Goffredo with the magic wand transforms the garden into a desert. Argante and Armida, now reconciled, review their troops and the Christian forces prepare for battle in which they are victorious, thanks to the heroism of Rinaldo. Argante and Armida are taken prisoner but are pardoned and become Christians.

Rinaldo was not only Handel's first opera for London but also the first Italian opera specifically written for the English capital. It won a popular success that led to Handel's return and subsequent involvement with Italian opera in London over the course of a number of years. The genre itself provoked conservative and xenophobic criticism, with Addison and Steele poking fun at the mixture of realism and impossible fantasy, the first element provided by a flock of birds set loose on the stage and thence in the auditorium. There is much fine music in the opera, but most notably the lament of the captive Almirena, *Lascia ch'io pianga (Let me weep)*, the counterpart of Rinaldo's own lament for her loss, *Cara sposa* (Dear spouse). The opera is spectacular in its effects, with a final transformation scene as Armida's garden and palace are changed to a desert with a distant view of Jerusalem, and a battle to bring the forces of good their final expected victory. The first staging in 1711 employed the alto castrato Nicolini as Rinaldo, but allotted the male rôle of Goffredo to Francesca Vanini-Boschi. Revival in 1731 transformed Goffredo into a tenor and Argante into a contralto, while the alto castrato Senesino sang the title-rôle. Intervening revivals, of which there were a number, allotted male rôles either to castrati or to women.

Recommended Recording: Lascia ch'io pianga ***Naxos 8.553751***

RING DES NIBELUNGEN, DER (THE RING OF THE NIBELUNG)

- Richard Wagner. *Bühnenfestspiel* (Stage Festival Play).
- First full performance of the cycle of four operas at the Festspielhaus, Bayreuth, from 13th to 17th August 1876.

(See *Das Rheingold*, *Die Walküre*, *Siegfried* and *Götterdämmerung*; The Rhinegold, The Valkyries, Siegfried and The Twilight of the Gods)

Rita

- Gaetano Donizetti. *Opéra comique* in one act. 1841.
- Libretto by Gustave Vaëz.
- First performance by the Paris Opéra-Comique at the Salle Favart on 7th May 1860.

The inn-keeper Rita maltreats her subservient husband Peppe, who is taught how to stand up to his wife by her former husband Gaspar, who has returned from Canada to secure an annulment of a marriage that had remained unconsummated. Peppe sees in Gaspar a chance of escape in gambling possession of Rita on a game of cards, the loser to win the woman. Matters are resolved when Peppe learns how to deal with his wife.

Rita, ou le mari battu (Rita, or The Beaten Husband) was written within the space of a week, after a chance meeting with Gustave Vaëz had elicited from him a short libretto. The work has eight numbers separated by spoken dialogue. It was not staged until after the composer's death.

Ritorno d'Ulisse in patria, Il (The Return of Ulysses to His Own Country)

- Claudio Monteverdi. *Dramma per musica* in a prologue and three acts. 1640.
- Libretto by Giacomo Badoaro, after Homer's *Odyssey*.
- First performance at the Teatro SS Giovanni e Paolo, Venice, in 1640.

Characters

L'Humana Fragilità (Human Frailty)	soprano
Il Tempo (Time)	bass
La Fortuna (Fortune)	soprano
Amore (Cupid)	soprano
Penelope, wife of Ulysses	soprano
Ericlea (Eurycleia), her old nurse	mezzo-soprano
Melanto, her young maid-servant	soprano
Eurimaco (Eurymachus), a courtier, Melanto's lover	tenor
Nettuno (Neptune)	bass
Giove (Jupiter)	tenor
Ulisse (Ulysses)	tenor
Minerva	soprano
Eumete (Eumaeus), a swineherd, old servant of Ulysses	tenor

Iro (Irus), a parasite	tenor
Telemaco (Telemachus), son of Ulysses and Penelope	tenor
Antinoo (Antinous), a suitor of Penelope	bass
Pisandro (Peisander), a suitor of Penelope	tenor
Anfinomo (Amphinomus), a suitor of Penelope	male alto
Giunone (Juno)	soprano

(Mercurio (Mercury), in the libretto only)

In the prologue Time, Fortune and Cupid claim to have control of human destiny and argue against Human Frailty. Penelope laments her situation, in the long absence of her husband, and beset by suitors. In a short scene of dalliance between Melanto and Eurymachus it becomes clear that the latter hopes that Melanto will persuade Penelope to give in. Elsewhere the Phaeacians return Ulysses to his country and Neptune, with the approval of Jupiter, punishes them for disobeying him, turning them into a rock. Ulysses, waking alone on the coast, is helped by Minerva, disguised as a shepherd, who tells him that he is now in Ithaca, his homeland, and explains the situation in his house. She advises him to adopt the disguise of an old beggar and leaves in order to bring Telemachus back from Sparta. In the palace Melanto tries to persuade Penelope to accept one of the suitors, but she refuses. Eumaeus, expelled from the court by the intruders, is happy in his pastoral life, mocked by Irus. Ulysses assures him that his master is alive, but does not reveal his identity. In the second act Telemachus returns and Ulysses reveals his identity to him, while Penelope, in the palace, rejects the suitors one by one. Eumaeus tells her that Telemachus has returned and Ulysses may soon follow. The suitors determine to kill Telemachus but are deterred by an omen. Helped by Minerva, Ulysses comes to the palace, still as a beggar, and seeks leave to compete with the suitors in drawing the bow that was his and that the suitors cannot bend. He kills the suitors, but it is only in the course of the third act that Penelope is eventually convinced of his true identity, leading to a final love duet.

Il ritorno d'Ulisse (The Return of Ulysses) is the first complete surviving opera of Monteverdi written for Venice, to be followed by *Le nozze d'Enea con Lavinia* (The Marriage of Aeneas and Lavinia), based on Virgil's *Aeneid*, the music of which is now lost, and his last opera *L'incoronazione di Poppea* (The Coronation of Poppaea), with its plot derived from the historian Tacitus and other sources. Penelope's lament *Di misera regina* (Wretched queen) opens the first act, while the third act brings a notable climax in the killing of the suitors. The operatic genre now allows elements of comedy and these are largely provided by the parasite Irus.

ROBERT LE DIABLE (ROBERT THE DEVIL)

- Giacomo Meyerbeer. *Grand opéra* in five acts. 1831.
- Libretto by Eugène Scribe and Germain Delavigne.
- First performance at the Paris Opéra on 21st November 1831.

CHARACTERS

Robert, a Norman duke	tenor
Bertram, his friend	bass
Alice, a Norman peasant	soprano
Isabelle, a Sicilian princess	soprano
Raimbaut, a Norman peasant	tenor
Alberti, a knight	bass
A Herald	tenor
Isabelle's Lady-in-waiting	soprano
A Priest	bass
Prince of Granada	silent rôle

On the shore near Palermo, knights prepare to compete for the hand of Princess Isabelle. Raimbaut sings to Duke Robert a ballad of a marriage between a fair princess of Normandy and a devil and of their issue, Robert the Devil, a person with whom Duke Robert at once claims identity, ordering Raimbaut to be hanged. He relents, when he learns of Raimbaut's betrothal, preparing to exercise his prior rights over Alice, who is. in fact, Robert's foster-sister. She tells him of his mother's death and her dying will and promises to carry a letter from him to Princess Isabelle. Led astray by Bertram, however, he gambles and loses all he has. Through the agency of Bertram Robert is kept away from the tournament where Isabelle had expected him. The third act brings further machinations from Bertram, who declares himself to be Robert's father. He must possess him before midnight, and he forces Alice, who has overheard his meeting with the infernal powers, to silence. Now he tells Robert that he must take a magic branch from the tomb of Ste Rosalie and this he does, as nuns rise from their graves to deter him by worldly delights. By the aid of the magic branch, Robert renders the Prince of Granada, his rival, and others immobile, when he comes again to Isabelle. She urges him to abjure the infernal powers. In Palermo cathedral Isabelle is to marry the Prince. Robert is torn between duty to Bertram, who now reveals himself as his father, and religious duty, supported in the latter by Alice. Miraculous intervention prevents the Prince from moving towards his intended bride, allowing Robert finally to take his place, to the approval of the celestial choir, while Bertram sinks into the earth.

Spectacular in its effects, *Robert le diable* (Robert the Devil) won wide popularity. The scene in which dead nuns rise from the grave was to provide Korngold with a key moment in his opera *Die tote Stadt* (The Dead City). Popular excerpts include the duet between Bertram and Raimbaut, *Ah! l'honnête homme!* (Ah! The honest fellow!), when the former tries to bribe the young man into abandoning Alice. Isabelle hopes to be united with Robert in her *En vain j'espère un sort prospère* (Vainly I hope for good fortune) and Bertram has a moment of sinister drama as he summons the nuns from their graves, *Nonnes, qui reposez* (Nuns, who rest here).

ROBERTO DEVEREUX (ROBERT DEVEREUX)

- Gaetano Donizetti. *Tragedia lirica* in three acts. 1837.
- Libretto by Salvadore Cammarano, after the play *Elisabeth d'Angleterre* (Elizabeth of England) by François Ancelot.
- First performance at the Teatro S Carlo, Naples, on 28th October 1837.

CHARACTERS

Elisabetta (Elizabeth), Queen of England	soprano
Duke of Nottingham	baritone
Sara (Sarah), Duchess of Nottingham	mezzo-soprano
Roberto Devereux, Earl of Essex	tenor
Lord Cecil	tenor
Sir Walter Raleigh	bass
Page	bass
Nottingham's Servant	bass

The Earl of Essex has returned from his expedition to Ireland. Sarah, Duchess of Nottingham, who loves him, is sad at the danger he is now in, about to stand trial for treason. The Queen, however, is perturbed rather at his infidelity to her. In defending himself he gives rise to her suspicion of his love for Sarah, a suspicion shared by the Duke of Nottingham, who has intended to support Essex in the Council. At Nottingham House he casts down a ring the Queen had given him and protests his love for Sarah, who had married in his absence and who now gives him a silk scarf, a token of her love. The Council sentences Essex to death and his infidelity to the Queen and his betrayal of his supporter Nottingham are revealed by the discovery of the scarf Sarah had given him. Sarah plans to use the Queen's ring to secure her lover's pardon, but is prevented by her jealous husband. In the Tower Essex awaits pardon, but this does not come. In the Great Hall the Queen too waits for the ring, which will ensure pardon for Essex. Sarah brings it to her, but it is too late. The sound of a cannon is heard, a signal for the execution of Essex, and the Queen, distraught, now sees in her mind the blood-stained victim and her own throne a tomb.

Roberto Devereux, ossia il conte di Essex (Robert Devereux, or the Earl of Essex) was successful at its first performance in Naples, although Donizetti continued to suspect that the work brought bad luck, having recently suffered the loss of both his parents and his wife. It includes *God save the Queen* in its overture, an anachronism, and treats historical characters with considerable freedom. The Queen's opening aria, *L'amor suo mi fe' beata* (His love makes me happy) establishes the central importance of the rôle, with its dramatic conflict of emotions. Essex himself has a scene of his own in the third act, where, in *Come un spirito angelico* (Like an angelic spirit) he thinks of his love for Sarah and hopes to exonerate her from accusations of infidelity to her husband. The last scene is dominated by the Queen, her hopes and fears and her final horror at what has happened, with a completely unhistorical announcement that she will now abdicate in favour of King James of Scotland.

Rodelinda

- George Frideric Handel. Opera in three acts. 1725.
- Libretto by Nicola Francesco Haym, after Antonio Salvi's *Rodelinda, regina de'Longobardi* (Rodelinda, Queen of the Lombards) and the play by Pierre Corneille *Pertharite, roi des Lombards* (Pertharite, King of the Lombards).
- First performance at the King's Theatre, London, on 13th February 1725.

Characters

Rodelinda, Queen of the Lombards	soprano
Bertarido, her husband	male alto
Grimoaldo, Duke of Benevento, a usurper	tenor
Eduige, sister of Bertarido,betrothed to Grimoaldo	soprano
Unulfo, a nobleman	male alto
Garibaldo, Duke of Turin	bass
Flavio, son of Rodelinda and Bertarido	silent rôle

The usurper Grimoaldo has forced Bertarido to make his escape from Milan, leaving behind his wife and son. Grimoaldo resolves to break faith with Eduige and marry Rodelinda, while Bertarido returns to Milan in disguise, assisted there by his supporter Unulfo. He is captured by his enemy and matters are further complicated by the machinations of Garibaldo, who seeks the love of Eduige and the throne for himself. Eventually Bertarido escapes from his prison, with the help of Unulfo, kills Garibaldo and pardons Grimoaldo, who is now united with Eduige once more, to rule in his own dukedom, while Bertarido is restored to the throne.

In the first production of *Rodelinda* Francesca Cuzzoni sang the title-rôle, with the castrato Senesino as Bertarido. His first aria *Dove sei?* (Where are you?), as he seeks his Rodelinda, is among the most famous, while Rodelinda is allowed the moving *Ombre, piante* (Shades, trees) as she mourns the supposed death of her husband.

Rodrigue et Chimène (Rodrigo and Jimena)

- Claude Debussy. Opera in three acts. Unfinished.
- Libretto by Catulle Mendès.

The plot of Debussy's unfinished opera is based on the same story as that of Massenet's *Le Cid*, where Chimène's father is killed by her lover Rodrigue, to avenge an insult to his own father, leaving her with a dilemma between love and filial duty that is eventually resolved through Rodrigue's bravery in the Christian cause.

Roi Arthus, Le (King Arthur)

- Ernest Chausson. *Drame lyrique* in three acts. 1895.
- Libretto by the composer.
- First performance at the Théâtre de la Monnaie, Brussels, on 30th November 1903.

Lancelot is in love with Queen Guinevere, the couple surprised together by Mordred. King Arthur celebrates his victory over the Saxons, giving particular honour to Lancelot. Mordred betrays the lovers to the King, who consults Merlin, learning of the coming disaster awaiting the round table. Lancelot fights with Arthur and is defeated by the magic sword Excalibur. Guinevere strangles herself in her own long hair, while Arthur, having forgiven the dying Lancelot, is borne away on a barge into the distant sunset.

Chausson's choice of subject bears witness to his interest in Arthurian legend and has its counterpart in Wagner's use of the story of Tristan and Isolde, lovers who betray a royal master. Chausson was aware of the similarity of subject and did his best to eliminate Wagnerian influence from his music for the opera. In this he was largely successful.

Roi l'a dit, Le (The King has Said It)

- Léo Delibes. *Opéra comique* in three acts. 1873.
- Libretto by Edmond Gondinet.
- First performance by the Paris Opéra-Comique at the Salle Favart on 24th May 1873.

The comedy is based on the predicament of the Marquis de Moncontour at the court of Louis XIV. With four daughters and no son to present at court, he disguises a servant as his son, with subsequent complications.

Roi malgré lui, Le (The King in Spite of Himself)

- Emmanuel Chabrier. *Opéra comique* in three acts. 1887.
- Libretto by Emile de Najac and Paul Burani.
- First performance by the Paris Opéra-Comique at the Salle Favart on 18th May 1887.

Henri of Valois, King of Poland, is bored with the country, but complications follow when he becomes involved in a love affair and, in disguise, is asked by conspirators to kill the king. A new king is elected and Henri gladly makes his way to the frontier, hoping to return to France, but forced to remain in Poland, when the newly appointed king refuses to take up the position.

Musically more distinguished than its plot, *Le roi malgré lui* (The King in Spite of Himself) includes, in a ball scene, the well known orchestral *Fête polonaise* and the same scene brings the gypsy *Chanson tzigane*. In the first act the King asks an Italian at court his opinion of Polish character and is told by the baritone Fritelli *Le polonais est triste et grave* (The Pole is sad and serious).

Roland

- Jean-Baptiste Lully. *Tragédie en musique* in a prologue and five acts. 1685.
- Libretto by Philippe Quinault, after Ariosto's *Orlando furioso* (Roland in Madness).
- First performance at Versailles on 8th January 1685.

Characters

Demogorgon, king of the fairies, leader of the genies	baritone
Fairy	soprano

Angélique, Queen of Cathay	soprano
Roland, nephew of Charlemagne	baritone
Médor, follower of an African king	haute-contre
Témire, Angélique's confidante	soprano
Ziliante, prince of the Eastern Islands	baritone
Astolfe, friend of Roland	haute-contre
Belise, a shepherdess	soprano
Coridon, a shepherd, her lover	haute-contre
Tersandre, a shepherd, father of Belise	tenor
Logistille, a wise fairy	soprano
La Gloire (Glory)	soprano
La Renommée (Fame)	silent rôle
La Terreur (Terror)	silent rôle

In a prologue Demogorgon, with fairies and genies, prepares to entertain Louis XIV with the story of Roland, distracted by love from the proper pursuit of glory. Angélique, Queen of Cathay, falls in love with the stranger Médor, whom she has tended after a battle, in spite of the fact that the knight Roland loves her. To escape him, she arranges a false assignation and Roland vents his anger on a shepherd wedding party, which has provided a pastoral diversion. Roland is restored to himself, as he sleeps, by the fairy Logistille, and sets out homeward with Glory, Fame and Terror.

The exploits of Roland (Orlando) provided composers of opera with familiar material. Lully's opera contains the necessary elements of spectacle and dance then expected in the French theatre, with the *Ritournelle des fées* (Ritornello of the fairies) among the instrumental excerpts transcribed for harpsichord by Jean-Henri d'Anglebert.

Roméo et Juliette (Romeo and Juliet)

- Charles-François Gounod. *Opéra* in five acts. 1866.
- Libretto by Jules Barbier and Michel Carré, after the play by Shakespeare.
- First performance at he Théâtre Lyrique, Paris, on 26th April 1867.

Characters

Juliette (Juliet)	soprano
Roméo (Romeo)	tenor
Frère Laurent (Friar Laurence)	bass

Mercutio, friend of Romeo	baritone
Stéphano, Romeo's page	soprano
Capulet	bass
Tybalt, Lady Capulet's nephew	tenor
Gertrude, Juliet's nurse	mezzo-soprano
The Duke	bass
Paris, a young count	baritone
Grégorio (Gregory), Capulet's servant	baritone
Benvolio, Montague's nephew	tenor
Frère Jean (Friar John)	bass

Romeo, with Mercutio and Benvolio, in disguise, takes part, uninvited, in a masked ball given by Count Capulet, traditional enemy of his family, the Montagues. Romeo falls in love with Juliet and in the second act in the garden below her balcony tells her of his love. At his cell, Friar Laurence marries the couple. In a scene outside the Capulet house, Stéphano, Romeo's page, sings a provocative song about a turtle-dove held prisoner in a cage of vultures and fights a duel with Gregory, resulting in a further quarrel in which Mercutio is wounded and in which Romeo kills Tybalt, to be banished by the Duke. Romeo leaves Juliet's room, as dawn breaks, but she then learns that her father intends her to marry Count Paris at once. She consults Friar Laurence, who gives her a potion to bring about the semblance of death. Romeo, returning and ignorant of the Friar's plan, finds Juliet seemingly dead, lying in the Capulet tomb. He kills himself, and she, waking and finding him dying by her side, seizes a sword and stabs herself, allowing time for one duet before they both die.

In the first act Capulet welcomes his guests with *Allons, jeunes gens!* (Come, young people!). Juliet shows her lack of interest in Count Paris in her waltz-song *Je veux vivre* (I want to live), while Mercutio has his Queen Mab song, *Mab, reine des mensonges* (Mab, queen of lies). Romeo expresses his love for Juliet in *Ange adorable* (Adorable angel) and in the Capulets' garden sings to her the moving aria *Ah! lève-toi soleil* (Ah! Rise, sun). Stéphano's song, in which he taunts the Capulets, *Que fais-tu, blanche tourterelle* (What are doing, white turtle-dove) is well enough known and in the duet *Va! Je t'ai pardonné* (Go! I have forgiven you) Juliet pardons Romeo's killing of Tybalt and they sing of their love for one another. There is an intensely moving final duet in the tomb, *Viens, fuyons au bout du monde* (Come, let us fly to the end of the world).

Romeo und Julia auf dem Dorfe (*see* Village Romeo and Juliet, A)

(see Village Romeo and Juliet, A)

Romeo und Julie (*Romeo and Juliet*)

- Jiři Antonín(Georg) Benda. *Ernsthafte Oper* in three acts. 1776.
- Libretto by Friedrich Wilhelm Gotter, after the play by Shakespeare.
- First performance at Schloss Friedenstein, Gotha, on 25th September 1776.

Benda's serious opera, in fact a *Singspiel*, follows Shakespeare's drama, although importance is given rather to Juliet than to her lover. The libretto was by the Gotha court archivist Friedrich Wilhelm Gotter, author of the text of Benda's melodrama *Medea*.

Rondine, La (*The Swallow*)

- Giacomo Puccini. *Commedia lirica* in three acts. 1917.
- Libretto by Giuseppe Adami, after a German libretto by A.M.Willner and Heinz Reichert.
- First performance at the Théâtre de l'Opéra, Monte Carlo, on 27th March 1917.

Characters

Magda de Civry, mistress of Rambaldo	soprano
Lisette, her maid	soprano
Ruggero Lastouc	tenor
Prunier, a poet	baritone/tenor
Rambaldo Fernandez, rich protector of Magda	baritone
Périchaud	bass-baritone
Gobin	tenor
Crébillon	bass-baritone
Yvette	soprano
Bianca	soprano
Suzy	mezzo-soprano
Butler	bass

Magda and her protector Rambaldo are entertaining their friends in a luxurious room of a Paris apartment. Prunier sings a song of Doretta, who dreams that one day the King favours her, but admits he cannot end the song. A young man has been waiting to see Rambaldo and now comes in.

Magda recalls earlier years of happiness, particularly at the café Chez Bullier, where she once met a man she loved but whose name she never knew. It is here that the young man, Ruggero, is sent for the evening, while Lisette, the object of Prunier's repeated complaints, now goes out with him, dressed in her mistress Magda's clothes. At Chez Bullier Ruggero sits alone, among the crowd of dancers and young people. He is joined by Magda, now simply dressed, and then by Prunier and Lisette, the girls so different in appearance as not to be sure of each other's identity. The arrival of Rambaldo, seeking some explanation of Magda's presence, allows her to tell him that she has found love and will leave him. In the third act, set on the Côte d'Azur, Magda and Ruggero are together, although their money is running out. He has sought his family's permission to marry her, but knows nothing of her life with Rambaldo. Prunier, who has failed to establish Lisette on the stage, now arranges that Magda take her back into service, while Magda herself makes it clear that she must part from Ruggero, who has received his mother's blessing on his proposed marriage to a virtuous wife. Now she will go back to Rambaldo, who is willing to take her back again as his mistress.

Puccini's opera was commissioned as an operetta for Vienna. The outbreak of war made further progress impossible and the work, with an Italian libretto, was first staged in neutral Monte Carlo. While not among the most frequently performed of Puccini's operas, *La rondine* (The Swallow) has provided sopranos with material in Magda's reaction to Prunier's story of Doretta, *Chi il bel sogno di Doretta potè indovinar* (Who could guess Doretta's lovely dream), in which she ends the story as she imagines it, with the girl falling in love with a student. Slightly less well known is her story of flirtation at Chez Bullier, *Ore dolci e divine* (Tender, heavenly hours).

Recommended Recording: Chi il bel sogno ***Naxos 8.550605***

ROSENKAVALIER, DER (THE KNIGHT OF THE ROSE)

- Richard Strauss. *Komödie für Musik* in three acts. 1910.
- Libretto by Hugo von Hofmannsthal.
- First performance at the Königliches Opernhaus, Dresden, on 26th January 1911.

CHARACTERS

Die Feldmarschallin Princess Werdenberg	soprano
Octavian, Count Rofrano (Quinquin)	soprano/mezzo-soprano
Baron Ochs of Lerchenau	bass
Herr von Faninal, a rich merchant	baritone
Sophie, his daughter	soprano
Marianne Leitmetzerin, her duenna	soprano

Valzacchi, an intriguer	tenor
Annina, his niece and companion	contralto
A Notary	bass
An Italian Singer	tenor
Three Noble Orphans	soprano, mezzo-soprano & contralto
A Milliner	soprano
An Animal Vendor	tenor
Faninal's Major-Domo	tenor
The Marschallin's Major-Domo	tenor
Four Footmen of the Marschallin	two tenors & two basses
Four Waiters	tenor & three basses
A Police Commissioner	tenor
An Inn-Keeper	tenor
A Flautist	silent rôle
A Hairdresser	silent rôle
A Scholar	silent rôle
A Noble Widow	silent rôle
Mohammed, the Marschallin's black page	silent rôle

The first act opens in the bed-room of the Marschallin where the young Octavian is kneeling by the Marschallin's bed, from which she has not yet risen. Octavian, taking advantage of the absence of the Field-Marshal hunting, would like to prolong the moment, but must hide as a servant brings breakfast for the Princess. They hear the sound of someone approaching, and Octavian hides behind a screen. Instead of the Field-Marshal, whose return they had feared, it is Baron Ochs von Lerchenau, the Marschallin's cousin, who eventually bursts in, while Octavian disguises himself as a maid, but is unable to escape the attentions of the Baron. He seeks the Marschallin's help in finding a Knight of the Rose to take the traditional token of intended marriage to Sophie von Faninal on his behalf. She proposes her young cousin Count Octavian as an emissary. There follows the Marschallin's levée, attended by various people who attempt to enlist her support. When they have gone, she recalls her own early marriage and realises that Octavian will soon turn his attention to a younger woman. Octavian goes, and the Marschallin sends after him, then despatching her page to him with the silver rose, which he will know what to do with. The second act opens in the Grand Hall of Herr von Faninal's house. Sophie awaits the arrival of the Knight of the Rose and is immediately attracted to Octavian, while repelled by the boorish manners of the Baron, who follows. Sophie's aversion and her feeling for Octavian lead her to refuse marriage with the Baron, who is slightly hurt in an immediate duel with Octavian. The intriguers Valzacchi and Annina, employed by the Baron but annoyed at his meanness, now offer their services to Octavian, who sends Annina with a note to the Baron making an assignation with Mariandel, the identity he had assumed to escape from the Marschallin's bed-room. In the third act, set in an inn near Vienna, the assignation takes place, with the Baron now confronted by a series of staged apparitions, culminating in the appearance of Annina disguised as his abandoned wife. The Baron summons the police and matters reach a degree of complication that is solved only by the intervention of the Marschallin, who now unselfishly encourages the love of Sophie and Octavian.

Der Rosenkavalier (The Knight of the Rose) evokes a past Vienna in music of great poignancy and beauty, with Strauss, like Brahms, able to encompass moods of autumnal sadness, epitomized in the love and self-sacrifice of the 32-year-old Marschallin for the seventeen-year-old Octavian. Baron Ochs, who has a penchant for memorable waltzes, is a splendid comic figure, uncouth in manner and to be pitied, nevertheless, in his final discomfiture. The work is scored for a large orchestra and Waltz Sequences from the second and third act of the opera are popular in the concert-hall. Possible vocal excerpts include the Italian singer's *Di rigori armato* (Sternly armed), rudely interrupted at the Marschallin's levée by the Baron, the Marschallin's poignant memories of her own earlier life and her arranged marriage, *Da geht er hin* (So there he goes) and her parting with Octavian at the end of the first act, *Die Zeit, die ist ein sonderbar Ding* (Time is a thing of its own). The presentation of the silver rose in the second act brings a particularly moving moment, with Octavian's hesitant *Mir ist die Ehre widerfahren* (To me has been given the honour). The young lovers are left together as the third act comes to a close, with Sophie wondering if love is a dream, *Ist ein Traum, kann nicht wirklich sein* (It is a dream, it cannot really be true).

Recommended Recordings:
Waltz Sequence 1 — ***Naxos 8.550182***
Waltz Sequence 2 — ***Naxos 8.550342***

ROTHSCHILD'S VIOLIN

- Venyamin Iosifovich Fleishman. Opera in one act. 1941.
  Completed by Dmitry Shostakovich. 1944.
- Libretto by the composer, after a story by Chekhov.
- First staged performance at Leningrad Conservatory on 24th April 1968.

The opera centres on the bitter central character, Yakov Ivanov, a coffin-maker and amateur fiddler, his gradual understanding of life and his bequest of his violin to Rothschild, who also plays in the Jewish band with Ivanov and whom he has treated with contempt.

Fleishman, a gifted pupil of Shostakovich, died in Leningrad in 1941 and Shostakovich was eventually able to trace the score and complete the work, which has recently begun to arouse some interest.

Rusalka

- Antonín Dvořák. Lyric fairy-tale in three acts. 1900.
- Libretto by Jaroslav Kvapil, after *Undine* by Friedrich de la Motte Fouqué.
- First performance at the National Theatre, Prague, on 31st March 1901.

Characters

Rusalka, a water nymph	soprano
Prince	tenor
Foreign Princess	soprano
Vodník, the spirit of the lake	bass
Ježibaba, a witch	mezzo-soprano
Huntsman	baritone
Forester	tenor
Kitchen Boy	soprano
Three Wood Nymphs	two sopranos & contralto

Rusalka, by the lake, seeks the advice of her father, Vodník, the spirit of the lake, since she has fallen in love with a mortal. He tells her to consult the witch Ježibaba, who allows Rusalka human identity, without speech, but warns her that infidelity from her lover will lead to damnation for them both. The Prince, out hunting, meets Rusalka and takes her with him to the palace. Wedding preparations are made, but the silence of Rusalka becomes wearing and the Prince turns his attention to a foreign princess. By the lake again, Rusalka wanders as a will-o'-the-wisp, told by the witch that release can only come by the death of a mortal. The Prince comes to the lake to find her again and in spite of her warnings embraces her and dies in her arms.

Dvořák's opera has debts to Hans Christian Andersen and Gerhardt Hauptmann, as well as to de la Motte Fouqué and to Czech traditional sources. The score includes an evocative overture that sets the mysterious opening scene by the lake and Rusalka's address to the moon *Mešíčku na nebi hlubokém* (O silver moon), with a polonaise in the second act, when a ball is held for the marriage of the Prince.

Recommended Recordings:
Overture, Polonaise — *Marco Polo 8.223272*
Song to the Moon — *Naxos 8.553166*

RUSLAN AND LYUDMILA

- Mikhail Ivanovich Glinka. Opera in five acts. 1842.
- Libretto by Valerian Fyodorovich Shirkov, with contributions from others, based on the poem by Pushkin.
- First performance at the Bolshoy Theatre, St Petersburg, on 9th December 1842.

CHARACTERS

Svetozar, Grand Prince of Kiev	bass
Lyudmila, his daughter	soprano
Ruslan, her betrothed	baritone
Ratmir, a Khazar prince	contralto
Farlaf, a Varangian prince	bass
Chernomor, an evil dwarf	silent rôle
Gorislava, Ratmir's slave	soprano
Finn, a good magician	tenor
Naina, an evil sorceress	mezzo-soprano
Bayan, a bard	tenor

The Grand Prince of Kiev entertains his daughter's suitors, with Ruslan preferred, but there is a sudden clap of thunder and Lyudmila disappears, leading the Grand Prince to promise her to the one who brings her back. Ruslan consults the magician Finn, who tells him that her disappearance is the work of the evil dwarf Chernomor; at the same time he should beware of the sorceress Naina, now consulted by Farlaf. She tells him to leave the search to Ruslan and then intervene. On a battlefield Ruslan comes across a gigantic head over which he triumphs, taking a sword to help him defeat Chernomor. At the palace of Naina Ruslan is distracted by sirens, but is saved by Finn. He finds Lyudmila in a trance in the magic gardens of Chernomor, whom he defeats in single combat. Although she is again abducted, now by Farlaf, who seeks to gain gratitude from the Grand Prince for her recovery, Ruslan succeeds in recapturing her. He is able to waken her from her magic trance and is finally joined to her in marriage.

The second opera by Glinka is replete with national colour, with scenes that allow the introduction of exotic elements. There is a brilliant overture that enjoys continuing popularity in the concert-hall, with Farfal's rondo welcoming the hope of triumph Naina gives him, Ruslan's second act aria addressing the deserted battlefield and the seductive oriental dances of the fourth act, in the magic gardens of Chernomor.

Recommended Recording: Overture **Naxos 8.550085**

RUTH

- Lennox Berkeley. Opera in three scenes. 1956.
- Libretto by Eric Crozier, based on the biblical text and narrative.
- First performance at the Scala Theatre, London, on 2nd October 1956.

Ruth, amid the alien corn, is protected by Boaz, with whom she is united in marriage.

Lennox Berkeley's *Ruth* was written for the English Opera Group that had been established by Benjamin Britten, Peter Pears and Eric Crozier. Peter Pears created the rôle of Boaz, and the work shows the clear influence of Britten.

S

Sacra rappresentazione di Abram e d'Isaac, La (*The Miracle Play of Abraham and Isaac*)

- Ildebrando Pizzetti. Opera in one act. 1928.
- Libretto by Onorato Castellino, after the miracle play by Feo Belcari.
- First performance at the Teatro Morlacchi, Perugia, on 2nd October 1937.

While Sarra (Sarah) remains at home, anxious, Abraham leads Isaac to the place where he will be sacrificed, an event hindered by the intervention of an angel.

Pizzetti's incidental music was later expanded into an opera. The original text is that of a 15th century miracle play, here set with relative simplicity.

Sadko

- Nikolay Andreyevich Rimsky-Korsakov. Opera in seven scenes. 1896.
- Libretto by the composer and others, based on traditional ballads and other sources.
- First performance by the Mamontov Opera at the Solodovnikov Theatre, Moscow, on 7th January 1898.

Characters

The King of the Sea	bass
Volkhova, his favourite daughter	soprano
Sadko, a singer in Novgorod	tenor
Lyubava Buslayevna, his young wife	mezzo-soprano
Nezhata, a psaltery-player from Kiev	mezzo-soprano
Viking Merchant	bass
Hindu Merchant	tenor
Venetian Merchant	baritone
Four Buffoons	two mezzo-sopranos, tenor & bass

Two Elders of Novgorod	tenor & bass
Two Wizards	tenors
Apparition of an Ancient Warrior	baritone
Tsaritsa-Vodyanitsa, wife of the Sea-King	dancer

Nezhata of Kiev entertains the merchants of Novgorod with a heroic ballad. They call for Sadko, whose song suggests riches if their ships had access to the sea. Sent away, Sadko sings by the side of Lake Ilmen, where swans approach him, changing into young women, with Volkhova, daughter of the Sea-King, who spends the night with him. When she leaves at dawn she promises that he will catch three golden fish in the lake and travel to a foreign country, while she will wait for his return. Lyubava, Sadko's young wife, wonders at his absence, and is saddened when he returns only to bid her goodbye. By Lake Ilmen there are foreign merchants and entertainers. Nezhata sings but Sadko is mocked again when he tells them of the three golden fish in the lake. These he catches and calls on brave young men to join him in his proposed journey. Three foreign merchants tell him of their own countries and Sadko chooses to travel to Venice. Twelve years later, returning with great treasure, Sadko's ship is becalmed and attempts are made to placate the Sea-King with treasure, but it is only when Sadko steps onto a floating plank thrown into the sea that the ship can sail on. In the depths of the sea Sadko sings to the King and Queen and is promised the hand of Volkhova. The excitement his singing arouses causes a storm that sinks ships, until an apparition warns that the Sea-King's reign is over. Sadko wakes by the side of the lake, watched over by Volkhova, who vanishes, leaving a great river, the Volkhova, that joins Novgorod to the sea. Lyubava seeks her husband, whose richly laden ships now return to Novgorod, of which he becomes one of the richest citizens.

It is above all the songs of the three foreign merchants that have provided material for recital. The song of the Indian merchant in particular has attracted arrangements for violin by Fritz Kreisler and for cello. The opera itself makes use of a traditional story already used by Rimsky-Korsakov in his 1869 musical picture of the same name.

Saffo (Sappho)

- Giovanni Pacini. *Tragedia lirica* in three parts. 1840.
- Libretto by Salvadore Cammarano, after the play by Pietro Beltrame.
- First performance at the Teatro S Carlo, Naples, on 29th November 1840.

CHARACTERS

Saffo (Sappho)	soprano
Faone (Phaon)	tenor
Alcandro (Alcander), high priest of Apollo	baritone
Climene (Clymene), his daughter	mezzo-soprano
Dirce, her handmaid	soprano
Ippia (Hippias), Chief Augur	tenor
Lisimaco (Lysimachus)	bass

The first act opens with the entry of the high priest of Apollo's temple in Leucadia, Alcander, angry at his reception by the people at the Poetic Games of the 42nd Olympiad. As he tells the Chief Augur Hippias, Sappho's elegy on the Leucadian leap, the enforced leap to death encouraged by the priests of Apollo, has given rise to popular resentment against him. Alcander, who feels attracted to Sappho, plans revenge through Phaon, in love with Sappho but a possible match for his own daughter Clymene. Phaon's jealousy of the poet Alcaeus can be provoked. Three months later Clymene is to marry Phaon. Sappho, whom she does not know, seeks her help in offering propitiation to Apollo and promises to recite her own verses in celebration of the marriage. When she discovers that the bridegroom is her own former lover Phaon, Sappho bursts out in grief and anger and desecrates the marriage altar, which she overturns. In the third act, on the Leucadian cliffs, Sappho seeks to put an end to her passion by leaping to her death in the sea below. At this point the old man Lysimachus reveals Sappho's true parentage, daughter of Alcander, who now tries to save her from the oath she has sworn, to die. The oracle and the auguries, however, ratify the decree of death and Sappho ascends the promontory, ready to plunge to her death, to the horror of a penitent Phaon, her father Alcander and her sister Clymene.

Giovanni Pacini was among the most prolific opera composers of the first half of the 19th century, with some fifty operas already to his credit by 1835, when his thoughts turned to other means of livelihood. His return to this form of composition in 1840 with his opera *Saffo* (Sappho) marked a new departure, with an original attempt to capture something of the technique as well as the spirit of ancient Greek music, at least in a study of ancient musical theory and the Greek modes, as he understood them.

Recommended Recording:
Saffo (2 CDs) — ***Marco Polo 8.223883-84***

SAINT FRANÇOIS D'ASSISE (ST FRANCIS OF ASSISI)

- Olivier Messiaen. Opera in three acts. 1983.
- Libretto by the composer.
- First performance at the Paris Opéra on 28th November 1983.

The scenes of the opera centre on various features of the life of St Francis. In the first act he preaches the acceptance of suffering, sings verses from his praises of all creatures and kisses and cures a leprous beggar. The second act brings the visit of an angel, demanding answers to questions of predestination, playing sweet music to the saint, who, in a further scene, preaches to the birds. In the third act St Francis receives the stigmata and prays as he dies, to meet a triumphant musical resurrection.

With a large orchestra and an even larger chorus, Messiaen's opera suggests the medieval in its modal writing, presenting a series of tableaux, isolated incidents from the religious life of the saint, and making full use of the various techniques Messiaen had at his disposal, with bird-song making its appearance in the final scene of farewell to the world.

SAINT OF BLEECKER STREET, THE

- Gian Carlo Menotti. Musical drama in three acts. 1954.
- Libretto by the composer.
- First performance at the Broadway Theatre, New York, on 27th December 1954.

CHARACTERS

Assunta	mezzo-soprano
Carmela	soprano
Maria Corona, a newspaper-vendor	soprano
Her dumb 16-year-old son	silent rôle
Don Marco, a priest	bass
Annina	soprano
Michele, her brother	tenor
Desideria, his mistress	mezzo-soprano
Salvatore	baritone
Young Man	tenor

In a poor apartment in Bleecker Street, in New York's Little Italy, it is Good Friday afternoon and neighbours anxiously await the appearance of the girl Annina, a stigmatic credited with miraculous powers. The priest Don Marco and Carmela try to hold the people back, and they are dispersed by Michele, her brother, angry at what he sees as mere delusions. Annina and her friend Carmela are preparing a costume for a child taking part in the procession of San Gennaro. They are joined by Assunta. Carmela now plans to marry, while Annina is still anxious to become a nun. Maria Corona, whose mute son, touched by Annina, can now make some noises, tells her that the Sons of Gennaro insist that their Little Saint accompany them in the procession. Michele opposes this, for her own good, but is overpowered, while Annina is taken to lead the procession. Desideria comforts her lover. At the wedding of Carmela and Salvatore, Desideria seeks out Michele, who has not brought her to the wedding. She accuses Michele of putting his sister Annina before her, of being in love with his own sister. Michele draws a knife and kills her. In a deserted passageway in a subway station Annina and Maria Corona meet Michele again, brought there by Don Marco. Annina urges him to give himself up and tells him that she is afraid of dying and will enter a convent. He rushes away in anger. A week later Annina is dying and a special dispensation allows her to take the veil on her deathbed, in spite of Michele's plea for her to change her mind.

As with other operas by Menotti, *The Saint of Bleecker Street* is dramatically strong, simple and effective in its music. It has not enjoyed the same attention as *The Consul*, which has a more generally applicable appeal in its plot.

SALOME

- Richard Strauss. *Musikdrama* in one act. 1905.
- Libretto by Hedwig Lachmann, translating Oscar Wilde's play.
- First performance at the Hofoper, Dresden, on 9th December 1905.

CHARACTERS

Herodes (Herod), Tetrarch of Judaea	tenor
Herodias, his wife	mezzo-soprano
Salome, his step-daughter	soprano
Jochanaan (John the Baptist)	baritone
Narraboth, Captain of the Guard	tenor
Page of Herodias	alto
Five Jews	four tenors, one bass
Two Nazarenes	bass & tenor
Two Soldiers	basses

A Cappadocian	bass
A Slave	soprano/tenor

On the terrace of Herod's palace, outside the banquet-hall, the young Syrian captain Narraboth shows his love for Salome, daughter of Herodias. The ominous voice of John the Baptist is heard from his dungeon below, urging repentance. Salome leaves the hall, watched by Herod, and fascinated sees now John the Baptist, who has condemned the wickedness of her mother, a woman who killed her own husband in order to marry Herod, and of Herod himself. She expresses her desire for him, vainly offering temptation, while Narraboth, in despair, kills himself. Jochanaan withdraws, while Herod and Herodias come onto the terrace, the former lusting after his step-daughter, whom he invites to sit with him. Herod fears Jochanaan, while five Jews dispute about his teaching. Herod promises Salome whatever she wants, if she will dance for him, after which she demands the head of Jochanaan. He is executed, his head brought in, now kissed passionately by Salome, whose death Herod commands. She is crushed to death under the shields of the guards.

The eroticism of *Salome*, both as a play and in the operatic version by Strauss, provided something of a sensation. The opera makes very heavy technical and dramatic demands on the singers, notably in the title-rôle and in the rôle of Herod. The sensual nature of the subject and the music that matched it led the way to operas by Franz Schreker and other contemporaries that explored a similar vein of eroticism. The famous *Dance of the Seven Veils* enjoys a separate existence in the concert-hall, as, less frequently, does Salome's final passionate Wagnerian outburst, when she sees the severed head, *Ach, du wolltest mich nicht deinen Mund küssen lassen* (Ah, you would not let me kiss your mouth).

Recommended Recording: Salome's Dance ***Naxos 8.550182***

Samson et Dalila (Samson and Delilah)

- Camille Saint-Saëns. *Opéra* in three acts. 1876.
- Libretto by Ferdinand Lemaire.
- First performance at the Grossherzogliches Theater, Weimar, on 2nd December 1877.

Characters

Samson	tenor
Abimélech (Abimelech)	bass
High Priest of Dagon	baritone
Two Philistines	tenor & bass

Philistine Messenger	tenor
Dalila (Delilah)	mezzo-soprano
An Old Hebrew	bass

Defeated by the Philistines, the Hebrews lament their fate. The Philistine Abimelech proclaims the superiority of Dagon and is struck dead by Samson, who, with his people, is cursed by the High Priest of Dagon. He plans to use Delilah in an effort to overcome Samson. She appears, as the day dawns, luring Samson with her charms. At her retreat in the valley of Sorek, Delilah is urged by the High Priest to capture Samson. When he appears, intending to leave her, she tries to elicit from him the secret of his strength, and as he goes into her house, Philistine soldiers emerge from hiding, to a signal from Delilah. Eyeless in Gaza, imprisoned and turning a mill-wheel, Samson offers his life in repentance. There is a bacchanale in the temple of Dagon and Samson is brought in. Delilah joins others in mocking him, telling him of her duplicity. Samson is led to the two pillars that support the building and in a final effort of strength brings the temple down on himself and the whole assembled company.

There is a Wagnerian element in *Samson et Dalila* (Samson and Delilah), an expression of the composer's contemporary preoccupations. The opera marks the height of the dramatic achievement of Saint-Saëns, the second of his thirteen operas to be conceived, the third to be completed and the only one with an assured place in contemporary international operatic repertoire. The best known aria must be Delilah's *Mon cœur s'ouvre à ta voix* (My heart opens at your voice) in the second act. She has exercised her charms earlier in the seductive *Printemps qui commence* (Spring that begins). The third act Philistine bacchanale provides a concert orchestral excerpt.

Recommended Recordings:

Bacchanale	***Naxos 8.550138***
Samson and Delilah (2 CDs)	***Naxos 8.110063-64***

Sancta Susanna (Saint Susanna)

- Paul Hindemith. Opera in one act. 1921.
- Libretto by August Stramm.
- First performance at the Opernhaus, Frankfurt, on 26th March 1922.

A novice nun gives in to erotic desires. Warned by Sister Clementia of a nun who succumbed to her feelings and was immured behind the altar, Susanna seizes the loin-cloth from the figure of Christ on the crucifix and calls for similar punishment for herself.

Hindemith's short opera, one of a trilogy, with *Mörder, Höffnung der Frauen* (Murderer, Hope of Women) and *Das Nusch-Nuschi,* caused a scandal, with its companion-pieces. The composer later regarded them as something of an aberration.

SANT'ALESSIO (ST ALEXIS)

- Stefano Landi. *Dramma musicale* in three acts. 1631.
- Libretto by Giulio Rospigliosi.
- First performance at the Palazzo Barberini, Rome, on 18th February 1632.

Alexis, who has embraced a life of holy poverty, returns from the Holy Land as a beggar to his father's house in Rome, but does not reveal his identity, even when his wife and mother determine to travel in search of him. He resists the temptations offered by the Devil, with the help of an angel, and dies in the poverty he has chosen, under the steps of his father's house, his identity now discovered in a letter he holds, as he dies.

Landi's religious opera *Sant'Alessio* (Saint Alexis), while in the Counter-Reformation spirit of Jesuit dramas, marks a new departure in the theatre in Rome, combining antiquarian interests in ancient drama with modern musical conceptions of recitative, ensembles and occasional arias. Musically the work has considerable variety, with elements of comedy and tragedy, and went some way towards establishing specifically Christian opera in a Rome that remained musically conservative. Singers for the opera, all male, were recruited from the Papal Chapel and included castrati. The Barberinis, noted patrons of the arts, owed their current influence to the Barberini Pope Urban VIII. The librettist Giulio Rospigliosi in 1667 became Pope Clement IX.

SAPHO (SAPPHO)

- Charles-François Gounod. *Opéra* in three acts. 1851.
- Libretto by Emile Augier.
- First performance at the Paris Opéra on 16th April 1851.

In a plot that leads to the death of Sappho, who leaps from the cliffs of Lesbos into the sea, her lover Phaon deserts her, much of the tragedy devolving upon the intrigues of Glycère, a courtesan who is in love with Phaon.

Written at the urging of the distinguished French mezzo-soprano Pauline Viardot, sister of Maria Malibran, Gounod's first opera *Sapho* (Sappho) was a popular failure, although it secured him a measure of critical esteem. Sappho's final *O ma lyre immortelle* (O my immortal lyre) remains well enough known.

Sapho (Sappho)

- Jules Massenet. *Pièce lyrique* in five acts. 1897.
- Libretto by Henri Cain and Arthur Bernède, after the novel by Alphonse Daudet.
- First performance by the Paris Opéra-Comique at the Théâtre Lyrique on 27th November 1897.

The artist's model Fanny Legrand, known as Sapho, befriends the young Jean Gaussin, newly arrived in Paris from Provence, whom she meets in the drawing-room of the famous sculptor Caoudal. Jean is to study in Paris and his parents, with their niece Irène, take their leave, allowing Fanny to emerge from hiding. She has seduced Jean and their love affair continues. A year later, among friends in the garden of a restaurant, Jean learns of Fanny's past and breaks with her, leaving her to express her anger at those she thought her friends. At home in Avignon Jean is sad. Fanny comes, seeking a reconciliation, but is dismissed by Jean's mother. Alone in the little house they had shared, Fanny remembers their love. Jean returns to her, but as he sleeps, she leaves, realising that they can never be united.

Massenet's opera, with its element of contemporary realism, has similarities of plot with *La traviata* and its French dramatic source, *La dame aux camélias* (The Lady of the Camelias), another story of the self-sacrifice of a fallen woman and an enamoured young provincial. Seldom revived, the opera contains Jean's *Ah! qu'il est loin mon pays* (Ah! It is far away, my country) and Fanny Legrand's *Pendant un an je fus ta femme* (For a year I was your wife).

Saul og David (Saul and David)

- Carl Nielsen. Opera in four acts. 1901.
- Libretto by Einar Christiansen, after the biblical narrative.
- First performance at the Royal Theatre, Copenhagen, on 28th November 1902.

Saul defies the prophet Samuel and Jehovah, and is comforted by the singing of the shepherd-boy David, friend of his son Jonathan. David, promised the hand of Saul's daughter Michal as a reward, defeats the giant Goliath and provokes Saul's jealousy. Escaping the king's anger, David takes Saul's sword, as he sleeps, demonstrating his power and his loyalty. The Witch of Endor, through the spirit of the dead Samuel, foretells Saul's death. Jonathan, as he dies after battle with the Philistines, swears loyalty to David, and Saul falls on his own sword.

Nielsen's opera has provided orchestral repertoire with three dramatic preludes. The work remains in operatic repertoire in Denmark, but international performances have been rare.

Savitri

- Gustav Holst. Chamber opera in one act. 1908.
- Libretto by the composer after an episode in the Mahabharata.
- First performance at the London School of Opera on 5th December 1916.

Savitri is confronted by Death, who has come to take her woodman husband Satyavan, who succumbs, but is brought to life again when Savitri is granted by Death the boon of fullness of life, something impossible for her without her husband.

Savitri is a reflection of Holst's deep interest in Hindu literature and religion, both in its subject and in its music, which remains, whatever its implications, thoroughly English and of its period.

Scala di seta, La (The Silken Ladder)

- Gioachino Rossini. *Farsa comica* in one act. 1812.
- Libretto by Giuseppe Maria Foppa, after the libretto by François-Antoine-Eugène de Planard's libretto for *L'échelle de soie* (The Silken Ladder) by Pierre Gaveaux.
- First performance at the Teatro S Moisè, Venice, on 9th May 1812.

Giulia's secret marriage to her lover Dorvil is happily revealed when she engineers the marriage of her guardian's chosen husband for her, Dorvil's friend Blansac, with her cousin Lucilla.

La scala di seta (The Silken Ladder) starts with a popular overture, a frequent concert opener, drawn from this early example of Rossini's skill in handling comedy of this kind.

Recommended Recording: Overture ***Naxos 8.550236***

Schatzgräber, Der (The Treasure-Seeker)

- Franz Schreker. Opera in a prologue, four acts and an epilogue. 1918.
- Libretto by the composer.
- First performance in Frankfurt on 21st January 1920.

The minstrel Elis seeks the Queen's lost jewels, guarantees of her youth and beauty. Els, daughter of an inn-keeper in the forest, has acquired the jewels by means of those who have courted her and been killed by her. She falls in love with Elis and in a tender love scene appears wearing the jewels, which she gives him. She is saved from punishment by the King's Fool, who has employed Elis in the search and now claims Els as a reward for his success. In an epilogue Elis visits Els as she dies and sings of a palace of dreams where they may have the treasure of happiness together.

Schreker's opera, set in the Middle Ages, explores again the element of eroticism released for operatic use by Richard Strauss's *Salome*. An orchestral *Interlude* from the opera provides an occasional concert item.

Recommended Recording: Interlude from Act III — ***Marco Polo 8.220392***

SCHAUSPIELDIREKTOR, DER (THE IMPRESARIO)

- Wolfgang Amadeus Mozart. *Singspiel* in one act. 1786.
- Libretto by Gottlieb Stephanie the younger.
- First performance at the Orangerie, Schönbrunn, Vienna, on 7th February 1786.

CHARACTERS

Vogelsang, a singer	tenor
Mme Herz, a singer	soprano
Mme Silberklang, a singer	soprano
Frank, an impresario	speaking part
Eiler, a banker	speaking part
Buff, an actor	speaking part
Herz, an actor	speaking part
Mme Pfeil, an actress	speaking part
Mme Krone, an actress	speaking part
Mme Vogelsang, an actress	speaking part

The impresario Herr Frank has high artistic standards, but the actor Buff, engaged by him, announces that permission has been granted for performances in Salzburg, where, it seems, anything goes. Actors and actresses are auditioned in a series of dramatic excerpts, and the jealous anger of the old-fashioned tragic actress Mme Krone is provoked when a higher fee is offered to Mme Vogelsang. The actor Herz introduces his wife, who sings an expressive aria. Mme Silberklang deigns to audition and is engaged at the same fee as Mme Herz and the title prima donna, now claimed by Mme Herz. The singer Vogelsang tries to mollify them. Eventually, after complaints from the actresses and the intervention of Mme Pfeil's banker friend, they agree to accept the fees offered and the singers add a final vaudeville, joined in the end by Buff, no great singer but a *buffo* (comic) actor.

The Emperor Joseph II arranged, early in 1786, an entertainment for his sister, the Archduchess Christine Marie, and her husband, Duke Albrecht Kasimir of Sachsen-Teschen, Governors-General of the Austrian Netherlands. In the Orangery at the palace of Schönbrunn there was a stage at each end of the room, separated by the dining-table of the 82 guests. Mozart's *Singspiel* was performed after the banquet by the German company, followed by the Italian company in Salieri's comic *Prima la musica, poi le parole* (First the Music then the Words), both works dealing, in one way or another, with back-stage intrigue. Mozart's work opens with a lively overture. Mme Herz shows her prowess in the aria *Da schlägt des Abschieds Stunde* (The hour of the vespers strike), rivalled by Mme Silberklang's *Bester Jüngling* (Best of boys), a virtuoso declaraton of love in spite of everything. The quarrelsome trio *Ich bin die erste Sängerin* (I am the prima donna) leads, in the end, to the final *Heder Künstler strebt nach Ehre* (Every artist strives for honour).

Recommended Recording: Overture ***Naxos 8.550185***

Schöne Galatee, Die (Fair Galatea)

- Franz von Suppé. *Operette* in one act. 1865.
- Libretto by Poly Henrion (Kohl von Kohlenegg).
- First performance at Meysel's, Berlin, on 30th June 1865.

Pygmalion, a sculptor, makes a statue of a beautiful woman, Galatea, which the rich Mydas wants to buy. Pygmalion prays that Venus will bring the statue to life, but Galatea, as a living woman, causes turmoil by her behaviour and Pygmalion's prayer for the reversal of the miracle is answered. Galatea is turned again to stone, with jewels that Mydas had given her, leaving Mydas now to buy the statue.

The overture to Suppé's *Die schöne Galatee* (Fair Galatea) is heard often enough, whether in its original form or in arrangement for brass band. Vocal excerpts include the *Trinklied* (Drinking-Song).

Recommended Recording: Overture ***Naxos 8.553935***

Schöne und getreue Ariadne, Die (The Fair and True Ariadne)

- Johann Georg Conradi. Opera in three acts. 1691.
- Libretto by Christian Heinrich Postel.
- First performance at the Theater am Gänsemarkt, Hamburg, in 1691.

Ariadne, daughter of Minos, King of Crete, helps the young Athenian Theseus to defeat the monster, the minotaur, at the centre of the labyrinth, and to escape. Theseus, however, in this version of the story, is in love with Ariadne's sister Phaedra and for this reason abandons Ariadne on

Naxos, where she enjoys the love of Bacchus and the company of Venus and the Graces, before being raised to the skies as a constellation.

Derivative in musical style, Conradi's opera has historical importance as the first surviving score from the Hamburg opera and is a further example of the popularity of Ariadne on Naxos as a subject for operatic treatment from Monteverdi onwards.

SCHWANDA THE BAGPIPER

- Jaromír Weinberger. Opera in two acts. 1927.
- Libretto by Miloš Kareš, based on traditional Czech children's stories.
- First performance at the National Theatre, Prague, on 27th April 1927.

The robber Babinski takes refuge in the farmhouse of Schwanda and his wife Dorota and he and Schwanda go to relieve the Queen of melancholy, as she suffers under the power of a wicked Magician. Schwanda plays his bagpipes and the Queen recovers, suggesting marriage, which Schwanda accepts, kissing her. The Queen is angry, however, when Dorota and the Magician appear, and Schwanda is condemned to death, escaping with the help of Babinski and his bagpipes. He swears to Dorota that if he ever kissed the Queen, he will go to hell, and promptly does so. There the Devil asks him to play, a request he refuses, and then seeks his soul. Babinski rescues him again, this time beating the Devil at cards. Schwanda is finally re-united with Dorota, although Babinski had had hopes of her himself.

Schwanda's bagpipe *Polka* enjoys great popularity, to which the second act *Fugue* comes a close second. The opera itself has enjoyed considerable success, with its use of Czech folk material.

SCHWARZE MASKE, DIE (THE BLACK MASK)

- Krzysztof Penderecki. Opera in three acts. 1986.
- Libretto by Harry Kupfer and the composer, after the play by Gerhardt Hauptmann.
- First performance at the Salzburg Festival on 15th August 1986.

Set in the Silesian town of Bolkenhain in 1662, at a time of plague and carnival, a variety of characters appear, a Jansenist, a Huguenot, members of the nobility, citizens and a black intruder, a symbol of death, with the mayor and his wife Benigna.

Musically Penderecki's opera make use of a wide variety of styles and resources in a characteristic whole, which reflects the curious diversity of Hauptmann's short play, the first of the two plays he grouped together as *Spuk* (Ghost).

Schwarzschwanenreich (The Kingdom of the Black Swan)

- Siegfried Wagner. Opera in three acts. 1910.
- Libretto by the composer.
- First performance at the Hoftheater, Karlsruhe, on 5th November 1918.

The opera is set in the period of the Thirty Years War and centres on the predicament of an outsider in the village, Linda, who has secretly killed her own child and is suspected by the villagers of witchcraft. Lured by the black swans of the Swan Kingdom, Satan's emissaries, she is induced to confess and is condemned to death at the stake.

Inspired in part by a visit to a prison in Canton, the opera has a characteristically German historical setting and uses the Wagnerian symbolism of the swan in a study of the predicament of an outsider in an age of superstition.

Recommended Recording: Schwarzschwanenreich — ***Marco Polo 8.223777-78***

Schweigsame Frau, Die (The Silent Woman)

- Richard Strauss. *Komische Oper* in three acts. 1935.
- Libretto by Stefan Zweig, after the play *The Epicene, or The Silent Woman* by Ben Jonson.
- First performance at the Staatsoper, Dresden, on 24th June 1935.

Characters

Sir Morosus, a retired admiral	bass
Widow Zimmerlein, his housekeeper	contralto
Schneidebart, a barber	baritone
Henry Morosus, the admiral's nephew	high tenor
Aminta, his wife	coloratura soprano
Isotta, an opera-singer	coloratura soprano
Carlotta, an opera-singer	mezzo-soprano
Morbio, an opera-singer	baritone
Vanuzzi, an opera-singer	bass
Farfallo, an opera-singer	bass
The Parrot	squawking part

Widow Zimmerlein tries to enlist the barber's help in persuading Sir Morosus to marry, with herself in mind as a possible bride. Morosus detests noise, and the barber, as he shaves him, suggests that he should find a silent woman to marry. His nephew Henry appears and Morosus is at first delighted, until he finds that his nephew is a member of an operatic troupe. He disinherits him and will not acknowledge Aminta, Henry's wife, turning them out of the house, and calling on the barber to find him a wife. As Morosus leaves them, the barber suggests that a silent wife may be found, if they present the old man with Isotta, Carlotta and Aminta. The next day the barber presents the three girls, Carlotta as a rough country-girl, soon rejected, Isotta meeting a similar fate as an affected young lady of fashion. Aminta, however, appearing under the guise of Timida, pleases him. The barber brings in members of the troupe disguised as priest and notary and Morosus and Aminta are married, the wedding celebrated by the noisy intrusion of other members of the company, pretending to be shipmates of the admiral. When they are left alone, Aminta begins, with some reluctance, to play the part demanded of her, making scenes of every kind. , Morosus is relieved when Henry promises to arrange an immediate divorce. The third act brings chaos, as Aminta re-organizes the house and has Henry, disguised as a music-master, give her a noisy lesson. Vanuzzi appears, in the guise of the Lord Chief Justice, and evidence is heard to Aminta's discredit, although these are not grounds for divorce, he maintains. Morosus is in despair, until Henry and Aminta tell him of the trick they have played, the humour of which he is eventually able to enjoy, as the opera ends.

Die schweigsame Frau (The Silent Woman) has a pot-pourri overture, as Strauss described it. There are distinct improbabilities in the plot devised by Zweig, which is rather less convincing than Ben Jonson's original play. The work ends with the converted Morosus paying music a back-handed compliment in *Wie schön ist doch die Musik* (How beautiful music is – when it stops). Hugo von Hofmannsthal, with whom Strauss had collaborated on six operas, from *Elektra* and *Der Rosenkavalier* (The Knight of the Rose) to *Arabella*, had died in 1929. *Die schweigsame Frau* began a collaboration with Stefan Zweig that was cut short by the anti-semitic policies of the Third Reich. These resulted in the cancellation of performances of the opera in Dresden in 1935 after the first four nights. The opera is in general light-hearted and provided Strauss with an opportunity for pastiche and comedy.

SCIPIONE (SCIPIO)

- George Frideric Handel. Opera in three acts. 1726.
- Libretto by Paolo Antonio Rolli, based on a libretto by Antonio Salvi and on the histories of Livy.
- First performance at the King's Theatre, London, on 12th March 1726.

Characters

Berenice, daughter of King Ernando	soprano
Lucejo (Allucius), her lover	male alto
Scipione (Scipio), a Roman general	male alto
Lelio (Laelius), a Roman commander	tenor
Armira, captive of the Romans	soprano
Ernando, King of the Balearics	bass

Scipio, in triumph, has conquered New Carthage. He is in love with the captive Berenice, but magnanimously releases her to her beloved Allucius (Lucejo), a Celtiberian Prince, while the Roman commander Laelius is finally united with his beloved Armira, released now from Roman captivity.

The overture and more particularly the march that precedes the first act of the opera are well enough known. Berenice, like later operatic heroines, remains firm as a rock against the suggestion of marriage to Scipio in her final second act aria *Scoglio d'immote fronte* (Immovable as a rock). In the third act *Come al nazio boschetto* (As to the native wood) Allucius expresses again his love for Berenice. Handel made various changes in the work for a revival in 1730, with Scipio now allotted to a tenor and a woman taking the part of Laelius.

Scipione africano (Scipio Africanus)

- Francesco Cavalli. *Drama per musica* in a prologue and three acts. 1664.
- Libretto by Nicolò Minato.
- First performance at the Teatro SS Giovanni e Paolo, Venice, on 9th February 1664.

The well known magnanimity of the Roman general Scipio Africanus is demonstrated again in his ultimate willingness to give up his pursuit of the beautiful captive Carthaginian princess, Ericlea, who is in love with and loved by Luceius. Matters are complicated by the intrigues of Scipio's supposed ally, Masinissa, the imprisonment and remarkable escape by parachute of the king Syphax (Siface) and the rescue of his wife Sophonisba. It is she who has the aria *Non è, non è crudel* (No, not so cruel).

Scylla et Glaucus (Scylla and Glaucus)

- Jean-Marie Leclair. *Tragédie en musique* in a prologue and five acts. 1746.
- Libretto by D'Albaret, after Ovid's *Metamorphoses*.
- First performance by the Académie Royale de Musique in Paris on 4th October 1746.

The nymph Scylla fears love and is angry at the approach of the sea-god Glaucus, who seeks the help of the sorceress Circe, who uses her magic to make him fall in love with her. The spell is broken soon enough, moving Circe in her turn to anger and desire for revenge. When Glaucus returns, he finds that Scylla now loves him, but their happiness is interrupted by the appearance, in a cloud, of the angry Circe. Glaucus at first agrees to save Scylla from Circe's threats by giving her up, but Circe now pretends compassion, while still plotting revenge. Hecate, summoned by Circe, provides a poison that sends Scylla mad and she drowns, turned now into a rock by the whirlpool of Charybdis.

The principal importance of Leclair lies in his music for his own instrument, the violin, works that introduce a further element of Italian taste to France, added to a violin technique that had its origin also in Italy. A further biographical distinction lies in his murder in 1764, either by his estranged wife or, more probably, by his nephew, also a violinist. *Scylla et Glaucus,* written when Leclair was fifty, marked what he thought might be a new stage in his career, but his hopes were disappointed. Extracts from the opera, however, found their way into later compositions in the form of trio sonatas.

Secret, The

- Bedřich Smetana. Comic opera in three acts. 1878.
- Libretto by Eliška Krásnohorská.
- First performance at the New Czech Theatre, Prague, on 18th September 1878.

A small Czech town below Bezděz is divided. There is a long-standing quarrel between the town-councillors Malina and Kalina, the first of whom had refused to allow the second to marry his sister Miss Róza. Friar Barnabáš, now dead, had told the widower Kalina that he would show him a secret that would bring them together, and a paper, with writing of the Friar, is found by the old soldier Bonifác when Kalina's new house is being built. Kalina takes the paper, and makes Bonifác promise silence. Soon news of the secret is passed on. Malina's daughter and Kalina's son are in love, defying the quarrelling of their fathers. On Bezděz Kalina dreams that the Friar reveals his secret, a treasure, which he digs to discover. In the third act, after Malina has agreed to his daughter's marriage, if Kalina himself asks him, Kalina digs his way through to Malina's house, finding there his treasure in the person of Miss Róza.

Intended as a successor to the popular *The Kiss*, *The Secret* has never had the same appeal, in spite of its very Czech setting and story. Smetana claimed to have constructed the opera from two principal motifs, one representing the secret and the other Kalina.

Segreto di Susanna, Il (Susanna's Secret)

- Ermanno Wolf-Ferrari. *Intermezzo* in one act. 1909.
- Libretto by Enrico Golisciani.
- First performance at the Hoftheater, Munich, on 4th December 1909.

Characters

Count Gil	baritone
Countess Susanna, his wife	soprano
Sante, their servant	silent rôle

Count Gil suspects his young wife, smelling tobacco, although neither of them, it seems, are smokers. Susanna's guilty secret is eventually revealed, after bouts of jealous rage on the part of her husband: once he is out of the way, she smokes. The Count's discovery of his wife's habit brings reconciliation.

Wolf-Ferrari's short opera, less than an hour in length, is the most often performed of his stage works. The tone of the piece is set by the witty overture. In *O gioia, la nube leggera* (O joy, the delicate cloud) Susanna sings of the delights of smoking.

Recommended Recording: Intermezzo ***Naxos 8.550240***

Semele

- George Frideric Handel. Opera in three acts. 1743.
- Libretto by William Congreve, after Ovid's *Metamorphoses*.
- First concert performance at Covent Garden, London, on 10th February 1744.

Characters

Cadmus, King of Thebes	bass
Semele, his daughter	soprano
Ino, her sister	contralto
Athamas, Prince of Boeotia	countertenor

Jupiter	tenor
Juno	contralto
Iris, messenger and attendant of Juno	soprano
Somnus, god of sleep	bass
Apollo	tenor

Semele is to marry Athamas, but pleads for delay, while Ino, who herself loves Athamas, is distressed. At the wedding ceremony in Juno's temple, thunder is heard and Semele is taken up to heaven by a great eagle. She has been seized by her lover Jupiter, arousing the jealousy of Juno. Semele, however, while enjoying the pleasures of the country whither she has been transported, longs for immortality. Jupiter, who appears to her in human form, changes the scene to Arcadia and brings Ino to be her companion. Juno recruits the aid of the god of sleep and approaches Semele, now alone, in the guise of Ino, persuading her to ask Jupiter to appear to her in his true form. When Jupiter returns to her, Semele makes him swear to grant her wish, which he does with reluctance. He appears as a cloud of flame, and Semele dies. Ino returns home with news of what has happened and the divine command that she marry Athamas. The ashes of Semele, Apollo now promises, will bring forth Bacchus, god of wine.

Congreve had intended his opera, with music by John Eccles, to mark the opening of the Queen's Theatre in London in 1706. The advent of Italian opera forestalled this. Handel's later setting was intended for concert performance, although it has, since his time, been staged. It was written at a period when Handel was increasingly involved in English oratorio and like other such works it makes considerable use of the chorus, an important element of the newly developed form. To contemporaries *Semele* seemed neither one thing nor the other. It contains music of great beauty, with Jupiter's Arcadian *Where'er you walk* among the best know of all Handel arias. Somnus, the god of sleep, wakens to *Leave me, loathsome light,* roused from his lethargy by Juno, who has earlier provoked Iris to immediate energetic action in *Hence, Iris, hence away*. Semele herself has a number of moving arias, including *O sleep, why dost thou leave me?*.

SEMIRAMIDE (SEMIRAMIS)

- Gioachino Rossini. *Melodramma tragico* in two acts. 1822.
- Libretto by Gaetano Rossi, after Voltaire's *Sémiramis*.
- First performance at the Teatro La Fenice, Venice, on 3rd February 1823.

Characters

Idreno, an Indian king	tenor
Oroe, high priest of the Magi	bass
Assur, a prince, descendant of Baal	bass
Semiramide, Queen of Babylon, widow of King Nino	soprano
Arsace, Commander of the Assyrian army	contralto
Azema, a princess, descendant of Baal	soprano
Mitrane, Captain of the Guard	tenor

Semiramide, with Assur, has secured the murder of her husband, King Nino. Her son, however, has escaped death and is now, as Arsace, a successful commander, his identity unknown to his mother. He is called back to Babylon, is in love with Azema and unwilling to support Assur in the latter's bid for the throne. Semiramide falls in love with him and declares him king and her consort, while Azema will marry Idreno. King Nino's ghost warns of crimes to be expiated and the high priest Oroe tells Arsace of the crime committed by his mother and Assur. Arsace, in the tomb of his father, meets King Nino's murderers, and seeking to strike Assur, kills Semiramis. He is finally declared King.

Semiramide was Rossini's last opera for Italy, the title-rôle written for his wife, Isabella Colbran. The work starts with an effective overture and in the first act includes Arsace's return, with *Ah! quel giorno ognor rammento* (Ah! I always remember that day) and the impressive aria *Bel raggio lusinghier* (Fair ray of hope). The opera calls for outstanding singers in the leading soprano and contralto rôles.

Recommended Recordings:

Overture	***Naxos 8.550236***
Eccomi alfine in Babilonia	***Naxos 8.553543***

Semyon Kotko

- Sergey Prokofiev. Opera in five acts. 1939.
- Libretto by the composer and Valentin Katayev, after a novella by the latter.
- First performance at the Stanislavsky Opera Theatre, Moscow, on 23rd June 1940.

The opera mixes the love of the protagonist, a returning soldier, for the daughter of an anti-Bolshevik class enemy, and his political development, after 1917. The work had no success and was, in any case, ill-timed, in view of the Russo-German alliance that had recently been agreed. The overture is occasionally heard in the concert-hall.

Seraglio, Il (The Seraglio) (see *Entführung aus dem Serail, Die*)

Serail, Das (The Seraglio) (see *Zaide*)

Serse (Xerxes)

- George Frideric Handel. Opera in three acts. 1738.
- Libretto adapted from Silvio Stampiglia's *Il Xerse*.
- First performance at the King's Theatre, London, on 15th April 1738.

Characters

Serse (Xerxes), King of Persia	male mezzo-soprano
Arsamene, his brother	mezzo-soprano
Amastre, betrothed to Serse	contralto
Ariodate, a vassal prince	bass
Romilda, his daughter	soprano
Atalanta, her sister	soprano
Elviro, servant to Arsamene	bass

Xerxes sings in praise of a tree's shade, while the voice of Romilda is heard. She is loved by Arsamene, but Xerxes resolves to marry her, to the relief of Atalanta, who also loves Arsamene, while Amastre, disguised as a man and deserted by Xerxes, looks for revenge. Atalanta's pretence that Arsamene really loves her and the insistence of Xerxes on marrying Romilda cause a series of complications, enlivened by the comic servant Elviro. Eventually matters are put right, with Xerxes united again with Amastre and Arsamene with Romilda.

Handel's opera has a mixture of the serious and the comic. It opens with one of the most celebrated of arias, as Xerxes praises the shade of a plane-tree, *Ombra mai fù* (Shade there never was), known, in arrangement after arrangement, as Handel's *Largo*. The work was a marked failure when it was first staged in London and was given only five performances. The resurrection of the so-called *Largo* was left to the 19th century.

Serva padrona, La (The Servant as Mistress)

- Giovanni Battista Pergolesi. Intermezzo in two parts. 1733.

- ◆ Libretto by Gennaro Antonio Federico, after the play by Jacopo Angello Nelli.
- ◆ First performance at the Teatro S Bartlomeo, Naples, on 5th September 1733.

CHARACTERS

Uberto, an elderly gentleman	bass
Serpina, his servant	soprano
Vespone, another servant	silent rôle

Uberto, planning to go out, complains that he has waited hours for his chocolate. His criticisms levelled at Serpina are amply repaid. He tries to send Vespone out to find him a wife, and Serpina proclaims her own eligibility, while Uberto would be glad to be rid of her. In the second part Serpina tries to win Uberto's sympathy by her account of her coming marriage to a tyrannical army officer, Vespone, bribed by a promise of continued employment and now in disguise. Uberto is induced to take the place of the gallant captain and marry Serpina himself.

La serva padrona (The Servant as Mistress) played an important part in the operatic quarrels in Paris between supporters of the traditional French opera of Lully and Rameau and those who supported the simpler more modern art of Italy, exemplified in Pergolesi's opera, when it was staged in Paris, not for the first time, in 1752. The disagreement, the so-called *Querelle des Bouffons* (Quarrel of the Actors) continued for the next two years, with Rousseau a keen supporter of the Italian against the French. Pergolesi's opera is modest in its proportions, both vocally and instrumentally. As an intermezzo its two parts were intended for performance between the acts of a more serious work. It makes use of three of the stock characters of the Italian *commedia dell'arte*.

SERVILIA

- ◆ Nikolay Andreyevich Rimsky-Korsakov. Opera in five acts. 1902.
- ◆ Libretto by the composer, after the play by Lev Alexandrovich Mey.
- ◆ First performance at the Mariinsky Theatre, St Petersburg, on 14th October 1902.

Set in the Rome of Nero, the opera deals with the conversion to Christianity of Servilia, daughter of a Roman senator and her death, which converts others to her faith.

For his opera Rimsky-Korsakov tried to devise a musical language that would suit the period and place of the plot. The work won what the composer described as a *succès d'estime* in St Petersburg and subsequently, with a private opera company, in Moscow, but was dropped quickly enough by both.

Si j'étais roi (If I were King)

- Adolphe Adam. *Opéra comique* in three acts. 1852.
- Libretto by Adolphe Philippe d'Ennery and Jules Brésil.
- First performance at the Théâtre Lyrique, Paris, on 4th September 1852.

In 16th century Goa, a young fisherman is in love with the Princess that he has saved from drowning and is allowed to be king for one day. This enables him to marry the Princess, in spite of the opposition of a wicked Prince.

In addition to the overture, the baritone drinking-song and the Princess's *De vos nobles aïeux* (From your noble ancestors) have an occasional place in recital repertoire.

Recommended Recording: Overture — ***Naxos 8.550473***

Siberia

- Umberto Giordano. Opera in three acts. 1903.
- Libretto by Luigi Illica.
- First performance at the Teatro alla Scala, Milan, on 19th December 1903.

Stefana, the mistress of Prince Alexis, has a lover, the young officer Vassili, who does not know of her position. Vassili comes to the house to bid farewell to his old nurse, Nikona, Stefana's housekeeper. He meets Prince Alexis and wounds him in a fight, after which he is arrested. Condemned to hard labour in Siberia, Vassili is accompanied by Stefana. In the prison-camp Gleby, Stefana's former pimp, suggests a way of escape with him, but she refuses, and when she tries to escape with Vassili she is shot and killed.

Alexis and two friends sing an aubade to Stefana in the first act, seeking to wake her, although she is out of the house, meeting Vassili. The song *O bella mia* (O my fair one) may be heard in operatic recitals, as may something of the horrors of Siberia in Vassili's *Orride steppe* (Terrible steppes). Giordano, who valued this opera very highly, made use of Russian thematic material and included the balalaika in the third act.

Siddharta

- Per Nørgård. Opera Ballet in three acts. 1979.
- Libretto by Ole Sarvig.
- First performance at the Royal Opera, Copenhagen, on 18th March 1983.

The birth of Prince Siddharta brings joy to his parents and in his childhood he is protected from the ills of life. With life a game for him, he chooses a wife, but later begins to wonder about the reality of his life. Finally sickness, old age and death are revealed to him and Siddharta turns his back on the life he has led, leaving the palace and his princely garments.

Siddharta, Play for the Expected One, was a collaboration between the composer and Ole Sarvig, one of the most important Danish poets of the time, who died in 1981.

Sieben Todsünden, Die (The Seven Deadly Sins)

- Kurt Weill. *Ballet chanté* in eight parts. 1933.
- Text by Bertolt Brecht.
- First performance at the Théâtre des Champs-Elysées, Paris, on 7th June 1933.

Anna I and Anna II, a singer and dancer respectively, set out on adventures throughout America, seeking to earn enough money to build a house for themselves in Louisiana. In the course of their travels they stop in seven places, corresponding to the seven deadly sins, Sloth, Pride, Anger, Gluttony, Lust, Covetousness and Envy, sins that are for the middle classes, but which, in Brecht's Marxist text, become virtues.

Die sieben Todsünden (The Seven Deadly Sins) was an expensive failure when it was staged in Paris and then in London. It follows the earlier Brecht-Weill collaborations, *Mahagonny* and the *Dreigroschenoper* (The Threepenny Opera).

Siège de Corinthe, Le (The Siege of Corinth) (see Maometto II)

- Gioachino Rossini. *Tragédie lyrique* in three acts. 1826.
- Libretto by Luigi Balocchi and Alexandre Soumet, after the libretto by Cesare della Valle for Rossini's *Maometto II*.
- First performance at the Paris Opéra on 9th October 1826.

An effective revision and simplification of *Maometto II*, *Le siège de Corinthe* (The Siege of Corinth), recast for Paris, changes the scene from Negroponte to Corinth and the breeches rôle of Calbo to a tenor, Néocles. The plot, however, remains largely the same, dealing, as it does, with the traditional operatic conflict between love and duty.

- Richard Wagner. Music-drama in three acts. The second day of *Der Ring des Nibelungen* (The Ring of the Nibelung). 1871.
- Libretto by the composer.
- First performance at the Festspielhaus, Bayreuth, on 16th August 1876.

CHARACTERS

Siegfried	tenor
Mime, a Nibelung	tenor
Alberich, his brother	bass-baritone
The Wanderer (Wotan)	bass-baritone
Fafner, last of the giants, disguised as a dragon	bass
Erda, goddess of Fate	contralto
Brünnhilde, daughter of Erda and Wotan	soprano
Forest Bird	soprano

The dwarf Mime works at his forge, grumbling as he makes a sword for Siegfried and hoping to piece together the sword Nothung, so that Siegfried may kill Fafner and regain the ring, which will then be Mime's. Mime, who has brought Siegfried up, seeks his love, but the latter must learn his true parentage, as the son of Sieglinde, who died as he was born. Wotan, disguised as the Wanderer, wagers his head on three questions from Mime, which he answers, then posing three questions in turn to Mime, who cannot tell him who will repair the sword Nothung, which will kill the dragon Fafner. Under suspended sentence of death, Mime tells Siegfried of the sword Nothung, which he cannot repair, and Siegfried melts the pieces and makes the sword again. Mime, meanwhile, plans to let Siegfried kill Fafner and then to drug him and take the ring from him. Outside Fafner's cave, Alberich and Wotan seek to warn the dragon of impending danger, in return for the treasure. They are unsuccessful. Siegfried is led by Mime to the cave and, left alone, hears the murmur of the forest and the singing of a bird, which he cannot imitate. With his horn he rouses and kills the dragon, whose blood enables him to understand the song of the bird, telling him to beware of Mime and to take the treasure from the cave and the Tarncap of invisibility. Now understanding Mime's murderous thoughts, Siegfried kills him and the forest bird tells him of love and of Brünnhilde. By her rock, Wotan summons up Erda, whose knowledge he now wills away, understanding that Siegfried must wake Brünnhilde, who will save the world. Siegfried meets the Wanderer, Wotan, and with his sword breaks the latter's spear and power. He makes his way through fire to the rock and wakens the sleeping Brünnhilde, who gives up Valhalla and the gods for love of the mortal hero, her love putting an end to her knowledge.

Siegfried, the third music-drama of the tetralogy, again weaves together the leit-motifs associated with the characters and ideas in the work. The opening *Prelude* to the first act foreshadows Mime's complaints, while that to the second act combines motifs associated with Fafner and those of the ring and the curse Alberich had put on it. The third act opens with music evoking the wandering of Wotan and his fate. There is an orchestral version of the so-called *Forest Murmurs*, as Siegfried rests under a linden near Fafner's cave. This last may be heard also as a vocal excerpt, others of which may include the final scene between Siegfried and Brünnhilde.

Recommended Recording: Forest Murmurs ***Naxos 8.550211***

Signor Bruschino, Il

- Gioachino Rossini. *Farsa giocosa* in one act. 1813.
- Libretto by Giuseppe Maria Foppa, after Alissan de Chazet and E.-T. Maurice Ourry's play *Le fils par hasard, ou Ruse et folie* (The Son by Chance, or Trickery and Folly).
- First performance at the Teatro S Moisè, Venice, on 27th January 1813.

Sofia and Florville are in love, but Sofia's guardian, Gaudenzio, is against the match. He is an enemy of Florville's father and when matters seem easier, with the latter's death, he presents a further obstacle, having promised Sofia to the son of his old friend Signor Bruschino. Florville impersonates young Bruschino, detained for an unpaid tavern bill, which Florville has actually settled on his behalf, and the complications that arise when old Bruschino appears are eventually solved when Signor Bruschino is induced to accept Florville as his son, for the present purposes, although well aware of the whole situation.

A witty comedy, *Il Signor Bruschino, ossia Il figlio per azzardo* (Signor Bruschino, or The Son by Chance) opens with an overture to match.

Recommended Recording: Overture ***Naxos 8.550236***

Silbersee, Der (The Silver Lake)

- Kurt Weill. Play with music in three acts. 1932.
- Text by Georg Kaiser.
- First performance at the Altes Theater, Leipzig, the Stadttheater, Erfurt and the Stadttheater, Magdeburg, on 18th February 1933.

Unemployed and starving, Severin leads a group of his friends in an attempted robbery and is shot and wounded by a policemen, Olim. The latter secures Severin's release from prison and, winning a lottery, buys a castle, where the servants are former members of the nobility. Severin had vowed to kill the man who shot him and eventually learns that Olim was responsible, through the innocent Fennimore, niece of Frau von Luber, one of the servants, to whom Olim is induced to make over the castle. The two men are eventually reconciled, as they set out together over the frozen surface of the Silver Lake.

The sixteen numbers of Weill's score are varied in style, with echoes of *Die Dreigroschenoper* (The Threepenny Opera) and earlier collaborations with Brecht. The simultaneous staging in three cities, eighteen days after the appointment of Hitler as Chancellor of Germany, provoked the vocal opposition of the Nazis. *Der Silbersee* (The Silver Lake) was the last of Weill's works to be performed in a Germany where his music was regarded as decadent. As a Jew, like Weill, Kaiser also was compelled to take prompt refuge abroad. Fennimore's *Ich bin eine arme Verwandte* (I am a poor relation) and her Ballad of Caesar's Death, *Rom hiess eine Stadt* (There was a city called Rome) may be heard in recital.

Silla (Sulla)

- George Frideric Handel. Opera in three acts. 1713.
- Libretto by Giacomo Rossi.
- First performed privately in London in 1713.

The Roman dictator Sulla behaves with great arrogance, seeking to take the wife of Lepidus, Flavia, or to enjoy the love of Celia, who is herself loyal to him but in love with the dissident Claudius. Matters are finally resolved by the departure, shipwreck and abdication of Sulla.

Details of the first staging of *Silla* are unknown and the surviving parts of the score do not fully match the word-book. The work was apparently written in haste.

Silvana

- Carl Maria von Weber. *Romantische Oper* in three acts. 1810.
- Libretto by Franz Karl Hiemer, after a work by Carl von Steinsberg.
- First performance in Frankfurt on 16th September 1810.

Characters

Graf Rudolph von Helfenstein	tenor
Krips, his squire	bass
Graf Adelhart	baritone
Mechthilde, his daughter	soprano
Klärchen, her maid	soprano
Albert von Cleeburg	tenor
Kurt, his squire	bass
Silvana	speaking rôle
Ulrich	speaking rôle
Fust von Grimmbach	baritone
Herald	tenor

Count Rudolph is betrothed to Mechthilde, who is in love with Albert von Cleeburg, son of an enemy of her father, Count Adelhart. Count Rudolph is out hunting, accompanied by his men and his bragging squire Krips, a Papageno to his Tamino. He comes across the mute Silvana and takes her back to Count Adelhart's castle, where he is a guest. Count Adelhart insists that his daughter must marry Count Rudolph, but matters are settled to general satisfaction when Ulrich, a former servant of Count Adelhart, who has protected Silvana from infancy in the forest, reveals that she is the daughter of Count Adelhart. The revelation allows Silvana to speak.

Derived in part from music written for Carl von Steinsberg's *Das Waldmädchen* (The Forest Maiden) Weber's *Singspiel* tackles the problem posed by the presence of a heroine who is largely mute. The work includes a lively comic part for Krips, boastful and cowardly in incidents that echo elements in Mozart's *Die Zauberflöte* (The Magic Flute), and heroic rôles for the two tenors and the soprano Mechthilde. There are suggestions of writing that was to come to fruition in *Der Freischütz* (The Marksman).

Recommended Recording:
Silvana (2 CDs) ***Marco Polo 8.223844-45***

Simon Boccanegra

- Giuseppe Verdi. Opera in a prologue and three acts. 1856.
- Libretto by Francesco Maria Piave, with contributions from Giuseppe Montanelli, after the play *Simón Bocanegra* by Antonio García Gutiérrez. Revised by Arrigo Boito for La Scala, Milan in 1881.

◆ First performance at the Teatro La Fenice, Venice, on 12th March 1857.

Characters

Simon Boccanegra, Doge of Genoa	baritone
Maria (Amelia Grimaldi), his daughter	soprano
Jacopo Fiesco (Andrea)	bass
Gabriele Adorno, a Genoese gentleman	tenor
Paolo Albiani, favourite of the Doge	bass
Pietro, a courtier	baritone
Captain	tenor
Maid to Amelia	mezzo-soprano

In the prologue Paolo and Pietro agree to put forward the name of the plebeian Boccanegra for election as Doge of Genoa. Boccanegra agrees, thinking to facilitate his marriage to Maria, daughter of the reigning Doge, Fiesco. Maria dies but bears him a daughter, who subsequently disappears. 25 years later Amelia is in the garden of the Grimaldi palace, serenaded by her lover Gabriele Adorno, and confiding in him her fears for his safety and that of her guardian Andrea, Fiesco in disguise, both conspirators against the Doge. Fiesco tells Adorno that Amelia is not a true Grimaldi but an orphan, but blesses their intended union. Boccanegra had intended that Amelia marry his courtier Paolo but when he realises that she must be his long-lost daughter he changes his mind. Paolo secretly plans to abduct her. In the second scene Boccanegra is accused of her abduction, but is exonerated by Amelia, who does not reveal the name of the perpetrator. Boccanegra insists that the guilty man be cursed, a curse in which Paolo is compelled to join, to his horror. In the second act Paolo plans to poison Boccanegra, but Fiesco will not join the plot. Gabriele accuses Amelia of infidelity. He determines to murder the Doge, now sleeping after drinking from the cup Paolo has poisoned. He is prevented by Amelia, who reveals herself as Boccanegra's daughter, leading to the reconciliation of the three. Sounds of popular rebellion are heard, and Gabriele promises to support the Doge. In the third act, the rebellion now quelled, Paolo admits his crimes and is led away to execution. The poison works gradually on Boccanegra, who is now reconciled with Fiesco, his own identity revealed and that of Amelia, his grand-daughter. As he dies, Boccanegra blesses Gabriele and Amelia, and appoints the former as Doge.

It is generally thought that the 1881 revision of *Simon Boccanegra* improved the work by adding some light to the general gloom and giving further prominence to Boccanegra himself. It is the revised version that is usually performed. The prologue provides Fiesco with his moving *Il lacerato spirito* (The tortured spirit). In the first act dawn breaks in the Grimaldi palace garden, leading to Amelia's *In quest'ora bruna* (In this dark hour), while the more spectacular second scene, in the

Council Chamber, brings Boccanegra's effective *Plebe! Patrizi!* (Plebeians! Nobles!) that quells incipient disturbance. Gabriele Adorno has his own particular moment of jealous anger in *Sento avvampar nell'anima* (I feel burning in my soul).

SINGENDE TEUFEL, DER (THE SINGING DEVIL)

- Franz Schreker. Opera in four acts. 1928.
- Libretto by the composer.
- First performance at the Staatsoper, Berlin, on 10th December 1928.

Lilian is in love with the monk and organ-builder Amandus, who is determined to complete the great organ that his father had begun. Lilian, representing paganism against the religious world of Amandus, burns down the monastery, with the organ whose sounds had seemed to the people a very singing devil. As she dies, the burning pipes of the organ play angelic music.

Characteristic of Schreker in its historical setting, *Der singende Teufel* (The Singing Devil) makes use of the composer's usual symbolism. The work followed hostile criticism of the opera *Irrelohe* and was written while Schreker was occupied with his penultimate stage work *Christophorus*, for which he had sought advice from Schoenberg, in spite of his own leading position in Berlin at the time.

SIR JOHN IN LOVE

- Ralph Vaughan Williams. Opera in four acts. 1928.
- Libretto by the composer, after Shakespeare's *The Merry Wives of Windsor*.
- First performance at the Royal College of Music, London, on 21st March 1929.

The fat old knight, Sir John Falstaff, is gulled by the merry wives of Shakespeare's play, who pretend love for him, only to tip him into the river, when he makes his escape from a supposed assignation in a basket of dirty laundry, and finally to tease and torment him, when he agrees to a midnight meeting in Windsor Forest.

Vaughan Williams treats the subject chosen by Verdi for his own opera *Falstaff*. There are additions from other Shakespeare plays and from the work of Ben Jonson, with a score that includes elements of English folk-song, notably in the *Fantasia on Greensleeves* drawn from the introduction to the third act.

Siroe

- George Frideric Handel. Opera in three acts. 1728.
- Libretto by Nicola Francesco Haym, adapted from the libretto by Metastasio.
- First performance at the King's Theatre, London, on 17th February 1728.

Emira, daughter of Asbite, King of Cambaya, killed by the Persian King Cosroe, disguises herself as a man, intent on revenge. Siroe, elder son of Cosroe, loves her and knows of her disguise, while his younger brother Medarse plans to displace him as heir to the throne. Laodice loves Siroe and spurned suggests to Cosroe that Siroe is a danger to him. Siroe is imprisoned, but all ends happily enough when his release is secured and the plot against Cosroe engineered by Medarse is foiled. Siroe ends as king, with Medarse and Laodice forgiven and Emira no longer sworn to revenge.

Handel's opera, the first to use a libretto by Metastasio, provided rôles for the two rival sopranos Faustina Bordoni and Francesca Cuzzoni, with the alto castrato Senesino in the title-rôle.

Snow Maiden, The

- Nikolay Andreyevich Rimsky-Korsakov. Spring tale in a prologue and four acts. 1881.
- Libretto by the composer, after the fairy-tale by Alexander Nikolayevich Ostrovsky.
- First performance at the Mariinsky Theatre, St Petersburg, on 10th February 1882.

Fairy Spring and Winter have a child, Snegurochka, the Snow Maiden. She is sixteen, but must still be protected from the sun-god, for if he sees her, she will die. She is to be guarded by the Wood Spirit and now goes free among the people. In the first act she vainly loves the shepherd Lel' and is pursued by the rich young Mizgir, who cancels his own wedding to Kupava. Kupava, in the second act, seeks redress from the Tsar, who, when he sees Snegurochka, offers a reward to anyone who wins her love. In the Holy Wood there is celebration, and a dance of tumblers. Lel' sings for the Tsar and is allowed to claim a kiss from any of the girls present. He chooses Kupava, while Mizgir urges his attentions on Snegurochka, his way finally barred by the Spirit of the Wood. She pleads with her mother and eventually shows her love for Mizgir. The sun-god Yarilo, however, has warmed her heart and she must die, melting away, while Mizgir drowns himself. The Tsar, however, welcomes the return of the sun.

Rimsky-Korsakov considered *Snegurochka* (The Snow Maiden) his best opera, although he felt bound to make various cuts in a score that initially was too long. The second version was first staged in St Petersburg in 1898. Orchestral excerpts include the *Introduction, Dance of the Birds,*

Procession and *Dance of the Tumblers*. While the songs of the shepherd Lel' form part of Russian contralto repertoire.

Recommended Recording: The Snow Maiden (Suite) **Naxos 8.550486**

SOGNO DI SCIPIONE, IL (THE DREAM OF SCIPIO)

- Wolfgang Amadeus Mozart. *Azione teatrale* in one act. 1772.
- Libretto by Metastasio.
- First performance at the palace of the Archbishop of Salzburg in May 1772.

CHARACTERS

Scipione (Scipio)	tenor
La Constanza (Constancy)	soprano
La Fortuna (Fortune)	soprano
Publio (Publius), adoptive father of Scipio	tenor
Emilio (Aemilius), Scipio's father	tenor
Singer in final Licenza	soprano

In his dream Scipio is offered a choice between Constancy and Fortune and in Elysium seeks the advice of his adoptive father and his natural father. He finally makes his own choice, to follow Constancy.

Mozart wrote *Il sogno di Scipione* (The Dream of Scipio) to celebrate the enthronement of Hieronymus, Count Colloredo, as Archbishop of Salzburg. The work includes nine arias, starting with Scipio's *Risolver non osa* (My mind dare not decide), followed by arias from Fortune and Constancy. The final *Licenza* is the customary epilogue, addressed to the Archbishop, pointing out the resemblance between him and the hero of the dramatic piece performed.

SOLDATEN, DIE (THE SOLDIERS)

- Bernd Alois Zimmermann. Opera in four acts. 1964.
- Libretto by the composer, after the play by Jakob Michael Reinhold Lenz.
- First performance at the Opernhaus, Cologne, on 15th February 1965.

Marie, daughter of Wesener, a Lille fancy goods merchant, has fallen in love with the Armentières draper Stolzius. She seeks her sister's advice, while, in the second scene, Stolzius is delighted to have a letter from her. In Lille again, Baron Desportes pays court to Marie, forbidden by her father to go with him to the theatre. The fourth scene, in Armentières, introduces the soldiers, young officers, arguing about the moral merits of the theatre and the sermon. In Lille Wesener asks Marie about the intentions of Desportes and advises her to continue her relationship with Stolzius until she has a firm offer from the baron. The second act opens in the Armentières café of Madame Roux, where the officers talk together, join in accompanying a dancing Andalusian waitress and tease Stolzius on the probable activities of Marie in Lille. In Lille Marie receives a letter of reproach from him and is seduced by Desportes, while the reaction of Stolzius in Armentières is seen. In the third act the officers in Armentières are again in discussion over the proposed move to Lille of Major Mary. Stolzius applies to be his batman. In Lille Marie accepts the attentions of Desportes's friend Major Mary, in the absence of Desportes. In the following scene the Countess de la Roche discourages her son's attentions to Marie. Deserted now by Desportes, Major Mary and the Count, Marie is invited to become companion to the Countess. The fourth act shows the steps in Marie's degradation, as she sinks to the level of a prostitute, after Desportes has subjected her to the attentions of his gamekeeper. Stolzius plans revenge and serves Desportes a poisoned soup, which he then drinks himself. The final scene shows Marie, destitute and not recognised by her father, while soldiers are shown as a symbol of those who cause misery to mankind.

Zimmermann's opera makes use of serial technique and a series of formal structures for each of the fifteen scenes. The work calls for very great theatrical resources in its attempt at total theatre. The play by Lenz was written in 1775 and presented a particular challenge in its changes of scene. *Die Soldaten* (The Soldiers) may be seen as a successor to Alban Berg's *Wozzeck* and *Lulu*.

Sonnambula, La (The Sleep-Walker)

- Vincenzo Bellini. *Melodramma* in two acts. 1831.
- Libretto by Felice Romani, after the ballet-pantomime *La sonnambule, ou L'arrivée d'un nouveau seigneur* (The Sleep-Walker, or The Arrival of a New Lord) by Eugène Scribe and Jean-Pierre Aumer.
- First performance at the Teatro Carcano, Milan, on 6th March 1831.

Characters

Count Rodolpho, lord of the village	bass
Amina, an orphan,	soprano
Teresa, her foster-mother, owner of the mill	mezzo-soprano
Lisa, hostess of the inn, in love with Elvino	soprano

Elvino, a young farmer	tenor
Alessio, a villager, in love with Lisa	bass
A Notary	tenor

There is general celebration in the village of the coming marriage of Amina and Elvino, a match that Lisa, herself in love with Elvino, deplores. She rejects the continued attentions of Alessio. Count Rodolpho arrives, after a long absence and generally unrecognised by the villagers. He is entertained for the night by Lisa in her inn, but Amina walks in her sleep and wakes to find herself in the Count's room, arousing further jealousy in an already suspicious Elvino, who now rejects her, in spite of the attempted intervention of the villagers and the support of the Count; now he will marry Lisa. Matters are resolved when Amina is seen perilously walking in her sleep, solving the village mystery of a suspected ghost and the allegations of her infidelity. Before her final reconciliation with Elvino she finds the occasion, as she sleeps, for a brief mad scene, from which she is gently wakened by her lover.

Among the best known of 19th century operas, a model of the pastoral genre, *La Sonnambula* (The Sleep-Walker) has provided an effective vehicle for sopranos from Giuditta Pasta, who created the title-rôle, to Jenny Lind, Maria Callas, Joan Sutherland and others of similar stature. Amina's happiness is reflected in her first act *Care compagne* (Dear companions) and her first love scene with Elvino. Most famous of all his her final sleep-walking scene, *Ah! non credea mirarti* (Ah! Scarcely could I believe the flowers would wither so soon), an opportunity for moving dramatic performance.

Recommended Recording: La Sonnambula (2 CDs) ***Naxos 8.660042-43***

Sosarme (Sosarmes)

- George Frideric Handel. Opera in three acts. 1732.
- Libretto adapted from Antonio Salvi's *Dionisio, re di Portogallo* (Dionysius, King of Portugal).
- First performance at the King's Theatre, London, on 15th February 1732.

Set in Sardis, the opera deals with the conflict between Argone and his father Haliate, King of Lydia. Sosarme of Media, in love with Elmira, daughter of Haliate, is wounded in battle by Argone and nursed by Elmira, while the intriguer Altomaro seeks to make his grandson, illegitimate son of Haliate, successor to his father. It is Altomaro who turns Haliate's suspicions against his wife, Erenice, accused of provoking her son Argone to single combat with his father. Matters are brought to a happy conclusion with the final suicide of Altomaro.

Handel at first sought to use the setting of the original libretto, Portugal, but English friendship with that country suggested that a more distant setting might be more suitable. The opera contains a number of fine arias.

Spanish Lady, The

- Edward Elgar. Opera in two acts. Unfinished. 1933.
- Libretto by Barry Jackson, based on the play *The Devil is an Ass* by Ben Jonson.

Elgar's opera occupied him for a number of years, but eventually came to nothing. The surviving sketches include a number of dances, which have an occasional place in concert repertoire.

Speziale, Lo (The Apothecary)

- Joseph Haydn. *Dramma giocoso* in three acts. 1768.
- Libretto by Carlo Goldoni, with possible revision by Carl Friberth.
- First performance at Esterháza in autumn 1768.

Characters

Sempronio, the apothecary	tenor
Mengone, his assistant	tenor
Grilletta, Sempronio's foster-daughter	soprano
Volpino, a man about town	soprano

Sempronio intends to marry his ward Grilletta. His chief interests lie in amazing items of news. Volpino comes for a prescription, hoping to address his attentions to Grilletta, but he is teased by her and Sempronio's apprentice Mengone and forced to go away. Grilletta, really in love with Mengone, makes things more difficult for him by seeming to accept Sempronio's proposal of a marriage, for which both Mengone and Volpino appear disguised as notaries. In the third act there is more deception, with Turkish disguises and music to match, before Mengone engineers his own successful alliance with Grilletta.

The third act of Haydn's opera remains incomplete, but contains a Turkish aria for Volpino, while earlier arias exploit Sempronio's credulous search for novelties and Mengone's professional disquisition on the merits of a laxative that he is preparing.

Spielwerk, Das (The Music-Box)

- Franz Schreker. *Mysterium* in one act. 1912.
- Libretto by the composer.
- First performance, as the two-act *Das Spielwerk und die Prinzessin* (The Music-Box and the Princess), in Frankfurt and Vienna on 15th March 1913. The revised one-act version was first performed at the Nationaltheater, Munich, on 30th October 1920.

The opera deals with the power of music, as represented by the mysterious music-box of Meister Florian, and the relative simplicity of the flute-playing of a young traveller, over the Princess of the original title.

Schreker's opera, set in a mysterious world of earlier times, again explores the elusive power of music and love, as he had done in *Der ferne Klang* (The Distant Sound), a work that immediately preceded the new opera and had won some success, and in works as early as *Die Flammen* (The Flames). *Das Spielwerk und die Prinzessin* (The Music-Box and the Princess) aroused immediate criticism for its mixture of musical language and seemingly obscure symbolism, although it had its champions.

Recommended Recording: Prelude ***Marco Polo 8.220392***

Stiffelio (see Aroldo)

- Giuseppe Verdi. Opera in three acts. 1850.
- Libretto by Francesco Maria Piave, after the play *Le pasteur, ou L'évangile et le foyer* (The Pastor, or Church and Hearth) by Emile Souvestre and Eugène Bourgeois.
- First performance at the Teatro Grande, Trieste, on 16th November 1850.

Characters

Stiffelio, a Protestant minister	tenor
Lina, his wife	soprano
Count Stankar, her father, an elderly colonel	baritone
Raffaele, a nobleman	tenor
Jorg, an elderly minister	bass
Federico di Frengel	tenor
Dorotea, Lina's cousin	mezzo-soprano

Stiffelio, returning from a journey to Count Stankar's castle, relates how his boatman had seen a young man and woman at a castle window and how the young man had leapt from the window to escape, leaving papers behind. Their behaviour suggests the guilt of Lina and Raffaele, but Stiffelio destroys the papers, without looking at them. Alone with his wife, Stiffelio becomes suspicious when he finds her wedding-ring gone. Stankar learns of her infidelity, but forbids her to tell Stiffelio, as she had planned. Raffaele writes to Lina and hides his letter in a book, Klopstock's *Messias*. Federico takes the book and is seen by Jorg, who tells Stiffelio that he suspects him. Stiffelio plans a sermon on betrayal and forces the locked book open. When the letter falls out, Stankar seizes and destroys it, to Stiffelio's anger. Lina visits her mother's grave, to seek help, and is joined in the graveyard by Raffaele. Stankar now arrives and fights with Raffaele, the two separated by Stiffelio, who seeks his own revenge. In the third act Stankar contemplates suicide. Stiffelio seeks divorce from Lina, but understands that she loves him and that Raffaele is at fault. Stankar returns, his drawn sword stained now with the blood of Raffaele. In a final church service Stiffelio reads of the woman taken in adultery, his forgiveness of his wife echoed by the congregation.

The subject of Verdi's *Stiffelio* might have seemed ill-suited to a Catholic audience and it proved unsuccessful, both in Italy and abroad, although more recent productions have proved effective enough. Verdi recast the work as *Aroldo*, the protagonist a 13th century Saxon knight, but the work, while it avoided controversy, fared no better.

STORY OF A REAL MAN, THE

- Sergey Prokofiev. Opera in four acts. 1948.
- Libretto by the composer and Mira Mendelson, after the novella by Boris Polevoy.
- First public performance at the Bolshoy Theatre, Moscow, on 8th October 1960.

The opera treats the heroic story of Aleksey Meresyev, a war-time Soviet fighter pilot, who was shot down and lost both legs, but made a triumphant return to duty, with artificial legs.

Prokofiev's opera, on a safe patriotic subject, was awarded the Stalin Prize, but could not deflect the condemnation of 1948, in spite of the secure position of Boris Polevoy in the official hierarchy of Soviet writers. The opera is unusual in that it deals with the exploits of a man still living at the time of its composition.

Straniera, La (The Stranger)

- Vincenzo Bellini. *Melodramma* in two acts. 1828.
- Libretto by Felice Romani, after the novel *L'étrangère* (The Stranger) by Victor-Charles Prévôt.
- First performance at the Teatro alla Scala, Milan, on 14th February 1829.

Characters

Alaide, the stranger	soprano
Il Signore di Montolino	bass
Isoletta, his daughter	mezzo-soprano
Arturo, Count of Ravenstal	tenor
Baron Valdeburgo, brother of Alaide	bass
Prior of the Knights Templar	bass
Osburgo, Arturo's confidant	tenor

In 13th century Brittany Arturo, Count of Ravenstal, is in love with the mysterious stranger Alaide, who is, in fact, Agnese, sister of Baron Valdeburgo and banished former wife of the King of France, who has been compelled to return to his wife Isemberga. Arturo is to marry Isoletta, daughter of the Lord of Montolino, but confides in Valdeburgo his love for the stranger. Observing the Baron's meeting with and recognition of his sister, Arturo suspects that they are lovers, attacks and wounds Valdeburgo and, learning the truth from Alaide, leaps into the lake where Valdeburgo has fallen, in order to save him. Meanwhile Alaide's cries for help have resulted in charges of murder. She is tried, together with Arturo, who admits his guilt, and both are released when Valdeburgo returns. He will now allow Arturo to see Alaide only if he promises to marry Isoletta. At the wedding Isoletta is unwilling to proceed, while Alaide, who has hidden in the chapel, now emerges to lead the couple back to the altar. News comes of the death of Isemberga, Queen of France, which allows Alaide to resume her position. Arturo kills himself and Alaide, praying for death, falls to the ground.

The second collaboration between Bellini and Felice Romani, *La Straniera* (The Stranger) includes a number of very effective choruses. The second scene, set by Alaide's hut in the woods, brings her sad *Ah! sventurato il cor che fida* (Ah! Unlucky the heart that trusts), an element in a major soprano rôle.

Street Scene

- Kurt Weill. American opera in two acts. 1946.
- Libretto by Elmer Rice, after his own play.
- First performance at the Shubert Theatre, Philadelphia, on 16th December 1946.

In a street in front of a house in New York City in the month of June, characters play out their drama. Ann and Frank Maurrant are unhappily married, and the janitor and neighbours discuss Ann's relationship with Steve Sanky and the love affair of the Maurrants' daughter Rose and the young Jewish student Sam Kaplan. Frank shoots his wife and her lover and is imprisoned, while Rose parts from her lover.

Weill's American opera, based on the work of one of the most distinguished of American playwrights, Elmer Rice, is in the form of a *Singspiel*, with 21 musical numbers joined by dialogue. As in earlier collaboration with Brecht in Berlin, Weill uses pseudo-jazz idioms in a work that is more Broadway musical than opera, but none the less effective in the theatre. The first act song *Lonely house* has proved particularly popular in isolation from its dramatic context.

Stubborn Lovers, The

- Antonín Dvořák. Comic opera in one act. 1874.
- Libretto by Josef Štolba.
- First performance at the New Czech Theatre, Prague, on 2nd October 1881.

A marriage is agreed by their parents between Toník and Lanka, but their known stubbornness involves their godfather in a variety of intrigues in order to bring them together, an enterprise in which he is finally successful.

Known also in English, less flatteringly, if alliteratively, as *The Pig-Headed Peasants,* the opera was badly staged in 1881, seven years after its completion, and temporarily withdrawn. It was the second of Dvořák's completed Czech operas, written after the first revision of *King and Charcoal-Burner*.

Suor Angelica (Sister Angelica)

- Giacomo Puccini. Opera in one act. 1917.
- Libretto by Giovacchino Forzano.
- First performance at the Metropolitan Opera, New York, on 14th December 1918.

CHARACTERS

Suor Angelica	soprano
The Princess, her aunt	contralto
The Abbess	mezzo-soprano
The Alms Sister	soprano
The Novice-Mistress	mezzo-soprano
Suor Genovieffa	soprano
Suor Osmina	soprano
Suor Dolcina	mezzo-soprano
Novices	mezzo-sopranos
Nursing Sister	soprano

Sister Angelica, as the mother of an illegitimate baby, expiates her sin in a convent. Her aunt, the Princess, seeking her signature to a document for her sister's marriage, tells her that the child died two years ago. In despair Sister Angelica takes poison, but prays for forgiveness, seeing, as she dies, a vision of the Blessed Virgin bringing her child to her.

Suor Angelica (Sister Angelica) formed part of Puccini's *Il trittico* (The Triptych), a group of three operas, with *Gianni Schicchi* and *Il tabarro* (The Cloak). The best known aria from the work is the moving *Senza mamma, o bimbo* (With no mother, my little child).

SURPRISES DE L'AMOUR, LES (THE SURPRISES OF CUPID)

- Jean-Philippe Rameau. *Opéra-ballet* in a prologue and two (or more) entrées. 1748.
- Libretto by Pierre Joseph Bernard.
- First performance at the Théâtre des Petits Cabinets, Versailles, on 27th November 1748.

In its original version, commissioned by Madame de Pompadour, Rameau's *opéra-ballet* celebrated the Treaty of Aix-la-Chapelle, with Cupid resolving the conflict in each entrée, notably, in the first *entrée*, between peace and war. The work was extended for later performance at the Paris Opéra in 1757.

Tabarro, Il (The Cloak)

- Giacomo Puccini. Opera in one act. 1916.
- Libretto by Giuseppe Adami, after the play *La houppelande* (The Great-Coat) by Didier Gold.
- First performance at the Metropolitan Opera, New York, on 14th December 1918.

Characters

Michele, a barge-owner, aged 50	baritone
Giorgetta, his wife, aged 25	soprano
Luigi, a stevedore, aged 20	tenor
Tinca, a stevedore, aged 35	tenor
Talpa, a stevedore, aged 55	bass
Frugola, his wife, aged 50	mezzo-soprano

On a barge moored in the Seine in Paris, Giorgetta suggests that Michele should offer the stevedores a drink, as they finish their work. In her husband's absence she dances with the men, most closely with Luigi, but dancing stops as Michele returns. They all have their dreams and Michele approaches Giorgetta with the plea that they renew their love for each other. She, however, has planned to meet Luigi. Michele sees her still dressed and is suspicious. He lights his pipe, unwittingly giving the signal agreed between Giorgetta and Luigi, who now steals aboard to be strangled by the wronged husband. Michele hides the body under his cloak, and when his wife comes to him, asking him to warm her under his cloak, he opens it, to reveal the body of her lover.

Il tabarro (The Cloak) is the first of the trilogy *Il trittico* (The Triptych), with *Gianni Schicchi* and *Suor Angelica.* The three form an interesting contrast of comedy and tragedy.

Tale of Tsar Saltan, The

- Nikolay Andreyevich Rimsky-Korsakov. Opera in a prologue and four acts. 1900.
- Libretto by Vladimir Nikolayevich Belsky, after the verse folk-tale by Pushkin.
- First performance at the Solodovnikov Theatre, Moscow, by the Mamontov Opera, on 3rd November 1900.

Characters

Tsar Saltan	bass
Tsaritsa Militrisa, the youngest sister	soprano
Tkachikha (Court Weaver), the middle sister	mezzo-soprano
Povarikha (Royal Cook), the eldest sister	soprano
Old Matchmaker Barbarikha, their mother	contralto
Prince Guidon	tenor
The Swan Princess	high soprano
An Old Man	tenor
Messenger	baritone
Court Jester	bass
Three Sailors	tenor, baritone & bass

In the prologue the three sisters express their wishes, to cook, to weave and, for the youngest, to marry the Tsar and bear him a son. The Tsar overhears her wish and marries her, while the older sisters become Royal Cook and Court Weaver, but seek to take revenge, when the Tsar goes off to the wars, leaving his young wife pregnant. In the first act the Tsaritsa waits for a reply from the Tsar to her message of his son's birth, but her letter has been intercepted and news of the birth of a monster conveyed to the Tsar. A messenger now brings his orders that mother and baby be cast into the sea. Washed up, after childhood in a barrel at sea, on the coast of an island, Prince Guidon saves the Swan Princess from an attacking kite and is rewarded with a magic city, of which he becomes king. On the advice of the Princess, Guidon transforms himself into a bee, and reaches his father's court with three sailors, who tell of the marvels of Guidon's island. The Tsar wants to visit the island and Barbarikha's objections are silenced when the bee stings her. On the island again, Guidon seeks a wife and finds one in the Swan Princess. The Tsar comes to the island and is eventually re-united with his wife, while Barbarikha and her two daughters are finally pardoned.

The so-called *Flight of the Bumble-Bee*, which serves as an entr'acte before Prince Guidon's arrival at court as a bee, has served as a show-piece for a variety of instruments, from the tuba and the double bass to a well known arrangement for violin by Jascha Heifetz and a brilliant vehicle for trumpet virtuosity. Excerpts from *The Tale of Tsar Saltan, of his Son, the Renowned and Mighty Bogatïr Prince Guidon Saltanovich, and of the Beautiful Swan-Princess* are heard often enough in a concert suite by Rimsky-Korsakov, *Musical Pictures*, including the Tsar's departure for war, the barrel at sea and the three wonders related by the sailors.

Recommended Recording:
The Tale of Tsar Saltan (Suite) — ***Naxos 8.550726***

Tamerlano (Tamburlaine)

- George Frideric Handel. Opera in three acts. 1724.
- Libretto by Nicola Francesco Haym, after a libretto by Agostin Provene.
- First performance at the King's Theatre, London, on 31st October 1724.

Characters

Tamerlano (Timurlenk), Emperor of the Tartars	male alto
Bajazete (Beyazit)Emperor of the Turks	tenor
Asteria, his daughter	soprano
Andronico (Andronicus), a Greek prince	male alto
Irene, Princess of Trebizond, betrothed to Timurlenk	contralto
Leone (Leo), friend of Timurlenk and Andronicus	bass
Zaida, friend of Asteria	silent rôle

Beyazit is a prisoner of Timurlenk and, released by his captor, threatens suicide, from which Andronicus dissuades him. Timurlenk is in love with Asteria and will allow her father to live in return for her love, while proposing to give Irene, his betrothed, to Andronicus, now appointed King of Byzantium but formerly Asteria's lover. Irene arrives at court, is excluded, but gains entry in disguise. She angrily upbraids Timurlenk, while Beyazit refuses to sanction Asteria's marriage with the Tartar Emperor. Asteria herself has planned, in any case, to murder Timurlenk. Father and daughter are imprisoned and prepare to take poison and Asteria and Andronicus openly declare their love for each other. After dire threats from Timurlenk, Beyazit takes poison, but his daughter and Andronicus are pardoned by Timurlenk, who is now united with Irene.

The subject of the tyrant known to Christopher Marlowe as Tamburlaine and in Turkish as Timurlenk, Timur the Lame, provided the Elizabethan theatre with two of its most popular tragedies. Operatic conventions of Handel's time demanded a happy ending, achieved only after the death of Beyazit. The work contains notable scenes of confrontation between conqueror and conquered.

TANCREDI

- Gioachino Rossini. *Melodramma eroico* in two acts.
- Libretto by Gaetano Rossi, after Voltaire's *Tancrède*.
- First performance at the Teatro La Fenice, Venice, on 6th February 1813.

CHARACTERS

Tancredi	contralto
Amenaide	soprano
Argirio, her father	tenor
Isaura, her confidante	mezzo-soprano
Orbazzano	bass
Roggiero, friend of Tancredi	mezzo-soprano

In 11th century Syracuse the feud between the leading families of Orbazzano and Argirio has been ended, in the face danger from attack by the Saracen leader Solamir. Argirio, now the leader of Syracuse, offers the hand of his daughter to Orbazzano, but Amenaide has been secretly engaged to the exiled knight Tancredi, whose return she has urged in a secret letter. Amenaide refuses to obey her father, and meets Tancredi, who has made his clandestine return, now urging him to make his escape. Orbazzano has possession of Amenaide's letter to Tancredi, which he supposes a traitorous communication with Solamir, and , angry at her rejection of him, demands her punishment. In prison she is condemned to death but her cause is defended in the lists by an unknown champion, the disguised and proscribed Tancredi. In combat he defeats Orbazzano, but believing Amenaide guilty leaves her. Away from Syracuse he is told of imminent Saracen attack and returns to fight, falling wounded. As he dies, he hears Amenaide's explanation of the letter and Argirio marries the couple. In the original happy ending Solamir, defeated by Tancredi, reveals the truth, allowing Tancredi and Amenaide to be happily united, to general rejoicing.

Rossini's *Tancredi*, regarded by Stendhal as his masterpiece, was staged in Ferrara soon after the first performance in Venice, but now, unusually, with a tragic ending, as in Voltaire's play. The opera includes the popular *Di tanti palpiti* (After such beating of the heart), after Tancredi has landed in Syracuse, and provides a challenging rôle for the protagonist and a remarkable combination of operatic tradition with dramatic requirements.

Recommended Recording: Tancredi (2 CDs) ***Naxos 8.660037-38***

Tannhäuser

- Richard Wagner. *Grosse romantische Oper* in three acts. 1845.
- Libretto by the composer.
- First performance at the Hoftheater, Dresden, on 19th October 1845.

Characters

Herrmann, Landgrave of Thuringia	bass
Tannhäuser, a Minnesinger	tenor
Wolfram von Eschenbach, a Minnesinger	baritone
Biterolf, a Minnesinger	bass
Walther von der Vogelweide, a Minnesinger	tenor
Heinrich der Schreiber, a Minnesinger	tenor
Reinmar von Zweter, a Minnesinger	bass
Elisabeth, niece of the Landgrave	soprano
Venus	soprano
A Young Shepherd	soprano
Four Pages	soprano & alto

Tannhäuser lies sleeping by the couch of Venus. Bacchantes revel, but Tannhäuser wakens with a desire to return to the world, away from the sensual delights of the Venusberg. He is warned, but puts his trust in Mary, the Mother of Christ, at whose name he finds himself by her shrine in a valley near the Wartburg. He hears a shepherd singing a welcome to spring, sees pilgrims setting out for Rome, and falls to his knees in repentance. He is urged by the Landgrave to join his hunting-party and eventually persuaded when he hears that Elisabeth, the Landgrave's niece, is pining for him. At the Wartburg he meets Elisabeth and they celebrate the power of love. The song contest on the Wartburg brings conflict between Tannhäuser and those who disapprove of the sensuous view of love that he expresses. Elisabeth saves Tannhäuser from the swords of the angry knights, who insist he should join the pilgrims to Rome, in order to seek absolution. In Rome he finds no pardon, while Elisabeth, accompanied by the knight and Minnesinger Wolfram, anxiously awaits his return, praying to the Blessed Virgin for his salvation. Eventually, after the other pilgrims, Tannhäuser returns. The Pope has cursed him, telling him that only when the papal crozier bursts into flower will he ever be pardoned. Now Tannhäuser seeks again the Venusberg. Wolfram restrains him by the mention of the name of Elisabeth, whose body is now born towards them in funeral procession. Tannhäuser kneels by the side of the bier, praying for her intercession, at which young pilgrims are seen returning, carrying the Pope's crozier, now miraculously blooming.

Tannhäuser und der Sängerkrieg auf Wartburg (Tannhäuser and the Singing Contest on the Wartburg) was Wagner's fifth opera and followed the staging in Dresden of *Der fliegende Holländer* (The Flying Dutchman). In Dresden it was not fully understood, while staging in Paris in 1861, with an extended *Bacchanale* in the first act, to provide the element of ballet required by French tradition, was an utter disaster. Elsewhere, however, the opera soon entered general repertoire. Wagner continued with revisions to the work into the 1870s, but it is usual to distinguish broadly between the Dresden and Paris versions. The opera opens with a prelude that makes use of motifs associated with the pilgrims and with repentance, leading to the Venusberg music and, in the Paris version, the *Bacchanale*. Tannhäuser, waking, sings his Hymn to Venus. Elisabeth's greeting, *Dich, teure Halle* (O dear halls of song) comes in the second act, with its grand march for the entry of the guests and the Landgrave's welcome. The *Pilgrims' Chorus* has appeared in a variety of arrangements, while Wolfram's *O du mein holder Abendstern* (O star of eve) has suffered a similar fate. The demanding rôle of Tannhäuser brings an account of his reception in Rome, *Inbrunst im Herzen* (Contrite in heart), before the final lure of the Venusberg and his ultimate attainment of forgiveness.

Recommended Recording:
Overture / Venusberg Music / Entrance of Guests / Pilgrimage ***Naxos 8.550136***

TAVERNER

- Peter Maxwell Davies. Opera in two acts. 1968.
- Libretto by the composer.
- First performance at Covent Garden, London, on 12th July 1972.

The Tudor composer Taverner is tried for heresy, convicted but reprieved by the Cardinal, who is seen in negotiation with King Henry over the proposed royal divorce. The Jester, identified with Death, observes this cynically and presents Taverner with the dilemma of distinguishing between Christ and Antichrist, good and evil. The symmetrical second act is set after the Reformation and Taverner now accuses his former accuser, who is condemned and put to death. The Cardinal now appears as an Archbishop of the new church and Taverner is compelled to abjure his own musical contribution to the old religion. The Jester here controls the Wheel of Fortune, which has turned.

Maxwell Davies makes use of Taverner's music, which is transformed, quoted, and serves as the seed from which the work develops. The opera came after the composer's earlier use of Taverner, notably in the *Seven In Nomine*, based on the traditional English consort form, with its contrapuntal use of a fragment from a Mass by Taverner.

Telemaco (Telemachus)

- Christoph Willibald von Gluck. *Dramma per musica* in two acts. 1765.
- Libretto by Marco Coltellini, after Carlo Sigismondo Capece.
- First performance at the Burgtheater, Vienna, on 30th January 1765.

Telemachus, son of Odysseus, searches for his father, long delayed on his return from the siege and capture of Troy. Shipwrecked, he finds him a captive of the sorceress Circe, who, for love of Odysseus, sets him free. Circe's unwillingness to allow her former captives to leave her magic island is eventually circumvented, with Telemachus now united with Circe's maid Asteria, who turns out to be the long lost sister of his own companion in the adventure, Meriones.

Gluck's *Telemaco, ossia L'isola di Circe* (Telemachus, or The Island of Circe) is a transitional work, not fully demonstrating the principles of operatic reform shown in the preceding opera *Orfeo ed Euridice* (Orpheus and Eurydice) and the succeeding *Alceste* (Alcestis). The librettist Coltellini based his work on an earlier libretto written for Alessandro Scarlatti. The subject of Telemachus owed its literary and dramatic popularity in the 18th century to the treatment accorded it by Fénelon in an early philosophical Bildungsroman that might even have had some influence on Mozart's *Die Zauberflöte* (The Magic Flute), a hundred years later.

Telephone, The

- Gian Carlo Menotti. *Opera buffa* in one act. 1946.
- Libretto by the composer.
- First performance at the Heckscher Theatre, New York, on 18th February 1947.

Characters

Lucy	soprano
Ben	baritone

Ben's attempts to propose to Lucy are constantly interrupted by the telephone. Eventually he resorts to the only possible means of communication and telephones her from a nearby kiosk, making his proposal, which she accepts, urging him not to forget her telephone number.

Menotti wrote *The Telephone* as a curtain-raiser for a revival of the tragic work, *The Medium*. In the composer's usual direct and tuneful idiom, it offers a witty and light-hearted operatic revue sketch.

Templer und die Jüdin, Der (The Templar and the Jewess)

- Heinrich August Marschner. *Grosse romantische Oper* in three acts. 1829.
- Libretto by Wilhelm August Wohlbrück, after various sources based on Walter Scott's novel *Ivanhoe*.
- First performance at the Stadtheater, Leipzig, on 22nd December 1829.

The Norman Brian de Bois-Guilbert, a Knight Templar, seeks to win Rebecca, daughter of the Jew, Isaac of York, while his compatriot, Maurice de Bracy, hopes to win Rowena, ward of the Saxon knight Cedric, who is herself in love with Cedric's disinherited son, Ivanhoe. Isaac, Rebecca and Ivanhoe are taken prisoner by the Normans, but Ivanhoe is rescued by the Black Knight and his outlaw followers, revealing himself as King Richard the Lion-Heart, returned from the crusades. The fate of Rebecca, accused of witchcraft, depends on the result of a tournament in which Bois-Guilbert, whose urgent suggestions of escape together she has rejected, has been compelled to serve as champion of the Templars, her accusers. In combat with Ivanhoe, who appears as her champion, Bois-Guilbert falls down dead.

Marschner's opera enjoyed great popularity in the 19th century and still deserves attention. It includes effective choruses and moments of exciting drama, particularly in the conflict and escapes of the end of the first act.

Recommended Recording: Overture ***Marco Polo 8.223342***

Teseo (Theseus)

- George Frideric Handel. Opera in five acts. 1713.
- Libretto by Nicola Francesco Haym, adapted from the libretto *Thésée* (Theseus) by Philippe Quinault.
- First performance at the Queen's Theatre, London, on 10th January 1713.

Theseus returns in disguise to fight for his father, the Athenian king, Aegeus, who, victorious, declares his intention of marrying Agilea, instead of the sorceress Medea. Agilea, however, is in love with Theseus, as is Medea, who is ready to accept the royal suggestion that she marry him. Theseus, in triumph, is acclaimed as king and declares his love of Agilea, causing Medea to seek revenge by provoking the jealousy of Aegeus. Catastrophe is averted when Aegeus recognises Theseus as his son, and Medea's final attempts at destruction, through her spectacular magic powers, are frustrated by the goddess Minerva.

Handel's third opera for London has a fine and largely original score, relying less on borrowing from earlier works than was often the case. Dramatically it suffered because of its libretto, designed for the conventions of the French theatre, and because of cuts made in the text and in recitative that made the complexities of the action more difficult to follow. It received thirteen performances, a successful outcome that would have been more profitable had not the Irish impresario Owen Swiney, manager of the Queen's Theatre, found it necessary to abscond, leaving the singers unpaid.

Teuzzone

- Antonio Vivaldi. *Dramma per musica* in three acts. 1719.
- Libretto by Apostolo Zeno.
- First performance at the Teatro Arciducale detto il Comico, Mantua, at Carnival 1719.

Zeno's libretto of 1706 was first set by Clemente Monari and Paolo Magni for Milan. Interest must lie in the libretto, with its attempt to make use of new anecdotal information about China, here largely misunderstood. The music avoids orientalism.

Thaïs

- Jules Massenet. *Comédie lyrique* in three acts. 1893.
- Libretto by Louis Gallet, after the novel by Anatole France.
- First performance at the Paris Opéra on 16th March 1894.

Characters

Thaïs, an actress and courtesan	soprano
Athanaël, a young Coenobite monk	baritone
Nicias, a young Sybarite philosopher	tenor
Palémon, an old Coenobite monk	bass
Crobyle, a slave	soprano
Myrtale, a slave	mezzo-soprano
Albine, an abbess	mezzo-soprano
La Charmeuse, a dancer	soprano
Servant of Nicias	baritone

The young monk Athanaël, in the desert, sees a vision of the famous actress Thaïs, the centre of adulation, and sets out for Alexandria, with the intention of saving her. He meets her at the house of his former friend, the young nobleman Nicias, and later convinces her of the righteousness of his cause, setting fire to her house and possessions and leading her with him to the salvation offered by a convent. They part, but Athanaël is haunted by thoughts of Thaïs and presentiments for the future. He sets out for the settlement of the abbess, Mother Albine, where he finds Thaïs dying. She sees angels prepared to welcome her, while Athanaël must finally admit his mortal love for her, so long repressed.

The name of Massenet's opera is all too well known from the *Méditation* that serves as an interlude expressive of the thoughts of Thaïs that lead to her conversion in the second act, as Athanaël waits at her door. The short piece has been arranged for a variety of instruments. In the first act Athanaël recalls how once he had approached the house of Thaïs in Alexandria, fascinated but now scandalized, *Hélas! Enfant encore* (Alas! Still a child). In the second scene he approaches the house of his friend Nicias, *Voilà donc la terrible cité* (There then is the terrible city). In her own house Thaïs looks at herself in the glass, reflecting on her beauty in *Dis-moi que je suis belle et que je serai belle éternellement* (Tell me that I am beautiful and shall be beautiful for ever). The theme of the fallen woman now redeemed is one much favoured by Massenet and his contemporaries and compatriots.

Recommended Recording: Méditation ***Naxos 8.550306***

THÉRÈSE

- Jules Massenet. *Drame musical* in two acts. 1906.
- Libretto by Jules Claretie.
- First performance at the Opéra, Monte Carlo, on 7th February 1907.

It is 1792 and Thérèse is married to André Thorel, who has possession of a château that had belonged to his boyhood friend Armand de Clerval, former lover of his wife. Armand takes refuge with the Thorels, staying with them eight months later in Paris. André finds a safe-conduct for Armand, who tries to persuade Thérèse to escape with him. She refuses, and when her own husband is arrested, to be sent to the guillotine, she shouts out her support of the King, finally joining her husband on the scaffold.

Massenet wrote two works for the 1907 season, the present opera for Monte Carlo and *Ariane* (Ariadne), based on the classical legend of the Cretan princess abandoned by Theseus on Naxos, for the Paris Opéra, the latter achieving more substantial contemporary success.

Thomas and Sally

- Thomas Augustine Arne. Dramatic pastoral in two acts. 1760.
- Libretto by Isaac Bickerstaff.
- First performance at Covent Garden, London, on 28th November 1760.

The milkmaid Sally laments the absence of her lover Thomas, a sailor, and is urged by Dorcas to enjoy life. The Squire urges his attentions on her. Thomas returns and is able to deter the Squire from his renewed pursuit of Sally.

Thomas and Sally, a light-hearted and very English comic opera, enjoyed considerable popularity in its day. Its instrumentation includes clarinets, relatively uncommon in orchestras at this time.

Threepenny Opera, The (see Die Dreigroschenoper)

Tiefland (The Lowlands)

- Eugen d'Albert. *Musikdrama* in a prologue and two acts. 1903.
- Libretto by Rudolph Lothar, after the play *Tierra Baixa* (The Lowland) by Angel Guimerà.
- First performance at the Neues Deutsches Theater, Prague, on 15th November 1903.

Two shepherds, Pedro and Nando, are in pastures high in the Pyrenees. They are happy with their lot, but Pedro wants a wife. The village elder Tommaso arrives, bringing with him Marta, as a wife for Pedro, but Nando warns him of the dangers of the world below. In a mill in the village below it transpires that Marta is the property of the rich land-owner Sebastiano and now must marry an ignorant peasant, Pedro. The couple marry, while Sebastiano intends to continue his liaison with Marta and visit her that night, a meeting that the presence of Pedro eventually prevents. A little girl, Nuri, tells Pedro the truth about Marta, the reason for the villagers' mockery of his marriage. Marta seeks Pedro's forgiveness and a final open quarrel with Sebastiano, whose proposed marriage has been prevented by information given by Tommaso, leads to a fight and Sebastiano's death. Pedro resolves to take Marta away with him to the mountain pastures.

Eugen d'Albert found in *Tiefland* (The Lowlands) a subject to be depicted with dramatic realism. Pedro's prayer for a wife, *Zwei Vaterunser bet'ich* (I prayed two Our Fathers) and his innocent present to Marta of a silver coin he had won for killing a wolf, *Schau her, das ist ein Taler* (See here is a taler) typify his simplicity, with his *Wolfserzählung* (Tale of the Wolf). While Marta gives a moving account of her own destitute childhood in *Ich weiss nicht, wer mein Vater war* (I know not who my father was).

Recommended Recording: Prelude and Intermezzo — ***Naxos 8.550240***

Tito Manlio (Titus Manlius)

- Antonio Vivaldi. *Dramma per musica* in three acts. 1719.
- Libretto by Matteo Noris.
- First performance at the Teatro Arciducale detto il Comico, Mantua, at Carnival 1719.

Titus Manlius is engaged in war with the people of Latium. Conflicts of love and duty arise, with his daughter Vitellia in love with the Latin commander Geminius, but loved by the Latin Lucius. Manlius, the son of Titus, kills Geminius, disobeying his father, and is condemned to death, in spite of the pleas of his beloved Servilia, sister of Geminius. He rejects the offer of Lucius to free him. There is eventual reconciliation between father and son.

Vivaldi wrote *Tito Manlio* (Titus Manlius) for the celebration of the marriage of the governor of Mantua, Prince Philipp of Hessen-Darmstadt, and the work is scored with particularly rich instrumentation. He also contributed arias to another opera of the same name, a *pasticcio*, for performance in Rome.

Tolomeo (Ptolemy)

- George Frideric Handel. Opera in three acts. 1728.
- Libretto by Nicola Francesco Haym, after a libretto by Carlo Sigismondo Capece.
- First performance at the King's Theatre, London, on 30th April 1728.

The banished joint ruler of Egypt, Ptolemy IX, lives on the island of Cyprus, under the shepherd name Osmin, accompanied by his wife Seleuce, known as Delia. The sister of the despotic Araspe, King of Cyprus, Elisa, is in love with Ptolemy, while her brother pursues Seleuce. Ptolemy is eventually, after various intrigues, re-united with Seleuce and restored to the throne by his younger brother Alessandro, who had taken his place.

Non lo dirò col labbro (I will not say it with my lips), the *cavatina* of Alessandro in the first act, is better known to English audiences as *Silent Worship*, with new words by Arthur Somervell. A less familiar recital item is taken from the last act, when Ptolemy thinks that he is taking poison, in fact a sleeping draught provided by Elisa, *Stille amare* (Bitter potion). *Tolomeo* (Ptolemy) was the last of the series of operas written by Handel for the troublesome rival sopranos Faustina Bordoni and Francesca Cuzzoni, with the parts of the Ptolemy brothers sung by the castrati Senesino and Antonio Baldi.

Torquato Tasso

- Gaetano Donizetti. *Melodramma semiserio* in three acts. 1833.
- Libretto by Jacopo Ferretti, after works by Giovanni Rosini, Goldoni, Goethe and Byron.
- First performance at the Teatro Valle, Rome, on 9th September 1833.

The poet Tasso is in love with Eleonora, sister of his patron, Alfonso d'Este, Duke of Ferrara, and is imprisoned as a madman. After an incarceration of seven years he learns that he is to be crowned laureate, with the laurel wreath of Petrarch, but is shocked to learn that Eleanora, with whom he might have shared his honour, is dead.

Tasso is another important baritone rôle, but the apparently tragic nature of the plot is vitiated by the inclusion of a *buffo* element in a comic villain, a rival of the poet.

Torvaldo e Doliska (Torvaldo and Dorliska)

- Gioachino Rossini. *Dramma semiserio* in two acts. 1815.
- Libretto by Cesare Sterbini, after *Vie et amours du chevalier Faublas* (Life and Loves of Chevalier Faublas) by Jean-Baptiste Louvet de Couvrai.
- First performance at the Teatro Valle, Rome, on 26th December 1815.

The Duke of Ordow is in love with Dorliska, who escapes a trap set for her and her beloved Torvaldo in the forest. Dorliska makes the mistake of seeking refuge in the Duke's castle, where she is welcomed by the comic servants Carlotta and Giorgio, and meets Torvaldo, who has entered the castle disguised as a woodsman. They are both eventually rescued, with the help of the servants and a renegade follower of the Duke, who is overthrown by the rebellious villagers.

Rossini's opera has a lively enough overture, but the work is relatively seldom performed, although Torvaldo's first act *cavatina*, *Fra un istante* (For a moment), may be heard in recital.

Tosca

- Giacomo Puccini. *Melodramma* in three acts. 1899.
- Libretto by Giuseppe Giacosa and Luigi Illica, after the play *La Tosca* by Victorien Sardou.
- First performance at the Teatro Costanzi, Rome, on 14th January 1900.

Characters

Floria Tosca, a famous singer	soprano
Mario Cavaradossi, a painter	tenor
Baron Scarpia, Chief of Police	baritone
Cesare Angelotti, a former Consul of the Roman Republic	bass
A Sacristan	bass
Spoletta, a police agent	tenor
Sciarrone, a gendarme	bass
Gaoler	bass
Shepherd-Boy	alto
Roberti, the executioner	silent rôle

In the church of S Andrea della Valle, the fugitive Angelotti takes refuge in a private chapel. The painter Cavaradossi returns to the canvas he is painting, a picture of Mary Magdalene, influenced by the features of his beloved Tosca and by a woman he has often seen in the church. The sacristan complains of the trouble Cavaradossi gives him. As he leaves, Angelotti emerges from hiding, explaining that he has escaped from imprisonment in the Castel Sant'Angelo. The voice of Tosca is heard and Angelotti hides again. Tosca is jealous of what she thinks may have been an assignation with another woman but agrees to meet her lover after her evening performance. The church fills for a celebration of a supposed victory over Napoleon and Baron Scarpia and his agents seek for signs of Angelotti, suspicion falling on Cavaradossi as a possible accomplice. Scarpia succeeds now in arousing further jealousy in Tosca, who has returned, showing her a fan found in the chapel, belonging, in fact, to Angelotti's sister. Scarpia orders his men to follow Tosca, when she leaves, as a victory *Te Deum* is sung. In Scarpia's apartment the sound is heard of an entertainment being given below for Queen Caroline, dancing and a performance by Tosca. Cavaradossi has been arrested and is interrogated and, when Tosca comes in, tortured in the next room, to elicit information from her. She betrays Angelotti's hiding-place at the well in the garden of Cavaradossi's villa. The painter is to be shot at dawn, but can be saved if Tosca will give in to Scarpia's demands on her. She pretends to agree and when he has signed a safe-conduct she kills him. In the third act, at Castel Sant'Angelo, Cavaradossi prepares for death, as dawn draws near. Tosca is brought in and,

left alone with him, explains how there is to be a mock-execution, after which they can escape together. In the event Scarpia has his revenge. His orders did not countermand the execution and Cavaradossi is shot. When Tosca realises that he is dead, she leaps from the battlements to her own death, while Scarpia's men draw threateningly near, having discovered their master's body.

Tosca remains a major work in operatic repertoire, although subject to relentlessly hostile criticism on the grounds of the brutal coarseness of its plot. It is, in fact, dramatically convincing, up to the moment of final irony. Cavaradossi is entrusted with his first moving aria in the opening act, *Recondita armonia* (Secret harmony), when he contrasts the dark-haired beauty of Tosca with the fair-haired stranger he has seen in the church, both combined in his painting. Cavaradossi's other great aria comes in the third act, as he prepares for death. In *E lucevan le stelle* (And the stars shone) he regrets his coming execution and parting from Tosca. The rôle of Tosca has a strong dramatic appeal. Her best known aria is *Vissi d'arte* (I have lived for art), as she despairs at the predicament that Scarpia has posed for her.

Recommended Recordings:

Tosca (2 CDs)	***Naxos 8.660001-02***
Highlights	***Naxos 8.553153***

Tote Stadt, Die (The Dead City)

- Erich Wolfgang Korngold. Opera in three acts. 1920.
- Libretto by the composer and his father, Julius Korngold (under the pseudonym Paul Schott), after the novel *Bruges la morte* (Bruges the Dead) by Georges Rodenbach.
- First performance in Hamburg and Cologne on 4th December 1920.

Characters

Paul	tenor
Marietta, a dancer & The Apparition of Paul's late wife, Marie	soprano
Frank, Paul's friend	baritone
Brigitta, Paul's housekeeper	mezzo-soprano
Fritz, the Pierrot	baritone
Juliette, a dancer	soprano
Lucienne, a dancer	soprano
Gaston, a dancer	dancer
Gaston's Voice (off-stage)	tenor

Victorin, a stage director	tenor
Graf Albert	tenor

In Bruges Paul keeps a room as a shrine to his dead wife Marie. Her portrait hangs on the wall and a lock of her hair is kept in a casket. Frank visits him and learns how he has met a woman who resembles Marie, to the life. Marietta, a dancer, comes to the house, dances and sings, resembling, as she realises, the portrait now revealed on the wall of the room. Paul is fascinated by her and when she has gone imagines that he sees Marie herself, stepping from the portrait and telling him to go out and live. The second act finds Paul waiting outside Mariettas Lied house by night. His housekeeper, in disapproval, has entered a convent and Frank has also succumbed to the fascination of Marietta. She and her companions come from the theatre, laughing and drinking, observed by Paul. Marietta acts the resurrection scene from Meyerbeer's *Robert le Diable*, to the amusement of her friends and the horror of Paul, who rails at her. She exercises her power over him, insisting that they go to his house. The next morning Paul finds her in Marie's room, while outside a procession passes. Marietta mocks Paul's devotion to Marie and his piety, provoking him until he murders her. Paul wakes up, to find that what had happened was a dream. He resolves, with Frank, to leave Bruges, a city of death, where there is no resurrection.

Korngold's opera won wide success after its first simultaneous performances in Hamburg and Cologne. The work is richly orchestrated, with music often of great intensity. The treatment of the symbolist novel of Rodenbach is characteristic in many ways of the literary and dramatic preoccupations of the period. It attracted the attention of a number of important singers in the two principal rôles of Paul and Marietta-Marie. Well known excerpts include the *Mariettalied*, Marietta's song of sadness, *Glück, das mir verblieb* (Joy, that I had) and Fritz's melancholy *Pierrotlied*, in the night dream-sequence by Marietta's house. The latter was also arranged as a violin solo by Fritz Kreisler, testimony to its wide contemporary popularity.

Recommended Recording: Die tote Stadt (2 CDs) ***Naxos 8.660060-61***

TRAUMGÖRGE, DER (GÖRGE THE DREAMER)

- Alexander von Zemlinsky. Opera in two acts and a Nachspiel. 1906.
- Libretto by Leo Feld, based on a fairy-tale by Richard Volkmann-Leander, a novel by Hermann Sudermann and other sources.
- First performance at the Opernhaus, Nuremberg, on 11th October 1980.

The orphan Görge is fascinated by the fairy-tales he reads, in spite of the attempts of Grete to bring him to a sense of reality, as exemplified by Hans, her former boy-friend. He dreams of a princess and sets out on his quest, finding himself, some three years later, in sympathy with Gertraud, daughter of an impoverished nobleman, but likely to be involved in a bloodthirsty village uprising, led by Kaspar. The villagers attempt to kill Gertraud, who is thought to be a witch, but she is saved by Görge, who now comes to his senses. In the sequel Görge and Gertraud return to his village, where he can help the villagers and understand that the relevance of fairy-tales lies in the real world.

Zemlinsky's opera was accepted by Gustav Mahler for production at the Vienna Court Opera. When Mahler was forced to resign, to be replaced by Felix Weingartner, the work, the composer's third and, in his view, best opera, was rejected.

TRAVIATA, LA (THE FALLEN WOMAN)

- Giuseppe Verdi. Opera in three acts. 1853.
- Libretto by Francesco Maria Piave, after the play *La dame aux camélias* (The Lady of the Camelias) by Alexandre Dumas fils.
- First performance at the Teatro La Fenice, Venice, on 6th March 1853.

CHARACTERS

Violetta Valéry, a courtesan	soprano
Flora Bervoix, her friend	mezzo-soprano
Annina, her maid	soprano
Alfredo Germont	tenor
Giorgio Germont, his father	baritone
Gastone, Vicomte de Letorières	tenor
Baron Douphol	baritone
Marchese D'Obigny	bass
Doctor Grenvil	bass
Giuseppe, Violetta's servant	tenor

Violetta, at a party in her house, is moved to learn that the young Alfredo Germont is in love with her. There are, however, hints already that she is suffering from consumption. They set up house together in the country, but Violetta secretly sells her jewels to meet the expenses they now incur. Alfredo learns of this from Violetta's maid, Annina, and goes to Paris to raise money. In his absence his father arrives, seeking to persuade Violetta to leave Alfredo, whose behaviour prejudices the marriage chances of his sister, as well as his own prospects. Violetta sacrifices her own feelings and

accepts an invitation from her friend Flora Bervoix which will take her back to her old life, now under the protection of Baron Douphol. She leaves a note for Alfredo, telling him of her decision, while old Germont tries to comfort his son, without revealing anything of Violetta's true motives. Alfredo then bursts into the party at Flora's house and insults Violetta, whom he finds with her new protector. She falls back, fainting, as the second act closes. In the third act Violetta is at home, near to death. Germont has told his son of the sacrifice she had made, and Alfredo now returns, holding her in his arms as she dies.

La traviata (The Fallen Woman) is one of those operas that has retained a firm position in current repertoire, never failing in its effect. The prelude to the first act uses the tender and melancholy music that will later precede Violetta's death, as well as her plea to him to love her. The first of these returns in the prelude to the third act. At Violetta's there is a lively drinking-song or *Brindisi*, *Libiamo* (Let us drink), led by Alfredo, and as the guests go into the next room, he declares his love for her in *Un dì felice* (One happy day). Her response to his declarations is heard in her later reflective *Ah, fors'è lui* (Ah perhaps it is he my heart desires). In the second act Alfredo considers the happiness that life with Violetta has brought him in *De'miei bollenti spiriti* (Fervent my dream of ecstasy). Germont's attempts to remind his son of their home, *Di Provenza il mar, il suol* (The sea, the land of Provence) have provided baritones with a moving aria, and there is later contrast in the masquerading gypsy and Spanish dances at the house of Flora Bervoix. There is, of course, much else in a work, which, although set in 1700, might equally be supposed to have a contemporary setting and relevance in the Paris of the 1850s, an element of realism less apparent in historical dramas of kings and princes.

Recommended Recordings:

La traviata (2 CDs)	***Naxos 8.660011-12***
Highlights	***Naxos 8.553041***

TRISTAN UND ISOLDE (TRISTAN AND ISOLDE)

- Richard Wagner. *Handlung* in three acts. 1859.
- Libretto by the composer.
- First performance at the Königliches Hof- und Nationaltheater, Munich, on 10th June 1865.

CHARACTERS

König Marke (King Mark)	bass
Tristan, his nephew	tenor
Kurwenal, Tristan's retainer	baritone

Isolde, an Irish princess	soprano
Brangäne, her companion	soprano
Melot, a courtier	tenor
A Shepherd	tenor
A Helmsman	baritone
A Sailor	tenor

Isolde, with her companion Brangäne, sailing on Tristan's boat to Cornwall, rails at her fate and vows to encompass Tristan's death, as he takes her from her native country to marry King Mark. Tristan had killed her betrothed, Morold, and now takes her to Cornwall as tribute, while she, haunted by Tristan's gaze, had earlier cured him through her inherited magic powers of healing. Isolde summons Tristan to her, but he demurs. She now tells Brangäne to bring her casket of magic potions and prepares a poisoned cup for Tristan. Before they land, she calls him to her, and they both drink, but Brangäne has substituted for the death potion a love potion, which has immediate effect. It is now a summer night and Isolde waits for Tristan, against whom the courtier Melot has been plotting. It is only in the night that Tristan and Isolde can realise their love, deluded by the light of day. As the lovers lie together, Brangäne, watching from the tower, cries out her warning, as night passes, but they are unwilling to part. The royal hunting-party bursts in and Tristan is reproached by King Mark. He allows Melot to wound him mortally. In the third act Tristan lies dying, cared for by Kurwenal, who has brought him home to his own castle. Isolde's ship is seen approaching, and soon she is with him, as he dies in her arms. A second ship appears, bringing Melot and King Mark. Kurwenal defends his master, killing Melot, and being killed himself in the struggle. King Mark is horrified, since he had come to unite the lovers, having learnt of the love potion from Brangäne. Isolde, who has swooned, wakes, only to die, as she gazes at the body of her dead lover.

The prelude to *Tristan und Isolde* (Tristan and Isolde) has been regarded by analysts as a cogent element in the development of later modes of harmony, offering, as it does, harmonic ambiguities that have been seen as leading to atonality. It interweaves a series of motifs of importance in the drama, motifs of longing, the gaze, the love potion and the death potion, love's yearning, Tristan and Tristan and Isolde. The prelude to the second act contrasts motifs associated with day and those associated with night and its joys, while the third act is introduced by motifs associated with despair, languid suffering and solitude. At the climax of the drama is the *Liebestod*, Isolde's love-death, *Mild und leise wie er lächelt* (Fair and gently he is smiling), as she herself dies. The music is also known in an orchestral version, with a vocal arrangement, a prelude and *Liebestod*, devised by Humperdinck. The second act, with its ecstatic night of love, brings music of great dramatic power and suggestion.

Wagner's opera was written during the period he spent in Switzerland, after his escape from Dresden in 1849, and coincided with his relationship with Mathilde Wesendonck, the wife of a benefactor who continued his support of Wagner, as others were to do in similar circumstances. It would be difficult to exaggerate the marked technical and dramatic effect *Tristan und Isolde* had on the later course of music and of other arts.

Recommended Recording: Prelude and Liebestod **Naxos 8.550498**

Troilus and Cressida

- Willam Walton. Opera in three acts. 1954.
- Libretto by Christopher Hassall, after Chaucer and other sources.
- First performance at Covent Garden, London, on 3rd December 1954.

Troilus is in love with Cressida, daughter of the High Priest Calkas, who advises surrender to the Greeks, following the Delphic oracle, and himself plans to desert to the Greeks. Pandarus, Cressida's uncle, succeeds in bringing her together with Troilus, but in the morning the Greek prince Diomede demands that Cressida be exchanged for the Trojan Antenor, taken prisoner by the Greeks. In the Greek camp Cressida hears nothing of Troilus, whose messages have been intercepted on the orders of Calkas. She is induced to give in to the urging of Diomede, but, when a truce has been arranged and ransom prepared for Cressida, Troilus arrives to find her newly married to the Greek. Troilus attacks Diomede and is killed by Calkas, who is sent back to the Trojans in chains, while Cressida kills herself.

Walton's romantic opera won some success in London at its first staging. Written in an idiom that might, at the time, have seemed dated, the work is uneven in quality. A concert suite derived from the score by Christopher Palmer in 1987 may be heard occasionally in the concert-hall.

Trovatore, Il (The Troubadour)

- Giuseppe Verdi. *Dramma* in four parts. 1853.
- Libretto by Salvadore Cammarano, completed by Leone Emanuele Bardare, after the play *El trovador* (The Troubadour) by Antonio García Gutiérrez.
- First performance at the Teatro Apollo, Rome, on 19th January 1853.

Characters

Il Conte di Luna, a young noble in the service of the Prince of Aragon	baritone
Leonora, a lady-in-waiting to the Princess of Aragon	soprano
Azucena, an old gypsy woman	mezzo-soprano
Manrico, an officer in the army of Prince Urgel and supposed son of Azucena	tenor
Ferrando, an officer in the Count di Luna's army	bass
Ines, attendant and confidante of Leonora	soprano
Ruiz, a soldier in Manrico's service	tenor
An Old Gypsy	bass
A Messenger	tenor

The four parts of the opera have the titles *The Duel, The Gypsy, The Gypsy's Son and The Execution.* Ferrando tells the story of the revenge taken by a gypsy for the death of her mother, the apparent destruction in the fire of the son of the old Count di Luna. In the palace gardens Leonora waits for her lover, the troubadour Manrico, mistaking the Count di Luna, who also loves her, for him, an error that ends with a duel between the two men. At the gypsy camp Azucena tells Manrico the story of the abduction of the son of the Count di Luna and admits that she threw the wrong baby on the fire, keeping, as her own, the Count's son. He tells her how he was held back from killing the young Count, in their duel. News comes that Leonora, thinking Manrico dead, is to enter a convent, a step that the Count seeks to prevent. The arrival of Manrico, with his men, allows him to take Leonora away with him. Azucena is captured by the Count's men, who are preparing to attack Castellor, Manrico's stronghold. In the castle the planned marriage of Manrico and Leonora is interrupted by news of Azucena's capture. Imprisoned by the Count, Manrico and Azucena are threatened with death, while Leonora seeks to save her lover, offering herself in return, although she has secretly taken poison. In the prison Azucena reveals to Manrico his parentage, as a son of the old Count and brother to his enemy. Leonora comes to bring news of Manrico's release, and dies, while the Count orders the immediate execution of Manrico, watched by Azucena, who has her final triumphant revenge when she reveals to the Count the identity of his victim.

Il trovatore (The Troubadour) followed close upon the success of Verdi's *Rigoletto* and was to be followed by *La traviata* (The Fallen Woman). It retains its place as a major element in Italian opera repertoire, in spite of the improbabilities of a plot in which Azucena might seem to have suffered a confusion of mind worthy of Miss Prism. This lack of verisimilitude is forgotten in the dramatic strength of the music. Ferrando's narrative, *Di due figli vivea padre felice* (There lived once a happy father of two boys), sets the opening. The second scene allows Leonora her *Tacea la notte*

placida (Silent was the night), as she tells Ines of when she first heard Manrico's serenade, *Deserto sulla terra* (Deserted on the earth). The second act starts with the famous *Anvil Chorus*, *Vedi! Le fosche notturne* (See! The darkness of night goes), as the gypsies in their encampment start their day, a chorus that has its third part parallel in the song of the Count's soldiers, *Or co' dadi* (Now we gamble). The second act also brings Azucena's powerful account of her mother's death, *Stride la vampa* (The fire roars). She has her moments again when she is interrogated by the Count, as his prisoner, *Giorni poveri vivea* (There in poverty) and *Deh! Rallentate o barbari* (Ah! Cruel men, loosen these chains), and in her final scene with Manrico. For Leonora herself there is the moving *D'amor sull'ali rosee* (Love, fly on rosy wings), as she hears the *Miserere* from within the castle, where Manrico is held prisoner, and her final scene with Manrico.

Recommended Recording: Il trovatore (2 CDs) ***Naxos 8.660023-24***

Troyens, Les (The Trojans)

- Hector Berlioz. *Opéra* in five acts. 1858.
- Libretto by the composer, based on Virgil's *Aeneid.*
- First performance of Acts 3 – 5, as *Les Troyens à Carthage* (The Trojans at Carthage), at the Théâtre Lyrique, Paris, on 4th November 1863. First complete performance in Carlsruhe on 6th December 1890.

Characters

Énée (Aeneas), Trojan hero, son of Venus and Anchises	tenor
Cassandre (Cassandra), Trojan prophetess daughter of Priam	mezzo-soprano
Didon (Dido), Queen of Carthage, widow of Sychaeus, prince of Tyre	mezzo-soprano
Chorèbe (Coroebus), a young prince from Asia, betrothed to Cassandra	baritone
Anna, sister of Dido	contralto
Narbal, minister to Dido	bass
Iopas, Tyrian poet at Dido's court	tenor
Hylas, a young Phrygian sailor	tenor
Panthée (Panthous), Trojan priest, friend of Aeneas	bass
Ascagne (Ascanius), son of Aeneas	soprano
L'ombre d'Hector (Ghost of Hector), Trojan hero, son of Priam	tenor
Priam, King of Troy	bass

Hécube (Hecuba), his wife	mezzo-soprano
Sinon, a Greek spy	tenor
Two Trojan Soldiers	basses
A Greek Captain	bass
Mercure (Mercury)	bass
Hélène (Helenus), a Trojan priest, son of Priam	tenor
A Priest of Pluto	bass
Polyxène (Polyxena), sister of Cassandra	soprano
Andromaque (Andromache), widow of Hector	silent rôle
Astyanax, her son	silent rôle

The Greeks have seemingly departed, and the Trojans, under siege for ten years, follow the treacherous advice of Sinon and drag the Wooden Horse into their city. Cassandra foresees what will happen. At night the ghost of Hector urges Aeneas to flee. Troy is destroyed, but Aeneas escapes to found a new Troy in the West. The Trojan women kill themselves, rather than fall captive to the Greeks. In Carthage Dido is established as queen of a prosperous city. Aeneas and his men arrive and help to protect the city from the attack of Iarbas. Returning victorious, Aeneas joins Dido in a hunt, during the course of which they shelter from a storm, while the voice of wood-nymphs still insist on Italy as the destination of Aeneas, reminding him of his duty. Dido and Aeneas sing of their love, but the god Mercury reminds him of Italy. Trojan ghosts appear to urge Aeneas on and he obeys, setting sail. Dido, abandoned, mounts her funeral pyre, calls for future revenge from Hannibal and kills herself with the sword of Aeneas, seeing, as she dies, the future power of Rome.

Berlioz had recourse to Virgil's *Aeneid*, a poem with which he had been familiar from boyhood, for the basis of his opera, a work that makes considerable demands on resources, although it should not last more than four and a half hours. It is a spectacular work and in its earlier history was divided into two parts, the first dealing with the capture of Troy and the second the events in Carthage. Most familiar of all to audiences are the orchestral *Royal Hunt and Storm* from the fourth act. The epic work is richly orchestrated, with off-stage effects that include groups of instruments set apart to give the impression of an approaching and passing procession in the first act, with an off-stage group of sax-horns. Over all is the grandiose historical perception of the destiny of Aeneas and the imperial future of Rome, a reflection of the concept behind his literary source.

Recommended Recording: Prelude and Royal Hunt and Storm ***Naxos 8.553195***

Tsar's Bride, The

- Nikolay Andreyevich Rimsky-Korsakov. Opera in four acts. 1899.
- Libretto by Il'ya Fyodorovich Tyumenev, based on an outline by the composer drawn from a play by Lev Alexandrovich Mey.
- First performance at the Solodovnikov Theatre, Moscow, by the Mamontov Opera on 3rd November 1899.

The nobleman Gryaznoy, a member of Tsar Ivan's special retinue, the *oprichniki*, wants to marry Marfa, daughter of the Novgorod merchant Vasily Stepanovich Sobakin, who is already promised to Ivan Sergeyevich Lïkov, a young nobleman. Gryaznoy seeks a love potion from his mistress, Lyubasha, who determines on revenge, providing a potion that will destroy her rival's beauty. The Tsar Ivan seeks a bride and chooses Marfa, who is now ill. Gryaznoy blames Lïkov, whom he kills, but eventually admits what he has done. Lyubasha now confesses how she has provided a different potion, and Gryaznoy kills her. Marfa is now out of her mind, and identifies Gryaznoy with her beloved Lïkov.

The Tsar's Bride is a thoroughly Russian work, both in its pseudo-historical setting and in its occasional recourse to folk-melodies. The overture has provided an item of occasional concert repertoire, while Lyubasha's aria *Haste thee, mother mine* is known also in instrumental arrangements.

Recommended Recording: Overture and Intermezzo — ***Naxos 8.553789***

Turandot

- Giacomo Puccini. *Dramma lirico* in three acts. 1924.
- Libretto by Giuseppe Adami and Renato Simoni, after the fairy-tale drama by Carlo Gozzi.
- First performance at the Teatro alla Scala, Milan, on 25th April 1926.

Characters

Princess Turandot	soprano
The Emperor Altoun, her father	tenor
Timur, the dispossessed King of Tartary	bass
Calaf, his son	tenor
Liù, a young slave-girl	soprano
Ping, Grand Chancellor	baritone
Pang, General Purveyor	tenor

Pong, Chief Cook	tenor
A Mandarin	baritone
The Prince of Persia	silent rôle
The Executioner (Pu-Tin-Pao)	silent rôle

By imperial decree, Princess Turandot is to marry the first royal suitor able to answer her three riddles, failure leading to execution, a fate to be suffered by the Prince of Persia. Calaf resolves to try his chance with the cold-hearted Princess, although Ping, Pang and Pong and his father try to dissuade him. Turandot poses her three riddles, which Calaf answers correctly, offering her a chance of escape, if, before morning, she can find out his name. Every effort is made to find out Calaf's name, with the slave-girl Liù tortured, but remaining loyally silent, killing herself rather than reveal it. Finally Calaf tells her his name, but now Turandot has learned that his true name is Love.

Puccini did not live to finish his opera, which was completed after his death by Franco Alfano, who based his work on the few sketches that Puccini had made for the final scenes. For musically and operatically irrelevant reasons, Calaf's *Nessun dorma* (None shall sleep) has won wide currency, an aria that, in its original context, marks the frantic search ordered by Turandot for the name of her apparently successful suitor. Liù tries to dissuade Calaf from his endeavour in *Signore, ascolta* (Listen, master), to which he replies by urging her not to cry, *Non piangere, Liù.* Turandot explains the reason for her apparent coldness and cruelty in her second act *In questa reggia* (In this royal palace), while Liù, under interrogation, is brave enough to tell the Princess of the power of love, in *Tu che di gel sei cinta* (You who are bound in ice). Puccini had recourse to Chinese melodies for his score, although the inflation of a simple Chinese folk-song into a theme of imperial splendour strikes a listener familiar with the original song as inappropriate.

Recommended Recordings:

Nessun dorma	***Naxos 8.554065***
Tu, che di gel sei cinta / Signore, ascolta	***Naxos 8.550606***

TURANDOT

- Ferruccio Busoni. *Chinesisches Fabel* in two acts. 1917.
- Libretto by the composer, after the fairy-tale drama of Carlo Gozzi.
- First performance at the Stadttheater, Zürich, on 11th May 1917.

Kalaf, son of the defeated King of Tartary, learns of the challenge Princess Turandot poses to possible suitors and answers the riddles she puts to him, after which she refuses to fulfil her promise. He puts to her the riddle of his own name, which is eventually revealed to her by Adelina, who has hoped to attract Kalaf. Turandot now seems about to order the execution of Kalaf, but instead proclaims her coming marriage.

Busoni made use for his opera of earlier incidental music for a staging of Gozzi's play, a work for Schiller's adaptation of which Weber had already provided music derived from exiguous secondary Chinese sources a century before. Busoni too has recourse to secondary sources for an oriental element in a work that retains much of its original *commedia dell'arte* source. There is a concert suite derived from Busoni's earlier incidental music to the play.

TURCO IN ITALIA, IL (THE TURK IN ITALY)

- Gioachino Rossini. *Dramma buffo* in two acts. 1814.
- Libretto by Felice Romani, after the libretto by Caterino Mazzola.
- First performance at the Teatro alla Scala, Milan, on 14th August, 1814.

CHARACTERS

Selim, the Turk	bass
Fiorilla, a young Neapolitan	soprano
Geronio, her husband	bass
Narciso, her lover	tenor
Zaida, a Turk	mezzo-soprano
Albazar, a Turk	tenor
Prosdocimo, a poet	baritone

The poet Prosdocimo finds the subject for a new comedy in the ill-matched Geronio and his flirtatious wife Fiorilla, prepared, already, to throw her cap at Selim, the Turkish Pasha, once loved by Zaida, a girl who has taken refuge in a gypsy encampment near Naples, accompanied by Albazar. Fiorilla entertains Selim, newly arrived in Naples, to coffee, and deals with both Geronio and Narciso. Prosdocimo advises Geronio to manage his wife with firmness, but his attempts at this prove unsuccessful. The principal characters gather at the gypsy camp, seeking their fortunes in one way or another. Selim meets Zaida again and Zaida and Fiorilla confront each other. Selim now suggests that he should buy Fiorilla from Geronio, a proposal he rejects. Prosdocimo, eager for a comic outcome, offers a further plan. At a masked ball Geronio should masquerade as Selim, to forestall the real Selim's planned abduction of Fiorilla. Narciso overhears the plan, and assumes the same disguise, so that there are three Selims at the ball. Matters are finally resolved when the real Selim decides to return home with Zaida, and Fiorilla is left to make the best of the revelation of her fickle behaviour.

There is a lively overture to Rossini's *Il Turco in Italia* (The Turk in Italy) and witty comedy in a work that follows earlier custom in its contrast of manners.

TURN OF THE SCREW, THE

- Benjamin Britten. Opera in a prologue and two acts. 1954.
- Libretto by Myfanwy Piper, after the story by Henry James.
- First performance at the Teatro La Fenice, Venice, on 14th September 1954.

CHARACTERS

The Prologue	tenor
The Governess	soprano
Miles	treble
Flora	soprano
Mrs Grose, the housekeeper	soprano
Miss Jessel, a former governess	soprano
Peter Quint, a former manservant	tenor

The Prologue introduces the story of the Governess, who had accepted a position at a country-house to take charge of two children, whose guardian, a young man-of-the-world, had no time for them. She is flattered at the trust he puts in her, and resolves to do her best to please him. At Bly, the house, she is welcomed by the children, Miles and Flora, and the housekeeper, Mrs Grose. The setting seems idyllic, but gradually she becomes aware that all is not well. Miles has been expelled from his school, although he, like his sister, seems angelic. It is little by little apparent that the children have been corrupted by the former governess, Miss Jessel, herself seduced by Peter Quint, the master's man-servant. Although both are dead, they continue to haunt the children, exercising their corrupting influence, against which the Governess struggles. In the end she challenges Quint for the soul of Miles, but the boy dies in her arms, while Flora, who has turned violently against the Governess, is taken away by Mrs Grose, in an effort to save her.

Britten's remarkable chamber opera takes the musical form of a twelve-note theme and following instrumental variations. These divide the sixteen scenes, and therefore have a practical theatrical purpose, as well as a musical one in providing the musical material from which each scene is derived. The work is symmetrically constructed, with each variation in a new key, and with miraculous scoring that evokes the atmosphere of evil that Quint and Miss Jessel offer. In spite of the actual appearance on stage of the ghosts, the mysterious nature of the original story by Henry James, where much is left unsaid, is preserved and extended.

Two Widows, The

- Bedřich Smetana. Comic opera in two acts. 1874.
- Libretto by Emanuel Züngel, after the play *Les deux veuves* (The Two Widows) by Félicien Mallefille.
- First performance at the Provisional Theatre, Prague, on 27th March 1874.

The two widows of the title, the lady of the manor Karolina and her cousin Anežka are compelled into an encounter with Ladislav, who gains entry to the house through appearing as a poacher and finally being apprehended by the comic gamekeeper Mumlal. Anežka is attracted to the very eligible Ladislav, but is resolved to remain loyal to her husband's memory, until provoked by the deliberate flirtation of her sister, designed to make her change her mind, which she finally does.

The original version of *The Two Widows*, with its spoken dialogue, was later expanded and given additional arias for performance in Prague in 1878. The overture and the second act Polka have provided an occasional concert item from a work that remains thoroughly Czech, in spite of its remoter French provenance.

Ugo conte di Parigi (Hugo, Count of Paris)

- Gaetano Donizetti. *Tragedia lirica* in four parts. 1832.
- Libretto by Felice Romani, after *Blanche d'Aquitaine*, by Hippolyte-Louis-Florent Bis.
- First performance at the Teatro alla Scala, Milan, on 13th March 1832.

Blanche (Bianca) loves Ugo (Hugues Capet), who is promised to her sister Adelia, while she herself is to marry King Louis V of France. She prepares to poison the King, but eventually takes the poison herself, resolving problems of loyalty that had confronted the Count of Paris.

Censorship and competition with Bellini's *Norma*, which employed the same distinguished cast in the same season at La Scala, ensured the failure of a minor and somewhat derivative work of Donizetti.

Ulisse (Ulysses)

- Luigi Dallapiccola. Opera in a prologue, two acts and an epilogue. 1968.
- Libretto by the composer, after Homer's *Odyssey*.
- First performance at the Deutsche Oper, Berlin, on 29th September 1968.

Calypso laments the departure of Ulysses, who, in a great storm, is washed up on the coast of Phaeacia, where he meets Nausicaa. At her father's palace, in the first act, Ulysses recounts his earlier adventures, with the Lotus-Eaters, with Circe and in Hades. In Ithaca, in the second act, Penelope's suitors plan to waylay her returning son, Telemachus. Ulysses makes his way back, as an old beggar, but reveals himself, using his bow to kill the suitors. The epilogue finds Ulysses wandering again, now seeking meaning in life and finding God.

Dallapiccola's twelve-note technique opera treats the classical hero Ulysses in a symbolic way that is influenced by post-Homeric versions of the story, including the novel by James Joyce. The search in which the hero is involved reflects the composer's own search for certainty.

UNDINA

- Pyotr Il'yich Tchaikovsky. Opera in three acts. 1869.
- Libretto by Vladimir Sollogub, after the story *Undine* by Friedrich Heinrich Carl de la Motte Fouqué.
- The water-spirit Undine loves a mortal, but her love leads her to jealousy of a mortal rival.

Tchaikovsky's opera was quickly written and never performed. He destroyed the score, of which three fragments are preserved.

UNDINE

- E.T.A.Hoffmann. *Zauberoper* in three acts. 1816.
- Libretto by Friedrich Heinrich Carl de la Motte Fouqué, after his story of the same name.
- First performance at the Königliche Schauspiele, Berlin, on 3rd August 1816.

Undine, a water-spirit, adopted by a fisherman after the loss of his own daughter, leaves her foster-parents and is warned by the spirit Kühleborn against mortals. She meets the knight Huldbrand and they fall in love. She warns him that if he is unfaithful she will return to the water or perhaps kill him. Undine becomes friendly with Berthalda, supposed daughter of the Duke and Duchess, but revealed by Kühleborn as the daughter of the fisherman. Undine makes this known, and Huldbrand comforts Berthalda, taking against Undine, who now returns to the water, warning Huldbrand to block the garden well. Huldbrand and Berthalda are to marry, and she orders the well unblocked. Undine now returns, embracing Huldbrand and drawing him down into the waters with her.

Hoffmann's most successful opera, *Undine* embodies his theories of romantic opera, effectively representing the various supernatural and human, courtly and humble elements in the story.

UNDINE

- Albert Lortzing. *Romantische Zauberoper* in four acts. 1845.
- Libretto by the composer, after the story by Friedrich Heinrich Carl de la Motte Fouqué.
- First performance at the Nationaltheater, Magdeburg, on 21st April 1845.

Hugo von Ringstetten takes refuge in the hut of a poor fisherman, meeting there the man's adopted daughter Undine, with whom he falls in love. Undine's father, the water-spirit Kühleborn, investigates the background of Hugo, now married to Undine. Hugo had been in love with Bertalda, supposed daughter of the Duke, but Kühleborn reveals her identity as daughter of the fisherman who had adopted Undine. Hugo transfers his affections to Bertalda, and Undine returns to the water. At the wedding of Hugo and Bertalda Undine returns through the well in their courtyard and embraces Hugo, who swoons, as water fills the room, now transformed into the palace of Kühleborn, who pardons Hugo's infidelity.

While treating the principal characters in his opera with high seriousness, Lortzing allowed a comic element in Hugo's squire and a castle cellarer. The tenor *Vater, Mutter, Schwestern, Brüder* (Father, Mother, Sisters, Brothers) has enjoyed some popularity as a recital item. The opera is in the form of a series of numbers, divided by spoken dialogue.

UNGDOM OG GALSKAB (YOUTH AND FOLLY)

- Edouard Dupuy. Singspiel in two acts. 1806.
- Libretto by N.T.Bruun, after *Une Folie* by Jean-Nicolas Bouilly.
- First performance at the Royal Theatre, Copenhagen, on 19th May 1806.

Captain Rose, with the help of his comic servant Johan, succeeds in outwitting the elderly painter who is the guardian of Vilhelmine. The couple is eventually brought together by subterfuge, when Captain Rose is able to take another's place as a model, with Vilhelmine, for a mythological painting on which the old artist is engaged.

Ungdom of Galskab enjoyed considerable popularity, after the original plan to use the music written by Méhul for a translation of the original French libretto had been rejected. Set in Copenhagen, the new opera included songs in Jutland dialect and a drinking-song for Captain Rose.

Vampyr, Der (The Vampire)

- Heinrich August Marschner. *Grosse romantiche Oper* in two acts. 1828.
- Libretto by Wilhelm August Wohlbrück, after the story by John Polidori and Byron's *Fragment of a Novel,* with plays based on these.
- First performance at the Stadtheater, Leipzig, on 29th March 1828.

Lord Ruthven, a newly recruited vampire, must find three young brides to sacrifice before midnight the next day, if he is to have a year's reprieve before eternal damnation. He sucks the blood of Janthe, daughter of Sir John Berkley, who vainly tries to kill him. Ruthven is helped to revive in the eerie monlight by his former friend Aubry, who realises that Ruthven is a vampire. Aubry is in love with Malwina Davenant, whose father intends her for the Earl of Marsden, who turns out to be Lord Ruthven. Aubry is in a dilemma, since he has sworn to keep secret the fact that Ruthven is a vampire. Ruthven finds his second young bride in Emmy, who is marrying George, a Davenant servant. George finds Emmy dead and shoots the vampire. As midnight approaches, Ruthven is to marry Malwina, but Aubry takes courage and reveals Ruthven's identity. The vampire is taken down to Hell, and Aubry and Malwina are united in marriage.

Marschner's opera, which has had television presentation as a modernised, serial thriller, follows Weber's *Der Freischütz* (The Marksman), in spite of its foreign setting. In particular there is a chance to show an eerie moonlight scene of melodrama, as Ruthven recovers, a parallel to the Wolf's Glen scene in Weber's opera, and comparison may be drawn between Weber's Agathe and Marschner's Malwina. There are elements of the melodramatic in Ruthven's gloating *Ha! Welche Lust* (Ha! How delightful) and in the machinations of a character without redeeming features.

Vanessa

- Samuel Barber. Opera in four acts. 1957.
- Libretto by Gian Carlo Menotti.
- First performance at the Metropolitan Opera, New York, on 15th January 1958.

In Northern Gothic surroundings, in 1905, Vanessa has waited, reproached by her mother, for twenty years for the return of her lover Anatol. Anatol's worthless son appears, greeted by Vanessa as her lover, before she understands her mistake. Vanessa's niece Erika vainly urges the young Anatol to leave. Erika is seduced by Anatol but refuses his proposal of marriage, while Vanessa and he prepare a New Year's Eve ball. Vanessa and Anatol announce their engagement, while Erika, pregnant, seeks an abortion, as she goes through the cold winter night to the lake. Vanessa and Anatol marry, while Erika declares that now she must wait, as her aunt had.

Erika's *Must the winter come so soon?* from the first act and Vanessa's *Do not utter a word, Anatol* enjoy an existence outside their operatic context, with the last act quintet *To leave, to break* and an orchestral interlude. Barber later revised the work, shortening it to three acts by amalgamating the first and second. The musical language is diatonic, with melodic writing that is well suited to voices, a reminder of the composer's background as a singer himself.

VENUS AND ADONIS

- John Blow. Tragic opera in a prologue and three acts. 1682.
- Text attributed, probably wrongly, to Aphra Behn.
- First performance as A Masque for the entertainment of the King in London or Windsor in 1683.

CHARACTERS

Cupid	soprano
Venus	soprano
Adonis	baritone
Shepherd	alto
Shepherdess	soprano
Huntsman	alto

Venus and Adonis are together, enjoying some of the delights of love, although the goddess does not wish to tire her lover. Huntsmen tell him of a raging boar, which he sets out to hunt down. Venus now teaches Cupid the art of love, and he passes the instruction on to lesser Cupids. Adonis is wounded in the hunt, and is carried in, dying, mourned by Venus and her Cupids.

Blow's masque is without spoken dialogue and served as a close model for his pupil Purcell's *Dido and Aeneas*, which may have been written very soon after. It may be supposed that both works have some topical relevance for the court of King Charles II and, perhaps, that of his brother and successor.

Vêpres siciliennes, Les (*I vespri siciliani/The Sicilian Vespers*)

- Giuseppe Verdi. *Opéra* in five acts. 1854.
- Libretto by Eugène Scribe and Charles Duveyrier, after their libretto *Le duc d'Albe* (The Duke of Alba).
- First performance at the Paris Opéra on 13th June 1855.

Characters

Guy de Montfort, Governor of Sicily under Charles d'Anjou, King of Naples	baritone
Le Sire de Béthune, a French officer	bass
Le Comte de Vaudemont, a French officer	bass
Henri (Arrigo), a young Sicilian	tenor
Jean Procida (Giovanni da Procida), a Sicilian doctor	bass
La Duchesse Hélène (Elena)	soprano
Ninetta, her maid	contralto
Daniéli (Danieli), her servant	tenor
Thibault, a French soldier	tenor
Robert (Roberto), a French soldier	baritone
Mainfroid (Manfredo), a Sicilian, adherent of Procida	tenor

It is the year 1282. In the great square in Palermo the occupying French soldiers vaunt their power and force Hélène, whose brother has been killed by the French, to sing for them. Her patriotic song rouses the Sicilians, who attack the French, the riot quelled only by the appearance of de Montfort. Hélène is greeted by Henri, released from prison and now offered fame if he will enter de Montfort's service, a suggestion he refuses. Outside the city Procida, a Sicilian patriotic leader, has returned, joined now by Henri, with Elena. Henri refuses an invitation from de Montfort to a ball, and is seized by the French soldiers. Procida suggests to the French that they carry off Sicilian women, aiming, successfully, to rouse the anger of the Sicilians. De Montfort learns that Henri is his son and the latter at least accompanies him to a grand ball, where conspirators prepare to murder de Montfort, presenting Henri with a dilemma, divided, as he now is, between loyalty to his newly found father and to his patriotic Sicilian associates. He eventually chooses to shield his father from Procida. The conspirators are seized and imprisoned. Hélène and Procida are to be executed, but de Montfort offers pardon, if Henri will call him father, which he eventually does. In the garden of de Montfort's palace the wedding of Hélène and Henri is to be celebrated. Procida has prepared another attack on the French, the signal for which, as he tells Hélène, will be the ringing of the church bells. She will not betray the plot, but seeks to frustrate it by refusing to marry. De Montfort, however, overrules her, the bells are rung and the massacre of the French takes place.

Verdi's first original opera for Paris conforms with the conventions of the Opéra. It opens with a long overture and includes, in its third act, an extended ballet of *Les quatre saisons* (Le quattro stagioni/The Four Seasons). Procida's patriotic greeting to his native country in the first scene of the second act, brings *O patrie* (O patria/My country) and *Et toi, Palerme* (O tu, Palermo/And you, Palermo). De Montfort muses on his life in *Au sein de la puissance* (At the heart of power), followed by Henri's *Quand ma bonté toujours nouvelle* (Quando al mio sen/When my ever new kindness), the start of the duet between father and reluctant son. The last act brings Hélène's *Boléro, Merci, jeunes amies* (Mercè, dilette amiche/Thanks, young friends). Verdi's grand opera has had relatively little success in its original form and was translated for performance in Italy, where censorship continued to cause difficulties. Verdi himself expressed dissatisfaction with Scribe's libretto, complaining about the portrayal of Procida as a common conspirator, and about the fate of the French in the final massacre, matters which seemed to reflect badly on both French and Italians.

Recommended Recordings:
Die Walküre (3 CDs) — ***Naxos 8.110058-60***
Overture — ***Naxos 8.553018***

Vera costanza, La (True Constancy)

- Joseph Haydn. *Dramma giocoso* in three acts. 1779.
- Libretto by Francesco Puttini.
- First performance at Esterháza on 25th April 1779.

Baroness Irene, her lover Marquis Ernesto, Villotto, intended husband of the fisher-girl Rosina and Lisetta, maid to the Baroness, are shipwrecked and rescued by Rosina and her brother Masino. The Baroness is searching for her errant nephew, Count Errico, to dissuade him from marrying Rosina, whom he had, in any case, secretly married some years before, fathering a son by her. Eventually Villotto is put off and the Baroness is induced to accept the marriage of Rosina and her nephew, who has now acquired some sense of responsibility, as a father and husband.

Haydn's opera starts with an effective overture. Rosina, in distress at her situation, has her moving *Care spiagge* (Dear shores), dispelled by the time she comes to the final love-duet *Rosina vezzosina* (Lovely Rosina).

Verratene Meer, Das (The Treacherous Sea)

- Hans Werner Henze. *Musikdrama* in two parts. 1989.
- Libretto by Hans-Ulrich Treichel, after the novel *The Sailor who fell from Grace with the Sea* by Yukio Mishima.
- First performance at the Deutsche Oper, Berlin, on 5th May 1990.

Characters

Fusako Kuroda, a 33-year-old widow	high soprano
Noboru, her 13-year-old son, Number Three	tenor
Ryuji Tsukazaki, a merchant-navy officer	baritone
The Youth Gang, Friends of Noboru:	
Number One	baritone
Number Two	tenor
Number Four	baritone
Number Five	bass-baritone
Ship's Mate	bass-baritone

In summer in Yokohama the widow Fusako puts her son Noboru to bed, locking the door so that he cannot go out with his friends. She dreams of a new lover and he of adventure at sea. The next day they visit a merchant ship in harbour and Fusako is fascinated by the young officer Ryuji Tsukazaki, who is impressed by Noboru's knowledge of the sea. The relationship between Fusako and Ryuji develops. He confides in her his disappointments and they sleep together, watched by Noboru through the wall. He tells his friends about Ryuji and then tries to make Ryuji into a hero, but without success. Ryuji and Fusako part, as his ship sails, and Noboru and his gang carry out the ritual killing of a cat, a symbol of their power over life and death. The second part, in winter, finds Ryuji on shore again, proposing to Fusako and planning to leave the sea. The gang discuss their frustration with fathers, and suggest that Ryuji is no better. Fusako and Ryuji discover the hole through which Noboru has spied on them, but Ryuji refuses to punish him. Ryuji is arraigned by the gang and still refuses to show life at sea as glamorous. The opera ends with his murder.

Henze associates various instrumental groups with the characters of his fourteenth opera in which he returns to a libretto in his own language. Piano and percussion predominate in music for the gang, wind instruments for Ryuji and strings for Fusako. The work includes a number of instrumental interludes between scenes, moments that carry forward the action or reflect the thoughts of the characters.

Vestale, La (The Vestal Virgin)

- Gaspare Spontini. *Tragédie lyrique* in three acts. 1805.
- Libretto by Etienne de Jouy.
- First performance at the Paris Opéra on 15th December 1807.

The Vestal virgin Julia finds herself divided between love and duty, drawn to her former betrothed, the victorious general, Licinius. He plans to abduct her from the temple, where she must watch over the sacred flame, and while he escapes blame for profaning the temple, she is condemned for his intrusion and for allowing the sacred flame to go out. Julia is about to be put to death, buried alive, when lightning strikes and the flame is renewed. This is taken as a sign of divine intervention on her behalf, and she and Licinius, whose attempts to exonerate her have failed, are re-united.

La Vestale (The Vestal Virgin) is among the most enduringly successful of Spontini's 24 operas. It includes an effective aria for Julia in the second act *Toi que j'implore avec effroi* (Tu che invoco con orrore/You whom I implore in fear), followed by *Impitoyables dieux!* (O Nume tutelar degli infelici/Pitiless gods – O guardian spirit of the unfortunate) and her third act *Toi, que je laisse sur la terre* (Caro oggetto/You whom I leave on earth – Dear one).

Viaggio a Reims, Il (The Journey to Rheims)

- Gioachino Rossini. *Dramma giocoso* in one act. 1825.
- Libretto by Luigi Balocchi, based on Madame de Staël's *Corinne, ou L'Italie* (Corinna, or Italy).
- First performance at the Théâtre Italien, Paris, on 19th June 1825.

A group of visitors from a number of countries gathers at the Inn of the Golden Fleur-de-lys, preparing to attend the coronation in Rheims. At their centre is the famous Roman poetess Corinna, with a Greek orphan girl, an elderly antiquarian, an English colonel and others. The comedy lies in the interaction of the various nationalities and characters, the whole piece ending in a final entertainment that includes a ballet and a series of national songs.

Rossini wrote *Il viaggio a Reims, ossia L'albergo del giglio d'oro* (The Journey to Rheims, or The Inn of the Golden Fleur-de-lys) in celebration of the coronation of Charles X. The work was also intended to serve his own reputation in Paris, where he was now proposing to establish himself. As a pièce d'occasion it was withdrawn by the composer after the fourth performance, some of the score later to be borrowed for *Le Comte d'Ory*. Revived only 150 years after its composition, when the score was rediscovered, the opera has a fascinating series of contrasted arias and admirable international ensembles.

Vida breve, La (The Short Life)

- Manuel de Falla. Lyric drama in two acts. 1905.
- Libretto by Fernández Shaw.
- First performance at the Municipal Casino, Nice, on 1st April 1913.

Characters

Salud, a gypsy girl	soprano
Paco, her lover	tenor
Her Grandmother	mezzo-soprano
Uncle Sarvaor	bass
Carmela, Paco's bride	mezzo-soprano
Manuel, her brother	baritone

Salud and Paco are lovers, but he agrees to marry a girl of his own richer class, Carmela. The wedding takes place, observed, from the street, by Salud. Her uncle Sarvaor offers to entertain the wedding-guests and Salud comes forward to accuse Paco, before falling down dead.

De Falla's opera is set in Granada and includes a series of dances that have appeared in a number of arrangements, notably, in the case of the first dance, that for violin and piano by Fritz Kreisler. Orchestral excerpts include the prelude and one or more dances.

Recommended Recording: Interlude and Dance ***Naxos 8.550174***

Vie parisienne, La (Parisian Life)

- Jacques Offenbach. *Opéra bouffe* in five acts. 1866.
- Libretto by Henri Meilhac and Ludovic Halévy.
- First performance at the Théâtre du Palais-Royal, Paris, on 31st October 1866.

Gardefeu is slighted by the courtesan Métella and arranges with a former servant, Joseph, employed at the Grand-Hôtel, to pass his own villa off as a hotel, to entertain an attractive Swedish baroness, with counterfeit guests that include the glove-maker Gabrielle, while providing other distractions for her husband. Gardefeu's friend Bobinet helps to arrange a reception for the countess at his aunt's villa, with servants masquerading as guests, but matters are complicated when Bobinet's aunt returns to Paris and decides to seek accommodation at the hotel where her friend the baroness is staying. General satisfaction is finally restored at a party given by a rich Brazilian. Here Gardefeu is re-united with Métella, allowing the work to end in Parisian gaiety.

La vie parisienne (Parisian Life) has a well known overture and includes a series of characteristic dances. Gabrielle, who finds final satisfaction with the rich Brazilian, enjoys herself by impersonating a colonel's widow, a guest at the supposed hotel at Gardefeu's house. Here she sings *Je suis veuve d'un colonel* (I am a colonel's widow), a high point in the second act.

Recommended Recording: Overture — ***Naxos 8.550473***

VILLAGE ROMEO AND JULIET, A

- Frederick Delius. Lyric drama in six scenes. 1901.
- Libretto by the composer, after the novel by Gottfried Keller.
- First performance at the Komische Oper, Berlin, on 21st February 1907.

The farmers Manz and Marti seek to encroach on land that should belong to the Dark Fiddler, who warns their children of danger, if the land be ploughed. The farmers quarrel and are ruined by the ensuing law-suit, while their children, Sali and Vreli, are drawn to each other. Her father tries to separate them and Sali strikes him. Impoverished, the two young lovers set out to wander, going to a fair and then to an inn where they are not known, the Paradise Garden. Here they meet again the Dark Fiddler and realise their love must end in death. To the sound of the fiddle, they board a hay-barge, their marriage-bed, and as it floats away, they sink it.

The best known excerpt from *A Village Romeo and Juliet* is the famous *Walk to the Paradise Garden*, a frequent enough concert item. The whole work is in the musical language that Delius made his own, an idiom now fully formed and suited to the dream-like quality imparted to the figures in the opera.

VILLI, LE (THE WILLIS)

- Giacomo Puccini. *Opera-ballo* in two acts. 1883.
- Libretto by Ferdinando Fontana, after the short story *Les Willis* by Alphonse Karr.
- First performance at the Teatro Dal Verme, Milan, on 31st May 1884.

Roberto is engaged to Anna, daughter of the head forester Guglielmo, but he leaves for the city, where he forgets her. Anna dies of grief, joining the Willis, the spirits of girls who have been abandoned by their lovers. Roberto returns, penitent and impoverished, and meets the Willis, who dance around him until he dies.

Puccini wrote his opera for a competition and although he did not win it, the work was staged in Milan with the support of Arrigo Boito, Ponchielli and Ricordi. Its relative success gave a promising start to his career, leading to a further commission. Anna's gift of flowers to Robert, whom she urges to remember her, is marked by *Se come voi piccina io fossi* (If I were tiny like you). The score opens with an evocative prelude and includes a ghostly dance for the Willis.

Recommended Recording: Prelude and La Tregenda ***Naxos 8.550240***

VIOLANTA

- Erich Wolfgang Korngold. Opera in one act. 1915.
- Libretto by Hans Müller.
- First performance at the Staatsoper, Munich, on 28th March 1916.

In 15th century Venice the sister of Violanta, wife of Simone Trovai, has been seduced by Alfonso, Prince of Naples. Violanta now demands that her husband seek revenge and arranges a meeting with Alfonso, so that Simone can murder him. As she talks with the prince, she feels pity for him and understands that she loves him. They embrace, as Simone rushes in, ready to kill the seducer, but in fact stabbing Violanta.

Korngold, now eighteen, offered a double bill, with his opera *Polykrates*, and won astonishing success both in Munich and in a more sceptical Vienna. The score includes a prelude and a Venetian carnival scene.

VOIX HUMAINE, LA (THE HUMAN VOICE)

- Francis Poulenc. *Tragédie lyrique* in one act. 1958.
- Libretto by Jean Cocteau, after his play.
- First performance by the Paris Opéra-Comique at the Salle Favart on 6th February 1959.

The soprano, Elle (She), spends some forty minutes on the telephone, sometimes talking to her lover, sometimes dealing with inefficiencies of the telephone service.

Unlike Menotti's cheerful little opera *The Telephone*, Cocteau's text has more serious implications, since it is clear that the girl has been deserted by her lover and has attempted suicide, in her depression. Poulenc saw himself as the protagonist, particularly in the coming absence of a close friend on military service. The work was written for performance by the soprano Denise Duval, who had sung the rôle of Blanche de la Force in the Paris première of *Dialogues des Carmélites.*

Volo di notte (Night Flight)

- Luigi Dallapiccola. Opera in one act. 1939.
- Libretto by the composer, after *Vol de nuit* (Night Flight) by Antoine Saint-Exupéry.
- First performance at the Teatro della Pergola, Florence, on 18th May 1940.

At the centre of the drama is the newly married pilot Fabien, whose plane is off course and without enough fuel. Rivière, the airfield director in Buenos Aires, has insisted and continues to insist, nevertheless, on night flights, whatever the risks involved, a responsibility which he must assume.

Volo di notte (Night Flight) is the first of Dallapiccola's stage works and uses twelve-note techniques in combination with other musical idioms in what is essentially a meditation on death.

Von heute auf morgen (From One Day to the Next)

- Arnold Schoenberg. Opera in one act. 1929.
- Libretto by Max Blonda (the composer's daughter Gertrud).
- First performance at the Opernhaus, Frankfurt, on 1st February 1930.

Wife, Husband, Friend and Singer are involved in cross-relationships, when the Husband falls in love with the Wife's Friend, and the Wife takes revenge, threatening to take a lover, the Singer. Eventually difficulties are settled, the Husband restored to his wife and the Wife now abjuring the 'modern' fashions she had espoused in order to provoke him.

Schoenberg made use of twelve-note technique in his opera, in a score that contains aria and arioso passages, connected by recitative. The obvious comedy of the plot is treated seriously enough, although all four characters have their affectations, innate or assumed.

Waffenschmied, Der (The Armourer)

- Albert Lortzing. *Komische Oper* in three acts. 1846.
- Libretto by the composer, after the comedy *Liebhaber und Nebenbuhler in einer Person* (Lover and Rival in One Person) by Friedrich Wilhelm von Ziegler.
- First performance at the Theater an der Wien, Vienna, on 30th May 1846.

In 16th century Worms Count von Liebenau has disguised himself as an apprentice, Conrad, to be near Marie, the daughter of his master, the armourer Hans Stadinger. The Count becomes his own rival when Marie prefers Conrad to the Count that she does not know, while Stadinger would rather she married another more industrious apprentice, Georg. In the end all turns out for the best, with Conrad rescuing Marie from the supposed clutches of the Count and Stadinger agreeing to their marriage.

Lortzing enjoyed a reputation as the leading composer of German comic opera of his time. *Der Waffenschmied von Worms* (The Armourer of Worms) includes an effective aria for the Count in *Man wird ja einmal nur geboren* (One is only born once) and, for the bass Hans Stadinger, the nostalgic *Auch ich war ein Jüngling mit lockigem Haar* (Once I too was a young man, with curly hair).

Recommended Recording: Overture — ***Naxos 8.550146***

Walküre, Die (The Valkyrie)

- Richard Wagner. Music-drama in three acts. The first day of *Der Ring des Nibelungen* (The Ring of the Nibelung). 1856.
- Libretto by the composer.
- First performance at the Königliches Hof- und Nationaltheater, Munich, on 26th June 1870.

Characters

Siegmund, son of Wotan	tenor
Sieglinde, his twin sister	soprano
Hunding, her husband	bass
Wotan, ruler of heaven and earth	bass-baritone
Fricka, his wife	mezzo-soprano
Valkyries, daughters of Wotan and Erda:	
Brünnhilde	soprano
Helmwige	soprano
Ortlinde	soprano
Gerhilde	soprano
Waltraute	mezzo-soprano
Siegrune	mezzo-soprano
Rossweisse	mezzo-soprano
Grimgerde	mezzo-soprano
Schwertleite	contralto

Siegmund staggers exhausted into Hunding's house and is entertained by the mysteriously attractive Sieglinde, Hunding's wife. Hunding returns home and Siegmund tells him how his mother had been killed and his twin sister abducted and how he had wandered with his father, whom he calls Wolfe. After his father's disappearance he had been unlucky and must call himself *Wehwalt* (Woeful). He tells of his last, unsuccessful battle, which, it seems, involved kinsmen of Hunding, for which the latter will seek revenge. Siegmund's father had promised him a sword and this Sieglinde shows him, the weapon, embedded in an ash-tree, where an old man, a visitor, had left it. The two recognise each other as brother and sister, and Siegmund draws the sword from the ash-tree, calling it *Nothung*, sword of need. They embrace. In the second act Wotan tells Brünnhilde to ensure victory for Siegmund in the coming battle with Hunding. Fricka, wife of Wotan, favours Hunding and marriage, as she angrily makes clear, while Wotan sanctions the love of Siegmund and Sieglinde. Fricka demands the withdrawal of Wotan's favour from Siegmund, a request that he unhappily grants. He explains to Brünnhilde his early search for power and love, Alberich's forging of the ring, Wotan's theft of it to pay for the building of Valhalla and Erda's prophecy of the end of the gods. Erda had born him the Valkyries, warrior-maidens who have brought together heroes fallen in battle, to defend Valhalla. Wotan needs a mortal to take back the ring, which he, by oath, cannot do himself. It is said that when Alberich has a son, the reign of the gods will be over. Now he orders Brünnhilde to ensure Siegmund's defeat, a task she accepts with sorrow. She meets Siegmund, with his sister, and tells him that he will die and go to Valhalla. At first, however, she protects him, in his battle with Hunding. The latter succeeds in killing Siegmund only after the intervention of Wotan, whose spear breaks Siegmund's sword. Brünnhilde rides away with Sieglinde, while Wotan dismissively brings death to Hunding and sets out angrily in pursuit of the Valkyrie. In the third act the Valkyries ride back from battle, joined by Brünnhilde, with Sieglinde, who must live to bear Siegmund's child and is now allowed away, before the arrival of Wotan. He condemns his favourite daughter to a rock, where she must lie senseless until roused by a mortal, who will be her husband. She begs that her husband may be the son of Sieglinde, who will be called Siegfried. Wotan leaves Brünnhilde, surrounded by protective fire to guard her as she sleeps her magic sleep.

Once again motifs are interwoven, adding a further dimension to a story that is complex and fraught with deeper and wider associations. Orchestral excerpts from *Die Walküre* (The Valkyrie) include the stormy prelude to the first act, the prelude to the second and the famous *Ride of the Valkyries* that introduces the third act. Siegmund recalls his father's promise in *Ein Schwert verhiess mir der Vater* (My father promised me a sword). Sieglinde's narrative, *Der Männer Sippe sass hier im Saal* (The men's kinsfolk sat here in the hall) tells of her unhappy forced marriage to Hunding. The joy that Siegmund brings to his sister is expressed in his *Winterstürme wichen dem Wonnemond* (Winter storms have waned in the moon of delight), while she greets his coming with *Du bist der Lenz* (You are the spring). The second act brings Fricka's denunciation of Wotan, the powerful *So ist denn aus* (Is all, then, at an end) and Wotan's explanation to Brünnhilde, *Als junger Liebe Lust mir verblich* (When young love's pleasure left me). Brünnhilde tells Siegmund of his coming death in her *Todesverkündigung* (Announcement of Death). Her own plea to her father is heard in *War es so schmählich?* (Was it so shameful?), after she has put love before duty to her father, following his desire rather than his command.

Recommended Recordings:

Die Walküre (3 CDs)	***Naxos 8.110058-60***
Ride of the Valkyries / Wotan's Farewell	***Naxos 8.550211***

WALLY, LA

- Alfredo Catalani. *Dramma musicale* in four acts. 1891.
- Libretto by Luigi Illica, after the story *Die Geyer-Wally* by Wilhelmine von Hillern.
- First performance at the Teatro alla Scala, Milan, on 20th January 1892.

CHARACTERS

Wally	soprano
Stromminger, her father	bass
Afra, a landlady	contralto
Walter, a strolling minstrel	soprano
Giuseppe Hagenbach, of Sölden	tenor
Vincenzo Gellner, of Hochstoff	baritone
The Messenger of Schnals	tenor

Stromminger mocks the skill of the young huntsman Hagenbach, son of his enemy, and abuses the young man's father, only to be thrown to the ground. Stromminger has been drinking with Gellner, who has been promised the hand of Wally, Stromminger's daughter, in marriage. She is in love with Hagenbach. A year later the landlady of The Eagle in Sölden, Afra, is betrothed to Hagenbach. Stromminger is now dead and Wally is rich and likely to come to the festival at Sölden, where she may see Hagenbach. She tries to rid herself of Gellner and dances with Hagenbach, who has wagered that he will have a kiss from her. His intentions are not serious, shown by the reversed feather in his hat, and he kisses her, to the amusement of the onlookers and to her anger. Wally tells Gellner that if he wants her, Hagenbach must die. In the third act Wally is at home, having second thoughts about her request. Gellner comes to her room, telling her that he has pushed Hagenbach to his death. Wally sets out to rescue him and succeeds in pulling him back from the abyss where he has fallen, returning the kiss he had given her so lightly. By the glacier near her house, Wally thinks of death. She is joined by Hagenbach, now recovered and professing his love. As he goes to find the path down, there is an avalanche and he is swept away. Wally now throws herself down, falling to her own death.

La Wally, with its Tyrolean setting, remains the most successful of Catalani's five operas. It provides sopranos with the first act aria *Ebben? Ne andrò lontana* (Well? I'll go far away). An orchestral interlude prepares for the last act, as Wally stands tired and in despair by the side of the glacier, in a work that maintains a certain level of operatic realism.

Recommended Recording: Ebben? Ne andrò lontana ***Naxos 8.550606***

WANDERING SCHOLAR, THE

- Gustav Holst. Opera in one act. 1930.
- Libretto by Clifford Bax, after an episode in Helen Waddell's *The Wandering Scholars*.
- First performance at the David Lewis Theatre, Liverpool, on 31st January 1934.

In medieval France a priest tries to seduce Alison, young wife of Louis, who is absent on a market errand. She is saved by a wandering scholar, Pierre, who subtly reveals the situation to Louis, before the priest is chased away.

The Tale of the Wandering Scholar, to give the work its original title, was Holst's last opera, written as a chamber work.

War and Peace

- Sergey Prokofiev. Opera in thirteen scenes. 1942.
- Libretto by the composer and Mira Mendelson, after the novel by Tolstoy.
- First complete staged performance at the Bolshoy Theatre, Moscow, on 15th December 1959.

At the estate of Count Rostov, Prince Andrey Bolkonsky, a widower, realises, in the beauty of the evening and the innocent beauty of the Count's daughter Natasha, that life still promises happiness. Natasha meets Prince Andrey at a ball in St Petersburg, to his happiness, but his father insists that he spend a year abroad and the behaviour of Andrey's father is intimidating. Natasha, meanwhile, is the object of affection of Prince Anatol, brother-in-law of Pierre Bezhukov, who plans to elope with her. The plot is divulged and foiled at the last minute, allowing Pierre to tell Natasha of his own feelings for her, were he free. The second part of the opera concerns war rather than peace, with the battle of Borodino. Pierre is an observer, but Andrey is wounded. Moscow is destroyed, in pursuit of the scorched earth policy that defeated Napoleon. Andrey, evacuated with the other wounded, dies in the presence of Natasha, who has found him again. Pierre has been taken prisoner by the French, but is rescued, as the opera draws to its patriotic close.

Prokofiev's opera, conditioned by the war-time circumstances in which it was written, is of epic proportions, calling for a large cast and spectacular effects. There is a concert suite from the work, including music from the ball scenes, the tranquil beauty of a May night, a snow-storm, battle and victory.

We Come to the River

- Hans Werner Henze. Actions for music in two parts. 1974.
- Libretto by Edward Bond.
- First performance at Covent Garden, London, on 12th July 1976.

The General celebrates his victory, but comes to realise the misery and destruction that his triumph has brought, while himself threatened with blindness. He inveighs against the Governor, who has him imprisoned. The General is in an asylum, where the inmates prepare an imaginary boat for their escape. One of his soldiers comes to tell him of the horrors that are taking place outside, urging him to lead an uprising, but the General refuses, as he does a request brought by the Governor for his help in quelling disturbance. The Governor is killed by the soldier. The Emperor considers the General responsible for this and orders him to be blinded, while the soldier has killed himself and his family. The lunatics, who imagine their sheets to be a river, decide that the General is a spy and drown him in their imagined river.

We Come to the River is a work of some theatrical complexity, making use of three stages and divided and varied instrumental groups, matched by varied styles of music, some of it amplified. The work, with its overt political implications, had no success in London, where it was staged with a cast of eighty singers, but has been mounted elsewhere.

WERTHER

- Jules Massenet. *Drame lyrique* in four acts. 1887.
- Libretto by Edouard Blau, Paul Millier and Georges Hartmann, after Goethe's novel *Die Leiden des jungen Werthers* (The Sorrows of the Young Werther).
- First performance at the Hofoper, Vienna, on 16th February 1892.

CHARACTERS

Werther, a poet, aged 23	tenor
Albert, aged 25	baritone
Le Bailli (The Magistrate), aged 50	bass
Schmidt, his friend	tenor
Johann, another friend	bass
Charlotte, daughter of the Bailli, aged 20	mezzo-soprano
Sophie, her sister, aged 15	soprano
Brühlmann	tenor
Käthchen	soprano
The Bailli's six other children	children's voices

It is July and the widower Bailli practises a Christmas carol with his children. His friends Schmidt and Johann call, inviting him to the inn to discuss a coming ball, at which Werther will partner Charlotte, in the absence of her fiancé Albert. Werther enters, praising the beauty of nature and watching Charlotte. Albert returns, but thoughts of love now arise in Werther, as he and Charlotte come back from the ball. He declares himself, but Charlotte recalls her promise to marry Albert. By the second act Charlotte and Albert have been married for three months. They join other townspeople in the church, where the pastor's golden wedding is being celebrated. Outside, Werther expresses his pain and bitterness, although he reassures Albert of his present friendship for him and his young wife. Werther has a meeting with Charlotte and resolves to take her advice and go away for a time, although even now he has thoughts of suicide. At Christmas Charlotte reads again the letters she has had from Werther, while Sophie, her younger sister, tries to comfort her. Werther returns and at first behaves calmly, until Charlotte draws his attention to a book of Ossian that he had once started to translate, the words of which fit his mood of growing despair. They embrace and Albert now shows signs of overt jealousy, as he questions Charlotte. Werther seeks to borrow Albert's pistols, as he plans a long journey, and Albert tells his wife to hand them to him. In the fourth act Charlotte finds Werther dying in his study, held in her arms, as children's voices sing outside of Christmas.

Goethe's novel of 1774, reflecting something of his own experiences and those of people he knew, had a strong influence on his contemporaries. In two parts, the first in the form of letters, the work was characteristic of the *Sturm und Drang* (Storm and Stress) period of German culture in the 1770s and had an influence even on dress and behaviour. Young men came to favour the blue coat and yellow breeches of Werther and some brought their lives to a similar conclusion, perhaps after his example. Massenet's operatic treatment of the work came more than a century later in an opera of marked dramatic contrasts. In 1902 Massenet made an arrangement of the part of Werther for a baritone. *Manon* and *Werther* remain Massenet's best known operas. Werther's song in praise of nature, *O Nature, pleine de grâce* (O Nature, full of grace) verbally echoes the Ave Maria in a suggestion of romantic pantheism and there is much that is moving in Charlotte's *Air des lettres* (Letters Aria) in the third act, in which Werther has his song from Ossian, *Pourquoi me réveiller?* (Why rouse me?).

Recommended Recording:
Pourquoi me réveiller ***Naxos 8.550343***

Wildschütz, Der (The Poacher)

- Albert Lortzing. *Komische Oper* in three acts. 1842.
- Libretto by the composer, after the play *Der Rehbock, oder Die schuldlosen Schuldbewussten* (The Roebuck, or The Guiltless, Conscious of Guilt) by August von Kotzebue.
- First performance in Leipzig on 31st December 1842.

The schoolmaster Baculus and his Gretchen celebrate their village betrothal, but Baculus is accused by the Count of poaching and is dismissed. Gretchen would intercede for him, but this task is undertaken by Baroness Freimann, a young widow and sister to the Count, whom she has not seen for some time. She has come, in fact, disguised as a boy, to see the husband her brother has proposed for her, Baron Kronthal, the Count's brother-in-law. Baron and Count are attracted to her in her disguise as Gretchen. The Countess, a woman of intellectual pretensions, does not recognise her brother, imagining the Baron has designs on her, and fails to persuade her husband to forgive Baculus. The Baron proposes to the supposed Gretchen, while the Count postpones a decision on Baculus, suggesting that the couple stay the night at his castle. Count and Baron come to blows, as they each try to prevent the other's approach to the false Gretchen. Found in a compromising situation by the Countess, the Baroness is taken by the Countess to her own room for the night, while the Baron tries to bribe Baculus to give up Gretchen, an offer he misunderstands. All misunderstandings are clarified in the third act, when identities are revealed.

Lortzing's opera *Der Wildschütz, oder Die Stimme der Natur* (The Poacher, or The Voice of Nature) follows the example of Weber in its opening peasant celebration. There is broad comedy in the portrayal of the old schoolmaster Baculus, ready to part with his own Gretchen, as he thinks, for the fine sum of *Fünftausend Taler* (Five thousand taler), money that will provide him with all kinds of things, allowing an element of topical invention to the singer. The Count sings of his eye for pretty girls in the third act *Wie freundlich strahlt die helle Morgensonne* (How friendly beams the morning sun).

Recommended Recordings:

Werther (2 CDs) — ***Naxos 8.110061-62***

Naxos 8.660072-73

Overture — ***Naxos 8.550146***

WOZZECK

- Alban Berg. Opera in three acts. 1922.
- Libretto by the composer, after Georg Büchner's play *Woyzeck*.
- First performance at the Staatsoper, Berlin, on 14th December 1925.

CHARACTERS

Wozzeck, a soldier	baritone
Drum Major	heroic tenor
Andres, a soldier, friend of Wozzeck	lyric tenor
Captain	tenor
Doctor	bass
Marie, Wozzeck's common-law wife	soprano
Margret, her neighbour	contralto
First Apprentice	deep bass
Second Apprentice	high baritone
Madman	high tenor
Marie's son	treble

Wozzeck is shaving the Captain, who tells him to go slower and makes fun of him, particularly over the matter of his illegitimate child. Eventually Wozzeck is roused into an indignant answer. The second scene finds Wozzeck and Andres cutting sticks in an inhospitable open field, where Wozzeck seems to fear the noises he hears. Marie, from her house, watches the band march past and is saluted by the Drum Major, who seems to show an interest in her. Wozzeck returns and tries to tell Marie of his fears, to her alarm. The Doctor diagnoses a fixed idea as the source of Wozzeck's difficulties, while the fifth scene returns to Marie, outside her house, where she is seduced by the Drum Major. Marie lulls her child to sleep again and Wozzeck comes in, suspicious of the earrings that the Drum Major has given, which she claims to have found in the street. In the street the Captain tells the Doctor to go slower and the Doctor diagnoses a fatal illness in the Captain. Both mock Wozzeck, when they meet him, laughing at Marie's relationship with the Drum Major. Wozzeck rushes away. He now threatens Marie, who leaves him to himself. In a tavern garden Wozzeck watches Marie and the Drum Major. Others dance and celebrate, but Wozzeck, at the prompting of a Madman, sees only blood. In the guard-room Wozzeck fights with the boasting Drum Major, full of his conquest, and is knocked down. The third act opens in Marie's room, where she reads in the Bible of the woman taken in adultery. In the half-light of evening Marie and Wozzeck walk together along a forest path. He talks of fidelity and love and stabs her. In a tavern

Wozzeck drinks to forget, his blood-stained hands noticed by Margret, Marie's neighbour. Wozzeck returns to the forest path, looking for his knife. Stumbling against Marie's body, he finally goes out of his mind, wading into the forest pool, where he drowns. The Doctor and the Captain pass by, unconcerned. The next morning, outside Marie's house, her child plays on his hobby-horse. Another child tells him what has happened, and they go together to see the woman's body.

Wozzeck, apart from the relevance and power of its plot, with its associated moral and social connections, is an elaborate musical structure. Berg makes use of a number of traditional forms, incorporated in an over-all pattern of symphonic complexity. The second act starts with a sonata form, followed by a fantasia and fugue, leading to an important slow movement, a scherzo, with two trios and a rondo. The first and third acts are more loosely constructed, but still in a series of established forms. The musical idiom, apart from the forms used, is in part atonal, in part diatonic, with other scale patterns used. Vocally it includes passages of *Sprechgesang* (sung speech). A concert version of excerpts from the opera, made in 1924, includes parts of all three acts in orchestral form, while Marie's scene, as the band marches past, has an occasional dramatic place in concert programmes.

XERSE (XERXES)

- Francesco Cavalli. *Drama per musica* in a prologue and three acts. 1654.
- Libretto by Nicolò Minato, based on Herodotus.
- First performance at the Teatro SS Giovanni e Paolo, Venice, on 12th January 1654.

The Persian king Xerxes prepares to mount a campaign against Athens, meanwhile competing with his brother for the attention of Romilda, daughter of Ariodate, Prince of Abydos. Amastre, Princess of Susa, who appears disguised as a soldier, has come in search of Xerxes, to whom she is betrothed. Eventually she is re-united with Xerxes, and Romilda duly married to the King's brother.

Cavalli's opera enjoyed relatively wide popularity. The libretto was to serve both Handel and his rival in London, Bononcini.

XERXES (SEE SERSE)

Yeomen of the Guard, The

- Arthur Sullivan, Operetta in two acts. 1888.
- Libretto by W.S.Gilbert.
- First performance at the Savoy Theatre, London, on 3rd October 1888.

In 16th century London, Colonel Fairfax, a prisoner in The Tower, escapes execution through the intervention of Sergeant Meryll and his daughter Phoebe. He falls in love with the strolling player Elsie Maynard, with whom he finds happiness, although there is only sadness for Elsie's jester partner.

The subject of *The Yeomen of the Guard* is of a more serious cast than usual in the collaborations between Gilbert and Sullivan. The operetta starts with an overture that is known also in arrangements for brass band.

Yerma

- Heitor Villa-Lobos. Opera in three acts. 1956.
- Libretto after the play by Federico García Lorca.
- First performance in Santa Fe on 12th August 1971.

The childless peasant-woman Yerma seeks out a sorceress, to no result. She visits a shrine, where she sees a pagan ritual carried out and, reproached by her husband Juan, she strangles him.

Set in rural Spain, the subject of *Yerma* suited Villa-Lobos very well. Here he was able to make use of his usual varied orchestral palette and appropriate elements of Iberian musical provenance, in the setting of a powerful village drama by one of Spain's greatest poets of the 20th century.

Youth and Folly *(see Ungdom og Galskab)*

Z

Zaide

- Wolfgang Amadeus Mozart. *Singspiel* in two acts. 1780.
- Libretto by Johann Andreas Schachtner, after *Das Serail* (The Seraglio) by Franz Josef Sebastian.
- First performance in Frankfurt on 27th January 1866.

Characters

Zaide	soprano
Gomatz	tenor
Allazim	bass
Sultan Soliman	tenor
Osmin	bass
Zaram, Captain of the Guard	speaking rôle
Four Slaves	tenors

Gomatz, enslaved, sleeps after his work, watched by the Sultan's favourite Zaide. They fall in love. With the help of Allazim, they escape. The Sultan expresses his anger. The lovers are captured and Zaide acknowledges the Sultan's former generosity, although she prefers freedom. She pleads for the life of her lover, and Allazim tells the Sultan of the brotherhood of man. It may be supposed that a magnanimous gesture from the Sultan would have ensued.

The full text of Mozart's unfinished opera is lost. Written in 1780, it may be seen as the precursor of *Die Entführung aus dem Serail* (The Abduction from the Seraglio), which he set two years later, when he had established himself in Vienna. The best known aria from the work is Zaide's *Ruhe sanft, mein holdes Leben* (Sleep softly, my dear one), as she watches over the sleeping Gomatz. Unlike the later work, *Zaide* makes no attempt at pseudo-Turkish music, although it may be supposed that there would have been some place in the completed opera for the Turkish effects with which Mozart and his contemporaries were very familiar.

Zaira

- Vincenzo Bellini. *Tragedia lirica* in two acts. 1829.
- Libretto by Felice Romani, after Voltaire's tragedy *Zaïre*.
- First performance at the Teatro Ducale, Parma, on 16th May 1829.

Zaira, a Christian captive, is to marry Sultan Orosmane. Her father Lusignano is also imprisoned and recognises her as his daughter, distressed that she has become a Moslem. Orosmane is jealous of the Christian knight Nerestano, who is, in fact, Zaira's brother, and after various complexities in the plot, kills Zaira. When he learns the truth, he kills himself.

Zaira won no success and Bellini later made use of parts of it for other works, designed for theatres of greater importance.

Zaïs

- Jean-Philippe Rameau. *Pastorale-héroique* in a prologue and four acts. 1748.
- Libretto by Louis de Cahusac.
- First performance at the Paris Opéra on 29th February 1748.

The air-spirit Zaïs assumes shepherd disguise to woo the shepherdess Zélide, whose constancy Cupid bids him try. Zaïs gives up his supernatural power for love of Zélide, allowing a transformation of the scene to that of a desert, but the king of the spirits allows him to resume his magic power, now allowed also to Zélide.

With a very original overture, later discarded, an illustration of primeval chaos, Rameau's opera includes appropriate pastoral music and a number of effective dances. The libretto combines the pastoral with the world of *féerie*, the magic genies and spirits, a fashionable literary preoccupation at the time.

Zampa

- Ferdinand Hérold. *Opéra comique* in three acts. 1831.
- Libretto by Mélesville.
- First performance by the Paris Opéra-Comique at the Salle Ventadour on 3rd May 1831.

The pirate Zampa, elder brother of Alphonse de Monza, returns, wanting now to marry his brother's betrothed, Camille. She is familiar with the story of Alice Manfredi, who had been betrayed and deserted by Zampa, and now, as Camille is forced to marriage, takes her revenge when her stone statue crushes him in its embrace.

Zampa once enjoyed great popularity. More recently it has been the overture that has retained a place in repertoire, in particular in arrangements for brass band.

Zar lässt sich photographieren, Der (The Tsar has his Photograph Taken)

- Kurt Weill. *Opera buffa* in one act. 1927.
- Libretto by Georg Kaiser.
- First performance at the Neues Theater, Leipzig, on 18th February 1928.

In Paris the Tsar wants his photograph taken by Angèle, a fashionable photographer. Her place, however, is taken by terrorists, who plan to shoot him. The Tsar, however, shows himself in a normal, human light, and, by a series of accidents, avoids being shot from the camera, which now conceals a gun. Warnings from the Tsar's equerry lead to the flight of the intended assassins and the release of the real Angèle and her staff.

Weill intended his comedy as a companion piece to *Der Protagonist*. For a time her preferred the double entendre of the title *Der Zar lässt sich* . . . . (The Tsar has himself . . . .), but eventually the longer title was restored. The work has a strong element of caricature in its treatment of all the characters.

Zar und Zimmermann (Tsar and Carpenter)

- Albert Lortzing. *Komische Oper* in three acts. 1837.
- Libretto by the composer, after the play *Der Bürgermeister von Saardam, oder Die zwei Peter* (The Mayor of Saardam, or The Two Peters) by Georg Christian Römer.
- First performance at the Stadttheater, Leipzig, on 22nd December 1837.

Characters

Peter the Great, Tsar of Russia	baritone
Peter Ivanov, a young Russian carpenter	tenor
General Lefort, Russian ambassador	bass
Van Bett, mayor of Saardam	bass

Marie, his niece	soprano
Widow Browe	contralto
Lord Syndham, English ambassador	bass
Marquis de Chateauneuf, French ambassador	tenor

Peter the Great is working in a Dutch shipyard, under the name of Peter Michaelov. News reaches the mayor that the Tsar is working in the shipyard, but he is puzzled when he finds two Russian Peters there. Peter Ivanov is in love with the mayor's niece Marie and Van Bett thinks he must be the Tsar, promising the hand of the girl, if he will reveal his identity. The French ambassador, meanwhile, has made contact with the real Tsar, while the English ambassador and the mayor centre their flattering attentions on Ivanov. The second act brings a celebration at an inn, with the ambassadors also disguised, Syndham and Van Bett with Ivanov, and the French and Russian ambassadors in discussion with the Tsar. Van Bett's attempt to have foreigners' papers checked still solves nothing. In the third act Van Bett arranges a cantata in honour of his supposed Tsar, Ivanov, while the true Tsar, provided through Ivanov with a safe-conduct from Syndham, makes his way to the ship the English ambassador has provided, leaving Ivanov a letter to be opened once he has gone. Eventually the Tsar is revealed, sailing from the harbour, and Ivanov opens his letter, which appoints him Imperial Overseer and allows him to marry Marie.

Zar und Zimmermann (Tsar and Carpenter) remains the best known of Lortzing's operas. Van Bett is a fine comic character, his nature first established in *O sancta justitia, ich möchte rasen* (O sacred justice, I should like to rage). At the inn in the second act the French ambassador, distracts the company with *Lebe wohl, mein flandrisch Mädchen* (Farewell, my Flemish maiden). The third act brings Van Bett's comic rehearsal of his cantata and in contrast the Tsar muses on his power in *Sonst spielt'ich mit Szepter, mit Krone und Stern* (Once I sported with sceptre, crown and star).

Recommended Recording: Hoch lebe die Freude — ***Naxos 8.550507***

Zarewitsch, Der (The Tsarevich)

- Franz Lehár. *Operette* in three acts. 1927.
- Libretto by Heinz Reichert and Béla Jenbach, after the play by Gabriele Zapolska.
- First performance at the Deutsches Künstlertheater, Berlin, on 16th February 1927.

The Tsarevich is lonely and seems disinclined to marry. It is arranged that Sonja, a dancer, disguised as a boy, should join him in his exercises. They fall in love, and the Grand Duke, who has arranged these matters, urges Sonja to break off the affair. The couple elope to Naples, but the death of the Tsar recalls the prince to his duty.

Lehár's operetta, with its serious ending, includes the Tsarevich's Volga song, *Allein! wieder allein!* (Alone! Alone again!). Sonja has her *Einer wird kommen* (One will come), while the third act brings the poignant *Warum hat jeder Frühling, ach, nur einen Mai?* (Why has every spring, ah, but one May?). The title-rôle of the Tsarevich was written for the tenor Richard Tauber.

Recommended Recording: Einer wird kommen / Wolgalied ***Naxos 8.550942***

Zauberflöte, Die (The Magic Flute)

- Wolfgang Amadeus Mozart. *Singspiel* in two acts. 1791.
- Libretto by Emanuel Schikaneder.
- First performance at the Theater auf der Wieden, Vienna, on 30th September 1791.

Characters

Sarastro, priest of the sun	bass
Tamino, a Javanese prince	tenor
Sprecher (Speaker), an elderly priest	speaking part
First Priest	speaking part
Second Priest	tenor
Third Priest	bass
Queen of the Night	coloratura soprano
Pamina, her daughter	soprano
Three Ladies, in the service of the Queen	two sopranos & mezzo-soprano
Three Boys	trebles or sopranos
Monostatos, a Moor	tenor
Papageno, a bird-catcher	baritone
Papagena	soprano
Two Men in Armour	tenor & bass
Three Slaves	speaking parts

Tamino tries to escape from a great serpent that is pursuing him. He faints and the Three Ladies dispose of the serpent, vying to stay behind and watch over him, while the others tell the Queen of what has happened. They leave and the bird-catcher Papageno makes his entrance, claiming, when Tamino comes to his senses, to have killed the serpent. The Ladies return and punish Papageno's lies by putting a padlock on his mouth. They give Tamino a portrait of a beautiful girl, by which he is immediately fascinated. This is Pamina, abducted, he is told, by a wicked magician. The Queen

of the Night makes her terrifying appearance, and tells Tamino that he must rescue Pamina, her daughter. The Ladies unlock Papageno's mouth and give Tamino a magic flute and Papageno silver bells, protection in their quest. In Sarastro's palace, Pamina has escaped but been caught again by Monostatos. Papageno and Monostatos confront each other, to their mutual terror. Papageno frees Pamina. Tamino, meanwhile, is confronted by three temples and, rebuffed at two of the temple doors, is questioned by the Speaker, an old priest from the Temple of Wisdom, who assures him that he will be re-united with Pamina. He plays his magic flute, to which animals emerge dancing. Papageno, captured by Monostatos, plays his bells, setting Monostatos and his slaves dancing and allowing their escape. The act ends with the entry of Sarastro and his priests, a prelude to the purification by ordeal of Tamino. The second act brings the ordeals through which Tamino, and to a limited extent Papageno, will pass. The first is of silence. Food is brought by the Three Boys, but Pamina's entrance has to be greeted in silence, to her distress. The Boys later prevent her killing herself with her mother's dagger. Tamino passes through the ordeals of fire and water, protected by the magic flute. Papageno has been tantalised by the occasional appearance of an old woman, claiming to be his bride. He is about to kill himself, when relief comes, through the Three Boys, when he makes use of the magic bells to bring a transformed young Papagena to his side. Monostatos and the Three Ladies, with their Queen, are still plotting against Sarastro, but are finally defeated by the power of light, with Tamino and Pamina now together in enlightenment.

The last of Mozart's operas to be staged in his lifetime, *Die Zauberflöte* (The Magic Flute) makes considerable use of masonic ritual and ideas. These are clear from the beginning of the overture, with its solemn ritual chords and use of ceremonial trombones. The opera that follows is of remarkable variety, mixing the comic and the heroic, the first found in Papageno, with his first entry, *Der Vogelfänger bin ich ja* (I am the bird-catcher) and his mixture of cowardice and peasant common sense, a stock character in contemporary German comedy. The heroic is represented by Tamino, in love at first sight with the portrait of Pamina in his *Dies Bildnis ist bezaubernd schön* (This picture is enchantingly beautiful). The Queen of the Night establishes her full coloratura power in her first appearance, *O zittre nicht* (O tremble not) and her vitriolic later *Der Hölle Rache* (Hell's vengeance). This is in contrast to the obverse character, Sarastro, with his calm and wise magnanimity, shown in its profundity in *O Isis und Osiris* (O Isis and Osiris) and *In diesen heil'gen Hallen* (In these sacred halls). Pamina's duet with Papageno on the happiness of love, *Bei Männern welche Liebe fühlen* (Those who feel love), won immediate popularity with audiences. Her own anguish is expressed in *Ach, ich fühl's* (Ah, I feel it has vanished), when greeted by Tamino's silence. There is much else that must be familiar in a score of prodigal invention.

Recommended Recordings:

Die Zauberflöte (2 CDs)	***Naxos 8.660030-31***
Highlights	***Naxos 8.553438***

Zelmira

- Gioachino Rossini. *Dramma* in two acts. 1822.
- Libretto by Andrea Leone Tottola, after *Zelmire* by Dormont de Belloy.
- First performance at the Teatro S Carlo, Naples, on 16th February 1822.

Zelmira's father, Polidoro, King of Lesbos, has been deposed, in the absence of his son-in-law Ilo, and is sheltered by his daughter Zelmira. The machinations of Antenore, who has subsequently seized power, involve calumny against Zelmira, whose husband Ilo thinks she has killed her father. He eventually realises the truth and is able to release his wife and her father from imprisonment and the threat of death.

Zelmira was Rossini's last opera for Naples, written with a view to a wider, international public. It was staged in Vienna two months after its first performances in Naples.

Zigeunerbaron, Der (The Gypsy Baron)

- Johann Strauss. *Operette* in three acts. 1885.
- Libretto by Ignaz Schnitzer, after a novel by Mór Jókai.
- First performance at the Theater an der Wien, Vienna, on 24th October 1885.

Sándor Barinkay returns to claim his father's estates, but is at first unsuccessful, obstructed by the illiterate Zsupán. He falls in love with the gypsy girl Sáffi and marries her in a gypsy ceremony that proves unconvincing to the authorities. His fortunes are finally restored after his triumphant return from an Austrian campaign in Spain.

Strauss introduces *Der Zigeunerbaron* (The Gypsy Baron) with an overture of the expected brilliance. The tenor Barinkay explains his wandering existence in his *Als flotter Geist* (As a cheerful soul). He explains his open-air gypsy marriage, attended by officiating birds, in *Wer uns getraut* (Who married us), and is greeted by a final march of victory, when he returns from Spain.

Recommended Recording: Overture / Als flotter Geist / Wer uns getraut   Naxos 8.550941

Zingara, La (The Gypsy Girl)

- Gaetano Donizetti. *Opera semiseria* in two acts. 1822.
- Libretto by Andrea Leone Tottola, after *La petite bohémienne* (The Little Gypsy) by Louis-Charles Caigniez, imitated from August von Kotzebue.
- First performance at the Teatro Nuovo, Naples, on 12th May 1822.

Argilla, the gypsy girl of the title, brings together the lovers Ferrando and Ines, saves the life of the Duke, whom she brings together again with his brother and frees Don Sebastiano, who turns out to be her father. Comedy is provided by the servant Pappacione, fooled into searching for gold in an old cistern.

The soprano aria *Fra l'erbe cosparse* (Sprinkled over the grass) enjoyed some popularity, not least in the repertoire of the Berlin Nightingale, Miliza Korjus. *La zingara* (The Gypsy Girl) was Donizetti's first opera for Naples.

Zoraide di Grenata (Zoraide of Granada)

- Gaetano Donizetti. *Melodramma eroico* in two acts. 1822.
- Libretto by Bartolomeo Merelli, after *Gonsalve de Cordove, ou Grenade reconquise* (Gonsalvez of Cordoba, or Granada Reconquered) by Jean-Pierre-Claris de Florian.
- First performance at the Teatro Argentina, Rome, on 28th January 1822.

Almuzir has usurped the throne and killed the king, father of Zoraide, whom he plans to marry. She is in love with Abenamet, who finally marries her, with the concurrence of Almuzir, whom he has rescued from popular anger.

Donizetti's opera won immediate success at its first staging, but failed to impress after its revision and revival two years later. In 1822 critics in Rome welcomed Donizetti as a promising new composer and the work won him, in consequence, further commissions, to be fulfilled in the same year.

ZOROASTRE (ZOROASTER)

- Jean-Philippe Rameau. *Tragédie en musique* in five acts. 1749.
- Libretto by Louis de Cahusac.
- First performance at the Paris Opéra on 5th December 1749.

Zoroastre, founder of the Magi, is exiled from Bactria, where the sorcerer Abramane yearns for power, to be achieved with the Bactrian princess Erinice. Zoroastre, banished, is parted from his beloved Amélite, heiress to the throne of Bactria. Through the help of Oromasès, King of the Genii, Zoroastre seeks to rescue Amélite, captured and tormented by Erinice. He is successful, but Abramane engineers, through his magic, further difficulties, championing the powers of darkness against the powers of light. Eventual victory allows Amélite to be crowned queen, with her consort Zoroastre.

Zoroastre was revised in 1756 and revived in Paris in 1770. Its plot is original in its study of conflict between darkness and light, evil and good, an idea that seems to suggest other contemporary preoccupations of the Enlightenment. The opera itself relies heavily on spectacular and repeated divine intervention for its eventual happy outcome.

ZWERG, DER (THE DWARF)

- Alexander von Zemlinsky. Opera in one act. 1921.
- Libretto by Georg Klaren, after Oscar Wilde's story *The Birthday of the Infanta.*
- First performance at the Neues Theater, Cologne, on 28th May 1922.

The Infanta, Donna Clara, is receiving her birthday presents, among them, from the Sultan, a dwarf. The Infanta amuses herself with her present, asking the Dwarf to sing and then to choose a bride. He chooses her but she is not serious, and orders her maid to let the Dwarf see himself in the glass, to understand his ugliness. The maid cannot bring herself to do this, but left alone the Dwarf kisses the cushion of the Infanta's throne and accidentally reveals a looking-glass. Seeing himself, he cries out in horror and when the Infanta returns he declares his love for her and seeks her assurance that he is not ugly. She tells him that she can only love a human being, not an animal. The Dwarf sinks down to the ground and dies, while the Infanta goes to find another toy to play with.

Zemlinsky's request to Franz Schreker to provide a libretto based on Oscar Wilde's story led, in the end, to Schreker's own opera, *Die Gezeichneten* (Those Marked with the Seal). Zemlinsky was preoccupied, it seems, with his own supposed ugliness, a matter that Alma Mahler, his pupil, had brought up in discussion with her future husband, Gustav Mahler. The opera is also known under the title *Der Geburtstag der Infantin* (The Birthday of the Infanta).

ZWILLINGSBRÜDER, DIE (THE TWIN BROTHERS)

- Franz Schubert. *Posse* in one act. 1819.
- Libretto by Georg von Hofmann, after the French *Les deux Valentins* (The Two Valentines).
- First performance at the Kärntnerthortheater, Vienna, on 14th June 1820.

Twin brothers, played by the same actor-singer, a baritone, return to their village, where there are predictable confusions, centring on Lieschen, who is betrothed to Anton, but is the object of attention of one of the brothers.

Dramatically achieving no great success, *Die Zwillingsbrüder* (The Twin Brothers) includes interesting music, most often heard now, if at all, out of its original context. Songs from the work include the baritone *Mag es stürmen, donnern, blitzen* (May it storm, thunder, lighten) and *Liebe teure Muttererde* (Beloved, dear mother-land).

Adam, Adolphe (1803-1856)

The son of a distinguished Paris Conservatoire piano-teacher, Adolphe Adam was born in Paris in 1803. He won popular success with his many compositions for the stage, much of his lesser work necessitated by the failure of a theatre venture in the revolution of 1848 and the consequent need to pay off heavy debts, cleared by the time of his death in 1856.

Operas

In addition to his well known ballet, *Giselle* or *Les Wilis*, Adam wrote some seventy operas, of which *Le Postillon de Lonjumeau* enjoyed great popularity in his lifetime. *Si j'étais roi* (If I were king) is now remembered principally for its overture and a drinking-song.

Adams, John (b.1947)

The American composer John Adams, son of a jazz saxophone player and a singer, has been associated with a more expanded form of minimalism, the fashionable movement in contemporary music that seeks its effects through developed repetition of very restricted harmonic or melodic material.

Operas

Adams first aroused interest in the opera-house with his very original *Nixon in China* (1987), which retains minimalist elements in a generally more lyrical context. He followed this in 1991 with *The Death of Klinghoffer*, centred on the murder of the wheel-chair-bound Jewish American of the title by Arab terrorists, a work that moves further away from minimalism into richer vocal territory.

d'Albert, Eugen (1864-1932)

Born in Glasgow in 1864, the German composer Eugen d'Albert had his early musical training in London, where his father was a ballet-master at Covent Garden. He won distinction as a virtuoso pianist and further fame as a composer of opera.

Operas

The best known of d'Albert's stage works is his music drama *Tiefland* (The Lowlands), one of twenty operas that he wrote between 1893 and his death in 1932. This was followed by a musical comedy on the subject of the flautist King of Prussia, Frederick the Great, *Flauto solo*.

Arne, Thomas (1710-1778)

One of the leading English composers of his time, as well as a violinist, Thomas Arne held an important place in English theatre-music of the 18th century, attempting to establish English opera, and serving as a successful composer of instrumental and vocal music.

Operas

Much of Arne's work for the theatre was in the form of songs and incidental music, including settings of Shakespeare songs that retain their place in recital, if not always in theatre repertoire. Among his most successful longer works for the theatre are his English opera *Thomas and Sally, or the Sailor's Return*, a work of considerable charm, his version of Milton's *Comus* and his attempt at an English *opera seria* in setting *Artaxerxes*, a translation of an Italian libretto by Metastasio, the most famous Italian librettist of his day.

Auber, Daniel-François-Esprit (1782-1871)

Daniel-François-Esprit Auber was a leading composer of French opera from the 1820s onwards, collaborating from then for some twenty years with the leading French librettist Augustin-Eugène Scribe.

Operas

Auber is particularly known for his contributions to the genre of *opéra comique*, although one of his most famous works is *Masaniello* or *La Muette de Portici* (The Dumb

Girl of Portici). For obvious reasons English audiences have preferred the first title. The staging of this work in Paris in 1828 began the era of French grand opera. Other successful operas, among the 47 by Auber, include *Fra Diavolo*, *Le cheval de bronze* (The Bronze Horseman) and *Les Diamants de la reine* (The Queen's Diamonds).

Bach, Johann Christian (1735-1782)

The youngest son of Johann Sebastian Bach by his second wife, Johann Christian was born in Leipzig in 1735 and after his father's death in 1750 moved to Berlin to live with his brother Carl Philipp Emanuel Bach, harpsichordist to King Frederick the Great. He travelled to Italy, studied with Padre Martini, became a Catholic and served as organist at Milan Cathedral before, in 1762, moving to London as a composer of Italian opera, as Handel had done fifty years before. He enjoyed a considerable reputation in England and abroad, organized subscription concerts in London with his friend Abel and exercised strong influence on the young Mozart, whom he met in London and in Paris. By the time of his death his popularity in London had begun to wane.

Operas

Johann Christian Bach wrote a dozen or so operas, some for the King's Theatre in London, with two in the 1770s for Mannheim and one for Paris, using a revised version of a libretto by Quinault written for Lully a hundred years earlier, *Amadis de Gaule*. His operas are now generally neglected.

Balfe, Michael William (1808-1870)

Born in Dublin in 1808, Balfe came to occupy a leading position in English opera during the 19th century. He made his earlier career as a theatre violinist in London and then as a singer, employed in Paris by Rossini at the Théâtre des Italiens, where he sang the rôle of Figaro in Rossini's *Il barbiere di Siviglia* (The Barber of Seville).

Operas

Balfe's early operas were designed for the Italian theatre, notably for La Scala, Milan, where he was engaged as a principal baritone. Most of his thirty operas, after his first London success in 1835, were written for London. Of these *The Bohemian Girl* is still remembered.

Barber, Samuel (1910-1981)

A native of Pennsylvania, the American composer Samuel Barber was among the first students at the Curtis Institute in Philadelphia, where he studied piano, conducting, singing and composition. Awards allowed him further study in Rome. He taught briefly at the Curtis Institute, but soon withdrew, sharing a house with his former fellow-student Menotti. His music remained neo-romantic in idiom, although not without contemporary influences.

Operas

Barber wrote three operas, the first, *Vanessa*, with a libretto by Menotti, in 1957. It was followed two years later by *A Hand of Bridge* and finally, in 1966, by his Shakespearean *Antony and Cleopatra*, with a libretto devised by Franco Zeffirelli.

Bartók, Béla (1881-1945)

Béla Bartók was one of the leading Hungarian and European composers of his time, proficient also as a pianist. He joined his friend Zoltán Kodály in the collection folk-music in Hungary and neighbouring regions, including, in his case, Anatolia. His work in this field deeply influenced his own style of composition, which is, however, very much more astringent in its apparent mathematical organization than much of what Kodály wrote. Out of sympathy with the right-wing government that replaced the immediate post-war republic in Hungary, he moved in 1940 to the United States, dying there in relatively straitened circumstances in 1945.

Opera

Bartók wrote only one opera, *Duke Bluebeard's Castle*, first staged in Budapest in 1918, after various revisions.

Beethoven, Ludwig van (1770-1827)

From 1792 Beethoven made his career in Vienna, after earlier experience in the service of the Archbishop-Elector of Cologne in his native Bonn, following the avocation of his father and grandfather. Fortified with introductions to leading families in the capital, he enjoyed initial success as a pianist and composer, but deafness, from about 1800 onwards, led to a concentration on the second activity. Building on the tradition of Haydn and Mozart, he expanded classical forms to breaking-point in his nine symphonies and his piano sonatas, pointing the way to a music of the future for his successors to explore. His musical language always had an academic element, a tendency to the exercise of contrapuntal skill, and this increased, as he grew older, deafer and, in his personal life, more eccentric.

Opera

Beethoven wrote only one opera, *Fidelio*, which had little success at its first performance in French occupied Vienna, but underwent various revisions for later revivals. He contemplated other subjects, but nothing came of them.

Bellini, Vincenzo (1801-1835)

Vincenzo Bellini was one of the most important composers of Italian opera in the earlier years of the 19th century. He died in Paris in 1835 at the height of his success. Bellini's influence was not confined to opera, and Chopin owes much to him, particularly in his handling of melody.

Operas

Bellini completed ten operas, the first in 1825 as a graduation piece at the Conservatory in Naples and the last, *I puritani* (The Puritans), for Paris in 1835. The best known of his operas in present repertoire must be the *opera semi-seria, La sonnambula* (The Sleepwalker), with the tragic *I Capuleti e i Montecchi* (The Capulets and Montagues) and *Norma*.

Benatzky, Ralph (1884-1957)

Benatzky started his musical career in Munich, before moving to Vienna and then to Berlin. He won a reputation as a writer of songs and of popular operetta.

Operettas

Benatzky achieved his most enduring success in the collaborative *Im weissen Rössl* (White Horse Inn), for which he provided the greater part of the music.

Benda, Georg (1722-1795)

One of a dynasty of Bohemian musicians, Georg Benda served in the orchestra of the King of Prussia, before appointment as Kapellmeister in Gotha, where he remained, intermittently, for the rest of his active career.

Operas & Melodramas

Benda's chief contemporary fame was as a composer of melodramas, works with spoken dialogue and musical accompaniment. His achievements in this genre impressed Mozart, who failed to complete his own first attempts at the form, and had a lasting effect on operatic practice, as in the prison scene of Beethoven's *Fidelio* or the scene in the Wolf's Glen in Weber's *Der Freischütz* (The Marksman). Benda's most important melodramas are *Ariadne auf Naxos* (Ariadne on Naxos), *Medea* and *Pygmalion*.

Bennett, Richard Rodney (b.1936)

A composer and pianist of great versatility, Richard Rodney Bennett studied in London with Lennox Berkeley and Howard Ferguson, and subsequently in Paris with Pierre Boulez. Although capable of writing in a variety of styles, with a parallel reputation as a jazz pianist and accompanist, he found what seems his own particular language in a lyrical form of serialism. Nevertheless he remains equally convincing in whatever style he chooses to write,

Operas

Bennett's five operas, written in the 1960s, won contemporary acclaim, notably the powerful *The Mines of Sulphur* of 1963, followed by the comic *A Penny for a Song* in 1966 and the romantic opera *Victory* in 1970. These interesting works have not held their place in contemporary repertoire.

Berg, Alban (1885-1935)

The so-called Second Viennese School of Arnold Schoenberg has exercised a strong influence over the course of music in the 20th century. Schoenberg's pupils Anton Webern and Alban Berg put into practice the general principles developed by their mentor, the latter in a lyrical approach to serialism, music based on the manipulation of a fixed order of the twelve semitones of the octave.

Operas

Berg completed the first of his two operas, *Wozzeck*, in 1922. This dramatic study of madness, based on a play by Georg Büchner, was followed by *Lulu*, an ambitious work based on plays by Franz Wedekind. This remained unfinished at his death in 1935, but the final act was eventually completed by others, to allow stagings of the whole work.

Berio, Luciano (b.1925)

A leading Italian composer of the avant-garde, Luciano Berio was influenced by Luigi Dallapiccola into new forms of serialism and thence into eclectic experiment of every kind.

Stage Works

Berio's dramatic compositions are varied and must include works for the concert-hall that have strong dramatic and histrionic possibilities. His operas include *Laborintus II*, if this collection of varied literary quotations can be so decribed, and *Opera*, a work that derives its theme of social degeneration and death from the sinking of the Titanic.

Berkeley, Lennox (1903-1989)

A pupil of Nadia Boulanger, the English composer Lennox Berkeley belongs rather to a continental than a national musical tradition. He enjoyed a successful career as a composer and as a teacher of composition at the Royal Academy of Music in London. His music, often written for particular performers, is skilfully constructed and generally lyrical.

Operas

Berkeley wrote four operas, *Nelson* in 1954 and in the same year *A Dinner Engagement*, first staged at the Aldeburgh Festival. 1956 brought the opera *Ruth*, followed, in 1967, by *Castaway*, again first staged in Aldeburgh.

Berkeley, Michael (b.1948)

The son of Lennox Berkeley, Michael Berkeley has established himself as a composer of versatility, writing in a generally approachable musical language.

Opera

Michael Berkeley's opera *Baa Baa Black Sheep*, first performed at Cheltenham in 1993, created an immediately favourable impression. The work is based on a story by Rudyard Kipling and includes an important rôle for a boy treble.

Berlioz, Hector (1803-1869)

In his own time Berlioz was something of an outsider to the French musical establishment, in spite of his eventual study at the Conservatoire and the award of the Prix de Rome. He is, nevertheless, typical of his period in his wide literary interests and the freedom of means of expression he sought in his music. Although his descriptions of apparent attempts to sabotage performance of his music are not always credible, there is no doubt that he encountered difficulties in gaining a hearing for his music in France, where he worked primarily as a music critic.

Operas

Berlioz completed four operas. The first of these, *Les francs-juges* was not performed and is remembered now for its surviving overture. *Benvenuto Cellini*, staged at the Paris Opéra in 1838, provided material for a later Roman Carnival, while the dimensions and demands of the Virgilian grand opera *Les troyens* (The Trojans) prevented its complete performance in the composer's life-time. His last opera, the Shakespearian *Béatrice et Bénédict*, was first staged at Baden-Baden in 1862.

Bernstein, Leonard (1918-1990)

The American conductor and composer Leonard Bernstein had a strong influence on American musical taste, particularly in his championing of Mahler. In some works, notably in his musical *West Side Story*, he attempted a fusion of American 'classical' and lighter styles.

Operas

In addition to musicals and ballets, Bernstein wrote two operas, the second of which, *Candide*, based on Voltaire, has won some popularity, particularly in its lively overture.

Berwald, Franz (1796- 1868)

Descended from a family of Swedish musicians of remoter German origin, Franz Berwald remains one of the most important figures in Swedish music in the 19th century.

Operas

Five completed operas by Berwald survive in various forms. Of these the last, *Drottningen av Golconda* (The Queen of Golconda), completed in 1864, *Estrella de Soria* ist the most significant.

Birtwistle, Harrison (b.1934)

Among the leading English composers of his generation, Harrison Birtwistle studied at the Royal Manchester College of Music and with Peter Maxwell Davies, Alexander Goehr and the pianist John Ogdon, formed the New Music Manchester Group. At first working as a clarinettist, he was later able to devote his time wholly to composition with a series of works that make use of varied experimental techniques.

Operas

Birtwistle's operas include the remarkable *Punch and Judy* of 1967, *The Mask of Orpheus*, completed in 1977, and *Gawain*, first staged at Covent Garden in London in 1991.

Bizet, Georges (1838-1875)

Bizet won early success as a composer and initially as a pianist. His later career in Paris was more variable and a number of stage works remained unfinished at the time of his early death.

Operas

Bizet's last opera, *Carmen*, is by far the best known, followed by the earlier *Les pêcheurs des perles* (The Pearl Fishers) of 1863 and *La jolie fille de Perth* (The Fair Maid of Perth), completed three years later.

Bliss, Arthur (1891-1975)

Master of the Queen's Musick from 1953 until his death, the English composer Arthur Bliss eventually followed the late romantic example of his compatriot Edward Elgar, after a more controversial earlier period as a young man.

Operas

Bliss wrote two operas, the first in 1949, with a libretto by J.B.Priestley, *The Olympians* and the second, in 1960, a television opera, *Tobias and the Angel*.

Bloch, Ernest (1880-1959)

Essentially a Jewish composer, Ernest Bloch was born in Switzerland and later took out American citizenship, serving as director of the Cleveland Institute from 1920 to 1925 and later of San Francisco Conservatory.

Opera

Bloch wrote his only opera, *Macbeth*, between 1904 and 1909.

Blomdahl, Karl-Birger (1916-1968)

Born near Stockholm in 1916, the Swedish composer Karl-Birger Blomdahl enjoyed an active career as a teacher and administrator. His music developed from the influence of Bartók and Stravinsky to an interest in serialism as exemplified in the work of Berg, later avoiding the more extreme innovations promoted at Darmstadt.

Operas

Blomdahl completed two operas, leaving a third incomplete. The first opera, *Aniara*, is of particular interest in its subject, travel in space, presented symbolically.

Blow, John (1649-1708)

John Blow was the most significant English composer in the generation before that of Henry Purcell, ten years his junior. Born in 1649, the year of the execution of King Charles I, he was able to benefit from the revival of church and theatre music with the Restoration of the monarchy in 1660.

Masque

John Blow's court masque *Venus and Adonis*, an opera in all but name, is important in itself, but has added interest as an obvious influence on Purcell's *Dido and Aeneas*.

Boieldieu, François-Adrien (1775-1834)

The principal composer of French opera in the first quarter of the 19th century, Boïeldieu was born in Rouen in 1775 and had his first theatrical success in 1793. Triumph in Paris was followed by failure in marriage and a period from 1803 spent as director of French opera in St Petersburg at the Russian court, whence he returned to Paris in 1811. By the time of his death in 1834 he had gone some way towards upholding French comic opera traditions against the inroads of the more popular Italian comedy of Rossini.

Operas

Boïeldieu wrote or collaborated in the composition of some forty operas, with *Le Calife de Bagdad* (The Caliph of Baghdad) and *La Dame blanche* (The White Lady) possibly the best remembered, at least in part.

Boito, Arrigo (1842-1918)

Boito is probably better known as a librettist than as a composer, notably for the texts that he provided for Verdi's *Simon Boccanegra*, *Otello* and *Falstaff*, as well as the libretto he wrote for Ponchielli's *La Gioconda*.

Operas

Boito's ambitious *Mefistofele* underwent various revisions, while his second, *Nerone*, was left unfinished.

Borodin, Alexander Porfir'yevich (1833-1887)

The Five, the Mighty Handful, so named by the Russian critic and librarian Vladimir Stasov, were the principal nationalist composers in later 19th century Russia, following the example of Glinka, their forerunner. Borodin, like some others of the group, followed another profession than music, winning distinction as a professor of chemistry. His work as a composer was limited by his other duties and preoccupations and at his death he left a number of compositions unfinished, to be completed by his friend Rimsky-Korsakov and others.

Operas

Borodin's operas include *The Bogatïrs*, a contribution to the collaborative opera *Mlada* and his best known but unfinished work *Prince Igor*, completed and partly orchestrated by Rimsky-Korsakov and Glazunov after the composer's death.

Boughton, Rutland (1878-1960)

A composer in the English pastoral tradition, with Wagnerian intentions, Rutland Boughton established à festival at Glastonbury, in the West of England, and was able to stage there his own ambitious operas, often with limited resources. After 1927 he attempted festivals at Stroud and at Bath, in the same part of England, but these did not continue.

Operas

Of Rutland Boughton's eleven operas *The Immortal Hour* remains the best known. He concentrated much attention on an Arthurian cycle of five operas, the last two of which, written bewteen 1943 and 1945, remained unperformed.

Britten, Benjamin (1913-1976)

Benjamin Britten must be accounted the most outstanding English composer of the mid-20th century, winning a national and international reputation and establishing, through the fundamental English sources of his inspiration, a language and sensibility that transcended the national barriers that many of his English predecessors had been unable to cross. His varied compositions include at their heart a series of vocal works inspired by the voice, literary perception and companionship of his friend, the singer Peter Pears.

Operas

Britten succeeded, as no English composer before him, in establishing English opera as an internationally viable form. His first great success came in 1945 with *Peter Grimes*, followed by the chamber operas *The Rape of Lucretia* and *Albert Herring*, *Billy Budd*, *Gloriana*, *The Turn of the Screw*, *A Midsummer Night's Dream*, the three church parables *Curlew River, The Burning Fiery Furnace* and *The Prodigal Son,* the television opera *Owen Wingrave* and the last of his operas, *Death in Venice.*

Bruneau, Alfred (1857-1934)

Alfred Bruneau was a pupil of Massenet and in his musical language seems to combine the Wagnerian with the lyricism of his teacher and the tradition of Gounod and Bizet. In a varied output, his collaborations with Zola are of particularly interest.

Operas

Bruneau wrote thirteen operas, nine of them based on the work of Zola, who directly provided libretti for four of these. His contemporary success came largely from his collaboration with or inspiration from the novelist. Operas that are particularly worthy of mention are *L'attaque du moulin* (The Attack on the Mill), *Messidor* and *Naïs Micoulin.*

Busoni, Ferruccio (1866-1924)

The son of an Italian musician father and a German pianist mother, Ferruccio Busoni represents a remarkable synthesis of two differing attitudes to music, while winning an outstanding reputation as a piano virtuoso. His varied compositions include orchestral works, music for voices and orchestra, chamber music and a quantity of music for the piano.

Operas

Busoni wrote five operas. Of these *Die Brautwahl* (The Bridal Choice), based on E.T.A.Hoffmann, aroused contemporary interest. Better known are the last three operas, *Arlecchino, oder Die Fenster* (Harlequin, or The Windows), *Turandot* and *Doktor Faust.*

Caccini, Giulio (c.1545-1618)

Giulio Caccini, a singer, lutenist and performer on the viol and harp, spent much of his life in the service of the Medici family in Florence. He is particularly associated with the new style of singing in recitative, the so-called *stile recitativo*, an alliance of music, in this case the single melodic line, with rhetoric, as the sung melody followed the intonations and stresses of speech. His ideas reflect those of the Florentine Camerata, with contemporary interests in dramatic music. The preface to his collection of songs published in 1601, *Le nuove musiche* (New Music), provides valuable insight into contemporary performance practice.

Operas

Caccini collaborated with Jacopo Peri in setting Rinuccini's libretto *Euridice* in 1600 and provided a further setting entirely his own in the same year, publishing it before the other work could be issued. His other opera is *Il rapimento di Cefalo* (The Abduction of Cephalus), to which other composers also contributed.

Cambert, Robert (c.1627-1677)

Skilled as a keyboard-player, the French composer Robert Cambert was an important figure in the establishment of French opera, in which he was a pioneer. He was displaced by Lully and in 1673 moved to London, where he seems to have achieved limited success, if any.

Operas

Cambert composed four operas, three of them bearing the descriptive title of *pastorale*. These only survive in fragmentary form. They include works that were revised for performance in London, notably *Pomone* and *Ariane, ou Le mariage de Bacchus* (Ariadne, or The Marriage of Bacchus), the latter yet another version of Ariadne's fate on the island of Naxos.

Campra, André (1660-1744)

Campra is an important figure in French music of his time, both sacred, as *maître de musique* at Notre Dame in Paris, and secular, as he turned his attention to music for the stage. In the theatre he won particular success during the regency of Philippe of Orleans and was reckoned one of the leading French theatre composers in the generation after Lully. He later received a royal pension and was in the service of the Prince of Conti. In 1723 he was appointed a *sous-maître* of the royal chapel, resigning for reasons of health in 1735.

Operas

Campra wrote some dozen operas, generally for performance at the Paris Opéra, where he directed performances after leaving Notre Dame in 1700. He was responsible for the creation of the French *opéra-ballet*, a work in which a number of scenes, with different characters, are presented, all generally related to one general subject that is indicated in the title. The first of these, *L'Europe galante*, staged first in 1697, introduces episodes under the titles France, Spain, Italy, Turkey. Campra won similar success, in particular, with *Les fêtes vénitiennes* (Venetian Festivals). He also composed a number of *tragédies-lyriques* in which he embellishes the form used by Lully, paving the way for the works of Rameau.

Casken, John (b.1949)

The English composer John Casken studied at the University of Birmingham and in Poland, his earlier music, at least, showing something of the influence of Lutoslawski.

Opera

Casken won particular recognition with his opera *Golem*, awarded the first Britten Prize for Composition in 1990, when it was first staged.

Catalani, Alfredo (1854-1893)

Alfredo Catalani had his musical training in his native Lucca, in Paris and in Milan, in this last city making friends with Boito. Treated with disdain by Verdi and by his nearer contemporary Puccini, he suffered from the negligence of his later publisher, Ricordi, but was championed by the conductor Toscanini, who called his daughter after the principal character in Catalani's best known opera.

Operas

Catalani completed five operas, of which *La Wally* alone survives in international repertoire.

Cavalieri, Emilio de' (c.1550-1602)

Of noble birth and wide culture Emilio de'Cavalieri served the Medici family and was involved both in the provision of elaborate court entertainments and in the secret diplomacy necessitated by changes in the papacy. He combined practical musical skills as a singer and organist, with ability as a dancer and in the 1590s provided music for a series of pastorals, developed from the literary fashions of the time. He left Florence after what he regarded as the failure of the festivities for the marriage of Henri IV of France and Maria de'Medici in 1600, at which he had directed the performance of the *Euridice* of Peri and Caccini. In his native Rome once more, he was involved in the provision of music for the Oratorio del Crocifisso.

Stage Work

Cavalieri, who declared his priority in the development of the new singing style which Caccini and Peri both claimed to have invented, is known in particular for his allegorical sacred dramatic work *Rappresentatione di Anima et di Corpo* (Representation of Soul and of Body), mounted at the Oratorio del Crocifisso in Rome in 1600.

Cavalli, Francesco (1602-1676)

Cavalli was recruited as a boy to the choir of St Mark's in Venice, where Monteverdi was *maestro di cappella*. He served as second and subsequently first organist at the basilica from 1639 onwards, his position kept for him during a two-year absence in France, at the request of Cardinal Mazarin, for the provision of opera. Cavalli had been involved in opera from 1639, two years after the opening of the first commercial opera-house in Venice. He won a wide reputation and held a leading position as an opera-composer in the generation after Monteverdi.

Operas

Cavalli wrote the music for over thirty operas, most of them intended for first performance in Venice, with the notable exception of *Ercole amante* (Hercules in Love), designed for Paris to celebrate the marriage of Louis XIV to the Spanish Infanta. There have been relatively recent revivals of his operas *Ormindo, Giasone* (Jason), *Calisto* and *Xerse* (Xerxes) and these and other works provide a valuable source for the understanding of Venetian operatic style at the most important period of its development.

Cesti, Antonio (1623-1669)

As a Franciscan friar for much of his life, Antonio Cesti found difficulty in reconciling his religious vocation with his work in the opera-house, both as composer and singer.

He enjoyed the patronage of the Medici in Florence, was released by the Pope from his vows as a religious and joined, briefly, the papal choir, but was later in the service of Archduke Ferdinand Karl in Innsbruck and of the court in Vienna. He was among the most celebrated Italian musicians of his time.

Operas

Of the dozen or so operas by Cesti the first, *Orontea*, enjoyed continuing popularity from its first staging in Venice in 1649 onwards. This was followed by *Alessandro vincitor de se stesso* (Alexander, Conqueror of Himself). The famous *La Dori* was written in 1657 for Innsbruck and the elaborate court opera *Il pomo d'oro* (The Golden Apple) for Vienna in 1666, to be staged there two years later.

Chabrier, Emmanuel (1841-1894)

Intended by his parents for a more conventional career than that of a musician, the French composer Emmanuel Chabrier was only able to devote himself fully to music in 1880, after employment for some nineteen years in the Ministry of the Interior in Paris. His compositions include some colourful orchestral works and piano pieces that had some influence over his immediate successors.

Operas

Chabrier wrote some ten stage works, including two early unfinished attempts at operettas with his friend Verlaine. Of the others *Gwendoline*, set in medieval Britain, had some success, with the *opéra comique Le roi malgré lui* (King in spite of himself). He finished only the first act of a major undertaking, *Brisëis*.

Charpentier, Gustave (1860-1956)

After Bohemian distractions in Paris, Gustave Charpentier eventually became a composition pupil of Massenet in 1885, when he was re-admitted to the Paris Conservatoire, winning the important Prix de Rome two years later. His chief activity as a composer came before 1914.

Operas

Charpentier seems to have completed only three operas and of these *Louise* remains the work by which he is most remembered.

Chausson, Ernest (1855-1899)

After a sheltered childhood in a cultured family and subsequent study of law, Chausson became a pupil of Massenet at the Paris Conservatoire, also attending the classes of César Franck. His music reflects something of the development of French music, from Massenet to the innovations of Debussy.

Operas

Of Chausson's three operas *Le roi Arthus* (King Arthur) was his most significant achievement in this field.

Cherubini, Luigi (1760-1842)

The Italian composer Cherubini came to occupy a leading position in French musical life. He was employed at the Paris Conservatoire from its foundation in 1795 and from 1822 served as its director, a position he held until his death twenty years later. His compositions include a variety of compositions, some of them necessitated by the political requirements of the French revolution, which he weathered, to occupy official positions under the restored Bourbon monarchy.

Operas

Cherubini wrote over thirty operas. Of these the most important is *Médée* (Medea), a work of strong dramatic power. His first operas were written for the Italian theatre and for London. His first French opera was written in 1788, followed by two escape operas, *Lodoïska* and *Eliza, ou Le voyage aux glaciers du Mont St-Bernard* (Eliza, or The Journey to the Glaciers of Mont St Bernard), both of which suggested new themes for opera, avoiding the more grandiose subjects usually accorded serious treatment in the opera-house. The escape opera *Les deux journées, ou Le porteur d'eau* (Two Days, or The Water-Carrier), in which humble water-carriers rescue unjustly persecuted aristocrats, although set in the 17th century, suggested situations all too familiar in France. The influence of the work is reflected in Beethoven's *Fidelio*.

Cilea, Francesco (1866-1950)

Francesco Cilea was trained at the Naples Conservatory and enjoyed a successful career as a teacher and administrator, for some twenty years as director of Naples Conservatory. His success as a composer was limited.

Operas

Of Cilea's six operas, *Adriana Lecouvreur*, written in 1902, alone retains some place in operatic repertoire. *L'arlesiana* (The Girl from Arles), based on Alphonse Daudet and musically associated more memorably with Bizet, has provided singers with one popular aria.

Cimarosa, Domenico (1749-1801)

Trained in Naples, Cimarosa became one of the most important composers of comic opera in the later 18th century. From 1787 he spent some years as *maestro di cappella* to Catherine the Great in St Petersburg and in 1791, the year of Mozart's death, was in Vienna as Kapellmeister to the Emperor Leopold II. He returned to Naples, with a court appointment, but association with the rebels of 1799 led to a brief period of imprisonment, from which he was released at the intercession of Lady Hamilton and others. He moved to Venice, where he died in 1801.

Operas

Cimarosa wrote well over sixty operas and has had a further series of works attributed to him, probably erroneously. He has a position of importance in the development of opera, the use of a chorus and of more complex structures. His most popular opera remains *Il matrimonio segreto* (The Clandestine Marriage).

Conradi, Johann Georg (d.1699)

Conradi served as court Kapellmeister at Ansbach and then to Duke Heinrich of Saxe-Gotha, before taking appointment in the mid-1690s in Hamburg, where he established an effective orchestra and successful opera.

Operas

Much of Conradi's work for the opera-house has been lost or survives only in libretti. *Die schöne und getreue Ariadne* (The Fair and Loyal Ariadne) has been rediscovered, its French operatic treatment of the story of Ariadne on Naxos important in establishing Conradi's prior position in German opera.

Copland, Aaron (1900-1990)

The son of immigrant Jewish parents from Poland and Lithuania, Aaron Copland was born in Brooklyn in 1900 and lived to become the doyen of all American composers. He was a pupil of Nadia Boulanger in Paris and is widely known, in particular, for his American ballets, among other works that seem to epitomize the spirit of America.

Operas

Copland's second opera, *The Tender Land,* has enjoyed relatively little success, but deserves attention, with its simple rustic American setting and homely plot, coupled with music that, as in the ballets, captures something of this rural American mood.

Corghi, Azio (b.1937)

The Italian composer Azio Corghi was born at Cirie, near Turin, in 1937 and trained there and in Milan. He has won a distinguished reputation in Italy, with music for the theatre and for the concert-hall.

Operas

Corghi wrote his opera *Divara – Wasser und Blut* (Divara – Water and Blood) in response to a commission from Münster, to commemorate the Anabaptist seizure of power there in 1534. This, and the earlier opera *Blimunda,* were collaborations with the Portuguese writer José Saramago.

Cornelius, Peter (1824-1874)

Peter Cornelius found congenial support for his ambitions in Weimar with Liszt. Gifted also as a poet, he set to music his own verses and opera libretti and eventually fell under the strong influence of Wagner, who encouraged him by arranging teaching and rehearsal appointments for him in Munich.

Operas

Cornelius completed only two operas. Of these the comic opera *Der Barbier von Bagdad* (The Barber of Baghdad) retains a place in modern repertoire.

Davies, Peter Maxwell (b.1934)

A contemporary of the composers Harrison Birtwistle and Alexander Goehr, and of the pianist and composer John Ogdon, in Manchester, Peter Maxwell Davies enjoys an exceptionally successful career as a composer in a number of different genres. His music-theatre works, combining concert performance with a visual dramatic element have proved both innovative and effective while his musical language has proved as acceptable as the witty pastiches of which he is capable.

Operas

Maxwell Davies's major opera is *Taverner*, completed in 1968 and revised in 1970. His chamber opera *The Martyrdom of St Magnus* has resulted from his long residence on Orkney and his consequent involvement in local traditions and cultural life. *The Two Fiddlers* is a children's opera, written for Orcadian performance, while the popular children's opera *Cinderella* has brought pleasure to many. *The Lighthouse* also draws on Scottish legend.

Debussy, Claude (1862-1918)

Claude Debussy has exercised a decisive influence over composers both at home, in France, and internationally. He was trained at the Paris Conservatoire, there deciding to become a composer rather than a concert pianist, his original intention. His highly characteristic musical language, thoroughly French in inspiration, extended the contemporary limits of harmony and form, with a remarkably delicate command of nuance, whether in piano-writing or in the handling of a relatively large orchestra.

Operas

Debussy attempted five operas, two of them based on the work of Edgar Allen Poe, but completed only one, *Pelléas et Mélisande*, based on the play by Maeterlinck.

Delibes, Léo (1836-1891)

At the Paris Conservatoire as a student, Delibes achieved no great distinction. His first major triumph came with the ballet *Coppélia* in 1870. He excelled as a composer of operetta, his career culminating in equally successful operas of a weightier kind.

Operas

Of some two dozen operatic works by Delibes, the majority lighter in character, it is the opera *Lakmé*, set in India, that has found particular favour, not least with advertisers in search of attractive promotional music. Written in 1883, it was followed by a lesser work, *Kassya*, which again has an exotic oriental element to its score.

Delius, Frederick (1862-1934)

Born in Bradford of German parentage, Delius was sent by his father to supervise an orange plantation in Florida, before persuading him to allow musical study in Leipzig, where he met Grieg. From there he moved to Paris, before settling with the painter Jelka Rosen, who later became his wife, at Grez-sur-Loing. His final years brought blindness and paralysis, the result of an earlier syphilitic infection, a period during which he was able to dictate his work to his musical amanuensis Eric Fenby. He owed much of his success to the strong advocacy of the conductor Sir Thomas Beecham. His musical language, instantly recognisable, is characterized by a rhapsodic harmony and lyricism of its own.

Operas

Of the six operas of Delius, *Koanga* owes its origin to the period the composer spent in Florida. This, and *A Village Romeo and Juliet* are better known in various concert excerpts than in the opera-house.

Destouches, André Cardinal (1672-1749)

From a well-to-do Parisian family, Destouches joined an expedition to Siam and later served as a musketeer, before turning to music as a career, taking lessons from Campra. He enjoyed royal favour and wrote principally vocal music, from the early drinking-songs of his army days onwards.

Operas

Destouches wrote some ten operas and *opéras-ballets* for Fontainebleau and the Paris Opéra. Among these were *Issé*, a work described as *pastorale-héroïque*, and a treatment of the well known story of Semiramis.

Donizetti, Gaetano (1797-1848)

For nearly a decade after the death of Bellini in 1835, Donizetti was the leading composer of Italian opera. A native of Bergamo, he had his first significant success in 1822 with his seventh opera, *Zoraida di Granata*. There followed a series of some sixty operas and removal to Paris, where Rossini had been induced to settle, to his profit. Donizetti wrote other music, in addition to his operas, including a quantity of other vocal music, chamber music and, in his earlier years, orchestral music.

Operas

From the long list of operas by Donizetti, those that retain a general place in repertoire must include *Anna Bolena* (Anne Boleyn), *L'elisir d'amore* (The Elixir of Love), *Maria Stuarda* (Mary Stuart), *Lucia di Lammermoor*, the French *La fille du régiment* (The Daughter of the Regiment), *Linda di Chamounix* (Linda of Chamonix) and *Don Pasquale*. There are other operas, serious and comic, that are staged with varying degrees of frequency today.

Dupuy, Edouard (c.1770-1822)

The French-born violinist, singer and composer Edouard Dupuy enjoyed a varied career from 1793 in Stockholm and in Copenhagen, where his career continued to resemble that of Don Giovanni, a part he took in Mozart's opera of that name. He achieved his greatest success as a composer of opera with *Ungdom og Galskab* (Youth and Folly) in Copenhagen in 1806.

Operas

Dupuy's stage work was *De ädelmodiga bönderna* (The Noble Peasant), staged in Stockholm in 1797. His comic opera *Felicie, eller Den romanska flickan* (Felicie, or The Maid of Rome) was staged in Stockholm in 1821.

Dvořák, Antonín (1841-1904)

The son of a Bohemian village inn-keeper-cum-butcher, Dvořák followed Smetana as the leading Czech nationalist composer. Encouraged by Brahms, he combined a national element with an inherited Central European classical tradition. He won acceptance abroad, while Vienna remained more grudging in its response to his work, and between 1892 and 1895 was employed intermittently in New York as director of the new National Conservatory. This period brought compositions that combine American with Bohemian inspiration. At home again, he was much honoured, preferring a relatively simple life in the Bohemian countryside to residence in Vienna, as others suggested.

Operas

Dvořák's ten operas have had limited popularity abroad, partly for linguistic reasons and partly because of his own dramatic limitations. As a viola-player under Smetana, he had worked in the opera-house in Prague and retained continuing interest in the genre, writing his first opera, *Alfred,* with a German libretto, in 1870 and his last, *Armida,* in the last years of his life. While *King and Charcoal-Burner, The Cunning Peasant, Vanda, Dimitrij, The Jacobin* and *Kate and the Devil* may contain musical elements very worthy of explorations, it is *Rusalka* that has proved internationally the most viable.

Einem, Gottfried von (1918-1996)

A war-time pupil of Boris Blacher in Berlin, Gottfried von Einem won himself a reputation as a composer of chamber and orchestral music. He held administrative positions at the Salzburg Festival and in Vienna, where he settled in 1953. Viennese operatic traditions had some influence on his later works for the theatre.

Operas

Gottfried von Einem's operas include *Dantons Tod* (Danton's Death), based on the play by Büchner, *Der Prozess* (The Trial), based on Kafka's novel of that name, *Der Zerrissene* (The One at Odds with Himself), *Der Besuch der alten Dame* (The Visit of the Old Lady), with the playwright Dürrenmatt, and a work based on Schiller's *Kabale und Liebe* (Cabal and Love).

Elgar, Edward (1857-1934)

Arguably the leading English composer of his generation, Edward Elgar was born into a relatively humble but musical family and began his career as an organist, violinist and teacher in his native West of England. He won considerable success with a series of orchestral and choral works and has popularly been identified, misleadingly, with an element of Edwardian jingoism. This, and his later preferred life as a country gentleman, belies his sensitivity as a composer and his position in European and specifically German late romantic tradition.

Opera

Elgar's only attempt at opera, *The Spanish Lady*, based on Ben Jonson's *The Devil is an Ass*, remained unfinished, when the composer ceased to work on the score which had occupied him intermittently in the early 1930s.

Enescu, George (1881-1955)

The greatest of Romanian musicians, Enescu was equally remarkable as a violinist and as a composer. He contributed significantly to the development of music in his own country, although much of his activity centred on Paris, where he was a pupil of the violinist Marsick and of the composers Massenet and Fauré.

Opera

Enescu's only opera is *Oedipe* (Oedipus). Based on the work of Sophocles, it was first staged in Paris in 1936.

Falla, Manuel de (1876-1946)

Manuel de Falla is representative of a group of Spanish composers who won international recognition. A native of Cádiz, he moved later to Madrid and spent some years in Paris, before returning to Madrid in 1914 and later settling in Granada, where his friend included the poet Lorca. In 1939 he accepted an invitation to Buenos Aires and died in Argentina in 1946.

Operas

In his earlier years Manuel de Falla contributed to the popular Spanish musical form of the *zarzuela*. His first success abroad came in 1913 with the staging of *La vida breve* (The Short Life). The ingenious puppet opera, *Il retablo de maese Pedro* (Master Peter's Puppet Show), based on an episode in the novel *Don Quixote* by Cervantes, was completed in 1922. His last work, *Atlántida*, described as a *cantata escénica* (stage cantata) was left unfinished at the time of de Falla's death in 1946, after intermittent work on the score for some twenty years.

Fauré, Gabriel (1845-1924)

Gabriel Fauré was a pupil of Camille Saint-Saëns at the Ecole Niedermeyer in Paris and remained something of an outsider to the official Conservatoire, until the death of the director Ambroise Thomas in 1896 allowed his appointment there. After the changes resulting from the rejection of his pupil Ravel as a contestant for the Prix de Rome, he became director of the Conservatoire, a position he held until 1920. His distinctive contribution to French music lies particularly in his songs and chamber music, and, to a lesser extent in his interesting piano music and orchestral compositions.

Operas

Fauré's contribution to opera rests mainly on *Prométhée* (Prometheus), a *tragédie lyrique,* and on *Pénélope*, described as a *drame lyrique*. The first of these is still nearer to incidental music in its musical interpolations into a dramatic text, while the second is the only real opera that Fauré attempted.

Fleishman, Venyamin Iosifovich (1913-1941)

A pupil of Shostakovich, Venyamin Fleishman entered Leningrad Conservatory in 1937 and at the outbreak of war volunteered for military service. His death followed soon afterwards.

Opera

Fleishman's only opera was the one-act *Rothschild's Violin,* based on a story by Chekhov. It was completed by Shostakovich after the composer's death.

Flotow, Friedrich von (1812-1883)

A member of the Prussian nobility, Flotow once enjoyed considerable popularity as a composer, with instrumental and vocal works to his credit, in addition to half a dozen melodramas and, his chief preoccupation, a number of operas.

Operas

Flotow wrote over thirty operas. Of these *Martha, oder Der Markt zu Richmond,* (Martha, or Richmond Market), is the only one to have made any lasting impression.

Gagliano, Marco da (1582-1643)

Marco da Gagliano spent most of his life in Florence, where he was associated with the poet and librettist Rinuccini, the composers Jacopo Peri, Giulio Caccini and others in a group that took the title Accademia degli Elevati. He enjoyed the support of Cardinal Ferdinando Gonzaga and thus had connection with the Gonzaga court in Mantua. He is among the early pioneers in contemporary exploration of the possibilities of dramatic monody.

Operas

Marco da Gagliano provided the Medici court with a number of dramatic musical entertainments. His best know work is *La Dafne*, written for carnival before the wedding celebrations in Mantua of Francesco Gonzaga and Margherita of Savoy.

Galuppi, Baldassare (1706-1785)

Remembered by Robert Browning, Baldassare Galuppi certainly wrote a quantity of keyboard music and was well known as a performer. His career took him from Venice to London and to St Petersburg as director of the court chapel, before his return to Venice to service at St Mark's and elsewhere.

Operas

Galuppi's career was largely spent as a composer of opera, with a very notable contribution to the development of the comic genre. He wrote over a hundred operas, among which may be singled out his *Il filosofo di campagna* (The Country Philosopher), one of his many collaborations with the playwright and librettist Carlo Goldoni. He enjoyed equal popularity as a composer of serious opera, particularly in settings of libretti by Metastasio.

Gerhard, Roberto (1896-1970)

Of Franco-Swiss parentage, Roberto Gerhard was born at Valls, in Catalonia and was a pupil of Granados and of Pedrell, before undertaking further study in Vienna and Berlin as a student of Schoenberg. He was involved in the Catalan separatist movement and after the Spanish Civil War moved, eventually, to England, where he remained for the rest of his life. His music draws, when occasion demands, on Spanish national elements, but also involves technical experiment that may sometimes appear astringent.

Opera

Gerhard's only opera is *The Duenna*, based on the text by Sheridan.

German, Edward (1862-1936)

Edward German was the successor to Arthur Sullivan in English operetta. He was a composer of some versatility, but wrote little after 1910, when it seemed to him that fashions had changed irredeemably.

Operettas

Edward German's six operettas include *The Emerald Isle*, which he completed after the death of Sullivan, *Merrie England*, also written for the Savoy Theatre, and *Tom Jones*.

Gershwin, George (1898-1937)

While composers such as Aaron Copland were establishing an American voice in the music of the United States of America, Gershwin, also the son of Jewish immigrant parents, sought to bridge the gap between Tin Pan Alley and the classical concert-hall, most notably in his jazz piano concerto *Rhapsody in Blue*. He was a fluent writer of popular songs and musical comedies.

Opera

Gershwin's distinctive contribution to American opera is his *Porgy and Bess*, set in black America and dealing with the tragedies of its characters in love, jealousy and murder.

Gibbons, Christopher (1615-1676)

The son of Orlando Gibbons, Christopher Gibbons served as a boy in the English Chapel Royal, was employed as organist at Winchester Cathedral, survived the Commonwealth interregnum as a teacher and resumed his career in the service of King Charles II after the restoration of the English monarchy in 1660. His compositions include church, consort and keyboard music.

Masque

The name of Gibbons is associated with that of Matthew Locke in the provision of music for Shirley's masque *Cupid and Death*, performed in 1659.

Ginastera, Alberto (1916-1983)

Alberto Ginastera occupied a leading position in the musical life of his native Argentina, where he exercised a strong influence over a generation of younger composers. He spent much of his later life in Geneva. Ginastera's musical style varies from the overtly national to the application of serialist techniques.

Operas

Ginastera's operas include lurid elements of tragedy in *Don Rodrigo, Bomarzo* and *Beatrix Cenci.* His fourth opera, *Barabbas,* was never finished.

Giordano, Umberto (1867-1948)

Trained at the Naples Conservatory, Giordano turned his early attention to the new realism, *verismo,* in opera, taking this to an initial extreme. His career in Italy was principally as a composer of opera.

Operas

Of his thirteen operas, *Andrea Chénier* (André Chénier) retains a place in present repertoire. To this may be added its successor, once enjoying almost equal popularity, *Fedora.*

Glass, Philip (b.1937)

The American composer Philip Glass has enjoyed some popularity as an exponent of minimalism, a style minimally defined as created with the minimum of means. The musical language of Glass, which has a certain affinity with popular commercial styles of composition, has proved effective in attracting a different audience to the opera-house.

Operas

Glass achieved his widest operatic success with *Einstein on the Beach,* followed by the less overtly minimalist *Satyagraha* and *Akhnaten.*

Glinka, Mikhail Ivanovich (1804-1857)

Glinka is commonly regarded as the founder of Russian nationalism in music. His influence on Balakirev, self-appointed leader of the group of nationalist composers known as The Five or The Mighty Handful, was considerable. Initially a talented amateur, he later studied in Berlin, acquiring a greater degree of assurance in his composition, which won serious attention at home and abroad.

Operas

Glinka's first Russian opera, *A Life for the Tsar*, was well received at its first staging in 1836. His second full opera, *Ruslan and Lyudmila,* with a libretto by Pushkin, proved less acceptable at its first staging in St Petersburg in 1842.

Gluck, Christoph Willibald von (1714-1787)

The name of Gluck is associated with the reform of opera that took place during the second half of the 18th century, when he and his librettist Calzabigi began to strive for a greater degree of realism, after the formal artifice of serious opera that had long been current. He was able to represent character in music and to combine music and drama on equal terms, the one subsumed in the other, after a period in which musical settings had proved disposable, never an integral part of the work. Gluck won considerable success in Vienna and Paris, as well as elsewhere in Europe, with revisions of his earlier Italian operas for the French stage.

Operas

Composer of over forty operas, Gluck collaborated first with Calzabigi in his thirtieth opera, *Orfeo ed Euridice,* first staged in Vienna in 1762, after a number of earlier settings of libretti by Metastasio and lighter French texts. *Alceste* followed in 1767 and *Paride ed Elena* (Paris and Helen) in 1770. For the French theatre he wrote *Iphigénie en Aulide* (Iphigenia in Aulis) and *Iphigénie en Tauride* (Iphigenia in Tauris), a version of Quinault's earlier French libretto in *Armide* and a French version of *Orfeo ed Euridice* (Orpheus and Eurydice).

Goehr, Alexander (b.1932)

Born in Berlin, Alexander Goehr moved to England in 1933, when his father, the conductor Walter Goehr, left Germany. He was a contemporary of Harrison Birtwistle, Peter Maxwell Davies and the pianist and composer John Ogdon at the Royal Manchester College of Music, developing his personal musical language from initial serialism into a more comprehensive idiom that derives much from earlier and remoter musical traditions.

Opera

Goehr's opera *Arden muss sterben* (Arden must die) is an effective and provocative treatment of the Elizabethan play, *Arden of Feversham.* His music-theatre pieces, *Naboth's Vineyard, Shadowplay* and *Sonata about Jerusalem* experiment with another form of dramatic realism in their insistence on moral themes that underlie the composer's thinking. The opera *Die Wiedertäufer* (Behold the Sun), dealing with the Anabaptist capture of Münster in 1534, revives something of 18th century musical practice, while his reworking of Monteverdi's lost opera *Arianna* involved an exceptional fusion of his own style with the surviving fragment of Monteverdi's opera which it frames.

Goldmark, Karl (1830-1915)

Born in Hungary in 1830 into a numerous Jewish family of very moderate means, Goldmark was eventually able to study for a time at the Conservatory in Vienna, before earning a living as a theatre violinist. Largely self-taught as a composer, he eventually established himself in Vienna. His contemporary reputation rested largely on his operas, but his violin concerto retains a place in current solo repertoire.

Operas

The first of Goldmark's operas, *Die Königin von Saba* (The Queen of Sheba) won wide success after its first staging at the Vienna Opera in 1875. Other operas include the large-scale *Merlin* and *Die Kriegsgefangene* (The Prisoner of War), *Das Heimchen am Herd* (The Cricket on the Hearth), based on Dickens, and *Götz von Berlichingen,* based on Goethe. His version of Shakespeare's *A Winter's Tale, Ein Wintermärchen*, explores the increasingly fashionable world of the fairy-tale opera.

Goldschmidt, Berthold (1903-1997)

Berthold Goldschmidt belongs to that group of German-born composers whose careers were disastrously interrupted by the events of 1933. A pupil of Schreker in Berlin, he moved to England in 1935. His work as a composer has recently received renewed attention.

Operas

Goldschmidt's first opera was *Der gewaltige Hahnrei* (The Mighty Cuckold), completed in 1931. In 1950 he was awarded a prize for his opera *Beatrice Cenci.*

Gounod, Charles (1818-1893)

Gounod held a dominant position in French music during the third quarter of the 19th century, notably after the great success of his opera *Faust*. He made a significant if occasionally sentimental contribution to church music and wrote a quantity of songs that retain their place in French repertoire.

Operas

Of the fifteen operas that Gounod completed, *Faust*, based on Goethe, is the best known, the standard operatic treatment of the subject. Second in popularity must be *Roméo et Juliette* (Romeo and Juliet), with others occupying a less favourable position. Among these last must fall *Philémon et Baucis, Mireille, La reine de Saba* (The Queen of Sheba) and *Sapho.*

Grabu, Louis (fl.1665-1694)

Louis Grabu was appointed court composer to Charles II in 1665 and later became Master of the King's Musick, to the annoyance of native English composers, who resented this French intrusion. He won favour, however, with the poet John Dryden, with whom he collaborated on the unsuccessful opera *Albion and Albanius.*

Operas

In addition to his collaboration with Dryden, Grabu contributed to the large number of operas on the subject of Ariadne on Naxos. The music for his *Ariane* (Ariadne) is lost.

Granados, Enrique (1867-1916)

Born in Lérida in 1867, Granados studied music in Barcelona and then in Paris. He won general distinction as a pianist and as a composer contributed to the popular *zarzuelas* of the Spanish musical theatre. His piano music is a representative achievement of Spanish musical nationalism.

Opera

Apart from his *zarzuelas* Granados wrote one opera of some importance, *Goyescas*, based on earlier piano music of the same title and other compositions.

Grétry, André-Ernest-Modeste (1741-1813)

Grétry is a composer of importance in the development of the *opéra comique* as well as of other genres of French opera. A native of Liège, he developed an interest in comic opera during a period of study in Rome and, on the advice of Voltaire, established himself in Paris in 1767, winning almost immediate success there. His work, however, did not fully survive the changes of taste and operatic requirements of the revolution.

Operas

Grétry wrote some sixty operas, over forty of them *opéras comiques*. He won his first success in Paris in 1768 with *Le huron* (The Huron), with a libretto by Marmontel, based on Voltaire.

Guridi, Jesús (1886-1961)

Born in 1886 in Vitoria in the Basque Country, Jesús Guridi won an early local reputation, before studying in Paris at the Schola Cantorum, where his teachers included Vincent d'Indy and Gabriel Grovlez. In Bilbao he served with distinction as an organist, notably at the Basilica de Santiago, where he won fame for his improvisations. Much of his music reflects his intense local patriotism.

Stage Works

Guridi contributed in particular to the zarzuela, in a number of works largely based on Basque material. These include *Mirentxu, Amaya* and *El caserio.*

Halévy, Fromental (1799-1862)

A pupil of Cherubini at the Paris Conservatoire, Fromental Halévy, as a teacher himself, boasted among his students Gounod, Bizet and Saint-Saëns. His reputation as a composer rested largely on his operas.

Operas

Halévy wrote nearly forty operas. By far the most successful was *La juive* (The Jewess), first staged in 1835, a work of which Wagner, casting aside anti-semitic prejudices, fully approved. Berlioz preferred Halévy in a lighter vein, shown in a number of *opéras comiques* of varying quality.

Handel, George Frideric (1685-1759)

Born in Halle, Handel began his fully professional career as a musician at the opera in Hamburg. A period spent in Italy was followed by appointment as Court Kapellmeister in Hanover and an almost immediate removal to England, where he spent the greater part of his life. His overwhelming influence on English music is seen most notably in his English oratorios, combinations of English Protestant piety with the more sensuous musical pleasures of Italian opera.

Operas

Handel's career was at first largely concerned with Italian opera, in Hamburg, in Italy and then, very considerably, in London, where his sixth opera, *Rinaldo*, was successfully staged in 1711. With some 45 Italian operas to his credit, he achieved varying financial success over a period of thirty years of involvement with the composition and staging of operas for the London theatre. Comparison of these, one with another, would be invidious, but among those that have enjoyed particular success in modern revival must be counted *Giulio Cesare* (Julius Caesar), *Alcina* and *Ariodante*, with *Tamerlano* and, now in a staged version, *Semele.*

Hanson, Howard (1896-1981)

The American composer and teacher Howard Hanson was director of the Eastman School of Music, in Rochester, New York, for forty years, from 1924 until 1964. He gave particular encouragement to American music, to which he contributed in a neo-romantic style in his own varied works.

Opera

Howard Hanson's only opera was *Merry Mount*, based on a story by Nathaniel Hawthorne and dealing with Puritan prejudices in the early 17th century, a subject to which Hawthorne and other more recent writers and playwrights have returned. The opera was commissioned by the Metropolitan Opera in New York, where the work was first staged in 1934. It has not retained a place in the repertoire.

Hartmann, Johan Peter Emilius (1805-1900)

Johan Peter Emilius Hartmann, grandson and son of musicians, was born in Copenhagen in 1805 and held important positions in Danish musical life, serving as organist of the Vor Frue Kirke and as a director of the Conservatory. Much honoured in his own country, he was regarded as pre-eminently a national composer in a new age of nationalism.

Operas

Hartmann's first opera was written in collaboration with Hans Christian Andersen. This was *Ravnen, eller Broderprøven* (The Raven, or The Brother Test), first staged in Copenhagen in 1832. A second opera, *Korsarerne* (The Corsairs) followed in 1853, with *Liden Kirsten* his third and last work in this form.

Haydn, Joseph (1732-1809)

The name of Haydn is associated with the development of the orchestral symphony and, indeed, of classical instrumental music in general, including string quartets, piano sonatas and other forms. After boyhood spent as a chorister in the Imperial Chapel in Vienna, Haydn eventually found his place in the service of the Esterházy Princes, notably under Prince Nikolaus at the palace of Esterháza, where he directed and provided music both for his orchestra and for the theatre.

Operas

Haydn's operas have in general enjoyed less attention than his instrumental music. He wrote some two dozen works for the theatre, much of it in the course of his duties at Esterháza, where there was also a marionette theatre for puppet operas. Works that have been successfully revived for modern performance include *Armida, La canterina, La fedeltà premiata* (Loyalty Rewarded), *L'incontro improviso* (The Unforeseen Encounter),

L'isola disabitata (The Uninhabited Island), *Il mondo della luna* (The World of the Moon) and *La vera costanza* (True Constancy).

Henze, Hans Werner (b.1926)

Hans Werner Henze is among the most prolific and successful of modern German composers, a pupil of Wolfgang Fortner and influenced by the serial principles propounded in the courses at Darmstadt. An extended period, from 1953, spent in Italy, had a strong influence on his writing, followed by a further development of Marxist political interests and an extension of musical material and media.

Operas

Henze's thirteen operas include two collaborations with W.H.Auden and Chester Kallman, *Elegy for Young Lovers* and *The Bassarids*. *König Hirsch* (King Stag) is based on a play by Gozzi, *Der Prinz von Homburg* (The Prince of Homburg) on Kleist, *Der junge Lord* (The Young Lord) on Wilhelm Hauff, *Das verratene Meer* (The Treacherous Sea) on Mishima and *The English Cat*, a collaboration with Edward Bond, on Balzac. It was with Edward Bond that he wrote his controversial *We Come to the River*.

Hérold, Ferdinand (1791-1833)

A pupil of the violinist Kreutzer and of the composer Méhul at the Paris Conservatoire, Hérold established himself in Paris as a theatre composer, more particularly in the genre of *opéra comique*.

Operas

Of the 23 operas that Hérold wrote, or in which he collaborated, the best known today must be *Zampa*, the overture to which may still be heard on many a bandstand. His greatest success, however, came with *Le Pré aux clercs*, which was still running at the Paris *Opéra-Comique* at the time of the composer's relatively early death in 1833.

Hindemith, Paul (1895-1963)

Respected as one of the most distinguished viola-players of his time, Hindemith devoted the earlier part of his career largely to performance, while developing his powers as a composer and his distinctive theories of composition and of the place of the artist in society. His name is particularly associated with the principles of

Gebrauchsmusik, the composer seen as a practical craftsman, supplying music as needed. Hindemith was able to supply a considerable amount of music that has proved extremely useful to players, all of it couched in his very recognisable musical language, with its idiosyncratic counterpoint.

Operas

Of the eleven operas completed by Hindemith, *Mathis der Maler* (Matthias the Painter), the basis of the symphony of that name, is the best known, for that reason. The cancellation of the planned performances in Berlin in 1934 by the intervention of the new National Socialist government, led to the resignation of Furtwängler and soon to Hindemith's emigration to America. Other operas by Hindemith include the trilogy of one-act operas *Mörder, Hoffnung der Frauen* (Murderer, Hope of Women), *Das Nusch-Nuschi* and *Sancta Susanna*. *Cardillac,* based on a story by E.T.A.Hoffmann, was first staged in 1926. Other operas include *Neues vom Tage* (News of the Day), the children's opera *Wir bauen eine Stadt* (We build a city), *Die Harmonie der Welt* (The Harmony of the World) and *The Long Christmas Dinner*.

Hoffmann, E.T.A. (1776-1822)

Trained as a lawyer, Hoffmann was gifted as a writer, painter and composer, and was an important influence in music criticism, particularly in his theories of proper operatic practice, in which words and music might spring from the same source. His stories provided material for other composers in opera and in ballets such as *Coppélia* by Delibes and Tchaikowsky's *Nutcracker*.

Operas

Undine, a magic opera, is probably the best of the six Hoffmann operas that survive. This was staged in Berlin in 1816.

Holst, Gustav (1874-1934)

Of Scandinavian ancestry on his father's side, Gustav Holst was born in the English spa town of Cheltenham in 1874 and studied music at the Royal College of Music in London. He worked for a time as a trombonist and later became director of music at St Paul's Girls' School in London, retaining this connection until the end of his life. His most popular composition remains his orchestral suite *The Planets*.

Operas

Holst wrote some ten operas or operettas. Of these the best known, by name at least, must be *Savitri, The Perfect Fool, At the Boar's Head* and *The Wandering Scholar*.

Honegger, Arthur (1892-1955)

Swiss by nationality, Honegger was born and died in France, where he had been for a time associated with the group of young French composers known as Les Six. He was a prolific composer in many genres.

Operas

Of Honegger's five surviving stage-works the opera *Antigone*, with a libretto by Jean Cocteau, based on Sophocles, was the one by which he set greatest store.

Humperdinck, Engelbert (1854-1921)

Influenced first by Lortzing and then by Wagner, Humperdinck won contemporary fame with his first opera, *Hänsel und Gretel* (Hansel and Gretel) and proved more successful in fairy-tale opera than in the comic operas he attempted. As a teacher, he exercised some influence over Siegfried Wagner, son of the composer, whose own explorations of German legend and folk-tale owe something to him.

Operas

The best known of Humperdinck's operas in the fairy-tale opera *Hänsel und Gretel* (Hansel and Gretel), followed at some distance by *Königskinder* (The King's Children) and *Die Marketenderin* (The Canteen-Woman).

Indy, Vincent d' (1851-1931)

A pupil of César Franck at the Paris Conservatoire, Vincent d'Indy later established the Schola Cantorum, providing an alternative to the Conservatoire for students. He was one of Franck's principal disciples and did much to propagate knowledge of his teacher's compositions.

Operas

Vincent d'Indy achieved some success with two of his dozen or so operas, *Fervaal* in 1897 and *L'étranger* (The Stranger) six years later. He was strongly opposed to the apparent formlessness of Debussy's *Pelléas et Mélisande* and by the time of his death seemed to have been overtaken by the developments of music in the 20th century.

Janáček, Leoš (1854-1928)

For many years Janáček enjoyed only a local reputation in his native Moravia, until his supporters were able to persuade Prague to mount his third opera, *Jenůfa*, in 1916. His style of writing, in instrumental as well as vocal works, often echoes the intonations of speech.

Operas

Janáček's success in 1916, when he was over sixty, was followed by the completion of his two *Mr Brouček* operas, *Katya Kabanova, The Cunning Little Vixen, The Makropulos Case* and *From the House of the Dead*. Earlier operas include *Šárka* and *Osud* (Fate).

Kabalevsky, Dmitry Borisovich (1904-1987)

Kabalevsky was a pupil of Myaskovsky at the Moscow Conservatory, where he himself later taught, throughout his career doing his utmost to conform with the official cultural policies of the Soviet Union and holding a number of important positions in the musical establishment. He writes, in consequence, in a generally easily intelligible musical style, with a number of useful educational compositions for children and students.

Operas

Of Kabalevsky's six operas *Colas Breugnon, The Master of Clamecy*, is the best known.

Kálmán, Emmerich (1882-1953)

A contemporary of Bartók and Kodály at the Budapest Academy, Kálmán eventually found his place as a composer of popular Viennese operetta.

Operettas

The most popular of Kálmán's operettas, and among the most popular of the whole Viennese operetta repertoire, are *Die Csárdásfürstin* (The Czardas Princess) and *Gräfin Mariza* (Countess Maritsa), closely rivalled by *Die Zirkusprinzessin* (The Circus Princess), works that have a pronounced Hungarian flavour.

Kodály, Zoltán (1882-1967)

Kodály, a colleague of Bartók in the early collection and collation of folk-music in Hungary and neighbouring regions, made his later career in his own country, where the system of musical education he devised has had a profound effect, as it has abroad. His own music is imbued with the spirit of Hungary and is in general less astringent than is sometimes the case with the music of Bartók.

Opera

Kodály's *Háry János*, a *Singspiel*, enjoys an existence also in the concert-hall in a suite derived from this essentially Hungarian work.

Korngold, Erich Wolfgang (1897-1957)

A precocious talent brought Korngold to the attention of Mahler while he was still a boy. In 1934 he moved to Hollywood and won considerable success for his film music, which generally can stand on its own, in musical terms. After 1945 he was able to return to other forms of composition, continuing the late Romantic tradition of Vienna in which he had been brought up.

Operas

Of Korngold's five operas, *Die tote Stadt* (The Dead City), first staged in 1920, is the most effective, while *Violanta*, first staged in Munich in 1916, is a testimony to his remarkable precocity.

Kraus, Joseph Martin (1756-1792)

An exact contemporary of Mozart, whom he outlived by one year, Kraus had his schooling in Mannheim, joined the *Göttinger Hainbund* as a university student and in 1778 went to Stockholm, where he remained for the rest of his life, occupying a leading position in cultural life in the service of King Gustavus III. His music reflects his years in Mannheim and his experience of European culture during travels abroad, undertaken with royal encouragement.

Operas

While Kraus's most significant opera may be *Aeneas i Carthago* (Aeneas in Carthage), his *Soliman II, eller De tre sultaninnorna* (Süleyman II, or The Three Sultanas), based on Favart, is an interesting example of the treatment of a fashionable Turkish subject.

Krenek, Ernst (1900-1991)

Born in Vienna, Krenek was a pupil of Schreker, but subsequently fell under the influence of Bartók and of Stravinsky, finally developing an interest in the teaching of Schoenberg and the principles of serialism. He was for a time married to Mahler's daughter Anna. In 1938, after the Anschluss, he moved to the United States.

Operas

Of Krenek's sixteen or so operas, it was *Jonny spielt auf* (Jonny Strikes Up) that caused the greatest sensation when it was staged in Leipzig in 1927. After the war Krenek returned to opera with the political *Pallas Athene weint* (Pallas Athene Weeps), and the modern satirical treatment of *Der goldene Bock* (The Golden Ram). The television opera *Der Zauberspiegel* (The Magic Mirror) is replete with the composer's usual irony and is chronologically and geographically wide-ranging.

Kunzen, Friedrich Ludwig Aemilius (1761-1817)

Member of a family of musicians settled in Lübeck, Kunzen eventually made his home in Copenhagen, where he became royal Kapellmeister in 1794. In his operas he was strongly influenced by Gluck and by Mozart.

Operas

Kunzen based the first of his operas, *Holger Danske* (Ogier the Dane) on a story by Wieland, the source of Weber's *Oberon*. This was followed by a dozen or more works for the Danish royal opera.

Landi, Stefano (1586/7-1639)

Landi was among the most distinguished Roman composers of his time and has a particular importance in the history of opera. He enjoyed the patronage of the Barberini family.

Operas

Landi's *Il Sant'Alessio* (Saint Alexis), first staged at the Palazzo Barberini in 1632, opened new operatic possibilities in its study of a historical character and in its religious dimension. Landi had earlier written a pastoral tragicomedy, *La morte d'Orfeo* (The Death of Orpheus), treating a story that had a particular fascination for composers.

Leclair, Jean-Marie (1697-1764)

The founder of the French violin school, Leclair had early training in Italy, before settling in France once more. His violin music adapts Italian style to the prevailing French taste.

Opera

Leclair's *Scylla et Glaucus* (Scylla and Glaucus) was completed and staged in Paris in 1746. It won contemporary favour and is his only opera.

Lehár, Franz (1870-1948)

A regimental bandmaster, like his father, Lehár definitively began his career in the theatre in Vienna in 1902, going on to provide a series of works that are at the heart of Viennese operetta tradition.

Operettas

Of the forty or so operettas written by Lehár, *Die lustige Witwe* (The Merry Widow) remains the best known of all, closely rivalled, however, by *Das Land des Lächelns* (The Land of Smiles). Other operettas include *Der Graf von Luxemburg* (The Count of Luxemburg), *Frasquita, Paganini* and *Der Zarewitsch* (The Tsarevich). His last operetta, *Giuditta*, was staged at the Vienna State Opera in 1934.

Leoncavallo, Ruggero (1857-1919)

Trained in his native city of Naples, Leoncavallo studied literature at Bologna University and had gifts as a librettist as well as in composition. In the latter field his success was intermittent and varied.

Operas

Leoncavallo is principally known for one work, the opera *Pagliacci*, which brought immediate fame at its first staging in 1892. Of his nine other operas, *La bohème* invites comparison with the contemporary version by Puccini. His attempts at the Wagnerian were unsuccessful, while his ten operettas have had no lasting position in operatic repertoire.

Linley, Thomas (1733-1795)

Father-in-law of the playwright Sheridan, Thomas Linley made a reputation for himself as a composer, performer and manager at Drury Lane in London, contributing songs and incidental music to plays staged there.

Operas

Linley was involved in a great many dramatic and musical projects for Drury Lane and for Covent Garden. These included the arrangement or composition of music.

Linley, Thomas (1756-1778)

Son of the Thomas Linley above and an exact contemporary of Mozart, with whom he established friendship in Italy when they met there in 1770, the younger Linley was prolific as a composer and equally talented as a violinist.

Operas

The younger Linley contributed to the setting of Sheridan's libretto *The Duenna* and in the year of his death had his comic opera *The Cady of Baghdad* staged at Drury Lane.

Locke, Matthew (1621/2-1677)

Among the most distinguished English composers of his time, Matthew Locke held positions at court under Charles II and served as organist in the Queen's Chapel, a position that suited his religion, as a Catholic, but did not always seem to match the Queen's more italianate tastes. He wrote music of all kinds, including English and Latin church music, chamber music and a quantity of compositions for the theatre.

Masque & Opera

Locke's masque *Cupid and Death* was written for performance in 1653 in collaboration with Christopher Gibbons. He contributed also to the supposed first English opera, Davenant's *The Siege of Rhodes* of 1656, both as composer and singer. The music is now lost. Like his friend Henry Purcell, he wrote a large amount of incidental music, overtures, dances and songs for plays of all kinds, including a jig and a witches' dance for Davenant's adaptation of Shakespeare's *Macbeth* and a *Masque of Orpheus* for Shadwell's *Psyche*.

Lortzing, Albert (1801-1851)

Lortzing's experience in the theatre as an actor, singer and conductor, helped in the creation of a series of operas that hold a firm place in German repertoire. His life was largely spent with travelling theatre and opera companies and he was never able to achieve the success that his gifts seemed to promise in the security of an established opera-house.

Operas

The best know of Lortzing's twenty operas is undoubtedly *Zar und Zimmermann* (Tsar and Carpenter). *Undine*, *Der Waffenschmied* (The Armourer) and *Der Wildschütz* (The Poacher) remain in repertoire, with *Hans Sachs* a lighter precursor of Wagner's *Die Meistersinger* (The Mastersingers).

Lully, Jean-Baptiste (1632-1687)

Italian by birth, Lully was taken to France as a boy and over the years established himself, through royal patronage, as the leading figure in French music and theatre. Skilled as a dancer and violinist he made a significant contribution to church music and was a key figure in the development of French opera.

Operas

Lully's compositions for the French theatre include court ballets, which have a vocal as well as instrumental content, *comédies-ballets*, a form that brought notable collaboration with Molière, and *tragédies lyriques*, a dramatic form that he created, with the collaboration of the poet Quinault. This last may be seen as the first true French opera. Lully wrote some sixteen *tragédies lyriques*, most of them on subjects drawn from classical mythology and allowing the necessary spectacle and element of dance that audiences in France expected. These include *Cadmus et Hermione* (Cadmus and Hermione), *Alceste* (Alcestis), *Thésée* (Theseus), *Atys, Isis, Psyché, Phaëton, Persée* (Perseus) and *Armide*.

Marschner, Heinrich (1795-1861)

Marschner occupies a position of great importance in German Romantic opera in the generation after Weber. He was a strong champion of German opera and spent much of his career as conductor at the Court Theatre in Hanover, where his talents were not always appreciated. In addition to his work in opera, he was a prolific composer of songs, with four hundred or more to his credit.

Operas

Marschner's great success came in 1831 with his romantic opera *Hans Heiling*, the twelfth of his seventeen operas. *Der Vampyr* (The Vampire) in 1827 explores the Gothic, while *Der Templer und die Jüdin* (The Templar and the Jewess) adapts Scott's *Ivanhoe* to the operatic stage.

Martin y Soler, Vicente (1754-1806)

A near contemporary of Mozart, the Spanish composer Martin y Soler won the Emperor's favour in Vienna, where he collaborated in opera with the librettist Lorenzo Da Ponte, to the detriment of Mozart, whom he outshone in contemporary popularity. Born in Valencia, he enjoyed a career in Italy, settling in Vienna in 1785. Three years later he moved, at the request of the Empress Catherine II, to St Petersburg, where he spent much of the rest of his life in positions of importance in the Russian court musical establishment. His stay in Russia was interrupted by a period of four years in London, where he collaborated with Salomon in the concerts that had brought Haydn to the city.

Operas

It was the opera *Una cosa rara* (A Rare Thing) that brought Martin y Soler particular popularity in Vienna. He set two Russian libretti, the first by the Empress herself, and collaborated again with Da Ponte in London in 1795.

Martinů, Bohuslav (1890-1959)

Born in a church tower in the Bohemian village of Polička, Bohuslav Martinů was a prolific enough composer as a child, before he entered Prague Conservatory as a violin student in 1906. Failing to complete his course there or at the Prague Organ School, to which he had been transferred, he worked as an orchestral player before moving, in 1923, to Paris. The approach of the German armies in 1940 forced him to make his way, as best he could, to the United States, where he was encouraged by commissions from Koussevitzky. Political events in Czechoslovakia prevented his return after the war and he spent his final years abroad, dying in Switzerland in 1959.

Operas

In opera, as in other genres of music, Martinů wrote quickly and prolifically. Of his seventeen operas, mention may be made, in particular, of *Julietta, Ariane, The Greek Passion* and his tetralogy *The Plays of Mary.*

Mascagni, Pietro (1863-1945)

An Italian composer and conductor, Mascagni is chiefly remembered in the first capacity and in particular for one opera. As a conductor he worked at La Scala, Milan, and was increasingly associated with the régime of Mussolini. He died in Rome in 1945.

Operas

Mascagni won particular success with the second of his seventeen operas, the one-act *Cavalleria rusticana* (Rustic Chivalry), an example of Italian operatic realism, or *verismo.* This was followed by *L'amico Fritz* (Friend Fritz). Other operas by Mascagni include a version of Heine's Scottish tragedy *William Ratcliff,* a subject earlier tackled by the Russian César Cui, *Iris,* set in Japan, the prior counterpart of Puccini's *Madama Butterfly,* and his last opera *Nerone,* staged at La Scala in 1935.

Massenet, Jules (1842-1912)

The leading operatic composer of his generation in France, Jules Massenet studied at the Paris Conservatoire and duly won the Prix de Rome, allowing a stay of three years at the Roman Villa Medici. He enjoyed great popularity, at least until the staging in Paris of Debussy's innovative opera *Pelléas et Mélisande.* He had considerable influence as a teacher at the Conservatoire, with pupils of distinction in France, including Charpentier, Koechlin, Florent Schmitt, Pierné and Reynaldo Hahn. His music had an undoubted and not always entirely beneficial effect on the writing of others, both at home and abroad.

Operas

Massenet won his first operatic success with *Don César de Bazan* in 1872, enhanced by the exotic *Le roi de Lahore* (The King of Lahore) five years later. Among over thirty operas, mention may be made of *Hérodiade, Manon, Le Cid, Esclarmonde, Werther, Thaïs, Cendrillon* and, perhaps, *Ariane*. The name, at least, of *Thaïs*, a characteristically bad girl turned good, a subject much favoured by Massenet and his contemporaries, has wide currency in the *Méditation* from the opera, beloved of violinists. *Manon* invites comparison with Puccini's treatment of the same subject, *Manon Lescaut*, while *Werther*, based on the romantic novel by Goethe, retains a special place in modern repertoire.

Méhul, Etienne-Nicolas (1763-1817)

Méhul occupies an important place in French music and in the development of the French symphony before Berlioz. His work during the period of revolution and under Napoleon brought him association with the newly established Paris Conservatoire and included a series of republican and Bonapartist works of celebration.

Operas

Méhul wrote some 35 operas, many of them innovative and daring in their musical and dramatic treatment of the subjects chosen. Of these *Ariodant*, based on a well known episode in Ariosto's *Orlando furioso*, holds an important historical position in French opera in the final decade of the 18th century.

Mendelssohn-Bartholdy, Felix (1809-1847)

Grandson of the great Jewish thinker Moses Mendelssohn and son of a prosperous banker, Felix Mendelssohn had the advantage of a cultured home, in Berlin from his early childhood, and the family connections with a circle of intellectual and artistic distinction. He showed early precocity as a musician, writing a quantity of music from the age of ten onwards, and took a leading part in the revival of public interest in the music of Johann Sebastian Bach. After a tour that took him as far South as Naples and as far North as the Hebrides, he embarked on a career as a conductor, pianist and composer, holding positions in Düsseldorf and later in Leipzig, with a brief and unsatisfactory return to Berlin. In his music he continued the tradition of Mozart in a mastery of classical form allied to romantic imagination.

Operas

Disappointingly Mendelssohn attempted little in the way of opera. As a boy he wrote comic operas, principally for home use, but his more ambitious *Die Hochzeit des Camacho* (Camacho's Wedding), based on an episode in Cervantes' *Don Quixote*, enjoyed a public performance in Berlin in 1827.

Menotti, Gian Carlo (b.1911)

Born in Italy, Gian Carlo Menotti studied at Milan Conservatory and later at the Curtis Institute in Philadelphia. Chiefly known for his operas, he has also written in a variety of other genres, always in an approachable musical language that remains based in Italian lyrical tradition.

Operas

Menotti has provided his own texts for some two dozen operas, some of which have enjoyed remarkable popular success for their dramatic and musical qualities. Particularly notable are *The Medium*, the light-hearted *The Telephone*, *The Consul* and the Christmas television opera *Amahl and the Night Visitors*, while *Help, Help, the Globolinks* provides children with an operatic glimpse of the extra-terrestrial. Other operas by Menotti include *Amelia al ballo* (Amelia Goes to the Ball), *The Old Maid and the Thief*, *The Saint of Bleecker Street*, *Martin's Lie*, *The Hero*, *The Most Important Man* and *Tamu-Tamu*.

Mercadante, Saverio (1795-1870)

Trained in Naples, Mercadante came to occupy an important position in Italian opera before the first successes of Verdi. His active career as a composer spans two generations, from 1840 as director of the Naples Conservatory, where he influenced a new generation of Italian composers.

Operas

Mercadante completed some sixty operas. He had his first significant success with the seventh of these, *Elisa e Claudio*, in 1821, while a commission in Paris at the invitation of Rossini brought acquaintance with the work of Meyerbeer and the subsequent opera *Il giuramento* (The Oath), based on the same Victor Hugo original work as Ponchielli's *La Gioconda*. Here, and in the operas that followed, he concentrated his attention on the dramatic, eliminating the more decorative excrescences of earlier Italian operatic style and preparing the way for Verdi. Other operas include *Elena da Feltre, Il bravo* and *La vestale*.

Messiaen, Olivier (1908-1992)

Olivier Messiaen has exercised a remarkable influence over composers both in his native France and elsewhere, although his own work remains unique. Educated at the Paris Conservatoire, where his teachers included the great French organist Marcel Dupré, he became principal organist at La Trinité in Paris, a position he held for many years. Messiaen's musical language is derived from varied sources, including bird-song, Greek metrical rhythms, Hindu tradition, serialism and Debussy, his work constantly imbued by the spirit of Catholicism.

Opera

Messiaen's only opera is *Saint François d'Assise* (Saint Francis of Assisi), a work of obvious religious relevance, first staged in Paris in 1983.

Meyerbeer, Giacomo (1791-1864)

Born near Berlin into a family of cultured interests, Meyerbeer was a pupil of Vogler and a contemporary of his fellow-pupil Weber. He made his career in Paris, where he became the most important composer of French grand opera, although maintaining wide cosmopolitan connections, particularly from 1842 in Berlin as General Music Director under King Friedrich Wilhelm IV of Prussia. As a man of independent means, Meyerbeer was able to take time and care over his work, both in their composition and in the choice of performers.

Operas

Meyerbeer wrote some seventeen operas. Of these the most substantial are the grand operas *Robert le diable* (Robert the Devil), *Les Huguenots* (The Huguenots), *Le prophète* (The Prophet) and *L'Africaine* (The African Maid). The semi-serious *L'étoile du Nord* (The Star of the North) belongs to the period of Meyerbeer's grand operas, while the earlier *Il crociato in Egitto* (The Crusader in Egypt) won particular success after its first staging in Italy in 1824.

Milhaud, Darius (1892-1974)

Born into a long-established Jewish family in Aix-en-Provence, Darius Milhaud enjoyed earlier association with the poet-diplomat Paul Claudel, whom he accompanied to Brazil when the latter was posted there. In Paris once more in 1918, he associated with the circle of Jean Cocteau and was a member of the diverse group of young French composers of the period known as Les Six. Extremely prolific, Milhaud spent the years from 1939 in the United States, where he taught, combining this with teaching at the Paris Conservatoire after 1947, while the constant weakness of his health allowed.

Operas

Milhaud wrote fifteen operas and provided a quantity of music for ballet, for the theatre and for the cinema. His operas include *Les malheurs d'Orphée* (The Misfortunes of Orpheus), a Theseus trilogy that includes *L'abandon d'Ariane* (The Abandonment of Ariadne), *Christophe Colombe* (Christopher Columbus), with Paul Claudel, and an opera *David* commissioned by Koussevitzky to celebrate King David's foundation of Jerusalem.

Millöcker, Carl (1842-1899)

Carl Millöcker enjoyed a reputation in Vienna as a composer of operettas. His career had brought engagements as a conductor in various theatres, in Vienna and elsewhere, principally of the kind of repertoire with which his name is associated as a composer.

Operettas

Of Millöcker's twenty operettas, representing a small fraction of the music he wrote for the theatre, *Der Bettelstudent* (The Beggar-Student) remains the most popular, while other works have often been subject to considerable re-arrangement and adaptation.

Monteverdi, Claudio (1567-1643)

Born in Cremona in 1567, Claudio Monteverdi served at the court of the Duke of Mantua from the early 1590s until 1611 and from 1612 was *maestro di cappella* at the basilica of San Marco in Venice, until his death in 1643. He is particularly associated with the new style of the early Baroque, with its dramatic attention to the rhythms, intonations and contents of speech and its innovative harmonies.

Operas

Monteverdi's first opera, and the earliest such work to have a place in modern operatic repertoire, is *L'Orfeo* (Orpheus), staged at court in Mantua in 1607. It was followed by *Arianna* (Ariadne) in 1608, but this work is now lost, except for the famous lament sung by the heroine, abandoned on the island of Naxos. For the public opera-house in Venice he wrote operas of which *Il ritorno d'Ulisse in patria* (The Homecoming of Ulysses) and *L'incoronazione di Poppea* (The Coronation of Poppaea) survive. Other dramatic works include *Il ballo delle ingrate* (The Dance of the Ungrateful Women) and *Il combattimento di Tancredi e Clorinda* (The Combat of Tancredi and Clorinda).

Mozart, Wolfgang Amadeus (1756-1791)

The genius of Mozart lay above all in his operatic gifts, reflected largely also in his instrumental music. Born in Salzburg, the son of the composer and violinist Leopold Mozart, he enjoyed wide international success as a child prodigy, but found the limitations of his native city offered too few opportunities, as he grew older. Failing to find suitable positions in Mannheim or in Paris, he eventually settled in Vienna, in independence of his father and of their patron, the ruling Archbishop of Salzburg. Here at last he was able to turn his attention to opera and to a full career as a performer and composer during the last ten years of his life, although frequently needing the help of friends, when the money he could earn proved insufficient for his needs and those of his wife and children. He remains one of the greatest composers in European musical tradition, combining classical clarity of form and texture with poignancy and, where appropriate, wit and exuberance.

Operas

Mozart's earlier operas were written either for occasional use in Salzburg or in response to commissions during childhood journeys to Italy. These include *Apollo et Hyacinthus* (Apollo and Hyacinthus) for Salzburg University in 1767, *La finta semplice*

(The Feigned Simpleton), *Bastien und Bastienne* (Bastien and Bastienne), *Mitridate, re di Ponto* (Mithridates, King of Pontus), *Ascanio in Alba* (Ascanius in Alba), *Il sogno di Scipione* (The Dream of Scipio), *Lucio Silla* (Lucius Sulla), *La finta giardiniera* (The Pretended Garden-Girl) and *Il re pastore* (The Shepherd King). Later operas, starting in 1781 with the Munich staging of *Idomeneo, re di Creta* (Idomeneus, King of Crete), continue in Vienna with the Singspiel *Die Entführung aus dem Serail* (The Abduction from the Seraglio), *Le nozze di Figaro* (The Marriage of Figaro), *Don Giovanni*, *Così fan tutte* (They All Behave Alike), *Die Zauberflöte* (The Magic Flute) and *La clemenza di Tito* (The Clemency of Titus). Of less significance is the one-act *Der Schauspieldirektor* (The Impresario).

Mussorgsky, Modest Petrovich (1839-1881)

Associated with Balakirev and the group of five Russian nationalist composers described by the polymath Stasov as the Mighty Handful, Mussorgsky spent the earlier part of his career as an army officer, while always pursuing musical interests. In 1858 he resigned his commission and later had employment in government service, until his way of life and the consequent state of his health made this no longer permissible. As a composer he left much unfinished, but showed particular genius in his songs and in his attempts at opera, aiming, as he declared, to convey human speech in his music.

Operas

Mussorgsky's great opera is *Boris Godunov*, a historical work that is essentially Russian both in its story and in its music. A number of other works remained incomplete or were merely considered as possible projects. *Khovanshchina*, however, was sufficiently far advanced to be completed by Rimsky-Korsakov and *Sorochintsy Fair* was eventually completed and orchestrated by Lyadov.

Nicolai, Otto (1810-1849)

A native of Königsberg, Otto Nicolai was educated largely in Berlin, through the intervention of a sympathetic patron, and made a name for himself there, without great material success. A period in Rome as organist at the Prussian Embassy aroused his interest in opera, an enthusiasm he was able to pursue at the Court Opera in Vienna. In the year before his death he returned to Berlin as director of the Cathedral Choir and of the Berlin Opera.

Operas

The best known of Nicolai's five operas is the Shakespearean *Die lustigen Weiber von Windsor* (The Merry Wives of Windsor), staged at the Court Opera in Berlin two days before the composer's death in 1849. His first opera, *Enrico II*, was completed in 1836, followed in 1840 by *Il templario* (The Templar), based on Sir Walter Scott's *Ivanhoe*. His two other operas are *Gildippe e Odoardo*, staged in Genoa in 1840 and now lost, and *Il proscritto* (The Proscribed), completed in 1841 and staged, in a German version, in Vienna in 1846.

Nielsen, Carl (1865-1931)

Carl Nielsen is the principal post-romantic Danish composer. He was the son of a painter and village musician and acquired practical musical experience as a child. After more formal study in Copenhagen, he was employed as an orchestral violinist, while starting to make his way as a composer. He wrote music of all kinds, but his principal achievement lies in his six symphonies.

Operas

Nielsen's first opera, *Saul og David* (Saul and David), was completed in 1901, followed in 1906 by *Maskarade*, based on the play by Holberg.

Nørgård, Per (b.1932)

Per Nørgård is among the leading Danish composers of his generation. A pupil of Holmboe in Copenhagen, he turned from a style influenced by Sibelius and other Nordic composers, to a musical language that took account of the work of Schoenberg and his successors and, more recently, in music that makes use of quotation, in the form of musical collages. From these stages in his creative procedures, he has developed a more varied style of his own, taking account of acoustical phenomena and mathematical theories of proportion.

Operas

Nørgård's operas include *The Labyrinth*, completed in 1963, *Gilgamesh* completed in 1972, and *Siddharta (Play for the Expected One)*, an opera based on the birth and youth of the Buddha, a collaboration with the poet Ole Sarvig, completed in 1979.

Offenbach, Jacques (1819-1880)

The son of a Cologne synagogue cantor, Offenbach and his violinist brother Julius were trained at the Paris Conservatoire, and Jacques thereafter initially found employment as a cellist at the Opéra-Comique, followed by a career as a virtuoso performer. For five years he served as conductor at the Paris Théâtre Français, but in 1855 rented his own theatre, where his early light-hearted stage-works were performed. He continued his successful career until his death in 1880.

Operas & Operettas

In a more serious vein, Offenbach's reputation must rest on *Les contes d'Hoffmann* (The Tales of Hoffmann), completed after the composer's death by Ernest Guiraud and first staged in 1881. This had been preceded by a very large number of lighter works, of which *Orphée aux enfers* (Orpheus in the Underworld) remains the best known. Other operettas that retain some place in international repertoire include *La Périchole, La vie parisienne* (Parisian Life), *Barbe-Bleue* (Bluebeard) and *La belle Hélène* (Fair Helen).

Orff, Carl (1895-1982)

The German composer Carl Orff is widely known for his work in music education and particularly for his exploration of the connection between music and movement. His style as a composer is idiosyncratic, often with considerable reliance on repeated musical patterns and insistent rhythms.

Stage-Works

Orff's *Carmina Burana,* internationally the best known of his works, at least in the concert-hall, was originally designed for staging, in a combination of medieval poems, music and movement. Other compositions for the theatre involved a re-arrangement of works by Monteverdi. His operas include *Die Kluge* (The Clever Young Woman) and *Der Mond* (The Moon), both based on the Grimm brothers' fairy-tales, and versions of Greek tragedy, Hölderlin's translations of the *Antigone* and *Oedipus Rex* of Sophocles and a setting of the Greek text of the *Prometheus* of Aeschylus.

Pacini, Giovanni (1796-1867)

The son of a distinguished operatic tenor, Giovanni Pacini studied music in Bologna and in Venice, before embarking on a career as a prolific composer of opera, his first work completed at the age of seventeen. Eclipsed for a time by Bellini and Donizetti, he returned to success in the opera-house in the 1840s, when Verdi was starting to make a name for himself.

Operas

Pacini wrote or contributed substantially to nearly ninety operas, in the course of a career that began in 1813 and continued until his death. His opera *Saffo* (Sappho), in 1840, marked a successful return to the theatre, after a pause of five years. In general his success was confined largely to Italy.

Paisiello, Giovanni (1740-1816)

Paisiello was among the most important composer of Italian opera in the late 18th century. He first established his reputation in Naples, where he had been a student, but soon won a measure of international fame, serving in St Petersburg from 1776 until 1783, before returning to Naples, where he received a court appointment. He wrote operas for Vienna and in 1802 accepted appointment in Paris, under Napoleon. His return to Naples and acceptance of a position under Joseph Buonaparte, who had ousted King Ferdinand, led, on the final defeat of Napoleon in 1815, to Paisiello losing his position and all pensions.

Operas

Paisiello wrote more than eighty operas. These included a version of *Il barbiere di Siviglia* (The Barber of Seville) that won great popularity and threatened the later success of Rossini's treatment of the same subject. His *L'idolo cinese* (The Chinese Idol) was a favourite with Nelson's mistress, Lady Hamilton, wife of the English Resident in Naples. Paisiello's earlier operas are chiefly but not exclusively comic, but there is a later concentration on more serious subjects.

Penderecki, Krzysztof (b.1933)

Penderecki occupies an important position in the music of his native Poland, while establishing an international reputation with music that has created a profound impression on audiences. His musical language, originally more experimental, was later modified by a return to more traditional sources of inspiration. His dramatic choral and vocal music on religious subjects has proved particularly impressive, both technically and in its effect on those who hear it.

Operas

Penderecki's operas include *The Devils of Loudun*, completed in 1968, and a work based on Milton's *Paradise Lost*, dramatized by Christopher Fry and completed in 1978.

Pepusch, Johann Christoph (1667-1752)

Born in Berlin, Pepusch settled in London in about 1704, remaining there for the rest of his life. He was closely concerned with the theatre, but also enjoyed a reputation as a teacher and scholar.

Stage-Works

Pepusch collaborated in the creation of masques for the London theatre, but is best known for his contribution to *The Beggar's Opera*, a collaboration with the poet John Gay for which he assembled and arranged popular tunes of the day. A second satirical ballad-opera *Polly* was banned by the censors.

Pergolesi, Giovanni Battista ((1710-1736)

Pergolesi was a composer of great importance in the development of Italian comic opera in the early 18th century, in the course of a very short career. Born and trained in Naples, he served in the musical establishments of members of the nobility and enjoyed some success also in Rome, before his death at the age of 26.

Operas

Pergolesi may properly be credited with some twelve operas and intermezzi. Of these the most far-reaching in its effect was *La serva padrona (*The Servant as Mistress*)*, which was at the centre of the so-called *guerre des bouffons*, the quarrel between supporters of Italian and French music in Paris in the early 1750s.

Peri, Jacopo (1561-1633)

Jacopo Peri, as a singer, composer and player, was an important figure in the cultural life of Florence, contributing in particular to the development of the Italian dramatic monody that is the basis of early Baroque opera. A number of his dramatic works were collaborative.

Operas

The music of Peri's *Dafne* of 1598 is lost, but the music of his *Euridice*, a collaboration with Caccini, survives, as the first example of the form.

Pfitzner, Hans (1869-1949)

A friend of Thomas Mann and of the conductor Bruno Walter, Pfitzner was among the leading composers of his generation in Germany, continuing the romantic German traditions of Schumann and Brahms.

Operas

Pfitzner's most important opera is *Palestrina*, first staged in Munich in 1917. Other operas include *Das Herz* (The Heart) and the early *Das Christ-Elflein* (The Christmas Fairy), an opera for children, written in 1906.

Piccinni, Niccolò (1728-1800)

Niccolò Piccinni holds a place of great importance in opera in Italy and France during the second half of the 18th century. His career as a composer of opera began in Naples, where he had studied, and his reputation soon spread to Rome and to major centres of opera in Italy. In 1776 he moved to Paris, at the invitation of the King, and was there involved in the partisan quarrels between those who favoured Gluck and the French opera and the supporters of the Italian opera. He contributed, however, to French operatic repertoire. He returned to Naples in 1791, but eventually, after family implication in revolutionary politics, made his way back once more to Paris, where he died in 1800.

Operas

Piccinni wrote some 120 operas, both comic and serious. Among the former *La Cecchina, ossia La buona figliuola* (Cecchina, or The Good Girl) in 1760, a version by Goldoni of Samuel Richardson's popular epistolary novel *Pamela, or Virtue Rewarded* was one of the most popular and was eventually even staged in Beijing by Jesuit musicians at the Chinese court. Richardson's novel was included on the *Index librorum prohibitorum. La buona figliuola maritata* (The Good Girl Married), in 1761, won rather less success. Other operas by Piccinni of particular note are *Catone in Utica* (Cato in Utica), the French operas *Didon* (Dido) and *Iphigénie en Tauride* (Iphigenia in Tauris) and *Ercole al Termedonte* (Hercules at Thermodon).

Pizzetti, Ildebrando (1880-1968)

Ildebrando Pizzetti was among the leading figures of his generation in Italian music. He enjoyed a close association with Gabriele d'Annunzio for some years and was associated primarily with more conservative musicians such as Respighi. He composed a variety of music, in a relatively conservative but distinctive musical idiom, in different genres.

Operas

Pizzetti's ambitions had always tended towards opera and in the course of his career he wrote some fifteen, including two radio operas. Of particular interest is his version of T.S.Eliot's *Murder in the Cathedral*, as *Assassinio nella catedrale*, while his interest in ancient Greek drama and legend, exemplified in incidental music for plays by Aeschylus and Sophocles, is heard in *Fedra* (Phaedra), with a libretto by d'Annunzio. He turned to biblical and sacred subjects in *Debora e Jaele* (Deborah and Jael) and *La sacra rappresentazione di Abram e d'Isaac* (The Miracle Play of Abraham and Isaac). His *Fra Gherardo* (Brother Gerard) is a study of the moral dilemmas faced by a 13th century friar.

Planquette, Robert (1848-1903)

Planquette's reputation rests chiefly on his operettas written for Paris and for London.

Operettas

Planquette's most popular operetta is *Les cloches de Corneville* (The Bells of Corneville), which found immediate favour abroad, as well as in Paris. For London he wrote *Rip Van Winkle*, which also achieved considerable success.

Ponchielli, Amilcare (1834-1886)

Ponchielli occupied an important position in Italian opera in the second half of the 19th century, coming next to Verdi in his achievement. His pupils in Milan, where he taught at the Conservatory, included Puccini and, for a time, Mascagni.

Operas

Of Ponchielli's twelve operas, it is *La Gioconda* for which he is best remembered. Other works of interest include an opera based on Mazzoni's *I promessi sposi* (The

Betrothed), *Il figliuol prodigo* (The Prodigal Son) and *I Lituani* (The Lithuanians), based on *Konrad Wallenrod* by the poet Mickiewicz, a writer who influenced Chopin.

Porpora, Nicola (1686-1768)

Nicola Porpora started his career in his native city of Naples. He won some distinction in Vienna and in Northern Italy, before being invited to London, when a group of amateurs set up the Opera of the Nobility, in opposition to the opera with royal support with which Handel was associated. Employment in Venice and in Dresden was followed by a move to Vienna, where Haydn served as his assistant and pupil. Other pupils of Porpora included the castrati Farinelli and Caffarelli and the composer Hasse.

Operas

From over fifty operas, the two versions of *Arianna e Teseo* (Ariadne and Theseus) are of particular interest, with his setting of Metastasio's libretto *Semiramide riconosciuta* (Semiramis Recognised).

Poulenc, Francis (1899-1963)

A member of Les Six, the group of young French composers coming to prominence in the 1920s, Poulenc wrote a wide variety of music, with a particularly distinctive contribution to French song, in performance associated with the singer Pierre Bernac, as well as to instrumental and orchestral music, often within the elegant restrictions of classical form.

Operas

Poulenc's principal operatic achievement lies in *Dialogues des Carmélites* (Dialogues of the Carmelites), based on Georges Bernanos and, in turn, on Gertrud von Le Fort's *Die letzte am Schafott* (The Last to the Scaffold), a study of martyrdom and moral conflict in the worst days of the French revolution. His *Les mamelles de Tirésias* (The Breasts of Tiresias), with a libretto by Apollinaire, deals light-heartedly with a surrealist fantasy, while his setting of Cocteau's *La voix humaine* offers an extended telephone conversation for the single singer employed.

Prokofiev, Sergey (1891-1953)

Prokofiev had already achieved a degree of musical notoriety in Russia by the time of the revolution of 1917. He spent some years abroad, but returned to Russia definitively in 1936, to experience political repression, the hardships of war and the difficulties of subsequent condemnation. With Shostakovich, he shares a position of the highest distinction among the Russian composers of his day, with music noted for its rhythmic impetus, irony and powerful lyricism, coupled, as occasion demanded, with an element of stridency more apparent in earlier compositions.

Operas

The seven completed operas of Prokofiev's maturity include a version of Tolstoy's novel *War and Peace* and the story of religious possession *The Fiery Angel.* He set a translation of Sheridan's libretto *The Duenna* and in 1919, for Chicago, *The Love for Three Oranges*, based on a play by Gozzi. *Semyon Kotko* and *The Story of a Real Man* occupy a less important position among his compositions.

Puccini, Giacomo (1858-1924)

Embarking on his career as Verdi's came to an end, Puccini may be seen as the older composer's popular successor in Italian opera. He has sometimes been associated with *verismo*, the realism in Italian opera exemplified rather in Mascagni's *Cavalleria rusticana* (Rustic Chivalry) or Leoncavallo's *Pagliacci* (Actors). Whatever realism there may be, this is mingled with strongly lyric writing in operas that verge on the sentimental and are still able to elicit tears from more sensitive audiences. An element of exoticism is found in operas set in Japan and in China, in the Wild West or in earlier periods of history.

Operas

Puccini's operas start in 1884 with *Le villi* (The Willies), its story familiar from the ballet *Giselle.* The operas that followed were *Edgar, Manon Lescaut, La bohème, Tosca, Madama Butterfly, La fanciulla del West, La rondine, Il trittico* and the final *Turandot*, left unfinished at his death. The last eight of these remain in popular repertoire and are likely to continue to do so.

Purcell, Henry (1659-1695)

Henry Purcell was among those English musicians who benefited from the Restoration of the monarchy in 1660. This allowed him training as a singer in the Chapel Royal and later employment in the royal service, with a final increased attention to the theatre, after the accession of William of Orange and Mary to the throne. French influences at the English court were developed further by additional influences from Italy, reflected by Purcell in music that is essentially English, particularly in the settings of texts, sacred and secular.

Operas

Although attempts had been made towards English opera, in Purcell's time there was little place for dramatic works set completely to music. Purcell's only opera, written either as a court masque or as an entertainment for a girls' school in Chelsea, was the short *Dido and Aeneas*. Later writers have used the term semi-opera to describe dramatic works of the period that include a large element of music which is often separable from the drama and its principal actors. The musical element here is often exotic or supernatural in function, as in Dryden's *King Arthur*. Other such works are *The Prophetess, or The History of Diocletian, The Fairy Queen, The Indian Queen* and *The Tempest or The Enchanted Island.*

Rachmaninov, Sergey (1873-1943)

One of the great pianists of his time, Sergey Rachmaninov had his training as a composer and as a pianist at the Moscow Conservatory and had embarked on what promised to be a highly successful career in Russia. 1917 brought an end to this and led to a life in exile during which he depended to a large extent on concert performance as a pianist and as a conductor, activities that left relatively little time for composition. His symphonies and his four piano concertos are supremely romantic in conception, with the latter providing an unfortunate model for less gifted composers.

Operas

Rachmaninov completed only three operas. These include the graduation piece *Aleko*, first performed in 1893, and the maturer *The Miserly Knight* and *Francesca da Rimini*, both completed in 1905.

Rameau, Jean-Philippe (1683-1764)

Rameau won his earlier distinction as a musical theorist, turning relatively late in his career, in 1733, to the opera, a genre that he dominated for some years to follow. As a composer of music for the keyboard, he continued the tradition of Couperin, as in his other instrumental works.

Operas

Rameau contributed notably to a number of French musical and dramatic forms. His first success came in 1733 with the *tragédie en musique* or *tragédie lyrique*, *Hippolyte et Aricie*, followed in 1735 by an *opéra-ballet*, *Les Indes galantes*. Other *tragédies en musique* are *Castor et Pollux*, *Dardanus*, *Zoroastre*, *Linus* and, in 1763, *Les Boréades*. *Opéras-ballets* include *Les fêtes d'Hébé* (The Festivities of Hebe), *Les fêtes de Polymnie* (The Festivities of Polyhymnia), *Le temple de la gloire* (The Temple of Glory), *Les fêtes de l'Hymen* (The Festivities of Hymen) and *Les surprises de l'Amour* (The Surprises of Cupid). There are *comédies-lyriques* in the satirical *Platée* and *Les Paladins*, with a number of *Actes de ballet* and *pastorales-héroïques* such as *Naïs*, *Acante et Céphise* and *Daphnis et Eglé*. Although by the time of his death in 1764 fashions had changed, in his day Rameau had few rivals, respected equally as a composer and as a scholar of musical theory.

Ravel, Maurice (1875-1937)

Although often coupled in name with Debussy, Ravel's contribution to French music is a distinctive one. While capable of elaborate figuration in some of his piano music, he also wrote at times in a much sparer, neo-classical style. At the same time he was able to display his gifts as an orchestrator in colourful and evocative scores. He contributed notably to the repertoire of French song, instrumental music and orchestral compositions and arrangements.

Operas

The first of Ravel's two operas was *L'heure espagnole* (The Spanish Clock), in 1907. This was followed, in 1925, by the remarkable *L'enfant et les sortilèges* (The Child and the Enchantments), with a libretto by Colette, a fascinating musical evocation both of childhood and of the animate and inanimate world of childhood.

Reimann, Aribert (b.1936)

The German composer Aribert Reimann, a pupil of Boris Blacher and Ernst Pepping in Berlin, has enjoyed a parallel career as an accompanist, often in recitals with Dietrich Fischer-Dieskau. His compositions have been influenced, in particular, by Webern, and, more recently, by Indian music.

Operas

The best known of Reimann's six operas is the Shakespearian *Lear*, written specifically for Dietrich Fischer-Dieskau. Other operas are *Ein Traumspiel* (A Dream Play) and *Die Gespenstersonate* (The Ghost Sonata), after Strindberg, *Troades*, after Euripides, and *Das Schloss* (The Castle), after Kafka.

Respighi, Ottorino (1879-1936)

With distinctive gifts as an orchestral colourist, Ottorino Respighi is best known internationally for his orchestral pictures of Rome, the *Fontane di Roma* (Fountains of Rome), *I Pini di Roma* (The Pines of Rome) and *Feste romane* (Roman Festivals), appropriate celebration of the ancient and modern glories of the city where he made much of his career. His gifts as a composer lay largely in his ability to capture a picture in his music, but this was coupled with deep roots in Italian musical traditions, of which he made special study.

Operas

Respighi completed nine operas, starting, in 1905, with the unpublished *Re Enzo*. Of particular interest are the marionette-opera *La bella addormentata nel bosco* (Sleeping Beauty), *Belfagor*, *Maria Egiziaca* (Mary of Egypt), *La fiamma* (The Flame) and *Lucrezia*.

Rimsky-Korsakov, Nikolay Andreyevich (1844-1908)

One of the Russian Five, the group of nationalist composers gathered, at first, under the influence of Balakirev, Rimsky-Korsakov survived the excesses of nationalist amateurism to reach a high degree of professional ability, exercised in completing and smoothing out the perceived crudities in the works of his colleagues Mussorgsky and Borodin. Gifted as an orchestrator, he wrote colourfully and is best known abroad for works such as *Sheherazade*, his *Capriccio espagnole* and the unavoidable *Flight of the Bumble-Bee*, from the opera *The Tale of Tsar Saltan*.

Operas

In Russia Rimsky-Korsakov earned a reputation particularly for his operas, but, perhaps for reasons of language, these have fared less well abroad. The first of his fourteen operas was *The Maid of Pskov*, followed by *May Night, The Snow Maiden, Mlada, Christmas Eve, Sadko, Mozart and Salieri, The Tsar's Bride, The Tale of Tsar Saltan, Servilia, Pan Voyevoda, Legend of the Invisible City of Kitezh* and *The Golden Cockerel*. In some cases these operas brought conflict with the official censors, an anxiety that continued with complaints and delays in the staging of the last of his operas, which was eventually mounted only after the composer's death.

Rossi, Luigi (1597/8-1653)

At first in the service of the Borghese family, Luigi Rossi later accepted the patronage of the Barberini. His compositions include a large number of secular cantatas and a smaller number of sacred works and he holds a position of some importance in the development and diffusion of dramatic vocal style, in the manner of Monteverdi.

Operas

For Cardinal Antonio Barberini Rossi wrote an opera based on an episode in Ariosto's *Orlando furioso* (Roland in Madness) that recurs later in operatic history. This was *Il palazzo incantato* (The Enchanted Palace). With the Cardinal's exile from Rome, Rossi travelled to Paris, where, for Cardinal Mazarin, he wrote his second and last opera, *Orfeo* (Orpheus), staged in Paris in 1647.

Rossini, Gioachino (1792-1868)

Born into a family working in the musical theatre, Rossini showed precocious gifts as a musician, embarking on a career as a composer of opera at the age of eighteen and retiring from it at the age of 38. He won widespread fame and popularity, and retained the respect and admiration of musicians even as fashions changed, during a retirement of nearly forty years. In the last decade of his life he returned to private composition, in styles that now suited well enough the new tendencies of the 1860s.

Operas

While Rossini may be widely remembered for the wit and brilliance of his comic operas, he also achieved much in a more serious vein. His vocal writing was demanding and masterly and in his final opera for Paris, *Guillaume Tell* (William Tell), staged there in 1829, he seems to enter the world of Weber or of Catalani, a more romantic ambience in the cantons of Switzerland. Rossini's most famous opera is *Il barbiere di Siviglia* (The Barber of Seville) and other comic operas include *La cambiale di matrimonio* (The Marriage Contract), *L'equivoco stravagante* (The Curious Misunderstanding), *L'inganno felice* (The Fortunate Deception), *La scala di sieta* (The Silken Ladder), *La pietra del paragone* (The Touchstone), *L'occasione fa il ladro* (Opportunity Makes the Thief), *Il Signor Bruschino, ossia Il figlio per azzardo* (Signor Bruschino, or The Son by Chance), *L'italiana in Algeri* (The Italian Girl in Algiers), *Il turco in Italia* (The Turk in Italy), *La gazzetta* (The Newspaper), *La Cenerentola, ossia La bontà in trionfo* (Cinderella, or Goodness in Triumph), *Adina, o il califfo di Bagdad* (Adina, or The Caliph of Baghdad), *Matilde di Shabran, ossia Bellezza, e cuor di ferro* (Matilda of Shabran, or Beauty and Heart of Iron), *Il viaggio a Reims, ossia L'albergo del giglio d'oro* (The Journey to Rheims, or The Golden Lily Inn) and the French *opéra comique, Le Comte Ory* (Count Ory). Operas in serious vein include *Ciro in Babilonia, ossia La caduta di Baldassare* (Cyrus in Babylon, or The Fall of Belshazzar), *Tancredi, Aureliano in Palmira* (Aurelianus in Palmyra), *Sigismondo, Elisabetta, regina d'Inghilterra* (Elizabeth, Queen of England), *Torvaldo e Dorliska* (Torvaldo and Dorliska), *Otello, ossia Il moro di Venezia* (Othello, or The Moor of Venice), *La gazza ladra* (The Thieving Magpie), *Armida, Adelaide di Borgogna* (Adelaide of Burgundy), *Mosè in Egitto* (Moses in Egypt), *Ricciardo e Zoraide* (Richard and Zoraide), *Ermione* (Hermione), *Eduardo e Cristina* (Edward and Christine), *La donna del lago* (The Lady of the Lake), *Bianca e Faliero, ossia Il consiglio dei tre* (Bianca and Faliero, or The Council of Three), *Maometto II* (Mehmet II), *Zelmira, Semiramide* (Semiramis), and the French versions of *Maometto II* and *Mosè in Egitto*, *Le siège de Corinthe* (The Siege of Corinth) and *Moïse et Pharaon, ou Le passage de la Mer Rouge* (Moses and Pharoah, or The Crossing of the Red Sea). Rossini's last opera was *Guillaume Tell* (William Tell).

Rousseau, Jean-Jacques (1712-1778)

Born in Geneva in 1712, Rousseau is best known as a writer and philosopher, an important influence on the thought of his time and on the revolutionary ideas that came to a head in the later 18th century. He was an opponent of French opera and the author of a *Dictionnaire de musique* (Dictionary of Music) that is a useful source for contemporary ideas on the subject. As a composer, he is of more limited interest.

Operas

Rousseau attempted the composition of various operas, but won most success with his French *intermède, Le devin du village* (The Village Magician), the source of Mozart's *Bastien und Bastienne.*

Roussel, Albert (1869-1937)

By early training a naval officer, the French composer Albert Roussel resigned from the service in order to devote himself to music. He was much influenced by a visit to India and to South-East Asia and developed a musical idiom of his own, based on earlier tradition and on the teaching he had received at the Schola cantorum, under the continuing influence of César Franck and that of Vincent d'Indy.

Opera

Roussel's only opera was *Padmâvatî*, an *opéra-ballet*.

Rubinstein, Anton (1829-1894)

Anton Rubinstein was among the greatest pianists of his generation. He was the founder of the St Petersburg Conservatory and played a fundamental part in the development of professional standards of musical training in Russia. As a composer, he won no favour with the nationalists, led, at first, by Balakirev, who took equal exception to the Conservatories and to a form of training that they stigmatized as German. There is no doubt that an element of anti-Semitism entered into judgements of this kind, so that, in spite of his very considerable achievements, the nationalists could finally use Rubinstein's name as a synonym for *kitsch*.

Operas

Rubinstein's twenty operas include *The Demon, Feramors, Kupets Kalashnikov* (The Merchant Kalashnikov), *Die Maccabäer* (The Maccabees), *Néron* and *Der Thurm zu Babel* (The Tower of Babel). His greatest success was with the first of these.

Saint-Saëns, Camille (1835-1921)

A musician who was prolific as a composer and versatile in his many interests, Camille Saint-Saëns wrote music in many different genres. He was a skilful craftsman and works such as his *Introduction et Rondo capriccioso* and his five piano concertos remain as essential to solo repertoire as his *Organ Symphony* is to purely orchestral fare. Although he had given strong support to younger musicians, and in particular to his former pupil and protégé Gabriel Fauré, by the time of his death in 1921 music had taken a very different course and his work seemed out of date in the world of Ravel or of Stravinsky.

Operas

The opera for which Saint-Saëns is best known is *Samson et Dalila* (Samson and Delilah). Of his other twelve operas, *Henry VIII* finds a brief place in modern repertoire in a series of dances extracted from the score.

Salieri, Antonio (1750-1825)

Born in Italy, Antonio Salieri occupied a position of fundamental importance in music in Vienna, where he was taken in 1766, until nearly the end of his life. His modern reputation has suffered through the attention accorded him in the play and subsequent film *Amadeus*, by Peter Shaffer, a reflection of an element of the earlier work by Pushkin, the basis of Rimsky-Korsakov's opera *Mozart and Salieri*, which seems to suggest professional failure as well as jealousy. In fact he enjoyed the highest reputation in Vienna as a composer, while as a teacher his pupils included Beethoven and Schubert, the latter over a period of some five years of continuing study. His compositions include a quantity of sacred and secular vocal works, in addition to a smaller number of surviving orchestral and instrumental compositions.

Operas

As a composer of opera, Salieri occupies an important position, from his first comic opera for Vienna, *Le donne leterate* (The Lady Literatae) in 1770. He wrote some forty operas and in the 1780s was held in particularly high esteem in Paris, where *Les Danaïdes* (The Danaids) was staged in 1784 and *Tarare*, with a libretto by Beaumarchais, in 1787. He set libretti by Goldoni and Metastasio, Casti and Da Ponte, and his *Prima la musica poi le parole* (First the Music then the Words) was staged at Schönbrunn at the same occasion as Mozart's *Der Schauspieldirektor* (The Impresario), in 1786. The year 1788 brought an Italian adaptation by Da Ponte of *Tarare*, under the title *Axur, re d'Ormus* (Axur, King of Ormus) and his *Falstaff* of 1799, based on Shakespeare's *The Merry Wives of Windsor*, retains the power to amuse in its light handling of the comedy.

Sallinen, Aulis (b. 1935)

Arguably the leading Finnish composer of his generation, Aulis Sallinen has been able to capture in sound the spirit and atmosphere of his native country.

Operas

Sallinen remarkable first opera *Ratsumies* (The Horseman) of 1974 was followed four years later by *Punainen viiva* (The Red Line), a graphic depiction of human suffering, in spite of political change.

Scarlatti, Alessandro (1660-1725)

The father of Domenico Scarlatti and member of an influential family of musicians in Naples, Alessandro Scarlatti played an important part in the development of opera in Naples. His compositions include a considerable amount of vocal music, sacred and secular, and a smaller quantity of instrumental music. He may be considered as one of the most important composers of his generation in Italian music of the period.

Operas

Scarlatti left some seventy operas, the first of these given its first performance in 1679 and the last, *La Griselda*, in 1721. It was with his operas that the Italian overture, the introductory, three-movement *sinfonia*, took shape and whatever the fate of his work in following generations, he succeeded in establishing Naples as an operatic centre and his own very considerable contemporary reputation, which brought him due public honour in Naples and in Rome. Arias by Scarlatti still hold an essential place in vocal training.

Scarlatti, Domenico (1685-1757)

Domenico Scarlatti is generally known for the five hundred or so keyboard sonatas that he wrote, particularly during the years he spent, from 1719 until his death, in Portugal and Spain. His music for the theatre came earlier in his career, before his departure for Lisbon.

Operas

Domenico Scarlatti at first followed his father's example, writing his first three operas for Naples, and then a further nine works for performance in Rome. While his father's influence is evident in his operas, there are ways in which he struck out on a new course of greater dramatic realism. Seven of his Roman operas were written for the Queen of Poland, Maria Casimira, in whose service he remained from 1709 until her departure from Rome in 1714.

Schoenberg, Arnold (1874-1951)

Arnold Schoenberg's influence on music of the 20th century has been incalculable, chiefly through the principles of serialism that he developed, the ideal of providing musical unity to a work from the use of a series of the twelve semitones of the octave, deployed in order, but otherwise in very varied ways. His theories led to fruitful and unfruitful exploitation by later composers, contributing, it must be said, to a divorce of serious contemporary music from popular taste, at a time when audiences were growing and general musical knowledge and understanding decreasing. His early music reflects many of the features of the Vienna of his day, breaking the bounds of tonality in a way that had been implied, at least, by Wagner. His later music presents greater difficulties of understanding in works that often seem characterized by the angularity of melodic lines and elements of dissonance. In general his compositional career may be divided into an early tonal period, a second period of atonality, moving away from a sense of key, a period some have chosen to call expressionist, serialism dominates the period from 1920 to 1936 and this is followed by a fourth period of eclecticism. Schoenberg's pupils in what has become known as the Second Viennese School, were Alban Berg and Anton Webern. In 1911 Schoenberg had moved to Berlin, to avoid the prevalent anti-semitism in Vienna from which Mahler had suffered. In 1933 he was compelled to leave Berlin and eventually made his home in Los Angeles, where he died in 1951.

Operas

From Schoenberg's expressionist period come the monodrama *Erwartung* (Expectation) and *Die glückliche Hand* (The Fortunate Hand). *Von heute auf morgen* (From One Day to the Next) was written in Berlin in 1928 and 1929, while the monumental *Moses und Aron* (Moses and Aaron) was put aside in 1932 and never completed.

Schreker, Franz (1878-1934)

Franz Schreker is among those composers whose careers were destroyed by the events of 1933 in Germany, with his music regarded as degenerate, for whatever reason. His compositions are chiefly vocal and dramatic, although he also left a small quantity of orchestral music.

Operas

Schreker created a musical and dramatic world of his own that is, nevertheless, very characteristic of the period in which he lived. *Der ferne Klang* (The Distant Sound) and *Die Gezeichneten* (The Sealed Ones) offer scores of rich sensuality to match their subjects, released from earlier restraint by the effect of Richard Strauss in his *Salome*, which had suggested new frontiers in this respect. Schreker's first, relatively minor work for the theatre was *Die Flammen* (The Flames), in 1900. His other operas include *Das Spielwerk und die Prinzessin* (The Music-Box and the Princess), *Der Schatzgräber* (The Treasure-Seeker), *Irrelohe*, *Der singende Teufel* (The Singing Devil), *Christophorus, oder Die Vision einer Oper* (Christopher, or The Vision of an Opera) and *Der Schmied von Gent* (The Smith of Ghent).

Schubert, Franz (1797-1828)

Born in Vienna, Franz Schubert had his early musical training as a chorister in the Imperial Chapel, after which he trained briefly as a teacher, following, intermittently, his father's employment. In Vienna he enjoyed the society of his friends in an increasingly flourishing middle class ambience, providing song after song, piano pieces and chamber music, all in some abundance. He lacked patronage, in a changing world, but had aroused the interest of publishers by the time of his early death, in a year in which he had risked the first public concert of his larger-scale works, an event that was successful and profitable. Schubert's gifts lie in his ability to invent melodies that always reflect his genius as a composer of songs, whether in his piano sonatas, chamber music or symphonies.

Operas

Although not primarily regarded as a composer of opera, Schubert was, by the time of his death, developing his dramatic powers in this medium. Among a dozen or so works for the theatre, the most worthy of attention are *Die Zwillingsbrüder* (The Twins), *Alfonso und Estrella* (Alfonso and Estrella), *Die Verschworenen* (The Conspirators) and *Fierrabras*.

Schumann, Robert (1810-1856)

Robert Schumann reflected in many ways the preoccupations of Romanticism, not least in his literary interests. After breaking off his university studies, he studied with the well-known teacher Friedrich Wieck, with the idea of becoming a concert pianist. When this proved impossible, while writing a number of piano pieces, often of extra-musical content, he turned his attention to song and to marriage with Wieck's pianist daughter Clara, a match that Wieck opposed through the courts. After his marriage in 1840, he worked on larger-scale compositions, while continuing to write chamber music, piano pieces and songs. The Schumanns had settled in 1844 in Dresden, but Schumann's first official position came in 1850, when he moved to Düsseldorf as director of music. The difficulties of his employment and his administrative inadequacies, coupled with depressive tendencies that had long plagued him, as they had his father and sister, led to final insanity during the last three years of his life.

Opera

Schumann's only completed attempt at opera was *Genoveva,* first staged in Leipzig in 1850. As so often, he had contemplated other operatic subjects, but had failed to finish his earlier *Der Corsar* (The Corsair), based on the poem by Byron, confining himself to concert works derived from Goethe's *Faust*, from Thomas Moore's *Lalla Rookh* and from Goethe's *Wilhelm Meister*.

Shostakovich, Dmitry (1906-1975)

Dmitry Shostakovich belongs to the generation of Russian composers trained after the revolution of 1917 at what was later to become the Leningrad Conservatory. He won distinction as a pianist and as a composer while still a student, and had established himself as an important enough figure in the Soviet musical world, until the condemnation, in 1936, of his opera *A Lady Macbeth of the Mtsensk District*. During the years of war Shostakovich found a measure of favour and his *Leningrad Symphony* received particularly wide publicity, but 1948 brought further official condemnation, relaxed after the death of Stalin in 1953. It has been suggested that there is a division in the music written by Shostakovich between the public and the private and certainly some compositions were held back until after 1953. While his initial sympathies would have followed those of his family in favour of political reform, it is clear that the nature of the new régime was such as to inspire a highly critical attitude, as biographical details emerging after his death in 1975 have suggested.

Operas

Shostakovich's first opera was *The Nose*, after a story by Gogol and he was later to attempt a second Gogol opera in *The Gamblers*. Apart from the musical comedy *Moskva, Cheremushki*, he wrote one other opera, *Lady Macbeth of the Mtsensk District*, later revised as *Katerina* Izmaylova.

Sidow (Seedo) (c.1700-c.1754)

Sidow, his other names unknown, worked in London in the 1730s in ballad opera at Drury Lane, after the success of his father's colleague Pepusch with *The Beggar's Opera*. He moved to Prussia, from where his father had come to London, in 1736.

Smetana, Bedřich (1824-1884)

Smetana was the first major Bohemian nationalist composer, his political sympathies involving him in the creation of national Czech opera and a series of works, such as the cycle of symphonic poems *Má Vlast* (My Country) that are filled with the spirit of Bohemia and its songs and dances.

Operas

The principal opera by which Smetana is known abroad is *The Bartered Bride*, with its simple Bohemian village setting. His first opera was *The Brandenburgers in Bohemia*, staged first in 1866, and others are *Dalibor*, *Libuše*, *The Two Widows*, *The Kiss*, *The Secret*, *The Devil's Wall* and the unfinished *Viola*, an intended version of Shakespeare's *Twelfth Night*.

Spohr, Louis (1784-1859)

Honoured still by violinists for his addition to their repertoire, Louis Spohr enjoyed a contemporary reputation as an innovative conductor and was an important figure in the development of German romantic opera. He was employed in Gotha, in Vienna and Dresden, and finally in Kassel, where he spent much of his later professional life. Although his music has been unduly neglected, it is now recovering, through recordings, something of the esteem in which it was held during the composer's lifetime, although this appreciation has not yet been extended to Spohr's operas.

Operas

Spohr wrote ten operas, of which *Jessonda* won the greatest popularity, regarded as the forerunner of Wagner's music-dramas. Other operas by Spohr are *Faust*, *Pietro von Abano* and *Zemire und Azor* (Zemire and Azor), while *Alruna, die Eulekönigin* (Alruna, the Owl Queen), *Der Zweikampf mit der Geliebten* (Duel with the Beloved), *Der Berggeist* (The Mountain Spirit), *Der Alchymist* and *Der Kreuzfahrer* (The Crusader) are often ambitious, but of lesser influence and historical importance.

Spontini, Gaspare (1774-1851)

Spontini's early career as a composer was in his native Italy, but in 1803 he moved to Paris, where he established himself in 1807 with the opera *La vestale*, a work much encouraged by the Empress Josephine. He continued to work in Paris after the fall of Napoleon, but in 1820 accepted an invitation to move to Berlin, where he reigned uneasily as music director of the Court Opera, opposed by those who resented the presence of a foreigner and urged a place for German opera. In 1842 he left Berlin, returning eventually to his birth-place in Italy, where he died in 1851.

Operas

Spontini left some 23 operas. Of these *La vestale* remains the best known. This was followed in Paris by *Fernand Cortez, ou La conquête de Mexique* (Fernand Cortez, or The Conquest of Mexico), with *Olympie* the last of his operas to be first staged in Paris. For Berlin he wrote, among other works, *Nurmahal, oder Das Rosenfest von Kaschmir* (Nurmahal, or The Rose Festival of Kashmir) and *Agnes von Hohenstaufen*.

Stockhausen, Karlheinz (b.1928)

Since the 1950s Karlheinz Stockhausen has been among the leading composers of the German avant-garde. He studied in Cologne with Frank Martin, at Darmstadt and in Paris with Messiaen and in his music has explored the possibilities of electronic music and of the human element in performance, moving, in his musical language, from total serialism to a more flexible idiom.

Operas

Stockhausen in 1977 turned his attention to the composition of seven operas, under the general title *Licht* (Light). The seven, which still await completion, have titles that follow the days of the week, *Montag aus Licht* (Monday from Light), *Donnerstag aus Licht* (Thursday from Light) and *Samstag aus Licht* (Saturday from Light).

Strauss, Johann (1825-1899)

The younger Johann Strauss followed his homonymous father in establishing his own dance-bands, an enterprise into which he enrolled his younger brothers, intended by their father, as he too had been, for other professions. The Strauss family came to dominate the music of ball-rooms in Vienna, with popular seasons elsewhere in Europe, and have come to be closely identified with the spirit of 19th century Vienna.

Operettas

Johann Strauss completed fifteen operettas, of which *Die Fledermaus* (The Bat) is the best known. Others are *Indigo und die vierzig Räuber* (Indigo and the Forty Thieves), *Carneval in Rom* (Carnival in Rome), *Cagliostro in Wien* (Cagliostro in Vienna), *Prinz Methusalem* (Prince Methusaleh), *Blindekuh* (Blind Man's Buff), *Das Spitzentuch der Königin* (The Queen's Kerchief), *Der lustige Krieg* (The Merry War), *Eine Nacht in Venedig* (A Night in Venice), *Der Zigeunerbaron* (The Gypsy Baron), *Simplicius*, *Ritter Pázmán* (Knight Pázmán), *Fürstin Ninetta* (Princess Ninetta), *Waldmeister* (Woodruff) and the unfinished *Die Göttin der Vernunft* (The Goddess of Reason).

Strauss, Richard (1864-1949)

The son of a distinguished horn-player and his second wife, the daughter of a well-to-do family of brewers, Richard Strauss received early encouragement in his musical ambitions. As a young man, he established his reputation as a conductor, serving first as assistant to Hans von Bülow in Meiningen. His early compositions were given public performance, through his father's influence, but no such support was necessary as he went on, writing in the 1880s and 1890s an important series of tone-poems that extended still further the aims of Liszt in expressing everything through music, coupled with the orchestral dimensions of Wagner. He was a regular conductor at the Court Opera in Berlin and served as co-director of the Vienna Staatsoper from 1919 to 1924. Strauss also contributed notably to the tradition of German Lieder and to other forms of orchestral and instrumental writing in an often rich musical language that could be tinged with autumnal melancholy, as in his *Four Last Songs*.

Operas

Strauss's first opera *Guntram*, in which his formidable wife took a leading rôle, did little to forward his reputation. This was followed in 1901 by *Feuersnot*, but his career as primarily a composer of opera was firmly established in 1905 with the controversial opera *Salome*, his first collaboration with the writer Hugo von Hofmannsthal. This led to *Elektra*, *Der Rosenkavalier* (The Knight of the Rose), *Ariadne auf Naxos* (Ariadne on Naxos), *Die Frau ohne Schatten* (The Woman without a Shadow), *Die ägiptische Helena* (The Egyptian Helen) and *Arabella*. Strauss provided his own libretto for *Intermezzo* and after Hofmannsthal's death collaborated with Stefan Zweig on *Die schweigsame Frau* (The Silent Woman). With Zweig's enforced exile after 1933, Strauss worked with a less effective librettist, Joseph Gregor, in three further operas, *Friedenstag* (Day of Peace), *Daphne* and *Die Liebe der Danae* (The Love of the Danae). His last opera, completed in 1941, was *Capriccio*. Strauss remains the most important composer of German opera of the first half of the 20th century.

Stravinsky, Igor (1882-1971)

Born in Russia in 1882, the son of a well known singer, Igor Stravinsky emigrated after the revolution of 1917, having already made a name for himself in Paris and elsewhere in his collaborations with Dyagilev and the Ballets russes, for which he wrote *The Firebird*, *Petrushka* and *The Rite of Spring*. Stravinsky spent part of the war years in Switzerland, returning afterwards to France. Eventually, however, he moved to the United States, where he lived from 1939 onwards. While his musical idiom is immediately recognisable, in whatever style, these styles did change during the course of his long career, from the overtly Russian to the sparer textures of the neo-classical and finally to serialism.

Operas

Stravinsky's early operas, *The Nightingale* and *Renard* were followed by *Mavra*. The opera-oratorio *Oedipus Rex* in 1927 and *Perséphone* in 1934, with texts by Cocteau and André Gide respectively, came as the composer found himself still involved in further scores for ballet. It was in 1951 that he achieved his most lasting operatic achievement with *The Rake's Progress*, with a libretto by W.H.Auden and Chester Kallman, drawing inspiration from Hogarth.

Sullivan, Arthur (1842-1900)

Of immediate Irish and Italian descent, Arthur Sullivan is now remembered chiefly for his collaboration with W.S.Gilbert in the Savoy operas, light-hearted works of musical and topical satire. His contemporary reputation in England and abroad was more considerable, with a quantity of vocal music and orchestral works and a knighthood from Queen Victoria.

Operettas

In 1862 Sullivan had made his first attempt at opera, the music for which is now lost, but a few years later he began to find his métier with *Cox and Box*. Collaboration with Gilbert began in 1871 with *Thespis*, but the first work to make its mark was *Trial by Jury*, staged in 1875, followed by *The Sorcerer, HMS Pinafore, The Pirates of Penzance, Patience, Iolanthe, Princess Ida, The Mikado, Ruddigore, The Yeomen of the Guard, The Gondoliers, Utopia* and *The Grand Duke*. *Ivanhoe* was a serious work based on the novel by Sir Walter Scott, with four other works that have failed to hold attention. The popularity of the Gilbert and Sullivan operettas has had an effect that has not been entirely beneficial, as topical satire has lost its relevance and is often misunderstood, while amateur music societies, in particular, have found too ready a field for musical exploitation, at the expense of other works that might deserve their attention and resources.

Suppé, Franz von (1819-1895)

A native of Spalato, the modern Split, Franz von Suppé established himself in Vienna as a leading composer of light opera, working at the Theater an der Wien from 1845 until 1862 and thereafter at the Kaitheater and from 1865 at the Carltheater, until his retirement in 1882.

Operettas

A list of the operettas written by Suppé or to which he contributed would be a very long one, including some 250 or more stage works. While *Boccaccio, Fatinitza* and *Die schöne Galathee* (Fair Galatea) may deserve particular attention, others, such as *Dichter und Bauer* (Poet and Peasant), *Flotte Bursche* (Gay Blades) and *Dis Leichte Kavallerie* (Light Cavalry), may be familiar from their overtures or from concert excerpts, even though they may not have won a place in international repertoire, beyond their country of origin.

Szymanowski, Karol (1882-1937)

Karol Szymanowski occupies a pre-eminent place among Polish composers of the first few decades of the 20th century. Influenced by German romanticism in his earlier years, he developed a very personal idiom, influenced by his interest in the ancient world, earlier Christian history and the culture of Islam. He was, at the same time, able to develop a distinctly Polish musical language, notably in the ballet-pantomime *Harnasie*.

Opera

Szymanowski's major operatic achievement is his opera *King Roger*, a work that combines his interest in early Christian history with the mythological figure of Dionysus and music that reflects his fascination with the Middle East, in a plot that recalls the *Bacchae* of Euripides.

Tchaikovsky, Pyotr Il'yich (1840-1893)

While presenting the outside world with a very Russian appearance, Tchaikovsky at home was subject to advice from Balakirev, but was never a member of the famous Five, nationalist composers with a lesser degree of professional competence. Tchaikovsky was trained at the St Petersburg Conservatory and taught for some years at the parallel institution in Moscow, before a pension from a benefactress who was to remain unseen, Nadezhda von Meck, allowed him to concentrate, for some fifteen years, on composition. His orchestral works, with highly coloured instrumentation, have won enormous popularity, and his three ballets, *Swan Lake*, *Sleeping Beauty* and *Nutcracker*, set new standards for composers. He had particular gifts that were well suited to ballet, with its need for short forms, but was capable of more sustained achievement in his six symphonies, his piano concertos and violin concerto.

Operas

The twelve operas that Tchaikovsky wrote have not won a universal place for themselves in international repertoire. Here two only are heard with any degree of frequency, *Eugene Onegin* and *The Queen of Spades*, both powerful and moving works, based on Pushkin. Tchaikovsky's other operas are *Voyevoda*, *Undine*, *Mandragora*, *The Oprichnik*, *Vakula the Smith* later revised as *Cherevichki*, *The Maid of Orleans*, *Mazepa*, *The Enchantress* and *Iolanta*. Tchaikovsky destroyed the first two of these, while the last, which had no great success, was written as part of a double bill with the ballet *Nutcracker*.

Telemann, Georg Philipp (1681-1767)

Born into a family with long-standing connections among the Lutheran clergy, Telemann also benefited from a university education, before embarking on a musical career that took him to Sorau, to Eisenach, to Frankfurt and finally, in 1721, to Hamburg, where he spent the rest of his life as music director of the five principal churches of the city. Enjoying esteem above that accorded by his contemporaries to his friend Johann Sebastian Bach, he was able, in Hamburg, to apply himself to a variety of music, instrumental and vocal, sacred and secular, which he did with great facility and versatility. He was succeeded in his position, after his death in 1767, by his god-son Carl Philipp Emanuel Bach, son of Johann Sebastian.

Operas

Telemann was not primarily a composer of opera, but he did contribute to opera in Leizig and to the music of the Hamburg theatre, notably in the comic opera *Der geduldige Socrates* (Patient Socrates), *Pimpinone* and *Der neumodische Liebhaber* (The New-Fangled Amateur).

Thomas, Ambroise (1811-1896)

The career of Ambroise Thomas followed the conventions of success in French musical life. A pupil of the pianist Kalkbrenner and, for composition, of Le Sueur, at the Paris Conservatoire, he duly won the Prix de Rome, forming a friendship with Ingres during his time at the Villa Medici. In Paris once more he continued to develop the tradition of the *opéra comique* in a series of works. In 1851 he succeeded Spontini among the immortals of the French Academy and five years later joined the teaching staff of the Conservatoire as professor of composition. He succeeded Auber as director of the Conservatoire in 1871, retaining the position until his death in 1896. In his later years he remained conservative in his opposition to the younger generation of French composers, with Fauré excluded from the Conservatoire until after his death. Thomas was much honoured in his life-time and won the respect of major figures in the musical world, both at home and abroad.

Operas

One of the most successful operas ever staged was *Mignon*, a work based on Goethe's *Wilhelm Meister*, in 1866, followed in 1868 by *Hamlet*. These remain the most significant achievements of Thomas, among twenty operas.

Thomson, Virgil (1896-1989)

A pupil of Nadia Boulanger, like other American composers of his generation, Virgil Thomson enjoyed a particular reputation as an acerbic critic. Between 1925 and 1940 he lived principally in Paris, collaborating in stage works with Gertrude Stein. From 1940 until 1954 he was music critic for the New York Herald Tribune. As a composer he wrote a varied quantity of music, including film scores and incidental music, and used varying styles in other works.

Operas

Virgil Thomson collaborated with Gertrude Stein on the first two of his three operas, *Four Saints in Three Acts* and *The Mother of Us All*. His third opera, *Lord Byron*, has been regarded as a summary of his work. It was completed in 1972 and the ballet music from it became the substance of Thomson's *Third Symphony*.

Tippett, Michael (1905 – 1998)

In English music of the 20th century Michael Tippett holds a unique and original position. A pacifist, like Benjamin Britten, he was for some years closely and altruistically involved with choral music at Morley College in London, an important centre for adult education, and it was primarily after 1945 that he won a sure place for himself among contemporary composers. His musical language is diverse and far-reaching in its terms of reference and his compositions include an important series of string quartets, concertos, four symphonies, songs and the movingly relevant oratorio *A Child of Our Time*, for which, as for his operas, Tippett wrote the words.

Operas

Tippett's first opera was *The Midsummer Marriage*, completed in 1952 and first staged at Covent Garden in 1955. It was followed by *King Priam, The Knot Garden, The Ice Break* and *New Year*.

Ullmann, Viktor (1898 - 1944?)

A pupil of Schoenberg in Vienna and later with Alois Hába in Prague, Viktor Ullmann occupied an important position in Bohemian music, cut short by his death in the concentration camp at Auschwitz, after a period of internment at Terezín.

Operas

Ullmann's *Der Sturz des Antichrist* (The Fall of Antichrist) was written in 1935. *Der Kaiser von Atlantis* (The Emperor of Atlantis) was written in Terezín in 1943.

Vaughan Williams, Ralph (1872-1958)

Holding a very special position in English music of the first half of the 20th century, Ralph Vaughan Williams studied composition with Parry, Charles Wood and Stanford, subsequently taking lessons from Ravel. Drawing in part on elements of English folk-song and pastoral tradition, he was by no means tied to this, developing in his nine symphonies a much more powerful musical language. His very considerable output is diverse, ranging from music for the theatre, for films and for the radio, to hymns, songs, choral pieces and instrumental and orchestral music. Like other major composers, Vaughan Williams has a very recognisable musical voice of his own, although his achievement has not always won recognition outside his own country, in which his music is very deeply rooted.

Operas

Operas or stage works by Vaughan Williams include *Hugh the Drover, or Love in the Stocks*, the Shakespearian *Sir John in Love, The Poisoned Kiss, Riders to the Sea* and the morality *The Pilgrim's Progress.*

Verdi, Giuseppe (1813-1901)

Giuseppe Verdi holds a commanding position in Italian operatic repertoire, dominating the form from his first considerable success in 1842 in a career that ended with his last opera, *Falstaff*, in 1893. Verdi's fame in Italy was allied, in part, to his association with the national aspirations of his compatriots as Italy was unified under a new monarchy. In addition to his operas, he left a certain amount of vocal and choral music. Of this the most significant is his monumental *Requiem*, to which the *Quattro pezzi sacri* (Four Sacred Pieces) provide a pendant. His operas, the main body of his work, are strongly dramatic, often grandiose in conception, expanding the possibilities of the traditional forms that he continued to use. His career, which took him to St Petersburg, to Paris and to London, was essentially that of an opera-composer, intimately concerned with the details of performance, from his first association with La Scala in Milan to his last operas in the same theatre.

Operas

Verdi was not immediately successful with his first operas, *Oberto, Conte di San Bonifacio* and the comic *Un giorno di regno* (King for a Day). Signal success came in 1842 with *Nabucco* (Nebuchadnezzar), followed by *I lombardi alla prima cruciata* (The Lombards at the First Crusade), *Ernani, I due Foscari* (The Two Foscari), *Giovanna d'Arco* (Joan of Arc), *Alzira, Attila, Macbeth, I masnadieri* (The Bandits), *Jérusalem, Il corsaro* (The Corsair), *La battaglia di Legnano* (The Battle of Legnano), *Luisa Miller, Stiffelio, Rigoletto, Il trovatore* (The Troubadour), *La traviata, Les vêpres siciliennes* (The Sicilian Vespers), *Simon Boccanegra, Aroldo, Un ballo in maschera* (A Masked Ball), *La forza del destino* (The Force of Destiny), *Don Carlos, Aida, Otello* and *Falstaff*.

Villa-Lobos, Heitor (1887-1959)

After gaining early experience, in his travels, of the various forms of music in his native Brazil, including that of the streets of Rio de Janeiro, Heitor Villa-Lobos was able to spend seven years in Paris, returning home in 1930 to take a leading place in national cultural life. His music, firmly rooted in Brazil, includes a series of *Chôros* and *Bachianas brasileiras*, with a valuable and now very familiar addition to the repertoire of the guitar. He also played an important part in the establishment of musical education in Brazil, based on the folk-music of the country.

Operas

The first opera by Villa-Lobos was *Izath*, in 1914, followed in his maturity by *Yerma*, based on the play by Federico García Lorca.

Vivaldi, Antonio (1678-1741)

Extraordinary in his feats as a violinist and prolific as a composer, Vivaldi spent the greater part of his life in his native Venice, intermittently employed at the Ospedale della Pietà, an institution for illegitimate, indigent or otherwise unwanted girls, with a strong musical tradition and reputation. Ordained priest in 1703, Vivaldi, for alleged reasons of health, did not celebrate Mass, but was able, in other respects, to lead a life that involved him in intensive musical activity both at the Pietà and in the opera-house. Since the modern revival of interest in his music, he has been chiefly known for his many concertos, some five hundred, in the solo form of which he was an important pioneer. His compositions were not confined to this form of instrumental music and include vocal and choral music, as well as works for smaller instrumental ensembles.

Operas

By 1739 Vivaldi claimed to have written 94 operas, but whatever the truth of this boast, there are certainly some fifty such works that are known by name, of which less than half survive in any degree of completeness. He made his operatic début in 1713 at the Teatro S Angelo, with which he continued to be intermittently associated for more than twenty years. His operas have not yet been extensively revived, although they contain music of much interest and variety, within the limits of the form. *Tito Manlio* was supposedly written in five days, evidence of the truth of the composer's boast that he could compose faster than a copyist could copy out parts. *Orlando* is based on Ariosto, a popular contemporary source for operatic libretti; *Teuzzone*, with a libretto by Apostolo Zeno, casts light on contemporary misunderstandings about China; *Dorilla in Tempe* offers an opera in heroic-pastoral fashion and *Griselda*, a favourite subject, takes as its heroine the patient wife, tested by her husband, whose virtues are celebrated in Boccaccio's *Decamerone* and in Chaucer's *Canterbury Tales*.

Wagner, Richard (1813-1883)

Richard Wagner fulfilled his ambition of creating a new form of German music-drama in works that brought together all the arts in a *Gesamtkunstwerk*, a comprehensive work of art, the whole conception, words, music and production stemming from his own genius. His early career had been as a conductor in a travelling theatre-company and in provincial opera-houses. A period in Paris proved disappointing but was followed by appointment as conductor in Dresden in 1843, after the successful staging there of *Rienzi* and *Der fliegende Holländer* (The Flying Dutchman). Involvement in the revolutionary activities of 1849 led to his escape to Switzerland, with the help of Liszt. There he was eventually given assistance by the Banker Otto Wesendonck, with whose wife he began a liaison. This was interrupted by the intervention of Wagner's wife, who had joined him in Switzerland. A visit to Paris brought a disastrous staging there of *Tannhäuser* but Vienna seemed likely to be more receptive. It was at this stage in his career, in 1864, that Wagner met King Ludwig II of Bavaria, with whose generous support his debts were paid off, allowing him, with the King's further financial help, to set about the completion of his major undertaking, the *Ring* tetralogy, while other operas were now staged in Munich at the Court Opera. Political intrigue necessitated a return to Switzerland at the end of 1865 and the death of his wife in

Dresden the following year allowed Wagner to contemplate marriage with Liszt's illegitimate daughter Cosima, wife of a strong supporter of Wagner, the pianist and conductor Hans von Bülow. In the final period of his life Wagner was able to build his own opera-house at Bayreuth and establish festivals of his works under his own conditions. Here the *Ring* was performed and, in 1882, Wagner's last opera, *Parsifal*. He died in 1883 during the course of a visit to Venice. His aesthetic principles defy succinct summary. In his music-dramas he made use of leit-motifs, leading motifs, themes or fragments of themes associated with particular characters or ideas, woven together in the seamless fabric of through-composed dramas. In his harmonies he explored new areas of possibility, extending the concept of tonality in a way that allowed some later composers to abandon it altogether. His theatrical techniques and his use of the orchestra again were innovative, part of a massive over-all achievement, accomplished through the sacrifice of many of those with whom he came into contact.

Operas and Music Dramas

Wagner's early operas include the unfinished *Die Hochzeit* (The Wedding), *Die Feen* (The Fairies) and *Das Liebesverbot* (The Ban on Love), based on Shakespeare's play *Measure for Measure*. His first real success came in 1844 with *Rienzi, der letzte der Tribunen* (Rienzi, the Last of the Tribunes), followed by *Der fliegende Holländer* (The Flying Dutchman)and *Tannhäuser und der Sängerkrieg auf Wartburg* (Tannhäuser and the Song Contest on the Wartburg). *Lohengrin* was staged by Liszt in Weimar in 1850, *Tristan und Isolde* (Tristan and Isolde) in Munich in 1865 and *Die Meistersinger von Nürnberg* (The Mastersingers of Nuremberg) in 1868. The first of the *Ring* tetralogy, *Das Rheingold* (The Rhine Gold) was staged in Munich in 1869, followed the next year by *Die Walküre* (The Valkyrie), completed at Bayreuth in 1876 with *Siegfried* and *Götterdämmerung* (The Twilight of the Gods). *Parsifal* was performed at Bayreuth in 1882.

Wagner, Siegfried (1869-1930)

The son of Richard Wagner and Cosima von Bülow, Siegfried Wagner had his birth celebrated by his father with the *Siegfried Idyll*, an *aubade* for Cosima, who had joined Richard Wagner in Switzerland in 1868, bringing with her her two daughters by Wagner. Siegfried Wagner studied with Engelbert Humperdinck, decided to follow another profession and then returned to music, working at Bayreuth as a conductor and then as general director until his death in 1930, a few months after the death of his powerful mother. Siegfried Wagner's operas took a very different course from his father's, following, rather, something of Humperdinck's example in works rooted in the German tradition of fairy-tales and legends of a more earthly kind than those of his father's gods. His musical language is late romantic, but, like Richard Wagner, he wrote his own texts. It is only in recent years that there has been a revival of interest in work that he himself saw as for future generations rather than his own.

Operas

Siegfried Wagner's first opera, in 1898, was *Der Bärenhäuter* (The Man in the Bear's Skin), followed by *Herzog Wildfang* (Duke Madcap), *Der Kobold* (The Goblin), *Bruder Lustig* (Brother Merry), *Sternengebot* (The Ban of the Stars), *Banadietrich*, *Schwarzschwanenreich* (Kingdom of the Black Swan), *Sonnenflammen* (Flames of the Sun), *Der Heidenkönig* (The King), *Der Friedensengel* (The Angel of Peace), *An allem ist Hütchen Schuld* (It's All the Fault of the Little Hat) and *Der Schmied von Marienburg* (The Smith of Marienburg).

Wallace, Vincent (1812-1865)

The Irish composer Vincent Wallace, like Arthur Sullivan, the son of a bandmaster, worked at first as a violinist and pianist, before establishing his reputation as a composer of opera in 1845 with *Maritana*. He moved to Tasmania and then to Australia, where he was hailed as an Australian Paganini. Adventures, partly musical, followed in South and North America, and in other parts of the world, but he is remembered now only for his first opera.

Operas

Wallace's first opera, *Maritana*, was staged at Drury Lane in 1845. His five next operas failed to win a similar success in London, while a further five or so stage works remained incomplete or unperformed.

Walton, William (1902-1983)

A chorister at Christ Church in Oxford, William Walton went on to study at the university, where his achievements remained purely musical. He received continuing encouragement from the Sitwell family, collaborating with Edith Sitwell on *Façade*, which remains one of his best known compositions. He won particular success with his oratorio *Belshazzar's Feast* in 1931 and his viola concerto from the same period is an essential part of solo repertoire. He remains among the most successful younger composers of the period before 1939, with significant additions to orchestral and instrumental repertoire after the war, when he completed his second symphony and cello concerto and wrote his two operas.

Operas

Walton's first opera was *Troilus and Cressida*, a work that seemed to some, at its first production at Covent Garden in 1954, to belong to an earlier age. It was subsequently revised. His second opera, *The Bear*, based on Chekhov, was first staged at Aldeburgh in 1967.

Weber, Carl Maria von (1786-1826)

A cousin of Mozart's wife Constanze, Carl Maria von Weber was trained as a musician from his childhood, spent largely with his father's travelling theatre company. He made a favourable impression as a pianist and then as a music director and conductor, notably in the opera-houses of Prague and Dresden. Here he introduced various reforms, as he had attempted as little more than an adolescent in Breslau, and was a pioneer of the craft of conducting without the use of a violin or keyboard instrument. As a composer he won a lasting reputation with his great German Romantic opera *Der Freischütz* (The Marksman). His varied compositions include a wide variety of music, and, notably, three clarinet concertos and a series of works for piano and orchestra.

Operas

The first surviving opera by Weber is *Peter Schmoll und seine Nachbarn* (Peter Schmoll and His Neighbours), completed in 1802. Little of its successor, *Rübezahl*, survives, but *Silvana*, in 1810, leads the romantic way towards *Der Freischütz*. *Abu Hassan*, in 1811, intervenes, while *Der Freischütz* in 1821 was followed in 1823 by *Euryanthe* and, three years later, by Weber's last opera, *Oberon*.

Weill, Kurt (1900-1950)

Kurt Weill was among the leading young composers in Germany during the Weimar Republic. He left Germany in 1933 and later became a citizen of the United States of America, turning his musical attention to compositions for Broadway, into which he was able to introduce something of the more astringent elements that had characterized his earlier work in Berlin with Bertolt Brecht.

Stage Works

Weill remains best known for his cogent *Dreigroschenoper* (Threepenny Opera), a collaboration with Brecht in 1928. With the expressionist playwright Kaiser he had written *Der Protagonist* and *Der Zar lässt sich photographieren* (The Tsar Has His Photograph Taken). Collaborations with Brecht included *Mahagonny, Happy End, Aufstieg und Fall der Stadt Mahagonny* (Rise and Fall of the City of Mahagonny), *Der Jasager* (The Affirmer) and *Die sieben Todsünden* (The Seven Deadly Sins). Among the works written in America *Street Scene* is one of the most effective.

Weinberger, Jaromir (1896-1967)

Born in Prague in 1896, Jaromir Weinberger studied with Max Reger, among other teachers, taught in America and then returned to work in Bratislava and Prague. In the 1930s events caused him to take refuge in the United States, where he remained until his suicide in 1967.

Operas

Weinberger won a degree of international fame with his second opera, *Schwanda the Bagpiper*, first staged in Prague in 1927. A polka and a fugue from the score have found a continuing place in orchestral repertoire.

Weir, Judith (b.1954)

A pupil of John Tavener and Robin Holloway, the Scottish composer Judith Weir has made interesting additions to operatic repertoire and other forms of instrumental and vocal music, often with open reference to Scottish material in a widely intelligible and acceptable musical language.

Operas

Judith Weir, in *A Night at the Chinese Opera*, makes use of the first Chinese drama to be known in Europe, *The Little Orphan of the House of Chao*, through a translation published, without music, in the 1730s. *The Vanishing Bridegroom*, first staged in 1990, makes use of three stories from the West Highlands. This was preceded, in 1989, by *Heaven Ablaze in His Breast*, based on a story by E.T.A.Hoffmann.

Williamson, Malcolm (b.1931)

A native of the Australian city of Sydney, Malcolm Williamson settled in London in the 1950s and has made his career there. In 1975 he was made Master of the Queen's Musick. His musical language, influenced in some respects by Messiaen, is generally accessible, a quality evident in a varied output of instrumental and vocal music.

Operas

Malcolm Williamson's children's operas, *The Happy Prince* and *Julius Caesar Jones*, have provided interesting repertoire for younger performers. His first opera, *Our Man in Havana*, based on the novel by Graham Greene, was followed by the chamber opera *The English Eccentrics*, with a text derived from Edith Sitwell's book of that title. The most effective has been *The Violins of Saint-Jacques*, with its exotic and highly dramatic West Indian setting.

Wolf, Hugo (1860-1903)

Hugo Wolf is known chiefly as an immensely prolific composer of songs. His last six years were clouded by mental disturbance that became acute in 1897, after more than twenty years of activity as a composer.

Opera

Wolf's only completed opera is *Der Corregidor*, based on Alarcón's *El sombrero de tres picos* (The Three-Cornered Hat).

Wolf-Ferrari, Ermanno (1876-1948)

Born of an Italian mother and a father of Bavarian origin, Ermanno Wolf-Ferrari divided his time and his loyalties between Munich and his native city of Venice. While much of his music has never reached a wide public, there are, in particular, operas that have found a continuing place in a repertoire of his work that is now growing.

Operas

Wolf-Ferrari wrote some fifteen operas. Of these *I gioielli della Madonna* (The Jewels of the Madonna), *Il segreto di Susanna* (Susanna's Secret) and *I quattro rusteghi* (known in

English as The School for Fathers) are the best known. Recent attention has been given to *Das Himmelskleid* (The Garment of Heaven).

Zemlinsky, Alexander von (1871-1942)

Friend, teacher and later brother-in-law of Schoenberg, Alexander Zemlinsky won growing importance in the musical world of Vienna in the early years of the 20th century. He taught Alma Mahler, who discussed with her future husband Gustav Mahler, the relationship between physical ugliness and spiritual beauty, this with reference to Zemlinsky. His earlier career was at the Vienna Volksoper, in Prague and in Berlin. He was forced to return to Vienna in 1933, thence to Prague and finally he moved to the United States of America, where he died in 1942.

Operas

Zemlinsky's more important operas are the two based on Oscar Wilde, *Eine florentinische Tragödie* (A Florentine Tragedy) and *Der Zwerg* (The Dwarf), based on Wilde's *The Birthday of the Infanta*. Other operas include *Sarema*, *Es war einmal* (Once Upon a Time), *Der Traumgörge* (Görge the Dreamer), *Kleider machen Leute* (Clothes Make the Man), *Der Kreidekreis* (The Chalk Circle) and the unfinished *Der König Kandaules* (King Candaules), this last on a libretto by André Gide.

Zimmermann, Bernd Alois (1918-1970)

Zimmermann occupies a special position in German music of the 20th century, with a musical language and techniques of relative originality. He taught, for much of his life, at the Cologne Musikhochschule and draws, in his own music, on his own wide cultural background and his roots in Catholic teaching and tradition.

Operas

Many have regarded Zimmermann's opera *Die Soldaten* (The Soldiers) as the most important German opera since Berg's *Lulu*.

Glossary

Affections

The so-called Doctrine of Affections, in Italian *affetti*, indicates the Baroque theory, derived from Greek and Roman rhetorical theory and practice, according to which one piece of music should aim to bring about a certain state of feeling in the hearer, of sadness, joy, anger (in the musical representation of which Monteverdi claimed to be a pioneer) or love. The original *affetti* developed in the 17th and early 18th centuries to cover a relatively wide range of human emotions and this had a clear effect on operatic requirements. The *opera seria* of the first half of the 18th century came to require a variety of arias for the principal singers, who would then be able to show their ability in expressing sorrow or anger, with other emotions.

Air

An *air* (*ayre*) is a song. The word is used by earlier English composers and has its counterpart in French usage.

Alto

The *alto* (= Italian: high) is the lower female or unbroken male voice at a pitch below that of the *soprano* and above that of the *tenor*. For female singers at this pitch, the term *contralto* is preferred (but see the entries under *contralto* and *mezzo-soprano*).

Aria

The word *aria* is the equivalent of the English *air*, in its most literal meaning. In opera it came to mean a separate song, usually for one voice, and distinguished, by the later 17th century, from *recitative,* which resembles heightened speech.

There are various forms of *aria*. These include the *da capo aria,* (from the beginning aria) originating in opera in the early 18th century. Here the singer repeats the first section of an *aria,* with appropriate additional ornamentation, to make a three-section lyrical form, with a generally contrasted middle section. This was not always dramatically suitable.

The *dal segno aria* (from the sign aria) is similar to the *da capo aria*, except that the repetition is from a sign in the earlier part of the score, not from the beginning. Both forms of *aria* would include instrumental introductions, conclusions and interruptions, the so-called *ritornello*, and might well involve further repetition of the sections.

The *aria* in one form or another, as a solo set-piece, has continued to have a place in opera, but it is, essentially, a closed form, with an element of completeness in itself.

The allocation of *arias* between rival singers and the necessary nature of these *arias* was often a matter of great importance. In the formal opera of the first half of the 18th century, entrances and exits needed to excite interest and applause from the audience.

ARIETTA

A short *aria*.

ARIETTE

Originally the French form of the Italian *arietta*, the word *ariette* came to signify a particular form of short aria, of lively character. The word is used in the descriptive title of French comic operas in the later 18th century, dialogue interspersed with songs (see *comédie mêlée d'ariettes*).

ARIOSO

Arioso suggests an aria-like passage in the middle of *recitative*. Various composers use the word in different ways, sometimes to indicate an *arietta* or *aria*. In general modern usage, however, used as a noun, it indicates a passage of melody within a passage that lacks formal melodic qualities. *Arioso* may also be an adjective or adverb.

BALLAD OPERA

Ballad opera is the form of English musical and dramatic entertainment that offers a play, usually comic, interspersed with songs set to popular tunes, whether traditional or borrowed from current operas or other repertoire. The form seems to have started in England in 1728 with John Gay's *The Beggar's Opera*. This had possible, if less satisfactory predecessors in the previous century, but essentially itself provoked a new genre, developed particularly by the dramatist and novelist Henry Fielding.

Ballata

Derived from the Italian *ballare* (to dance), the word *ballata* has connection also with *ballad*, a narrative song. In opera it is used to indicate a dance-like song or a sung narrative.

Ballet

Ballet, the art of dance and mime, has held an important place in opera, providing an element of spectacle and of variety, and found in the earliest period of operatic history, in particular with the court *masque* (see also *opéra-ballet*). The place of ballet in France was of particular importance, at one time of symbolic significance in supporting the power of the monarch. In later periods ballet continued to be an essential element in French opera, leading, in some cases, to the addition of a ballet to make a foreign opera more acceptable to the Parisian public.

Ballet-héroïque

The *ballet-héroïque* was a form that developed in France in the second and third quarters of the 18th century. Generally celebratory in tone and purpose, the genre involved heroic figures in a series of episodes based on a general theme. Rameau was the principle exponent of a form of distinct political relevance in its own time.

Barcarolle

A *barcarolle* (= Italian: *barcarola*) is a boating-song, generally with a characteristic swaying rhythm. The best known operatic example is found in Offenbach's *Les contes d'Hoffmann* (The Tales of Hoffmann), setting the scene in Venice.

Baritone

The word *baritone* indicates a male voice that is lower than *tenor* and higher than *bass*. The range corresponds to that of the normal male speaking voice. In fact the baritone range can vary very considerably, leading to a necessary distinction between high baritone and bass baritone. Operatic repertoire includes a number of leading baritone rôles, from Mozart's *Don Giovanni* to the dramatically and technically demanding parts offered by Verdi in operas like *Rigoletto* or *Falstaff*.

Bass

The *bass* is the lowest male voice, originally cast in majestic rôles like those of Plutone, King of the Underworld, or of Caronte (Charon), sinister ferryman of the dead, in Monteverdi's *Orfeo*. Composers sometimes call for a wide range of voice, rising from the depths to the heights. In French opera of the 19th century distinctions were made between types of bass, according to the character and range of the rôles, whether noble or lyrical.

Bass-baritone

The *bass-baritone* voice lies between *baritone* and *bass* and there are rôles that may be allocated to a bass-baritone instead of to a bass. Such rôles include that of Boris Godunov in Mussorgsky's opera and a number of rôles deliberately allotted by Wagner to 'high bass'.

Basso buffo

The *basso buffo* is the comic bass, as exemplified by the comic slave overseer Osmin, in Mozart's *Die Entführung aus dem Serail* (The Abduction from the Seraglio) or by Donizetti's Don Pasquale.

Basso cantante (= French: basse chantante)

A *basso cantante* is a singing bass, a bass singing a more lyrical melodic line, as, perhaps, in the title-rôle of Mussorgsky's *Boris Godunov*.

Basso profondo

The *basso profondo* is a deep bass, of rich lower sonority, the kind of bass for which Russia is well known. In opera the *basso profondo* is generally used for rôles of some solemnity, but the range demanded of Osmin in Mozart's *Die Entführung aus dem Serail* (The Abduction from the Seraglio) qualifies him for this description; his range is *profondo* in a rôle that is *buffo*.

Breeches rôle (= French: travesti; German: Hosenrolle)

A *breeches* part is one in which a female singer takes a male part. This occurred, for example, in the time of Handel, when leading male castrato parts were sometimes, alternatively, allocated to women. Famous *breeches* rôles must include that of Octavian in *Der Rosenkavalier* (The Knight of the Rose) and that of the Composer in *Ariadne auf Naxos* by Richard Strauss, but operatic history offers many more examples, from Monteverdi to Massenet.

Buffo

Buffo describes a singer or a rôle that is comic. The word is most often applied to the comic bass (see *basso buffo*), but tenors are occasionally allowed to indulge in comedy, as, for example, in the case of the *tenore buffo* Goro, the marriage-broker in Puccini's *Madama Butterfly*.

Burlesque (= Italian: burlesca; German: Burleske).

A *burlesque* is, in its earlier meaning, a comic piece for the theatre, often including an element of parody or caricature. The word is derived from the Italian *burlare* (to make fun of) and performances of this kind were often used in seasonal festivities to mock more serious theatrical works. In the United States of America the term took on a markedly less respectable meaning from the later 19th century onwards.

Burletta

Although the word *burletta* was used in England from the late 18th century for a form of light English opera, it had a use in Italy to indicate a category of comic opera, during the same period. An example is found in Rossini's *L'occasione fa il ladro* (The Occasion makes the Thief).

Cabaletta

A *cabaletta*, the word used first in the earlier 19th century, is the second, quicker part of an Italian aria in two parts. An example would be Rosina's *Io sono docile* (I am biddable), after her *Una voce poco fa* (A voice, a little while ago), in Rossini's *Il barbiere di Siviglia* (The Barber of Seville). The word can also describe the later part of an operatic duet.

Cadenza

As in concertos, a *cadenza* is a passage of added virtuoso ornamentation, often over a chord that immediately precedes the final cadence. Vocal *cadenzas* involve various degrees of elaboration and may sometimes be extended.

Cantabile

The Italian word *cantabile* means *singable* and is more usually found in directions for instrumental performance in a singing manner. It has appeared also as a noun to indicate the first part of a two-section Italian aria.

Canzone

A *canzone* is a song. In opera the word is used to indicate a song that appears as such in the dramatic context. An example might be Cherubino's song *Voi che sapete* (You who know what love is) in Mozart's *Le nozze di Figaro* (The Marriage of Figaro).

Canzonetta

A *canzonetta* is a little *canzona*.

Castrato

The *castrato*, the castrated male singer, held a position of essential importance in opera of the 17th and 18th centuries, in particular in Italian works. Many principal male rôles in Italian Baroque opera were allocated to male sopranos or altos, who enjoyed great fame and high fees. Outstanding castrato singers include Farinelli, whose career flourished in the 1720s and 1730s. The *castrato* voice went out of fashion during the later 18th century, although there are rare and isolated *castrato* rôles in operas by Rossini and Meyerbeer.

Cavatina

A *cavatina* is a short aria, an example of which, so specified, would be Figaro's *Se vuol ballare* (If you would dance) in Mozart's *Le nozze di Figaro* (The Marriage of Figaro). In Italian opera of the 19th century it came to indicate an opening aria for a leading character or an aria of particular virtuosity.

Coloratura

In its earlier meaning *coloratura* signifies *colouring*, and, in music, ornamentation. The word now generally indicates a rôle or a singer specialising in a kind of rôle that includes elaborate ornamentation, often involving a high soprano in exploration of the musical stratosphere. A well known example is found in the rôle of the Queen of the Night in Mozart's *Die Zauberflöte* (The Magic Flute), with her dazzling vocal acrobatics.

Comédie-ballet

The French Baroque *comédie-ballet* makes use of spoken dialogue, song and dance. A well known example of the form is found in Molière's collaboration with the composer Lully in *Le bourgeois gentilhomme* (The Bourgeois Gentleman).

Comédie larmoyante

The French *comédie larmoyante* (tearful comedy) became fashionable in France in the later 18th century, providing a plot in which a tearful element leads to a happy ending. The genre has wider cultural connection with novels such as Samuel Richardson's *Pamela, or Virtue Rewarded* and with the German *Empfindsamerstil* (sentimental style).

Comédie lyrique • Comédie en musique

Lyric comedy, comedy in music, comedy set to music, are terms applied to French operas of the later 18th century that are to be distinguished from the *tragédie lyrique* of the period. It represents a form that has less dramatic pretensions than lyric tragedy but rather more than the *comédie mêlée d'ariettes*.

Comédie mêlée d'ariettes

Comedy mingled with little arias was a form that gained currency in France in the second half of the 18th century. The musical element, in the shorter songs involved, is relatively simple and straightforward.

Commedia dell'arte

The conventions of the semi-improvised Italian *commedia dell'arte*, with its stock characters of Harlequin, Pantaloon and Columbine, are reflected in early opera until the middle of the 18th century, and beyond that in the plays by Gozzi, sources of later operatic exploitation. The character of Harlequin (Arlecchino), protagonist of Busoni's opera of that name, is that of the ordinary man, set, time and again, in inappropriately exotic or majestic surroundings, which he then brings into ridicule. His German equivalent is found in Hanswurst and then in characters such as Mozart's bird-catcher Papageno in *Die Zauberflöte*. Shakespeare's Bottom in fairy-land explores much the same vein of humour. The characters and the genre of the *commedia dell'arte* continue to have their place, as, for example, in the opera *Ariadne auf Naxos* (Ariadne on Naxos) by Richard Strauss.

Comprimario

Comprimario rôles are operatic rôles of secondary or even lesser importance, however vital their existence may be to a plot.

Contralto

The *contralto* voice is the lowest female voice, now often identified with the *mezzo-soprano*. It is, however, possible to distinguish between the two types of voice and the kinds of rôles allotted to them in opera. A characteristic *contralto* rôle is that of Tancredi in Rossini's opera of that name, a breeches part that demands a rich lower register, as well as the usual vocal agility. In general, however, the *contralto* has had to be content as a mother, mother-in-law or nurse, or as any other female of formidable power or sinister suggestion, such as the gypsy Azucena in Verdi's *Il trovatore* (The Troubadour), which might properly be thought to belong to a *mezzo-soprano*, because of the part's slightly higher range.

Countertenor

The *countertenor* voice is the adult male alto voice. It has been used to replace the *castrato* in modern performances of Italian Baroque opera and has a special place in 20th-century opera in Britten's *A Midsummer Night's Dream*, where Oberon is cast as a countertenor, and in the same composer's *Death in Venice*, where the voice of Apollo is a countertenor. The voice has an obvious place in the performance of English music of the period of Purcell.

Da capo

Da capo (from the beginning) is used as a direction to performers to repeat a piece from the beginning. The *da capo aria* was a form that won acceptance in later Baroque opera and other forms of vocal music. It indicates an aria in three sections, the third of which repeats the first, with additional ornamentation.

Dal segno

Dal segno (from the sign) is used as a direction to performers to repeat a piece from a sign written above the music at some point after the beginning. A *dal segno aria* is an aria with a repeated element of this kind.

Dramatic soprano

The *dramatic soprano* voice is needed for rôles that make demands on the power and intensity of the soprano. Examples would include the rôle of Isolde in Wagner's *Tristan und Isolde* and a number of other Wagnerian heroines. Sometimes lyrical elements may predominate over the heroic, as in Tosca or in Cio-Cio-San, Madama Butterfly, calling for a combination of the dramatic and the lyrical.

Drame lyrique

The French *drame lyrique* (lyric drama) was, from the 1750s until the early 19th century, a form of opera that dealt seriously enough with characters of lower degree than the kings and demi-gods of French *tragédie lyrique*. The term later came into very general use, as, in the later 19th century, in Massenet's *Werther*, with its middle-class setting.

Dramma giocoso

The *dramma giocoso* (cheerful drama) is found principally in Italian opera of the 18th century and notably in libretti by Carlo Goldoni. It indicates an opera that is, in general, comic, but includes more serious rôles. The librettist Lorenzo Da Ponte used the term for his libretto for Mozart's *Don Giovanni*.

Dramma per musica

Dramma per musica (drama for music) would appear to have been largely a librettists' term for their work, particularly in contributions to what became known as *opera seria*, in the first part of the 18th century.

Duet

A *duet* is part of an opera intended for two voices. It has always been of importance in opera, from Cavalieri's duet for Body and Soul in his *Rappresentatione di Anima e di Corpo* (Representation of Soul and Body) in 1600 and Monteverdi's famous closing duet for Nero and Poppaea in *L'incoronazione di Poppea* (The Coronation of Poppaea) to *Sous le dôme épais* (Under the thick canopy of jasmine) in *Lakmé* by Delibes, with voices joined in mellifluous parallel. Examples continue, often as expressions of love between the two singers.

Echo

The practical use of an echo effect, sometimes by the sound of the goddess Echo herself, provided additional interest in early Baroque opera. Well known examples occur in Cavalieri's *Rappresentatione di Anima e di Corpo* (Representation of Soul and Body), where Soul calls on Heaven for an answer to her questions, which comes in syllables derived from the last words of each question. There is a similar use of the device in the fifth act of Monteverdi's *Orfeo,* where Echo herself answers the distraught Orpheus, his Eurydice now lost to him.

Ensemble

An *ensemble* is part of an opera sung by a group of singers together. This became a special feature of opera, since, in an operatic ensemble, it is possible to present simultaneously the feelings and ideas of a number of contrasting characters in such a way as to make each of them intelligible to an audience. Benjamin Britten provides an instructive example in his opera *The Little Sweep*, explained in the introductory, spoken *Let's Make An Opera*, of which it forms a part.

Entr'acte (= German: Zwischenspiel)

An *entr'acte* is an interlude between the acts or scenes of an opera or other such dramatic and musical work. While the function of the *entr'acte* may be dramatic, it may also be practical, allowing the necessary time for changes of scene, if some element of over-all continuity is needed.

Entrée

The French word *entrée* has two possible meanings in opera. It may refer to the entrance, or first appearance, of a character (= German: *Eintritt*), or, more particularly, in the French *ballet de cour*, to one unified scene.

Fairy-tale opera (see Märchenoper)

Falsetto

The *falsetto* voice is the treble register, used for special effect by a male adult singer. Falsettists, singers who normally use this register, if not elevated to the rank of countertenors, may be found singing the alto line in English cathedral choirs. In opera the register is generally used for comic effect, as of a man imitating a woman, for example in Verdi's *Falstaff,* where Falstaff imitates the words of Mistress Ford, or to marked dramatic effect in innovative works of the later 20th century. There is a general view that a tenor who uses *falsetto* to reach his top notes is cheating.

Farsa

The Italian *farsa* (farce) was a shorter form of comic opera, popular in Venice in Rossini's heyday. He himself used the descriptive title for *La cambiale di matrimonio* (The Marriage Contract), *La scala di seta* (The Silken Ladder) and *Il Signor Bruschino*.

Favola in musica

The Italian *favola in musica* (story in music) is descriptive of early baroque opera at the beginning of the 17th century. The term, borrowed from earlier literary examples, where the word *favola* was in common use in narrative titles for works of a mythological or pastoral content, is used by Monteverdi on the title-page of his opera *Orfeo*, where the dramatic content is of a similar kind.

Festa teatrale

The descriptive title *festa teatrale* (theatrical festivity) was applied, from about 1650 to 1750, to dramatic and musical works, including, on occasions, operas and *serenatas*. They are often celebratory in content.

Finale

The *finale* is the last part of an act or scene in opera, and is often extensive in length, combining a number of distinct sections or movements, usually with an ensemble before the end. This type of *finale* is exemplified in the operas Mozart wrote with the librettist Lorenzo Da Ponte. There clearly continued a need for a general conclusion in which the confusions and conflicts of all characters might in the end be resolved. The ending itself, the *ultimo finale*, however, might be relatively perfunctory, with a concluding chorus expressing happiness or sorrow, or drawing a moral from what has passed.

Grand opéra

French *grand opéra* developed in the 19th century, notably with Meyerbeer, although it had historical precedent as early as Lully in the late 17th century, with the then demand for elaborate spectacle. The usual form of *grand opéra* is as a five-act work, making use of grandiose effects on a large scale. The genre was of considerable social and cultural importance in Paris, with a consequent effect on techniques of staging, which were often innovative and had to be impressive. It had influence outside France on composers such as Wagner and Verdi, specifically in the former's *Tannhäuser* in the version arranged for Paris and the latter's spectacular *Aida*. Examples of the genre from Meyerbeer include *Les Huguenots* and *L'Africaine*.

Haute-contre

The *haute-contre* voice is the highest male voice in French opera. In range it is equivalent to the alto and was normally written in the alto clef, corresponding to the highest of the three middle parts of the Lully five-part string orchestra, taken by a smaller form of viola. There is argument as to whether the *haute-contre* is a high tenor, with some use of *falsetto*, or a *falsettist*, but it would seem probable that, following the definition given by Berlioz, the voice is that of a very high tenor. A number of leading male rôles in French Baroque opera were allotted to the *haute-contre*.

Heldentenor

The German *Heldentenor* (heroic tenor) is a tenor of considerable power and stamina, necessary for a number of leading Wagnerian rôles.

INTERLUDE (= FRENCH: ENTR'ACTE; GERMAN: ZWISCHENSPIEL)

An *interlude* is an orchestral passage between acts or scenes, sometimes for dramatic purposes and sometimes designed to allow time for scene changes in a work that is continuous.

INTERMÈDE

An *intermède* is a work, often including singing and dancing, that was intended to be performed between the acts of a play or in a bill with an opera. Originating with the French court masque of the early Baroque period, the term continued in use, later as a translation of the Italian *intermezzo*, and hence as a description of works such as Pergolesi's *La serva padrona* (The Servant as Mistress), when it had its first influential performances in Paris in 1754.

INTERMEDIO

The Italian *intermedio* is a dramatic and musical work to be performed between the acts of plays. It developed in the 16th century as one of the forerunners of opera and often served a celebratory purpose, continuing into the 17th century as a court entertainment.

INTERMEZZO

The Italian *intermezzo* replaced the *intermedio* in 18th- century opera as an entertainment between the acts of an opera or play, relevant or irrelevant in plot to the work that framed it. It was often in the form of a short comic opera, providing, therefore, comic relief from the weightier matters of *opera seria*, and drawing, often enough, on the traditions and forms of the *commedia dell'arte*, with its stock characters.

LAMENT

The *lament*, a standard element of ancient Greek tragedy and of subsequent European literature, not least the *Heroides* of Ovid, complaints of heroines of antiquity, found an early place in opera, where it soon took on a standard musical form, based on four descending notes in the bass, a repeated pattern. Monteverdi in 1607 provided Orpheus with a heartfelt lament in his opera *Orfeo*, but more influential still was the lament of Ariadne, deserted by Theseus on the island of Naxos, the only part of Monteverdi's second opera, *Arianna*, to survive. Later in the 17th century Purcell's

Dido and Aeneas offers a further well known example of the form, which also provided poets and composers with the basis of separate compositions, as a *castrato* laments the limits imposed on his performance or yet another deserted heroine bewails her lot.

Leitmotif

The German *Leitmotif* or leading motif is distinguished by analysts of the operas and music-dramas of Richard Wagner, where a motif, here a theme or fragment of a theme, of whatever length or form, is used to represent a person, action or idea. It has obvious connection with earlier practice, in the use of the reminiscence motif, the use of a theme or fragment of a theme to remind the listener of its earlier dramatic associations. Wagner's leading motifs are of much greater complexity, but contribute notably to the musical unity of a work.

Libretto

The *libretto* of an opera is the text, an element that at one time seemed of greater importance than the music, which was disposable. Clearly the contribution of the writer is of fundamental importance in an opera, a fact that modern audiences sometimes forget. The librettist has generally been restricted to some extent by musical requirements, matters of length and of possible verse forms and choice of language, and has often worked closely with the composer to produce a unified work of art. Famous librettists range, historically, from Rinuccini and Striggio in the early Baroque period to Busenello, Zeno and Metastasio, Quinault, Calzabigi and Lorenzo Da Ponte, Scribe, Pavia and Boito, Richard Wagner and, to continue a list that becomes increasingly invidious in its omissions, W.H.Auden and Chester Kallman with their libretti for Stravinsky and for Henze. The history of the libretto is admirably discussed in Patrick Smith's book, *The Tenth Muse.*

Lieto fine

The *lieto fine* (happy ending) soon became a standard requirement of opera in the 17th and 18th centuries. Rinuccini's tragic ending to his original libretto for *Orfeo,* with Orpheus torn apart by savage bacchantes, was replaced, in Monteverdi's subsequently published score, by the happy elevation of Orpheus to the heavens, and 36 years later Nero and his mistress Poppaea end the same composer's *L'incoronazione di Poppea* (The Coronation of Poppaea) in loving happiness, although audiences would have been aware of the latent irony in this, in view of the later fate of both of them. While Ariadne, abandoned by Theseus on the island of Naxos, may find happiness with

Bacchus and his train, Dido provides an almost inevitable exception to the common convention, at least in Metastasio's treatment of the story, set by over sixty composers, during the course of a century.

Lyric soprano

The *lyric soprano* voice is that usually required for the generality of operatic heroines. Typical rôles of this kind include that of Mimi in Puccini's *La bohème.* There are occasions when the dramatic nature of a rôle may require a combination of the lyric and the dramatic.

Lyric tenor

With the increasing prominence of the tenor voice in later 18th century opera, leading to its predominance in heroic or amatory rôles, there was a need for the qualities of a *lyric tenor* voice, essential in a lover, such as Don Ottavio in Mozart's *Don Giovanni* or Rodolfo in Puccini's *La bohème.* As with the lyric soprano, there are times when a stronger dramatic element is also needed.

Mad scene

Music and madness are close allied, as Ophelia and King Lear both demonstrated. Madness soon found a place in opera and even the 17th century lament found room for madness in distinct solo repertoire. It was above all the 19th century that found itself able to explore more fully the phenomenon of the madness, usually temporary, of operatic heroines. The most famous of these mad scenes is probably the dangerous seizure of Lucia in Donizetti's *Lucia di Lammermoor*, but even Meyerbeer's *L'étoile du nord* (Star of the North) needed to allow the heroine a culminating moment of mental abstraction, assisted by an equally agile flute, an attack from which she quickly recovers. This is very different from the madness of Wozzeck in Berg's opera or other examples of the more clinically accurate portrayal of lunacy in the later 20th century.

Madrigal comedy

The Italian *madrigal comedy* has some importance as a precursor of opera in the later 16th century. It was derived, as its name suggests, from the contemporary fashion for madrigals, part-songs often on a pastoral subject, and from the *commedia dell'arte.* Characteristic examples are found in Orazio Vecchi's *L'Amfiparnasso* and *Il convito musicale.*

Magic opera (see Zauberoper)

(see Zauberoper)

Märchenoper

Märchenoper (fairy-tale opera) has a particular place in German opera towards the end of the 19th and into the 20th century. It exemplifies and stems from a German national interest in traditional stories, notably those collected and published earlier in the 19th century by the Brothers Grimm. Among the best known example of the genre is Humperdinck's *Hänsel und Gretel*, and there are a number of further examples from his pupil Siegfried Wagner, son of Richard Wagner, who explores the same vein in *Der Bärenhäuter* (The Man in the Bear's Skin), *Schwarzschwanenreich* (The Kingdom of the Black Swan) and other works.

Masque

The *masque* was a court entertainment in England principally in the late 16th and early 17th century. It involved, drama, dance and music, with an important element of spectacle. Later in the 17th century *masques* were included in theatrical entertainment, as in the Chinese *masque* appended to Purcell's *The Fairy Queen*. It has been suggested that the same composer's short opera *Dido and Aeneas*, like John Blow's *Venus and Adonis*, was first presented as a *masque* at the court of Charles II. As with French court ballet, the dancers, and in England singers and actors in court *masques* were often amateurs, courtiers or members of the royal family.

Melodrama

Melodrama makes use of spoken words, accompanied by or framed by music. The form was developed, in particular, by Georg Benda in Gotha, following the example in France of Jean-Jacques Rousseau. Benda's very successful *melodramas* included *Medea*, *Ariadne auf Naxos* and *Pygmalion*, the first two of which suggested to Mozart that he too should attempt the form, although this plan came to nothing. It is possible to distinguish a *monodrama*, which employs one performer, from a *duodrama*, which calls for two. *Melodrama* took a place within opera itself, when spoken dialogue was accompanied by music. A notable example of this can be seen in Weber's *Der Freischütz* (The Marksman), when magic bullets are cast, by diabolical means, in the midnight depths of the forest, and there is a sinister dungeon example in Beethoven's only opera, *Fidelio*. It has since found an important dramatic place in contemporary opera and music theatre.

Melodramma

The Italian word *melodramma* is sometimes used in the 19th century as a synonym for opera, but usually with reference to the libretto rather than the music.

Mezzo-soprano

The *mezzo-soprano* voice is the female voice immediately below the *soprano*, calling for a more substantial lower range. The term is sometimes used as a synonym for *contralto*, but a distinction should be made between the two types of voice. The *mezzo-soprano* assumed operatic importance as a distinct category of voice in the 19th century, as the soprano was urged to new heights. Those unable to reach these with any degree of comfort could be honourably accommodated in the category of *mezzo-soprano*. The voice came to be more often used for secondary rôles, for the *seconda donna* rather than the *prima donna*, but exceptions to this include Bizet's Carmen and a number of Rossini heroines, including Rosina in *Il barbiere di Siviglia* (The Barber of Seville), although this rôle is sometimes adapted to suit a coloratura soprano. There has often been some flexibility in casting, although a rôle such as that of the gypsy Azucena in Verdi's *Il trovatore* (The Troubadour) or, at a more elevated social level, Princess Eboli in the same composer's *Don Carlo*, are essentially for *mezzo-soprano*.

Monody

In the development of opera, the word *monody*, essentially music for a single voice, is associated with the *dramatic monody* of the early Baroque, in which the vocal line, accompanied by *basso continuo* of a chordal and a bass instrument, follows the contours and dramatic stresses of the text. The word covers *recitative*, *arioso* and *aria* at a period when the first and last were not formally distinguished.

Music drama

Although the words *music drama* might well have been and were used for a long period to signify *opera*, they are now most aptly applied to the later musical and dramatic works of Richard Wagner, the *Gesamtkunstwerk* in which he combined all the arts, in particular works such as *The Ring* and *Parsifal*.

Music theatre

The descriptive term *music theatre* found favour in the second half of the 20th century in a reaction against the traditional opera-house and all that it involved. It suggested an emphasis on the theatrical element, as in Alexander Goehr's *Naboth's Vineyard* or the *Eight Songs for a Mad King* and other such works by Peter Maxwell Davies, to be performed by actor-singers or, in some cases, dancers. The genre attracted the attention of Stockhausen and Henze in Germany, Nono and Berio in Italy, Ligeti and, in America, John Cage and his disciples.

Number opera

Number opera is opera that is made up of distinct and separate sections, complete in themselves. This form is not present in opera that is continuous and through-composed.

Obbligato

An *obbligato* (obligatory) instrumental part is one of essential importance in accompanying an aria in opera. Well known examples must include the horn *obbligato* in *Va tacito* (Go silently) in Handel's *Giulio Cesare* (Julius Caesar) or the flute in Catherine's mad scene in Meyerbeer's *L'étoile du nord* (The Star of the North).

Opera

Originally derived from the plural of the Latin word *opus* (work), the word *opera* is used in the singular to indicate a dramatic work that is set to music throughout. Distinctions have been drawn between works that avoid speech altogether and those that include spoken dialogue, as in the German *Singspiel*. In common usage, however, English makes no ordinary distinction between the two, although it may draw the line at lighter forms of musical and dramatic entertainment, the *operetta* or the *musical*.

Opéra

The French word *opéra* is generally used in the strict sense of a dramatic work set to music throughout, but historically there has been some flexibility in usage. It was customary in French, however, to indicate the nature of musical and dramatic works with much more precise nomenclature.

Opéra-ballet

French *opéra-ballet* flourished in the first three-quarters of the 18th century and combined elements of opera and ballet in a work that might or might not be unified by plot. A well known example is Rameau's episodic *Les Indes galantes*, staged in Paris in 1735.

Opéra bouffe

Opéra bouffe is the term used for French comic opera of the middle and later 19th century, witty in its dialogue and light-hearted in its music. The genre is exemplified by works such as Offenbach's *Orphée aux enfers* (Orpheus in the Underworld).

Opera buffa (= French: opéra bouffon)

Although not at first regarded as a classification of opera in the earlier 18th century, the term *opera buffa* came into gradual formal use to signify Italian comic opera. The later 17th century had brought a mixture of the serious with episodes of comic relief. The 18th century introduced a reform that tended to the separation of the two elements, the comic and the serious. The *opera buffa* was developed in Naples, thereafter spreading north to Rome and to Venice, assisted by the activity of the playwright and librettist Carlo Goldoni and culminating in the work of Mozart and Lorenzo Da Ponte, *Le nozze di Figaro* (The Marriage of Figaro), *Don Giovanni* and *Così fan tutte*, between 1786 and 1790. Less important as the 19th century went one, there are still notable examples in Rossini's *Il barbiere di Siviglia* (The Barber of Seville) and Donizetti's *L'elisir d'amore* (The Elixir of Love) and *Don Pasquale*.

Opéra comique

Having its origins in the music of the *Foires* (Fairs) in Paris, *opéra comique* developed as a musical and theatrical entertainment usually also involving spoken dialogue. This form and distinction belongs essentially to the 19th century. The fair theatres offered generally popular entertainment, but the form changed under the influence of Italian *opera buffa*, after the rivalries of the 1750s between the Italian form and French formal opera. There were inevitable changes with the Revolution, when Viotti's attempts to introduce naturalised Italian comic opera failed. In the new century *opéra comique*, staged by the theatre company of that name that had been first established in 1714 and continued, in one form or another, until relatively recently, included works of relatively serious content, such as the earlier version of Gounod's *Faust*, with its element of spoken dialogue. There was less of a place for spectacle or ballet, and various conventions of casting became established.

Opéra féerie

Opéra féerie (fairy opera) is the French counterpart of the German *Märchenoper* (fairy-tale opera). At the end of the 19th century Massenet's opera *Cendrillon* (Cinderella) provides an example of the genre, which, as far as plot and characters are concerned, had its roots in the operas and *opéra-ballet* of the 18th century.

Opera semiseria

The Italian *opera semiseria* of the earlier 19th century includes serious and lighter elements, as in Bellini's *La sonnambula* (The Sleep-Walker).

Opera seria

A retrospective classification of Italian opera on a serious subject, *opera seria* itself had its origin in a reaction against the mixture of the comic and the serious that had prevailed in the later 17th century, defying the rules of Aristotle and provoking criticism from proponents of French classical theatre. The chief librettists in this reform were Apostolo Zeno and the writer known as Metastasio. With them the form took a precise shape, depending on a number of distinct arias, properly allocated, with the necessary variety of feeling (*affetto*) and of versification. The form, reflected by the work of Handel in London, was modified by the realism introduced by Gluck and the librettist Calzabigi in the third quarter of the 18th century and the elimination of some practices that had become established in spite of clear dramatic needs. By the end of the century the era of the Italian *opera seria* was over, although Mozart, in 1791, could set a modified version of Metastasio's *La clemenza di Tito* (The Clemency of Titus), first used by Caldara in 1734, for a coronation performance in Prague, when the new Empress described the opera as *porcheria tedesca* (German pig-stuff).

Operetta

Operetta is light opera, a form that came into its own in the second half of the 19th century. Its provenance is usually considered to be Paris, where Offenbach was at work, followed soon by Vienna, with Johann Strauss, Suppé, Ziehrer and their successors, including Franz Lehár, Emmerich Kálmán and others. The English counterpart is found in the operettas of Gilbert and Sullivan. Although these last keep some place in national repertoire, where they have had no lasting successors, Viennese operetta still holds its own in revival, as do some of the works of Offenbach. Lighter musical stage works, however, have been influenced by the musical comedy of the earlier 20th century and the musicals that have emerged from American influence and from the more recent developments of spectacular stage effects in a variety of musical entertainments.

Oratorio

Originating in works of religious content, generally unstaged, for the edification of those associated with the Oratorian movement of St Philip Neri in later 16th-century Rome, the *oratorio* has some claim to inclusion in a consideration of opera through the staging in Rome in 1600 of Cavalieri's *Rappresentatione di Anima e di Corpo* (Representation of Soul and Body), which combines elements of a medieval morality play with the new dramatic music of the period. For some this was regarded as the first *opera* of all. Both in its Italian and, with Handel, its English form, as elsewhere, *oratorio* continued to have a strong musical and often dramatic connection with opera, although designed for unstaged performance.

Overture

The *overture* (= French: *Ouverture;* German: *Ouvertüre*) is, in opera, the music, generally instrumental, that opens a work. The word itself was used in the early 18th century as a title for an instrumental suite and from the 19th century as the designation of a form of instrumental concert-piece, often with narrative or descriptive extra-musical associations. A broad distinction may be made between the Baroque French overture of Lully, with its opening, stately dotted rhythms and following fugue, and the Italian overture of Alessandro Scarlatti, the *sinfonia avanti l'opera* (symphony before the opera), from which the three-movement Italian symphony was derived. While early overtures may be little more than an instrumental call to attention, a sign that the opera is about to start, and many 18th-century overtures may have little relevance to what follows, later composers tended, more and more, to relate the overture, thematically or in mood, with the work that was to follow.

Pantomime

While English *pantomime* has developed from its 18th- century origins into a popular Christmas entertainment that incorporates elements of the earlier music hall, the international meaning of the word reflects its etymology, indicating performance completely in mime. This meaning is found in sections of opera, where mime replaces the verbal indications of the course a plot is taking.

Parlando

The direction *parlando* (speaking) indicates that a singer should use a speaking style of delivery.

Pasticcio

A *pasticcio* (= French: *pastiche*) is an opera that makes use of arias and other musical elements drawn from a number of different sources. The practice of concocting such works, a procedure that brought obvious advantages, became current in the second half of the 17th century and continued at least until the end of the 18th century.

Pastoral

The *pastoral* tradition in European culture has its origins in the ancient world, notably in the work of the Alexandrian poet Theocritus and the Roman poet Vergil. The convention developed by which Arcadia, the land of the shepherds, was presented as an idyllic place and the life of the shepherd as one free from care, the only danger lying in death from unrequited love. Latin traditions allowed allegorical interpretation of the pastoral, an element exploited by later writers. While *pastoral* had a continuing history, it was particularly in the Renaissance of the 16th century that it became very fashionable, expressed in plays, poems, stories and madrigals. Shakespeare allows mockery of the *pastoral* in *As You Like It*, as does Cervantes in part of *Don Quixote*, where his hero decides to sample simple shepherd life. *Pastoral*, which provided much of the verbal content of madrigals, continued into early opera, which often dealt with *pastoral* subjects, as in Monteverdi's *Orfeo* and a *pastoral* element continued in the Academies of Italy, the learned societies that continued to interest themselves in opera and related arts and sciences. The *pastoral* convention is carried forward into later opera and music, its essence lying in the romanticisation of pastoral life, in which shepherds, as in paintings of such subjects, may sit idly on the rocks and see others feed their flocks, while melodious birds sing madrigals. The *pastoral* is in essence an urban view of the country, idealisation of a way of life that neither Versailles nor Dresden sought accurately to represent.

Preghiera

The *preghiera* (prayer; French: *prière*) has found a poignant place in opera, as in Desdemona's prayer in Rossini's and Verdi's *Otello*. It has its counterpart in German opera (= German: *Gebet*) in the work of Wagner and others.

Prelude

A *prelude* (= German: *Vorspiel*; French: *Prélude*; Italian: *Preludio*) introduces an act or scene, usually instrumentally and generally in a shorter form than the formal *overture*. Nevertheless the word is sometimes used to indicate the latter.

Prima donna

The *prima donna* is the first lady in an opera, with rights and privileges that she has traditionally used every way of ensuring.

Primo uomo

The *primo uomo* is the first man, usually a *castrato*, in 18th century opera, of similar or greater importance than the *prima donna* and capable of taking equal measures in support of his claims.

Querelle des bouffons

The *querelle des bouffons* (quarrel of the comedians) was the quarrel between supporters of the French and the Italian forms of opera in Paris in the early 1750s, particularly with the performance there of Pergolesi's *La serva padrona* (The Servant as Mistress)and a series of other works of similar provenance. The dispute had political significance, as the King was identified with traditional French opera, which had always had its own dynastic purposes. Matters were, for the moment, resolved with the departure from the Paris Opéra of the Italian company engaged there, after a successful stay of some twenty months.

Rappresentazione sacra

The *rappresentazione sacra* (sacred drama) had its origins in medieval Italy, further developed in the 15th and 16th centuries and revived by Cavalieri in 1600 with his *Rappresentatione di Anima e di Corpo* (Representation of Soul and Body) for the Oratorian movement. The genre has brought its modern revival in Pizzetti's *La sacra rappresentazione di Abram e d'Isaac* and other works of the 20th century.

Recitative

Recitative is a form of musically notated dramatic speech, relatively free in form. It is later formally distinguished from the *aria*, the set song, which it frames, and came generally to carry the dramatic dialogue of a plot. By the early 18th century *recitative* had become largely stylized, with a conventional chordal accompaniment, usually provided on a keyboard instrument. Early *recitative*, with its origin in rhetorical theory and practice, allows a greater variety of expression than the more formal *recitative* of the 18th century or later.

Recitativo accompagnato

Recitativo accompagnato (accompanied recitative) or *recitativo stromentato* (recitative with instruments) is recitative with an orchestral accompaniment.

Recitativo secco

Recitativo secco (dry recitative) or *recitativo semplice* (simple recitative) is accompanied only by a keyboard or other chordal instrument in the form of a *basso continuo*.

Répétiteur

The *répétiteur* is the musician employed to teach singers their parts and to accompany and advise them in rehearsal. He needs to possess musical and linguistic skills for this sometimes demanding task.

Rescue opera

The term *rescue opera* has been used to describe operas such as Beethoven's *Fidelio*, dealing with the subject of rescue, particularly, after 1789, from political victimisation.

Rondo

Originally a two-part aria, a slow ternary section followed by a quicker section, the Italian vocal *rondo* came to be a reflection of the instrumental *rondo*, a form that frames two or more episodes between a recurrent refrain.

Sacred opera

Sacred opera simply indicates opera on a religious subject and may range from Cavalieri's *Rappresentatione di Anima e di Corpo* (Representation of Soul and Body) to Wagner's *Parsifal*. It is not, however, an established category of opera, merely a descriptive term which may have occasional use.

Scena

In 19th-century opera a *scena* is a dramatic scene that leads, in one way or another, to an aria or duet or more formal movement.

Scene

As part of an act, a *scene* may simply mark the arrival of a new character or indicate a dramatic division, with a possible change of 'scene' or place.

Semi-opera

While formal opera was slow to find a place in England, the *semi-opera*, a modern term to describe a later 17th-century form, allowed an amalgamation of a strong musical element with spoken drama. This is exemplified in works such as *King Arthur* by Dryden and Henry Purcell, where music distinguishes spirits, magicians and goblins from the more human protagonist and his heroine.

Serenade

The *serenade*, suggesting, in popular if erroneous etymology, an evening piece, has a place in opera in its common meaning of a musical performance to be sung beneath the balcony of the beloved, in an attempt to attract her amatory attention. There are well known examples in the mock-serenade of Mozart's *Don Giovanni* and in Rossini's *Il barbiere di Siviglia* (The Barber of Seville).

Serenata

A *serenata* is a piece of vocal and instrumental music, sometimes with a measure of dramatic content, current in the 17th and 18th centuries and often designed for the immediate celebration of some event or anniversary. The word is used, for example, for Mozart's *Il re pastore* (The Shepherd King) and might indicate an occasional work of some theatrical elaboration.

Singspiel

The accepted modern sense of the German word *Singspiel* is that of a German opera with spoken dialogue, such as Mozart's *Die Entführung aus dem Serail* (The Abduction from the Seraglio) and *Die Zauberflöte* (The Magic Flute), both called operas by Mozart himself. The word *Singspiel* in German often had a more general meaning, frequently as a synonym for *opera*, although its specifically German linguistic nature is reflected in the use of the term under the Emperor Joseph II, in his attempts to establish German opera in Vienna.

Soprano

The *soprano* voice is the highest female voice, required for many leading female operatic rôles. The same word may be used for the male *soprano*, the *castrato* voice used in *opera seria*. The female *soprano* voice assumed increasing importance in the late 16th century and had a continuing influence on and importance in opera, as it developed. It is usual to distinguish different types of soprano, lyric, lyric-dramatic, lyric coloratura and so on. Since it has been customary for principal rôles in opera to be written for a particular singer, as Rossini for Colbran or Britten for Peter Pears, specific vocal requirements have become established for certain rôles, generally reflecting the qualities of their original creators.

Spinto

The *spinto* tenor or soprano has a voice capable of incisive dramatic performance. The Italian word means 'pushed'.

SPRECHGESANG • SPRECHSTIMME

Sprechgesang (speech song) or *Sprechstimme* (speech voice) describe the technique of musically notated speech, as used notably by Schoenberg in *Pierrot lunaire* and elsewhere. He is followed in this by his pupil Berg in the operas *Wozzeck* and *Lulu*, and the practice has been interestingly explored by one or two recent Chinese composers, who have thus been able to secure greater clarity of meaning in the setting of a tonal language.

STILE CONCITATO

The *stile concitato* (agitated or excited style) was developed by Monteverdi as a means of expressing anger, in accordance with ancient Greek philosophical principles, to be added to two other states of mind, that of the humble supplicant and that of the moderate man. He intended the *stile concitato,* exemplified in his *Combattimento di Tancredi e Clorinda* (Combat of Tancredi and Clorinda), to represent, in its rapidly repeated notes, the mode associated by Plato, in *The Republic*, with bravery.

STILE RAPPRESENTATIVO

The *stile rappresentativo* (theatre style) is the style developed by Monteverdi and his contemporaries in the late 16th century in the *seconda prattica* (second practice), the new Baroque style of rhetorical recitative and *arioso.* The *seconda prattica* of the early Baroque, with its use of monody and *basso continuo*, was to be distinguished from the so-called *prima prattica* (first practice) of composers in a traditional polyphonic style, like Palestrina (*stile antico*).

TENOR

The *tenor* voice is the high male voice, above that of the baritone. While the protagonist in Monteverdi's opera *Orfeo* is a tenor, the voice was later used primarily in lesser, character parts, only later gradually assuming again a leading position, as the *castrato* lost favour. By the 19th century the tenor had taken the lead, coupled with the soprano in scenes of love and conflict. Musical and technical demands have led to the establishing of various categories of tenor, heroic, lyric, dramatic, *spinto* or even, at the highest, *altino*. The *tenor altino* is the highest form of tenor, able to use a treble register, but not, it is claimed, through the use of *falsetto*. An example of this last is seen in the rôle of the Astrologer in Rimsky-Korsakov's opera *The Golden Cockerel*. Here it is used to very special effect and is rare elsewhere in opera. Other categories of tenor include the *Heldentenor* (heroic tenor) of Wagner, in Italian described as *tenore robusto*, the *tenore di forza* (strong tenor), the *tenore di grazia* (the graceful tenor), as, for example, the young lover Alfredo in Verdi's opera *La traviata*, and the maligned *tenore spinto* (pushed tenor), in which the strenuous may overwhelm the lyrical.

Tragédie en musique • Tragédie lyrique

The *tragédie en musique* (tragedy in music) or *tragédie lyrique* (lyric tragedy) indicate the French operas of serious subject developed by Lully and continued by Rameau. The second term, although accurate, was not generally used in the period of either composer. The form flourished in parallel with the French classical theatre, although the need for spectacle involved the abandonment of the Aristotelian dramatic unities of place and time. The genre had certain formal requirements that were generally followed with some care, each scene bringing an element of dance and spectacle suited to the plot, the whole decidedly influenced by the very strong French traditions of spoken drama. Gluck introduced changes in the direction of a simpler realism. The form, as described, came to an end with the Revolution.

Vaudeville

Vaudeville indicates a relatively simple form of French song or a theatrical entertainment using such songs, or songs borrowed from elsewhere and often satirical in intention. These find popularity in the later 17th century, soon finding a place in the *Foires* (Fairs) of Paris, from which came the *Opéra-Comique*, established in 1714 and drawing, now with some official support, on this tradition.

Verismo

Operatic *verismo* (realism) reflected contemporary literary trends in Italy in the late 19th century. In opera it is seen in Mascagni's opera *Cavalleria rusticana* (Rustic Chivalry) and Leoncavallo's *Pagliacci* (Actors), which deal with relatively lower levels of society and conflicts that might, in this context, seem relatively mundane. The genre, if it can be so regarded, had an influence, at least, on Puccini, who amalgamated this new realism with more exotic settings.

Zarzuela

The *zarzuela* is a form of Spanish dramatic and musical form, making use of song and dance and attracting the attention of leading Spanish composers, who found in its popular form a means of subsistence. The *zarzuela* has its own varied history, but this has little bearing on the general history of European opera outside the Iberian peninsula.

Zauberoper

The *Zauberoper* (magic opera) found particular favour in Vienna in the last quarter of the 18th century. Among works of this kind the best known is Mozart's *Die Zauberflöte* (The Magic Flute), but contemporary composers had made use of other magic instruments, bassoons and harps among them. These works mingle comedy with the supernatural and draw on an older popular tradition, often dealing with the exploits of the common man in uncommon surroundings.

List of Illustrations

Index of Works by Composers

[A]

[B]

[C]

[D]

[E]

[F]

[G]

[H]

[I]

[J]

[K]

[L]

[M]

[N]

[O]

[P]

[R]

[S]

[T]

[U]

[V]

[W]